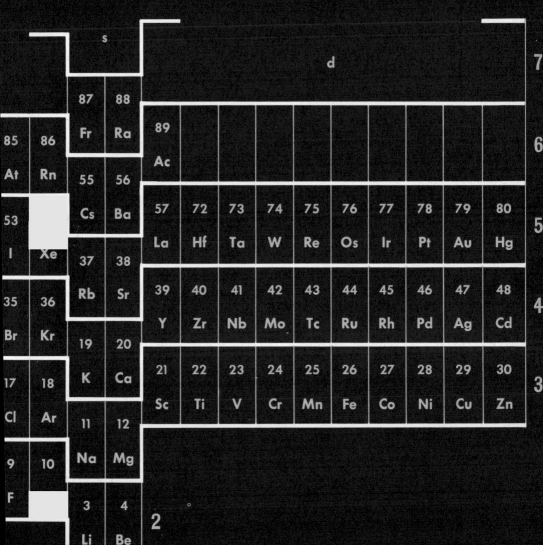

PHYSICAL CHEMISTRY

PHYSICAL

BOSTON, 1961

CHEMISTRY

William F. Sheehan

Department of Chemistry   *University of Santa Clara*

ALLYN AND BACON, INC.

PREFACE

Almost everyone has heard that a physical chemist is a mathematician who can blow glass. Not as many unfortunately have heard the description of a physical chemist given by the late Professor Ward V. Evans. He said, in his very special way, that a physical chemist is a chemist who sits behind a big mahogany desk with a platinum slide rule. The development of thermodynamics in the last century and the quantum mechanical revolution in physics thirty years ago have in fact provided chemistry with a comprehensive theoretical basis. Without apology, then, mathematical chemistry is presented here in the way mathematical physics is commonly and justifiably presented to physicists. It is mathematics.

This text is, it is hoped, remarkable in these ways. The logic of mathematics, as expressed in the allowed and defined operations of algebra and the calculus, is used in preference to lengthy and often unavoidably inaccurate verbalizations. Clarity, order, and simplicity are achieved through emphasizing that thermodynamic functions are functions of state. In introducing thermodynamics, a deliberate effort is made to bridge the gap between elementary physics and chemistry. Finally, modern physical chemistry — in particular, structural chemistry, quantum mechanics, valence theory, statistical mechanics, and absolute reaction rate theory — displaces traditional descriptive matter which is now included in general chemistry or no longer advances theory.

Many people have contributed to this book. It holds the lifework of many scientists. In particular, I should like to thank all my former teachers, especially Professors Verner Schomaker, Frank P. Cassaretto, John G. Kirkwood, and J. H. Sturdivant. Whatever excellence is found here is due to them. Professors Joseph F. Deck and John B. Drahmann have continually encouraged the writing. I am grateful to J. B. Deck and D. P. Waligora for numerous biological examples of osmosis.

Besides these, others have contributed more directly. The University of Santa Clara and the publisher have extended generous financial aid for which I am most grateful. Many thanks are due the publisher and its staff for their expert work and frequent help. In particular, many thanks are due George A. Bogden, the editor, for his sound advice on many things. To Ted Riley, who as associate production editor has designed the book and has produced it with care, go my sincerest thanks. I thank Mrs. Martha G. Allen for her careful and thorough work as copy editor and proofreader. And finally it is a pleasure to thank Mrs. V. Faye Wharton, whose skill in typing the manuscript and attention to detail have been most valuable.

W.F.S.

CONTENTS

1 / KINETIC THEORY OF GASES

AND EQUATIONS OF STATE

A. EQUATIONS OF STATE

1.1 Energy of a Perfect Gas

The kinetic theory of gases provides a mechanical model exhibiting average mechanical properties that are identified with macroscopic properties like pressure. In this model, a pure gaseous substance consists of an aggregation of myriads of minute identical particles called *molecules*. Further division of the molecule is not possible because such division would lead to a chemical transformation of the gaseous substance. Repulsive forces, attractive forces tending toward such things as chemical reaction or liquefaction, and gravitational forces are assumed to be negligible. Because the molecules do not attract each other and because they repel each other only when in contact, the system is devoid of potential energy.

The molecules are conceived as almost point masses, but collisions do occur. The collisions are perfectly elastic; that is, the laws of classical mechanics concerning forces and transfer and conservation of momentum by these free bodies are assumed to hold. The total energy E of this system of

N particles, each of mass m, is merely the sum of the average kinetic energies of all, namely,

$$E = \tfrac{1}{2}Nmu^2 , \qquad (1.1)$$

where u^2 is the average of the squares of the velocities of the molecules.

As it suffers continual changes of momentum through collision with other particles, any individual particle acquires velocities ranging from zero to very large values. If followed for a sufficiently long time, any particle exhibits an average velocity of zero because movement in any direction is equally likely. The square of its velocity is, however, always greater than zero; hence, the mean square velocity is greater than zero. If one particle were followed for a sufficiently long time, its mean square velocity would approach u^2, the mean value for the system of N particles. In other words, each particle has an average energy that is equal to the average energy per particle in the entire system.

The walls of the containing vessel are fixed and any particle that collides with the wall rebounds elastically. The changes of momentum that occur at opposite walls will on the average cancel so that the vessel is not accelerated and the energy of the gas is constant. The gas exerts a constant outward force on the walls due to the time rate of change of momentum at the walls. The average value of this rate of change of momentum per unit area is the *force per unit area*, or *pressure*, of the gas. Pressure is, then, attributed to mechanical behavior.

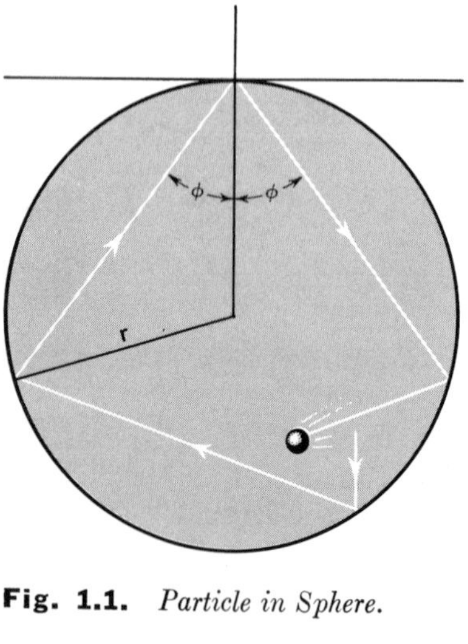

Figure 1.1 is a planar section through the center of a spherical vessel of radius r. A particle that collides elastically with the wall of this vessel rebounds from the vessel at an angle ϕ equal to its angle of approach. Moreover, since the sphere is symmetrical, one particle in such a vessel will remain in the same plane, and this plane passes through the center of the sphere. The distance between collisions is $2r\cos\phi$. If u be the velocity of this particle, the time Δt between collisions is $(2r\cos\phi)/u$. Hence, the number of collisions of a particle with the vessel per unit time is

$$\frac{1}{\Delta t} = \frac{u}{2r\cos\phi}. \qquad (1.2)$$

Fig. 1.1. *Particle in Sphere.*

The component of velocity along the perpendicular to the spherical surface is $u\cos\phi$. Since this component of momentum of a particle of mass m before collision is $-mu\cos\phi$, and afterward is $+mu\cos\phi$ because the component of velocity is in the opposite direction, the change in momentum Δp per collision is

$$\Delta p = +mu\cos\phi - (-mu\cos\phi) = 2mu\cos\phi . \qquad (1.3)$$

The total outward force exerted equally on the average in all directions by the collisions of N molecules is N times as great as that due to one average molecule. If collisions between or among molecules should prevent any one particular molecule from traversing a simple path along a chord, its momentum is in any event conserved and ultimately reaches the wall and is reflected. Hence, for N molecules, the total outward force is the time rate of change of momentum, which by (1.2) and (1.3) is

$$N\frac{\Delta p}{\Delta t} = N\frac{mu^2}{r}.$$

Since this force is exerted upon the area $4\pi r^2$ of the sphere, the force per unit area, or pressure P, is

$$P = \frac{Nmu^2/r}{4\pi r^2}.$$

And since the volume V of the sphere is $\frac{4}{3}\pi r^3$, it follows that

$$PV = \tfrac{1}{3}Nmu^2. \tag{1.4}$$

Equation (1.4), which relates pressure and volume to the mechanical variables N, m, and u, can be derived in an analogous way for a cubic vessel.

The kinetic theory links the energy of this idealized gas to the macroscopic observables pressure and volume. For by (1.1) and (1.4)

$$E = \tfrac{1}{2}Nmu^2 \tag{1.1}$$

$$= \tfrac{3}{2}(\tfrac{1}{3}Nmu^2)$$

$$= \tfrac{3}{2}PV. \tag{1.5}$$

The theory thus provides a mechanical model exhibiting average mechanical properties that are identified as familiar macroscopic properties.

1.2 Perfect Gas Equation of State

Historically the first equation of state of a gas was that discovered by Boyle in 1662. He found the volume V of a fixed amount of air to be inversely proportional to its pressure P under the experimental conditions in his laboratory. Mathematically, if k_B is the proportionality constant found experimentally by Boyle and many experimenters after him who have verified his findings for many kinds of gas, the inverse proportion is

$$PV = k_B. \tag{1.6}$$

The curves of Figure 1.2 show how volume V depends upon pressure P as k_B assumes various constant values. Two hundred years in anticipation of the kinetic theory of gases, Boyle had performed experiments on gases at constant energy, as Equation (1.5) states.

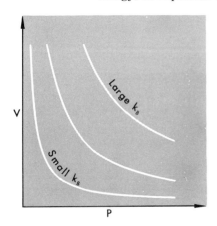

Fig. 1.2. *Boyle's Law:* $PV = k_B$.

Boyle was well aware that the flame of a candle destroyed his inverse proportion, but the effects of a change of temperature upon gas behavior were only qualitatively understood until more than a century after Boyle's discovery. Charles in 1787 and Gay-Lussac in 1802 concluded that all gases have the same coefficient of expansion at the same temperature if the pressure and amount of gas are fixed. If V_0 is the volume of gas at zero degrees while V is the volume of the same amount of gas at the temperature τ, then Charles' law says that at constant pressure the value of the coefficient of expansion α is the same for all gases, where

$$V = V_0(1 + \alpha\tau). \tag{1.7}$$

In terms of the modern Celsius scale of temperature, zero degrees is the temperature at which pure ice and water coexist in equilibrium with air at one atmosphere pressure, and one hundred degrees is the temperature at which pure water boils at a pressure of one atm. The average value of α over this interval of 100 centigrade degrees is, by (1.7),

$$\alpha = \frac{V_{100} - V_0}{100V_0}, \tag{1.8}$$

where V_{100} is the volume of gas measured at 100° on the Celsius scale. Here V_{100} and V_0 are measured under circumstances such that intermolecular forces are negligible, namely, for gases that have very low boiling points, and under very low pressures such that intermolecular distances are great. As the pressures of gases like He, N_2, and H_2 are reduced, their values of α as found by (1.8) approach, in the limit of zero pressure, the numerical value of 1 divided by 273.160 ± 0.010.[1] The value of this number depends upon the arbitrary zero of the Celsius scale of temperature τ and upon the arbitrary size of the centigrade degree.

The form of Charles' law (1.7) can be greatly simplified by the simple transformation

$$T = \tau + \frac{1}{\alpha}. \tag{1.9}$$

For substitution of (1.9) into (1.7) yields

$$V = V_0\left[1 + \alpha\left(T - \frac{1}{\alpha}\right)\right] = (V_0\alpha)T.$$

If k_C replaces $V_0\alpha$, the product of two positive constants, then the law of Charles and Gay-Lussac takes the simple form of a direct proportion,

$$V = k_C T. \tag{1.10}$$

The value of k_C depends upon the pressure and the amount of gas.

When the pressure and amount of a gas are fixed, the kinetic theory through Equation (1.5) requires that the energy of a gas be proportional to its volume. Because of (1.10), the energy is proportional to the new temperature variable T. For reasons soon to be evident, the positive proportionality constant linking E and T is commonly chosen to be $\frac{3}{2}R$; hence,

$$E = \tfrac{3}{2}RT. \tag{1.11}$$

Negative temperatures T are without physical meaning inasmuch as they would require that an ideal gas have negative kinetic energy if the kinetic theory is true. Even if the kinetic theory be ignored, Charles' law (1.10) would require a physically meaningless negative volume for negative values of T. Moreover, long before T reaches zero all real gases are observed to condense; hence, even the zero volume predicted by (1.10) at $T = 0$ is without its physical counterpart. Figure 1.3 illustrates graphically the dependence of V upon T.

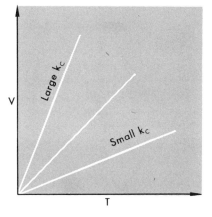

Because the new temperature scale T is restricted to positive values, it is called the *absolute scale of temperature*. The perfect gas equation of state is found from (1.5) and (1.11) by eliminating E to be

$$PV = RT. \tag{1.12}$$

Fig. 1.3. *Charles' Law: $V = k_C T$.*

If $RT = k_B$, (1.12) reduces to Boyle's law (1.6); in words, Boyle's law requires that the volume of a fixed amount of any gas be inversely proportional to its pressure at constant temperature. If $R/P = k_C$, (1.12) reduces to Charles' law (1.10). If R/V is constant, the perfect gas law (1.12) becomes

$$P = k_V T. \tag{1.13}$$

Equation (1.13) serves to define the absolute temperature scale T, for the ultimate experimental standard is the constant-volume gas thermometer containing hydrogen as thermometric fluid.

Example 1.1. The volume of 32.000 g oxygen at 0.00°C at 1.0000 atm is 22.394 l. Predict the volume of these 32.000 g oxygen at 50.00°C at 0.8000 atm.

The existence of an equation of state for oxygen implies that this amount of oxygen occupies a definite volume at 50.00°C at 0.8000 atm. The change of volume could be effected in many ways, but two simple ways are at once obvious. The temperature could be raised from 0.00°C to 50.00°C while the pressure was held constant at 1.0000 atm; and, in a second step, the pressure could be lowered to 0.8000 atm at 50.00°C. An alternate route would be to lower the pressure to 0.8000 atm at 0.00°C and then raise the temperature from 0.00°C to 50.00°C at 0.8000 atm. The following is a diagram of these simple routes.

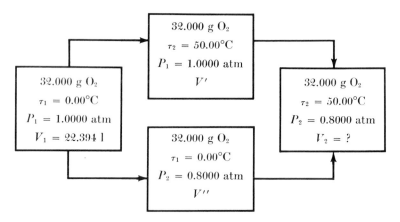

The temperatures that are appropriate for these processes are the absolute temperatures of 273.16°K and 323.16°K. As the temperature is raised at 1.0000 atm, by Charles' law (1.10),

$$k_C = \frac{V_1}{T_1} = \frac{22.394}{273.16} = \frac{V'}{T_2} = \frac{V'}{323.16}$$

$$V' = \frac{323.16}{273.16} \times 22.394 \text{ l.}$$

As the pressure decreases at 50.00°C, by Boyle's law (1.6),

$$k_B = P_1 V' = 1.0000 \times V' = P_2 V_2 = 0.8000 \times V_2$$

$$V_2 = \frac{1.0000}{0.8000} \times V' = \frac{1.0000}{0.8000} \times \frac{323.16}{273.16} \times 22.394 = 33.115 \text{ l.}$$

Although $V'' \neq V'$, the alternate route yields the same expression for V_2. The original volume V_1 increases by the factor (1.0000/0.8000) as the pressure decreases at constant temperature (0.00°C or 50.00°C), and the intermediate volume increases by the factor (323.16/273.16) as the temperature increases at constant pressure (0.8000 atm or 1.0000 atm). The observed value is 33.137 l.

In 1829, Graham discovered that, at constant pressure, the rates at which various gases escape through a tiny orifice are inversely proportional to their densities. If the rate of escape is proportional to u (see Section 1.8, Example 1.8) and if ρ is the density of the gas, then

$$u = \frac{k_G}{\sqrt{\rho}}. \tag{1.14}$$

A relation of this same type can be deduced from (1.4). Since density is mass per unit volume, the density ρ of a gas containing N particles each of mass m in a volume V is Nm/V. By (1.4),

$$u^2 = \frac{3PV}{Nm}$$

or

$$u = \sqrt{\frac{3P}{\rho}}. \tag{1.15}$$

The kinetic theory says that the value of k_G in (1.14) is $\sqrt{3P}$. As long as the orifice is small enough that each molecule escapes as an individual without colliding with others as it escapes, Graham's law obtains. This means essentially that the orifice must be small relative to the usual distance between collisions. If the orifice is larger than this distance, the flow becomes hydro-dynamic and a stream of gas issues through the orifice. Graham's law finds application in the separation of isotopes, such as in the separation of $U^{235}F_6$ from $U^{238}F_6$, and in the recovery of He from high molecular weight gases.

Example 1.2. At the same temperature and pressure, gaseous argon is ten times as dense as gaseous helium. At what temperature will argon at 1 atm diffuse through a tiny orifice at the same rate as helium at 1 atm at 0°C?

The rates of diffusion of argon and helium will be equal when their densities at 1 atm are equal. For a fixed mass of gas, density is inversely proportional to volume; hence, the volume of argon at the unknown temperature must be ten times that of helium at 0°C. Since volume is directly proportional to absolute temperature by Charles' law, the argon temperature is 2732°K.

1.3 Molecular Weight

With the synthesis of the unsymmetrical ethers R'OR'' by Williamson in the years following 1850, it was clear that the simple formula HO for water should be H_2O. But then, if the smallest chemical combining weight of hydrogen was to be unity, the smallest relative weight of oxygen would be 16 instead of the value 8 that went with the formula HO because of the incontrovertible fact that water is 89% by weight oxygen. Long before Williamson's critical experiment, Avogadro had suggested in 1811 a hypothesis which readily explained the law of combining volumes. He proposed that equal volumes of gases at the same temperature and pressure contain equal numbers of mole-cules. But since this hypothesis required the formula H_2O, it was unpopular until Williamson's synthesis of the unsymmetrical ethers.

The proof of Avogadro's hypothesis become law is brief. If gas of kind 1 has a kinetic energy per molecule of $\frac{1}{2}m_1u_1^2$ while kind 2 has a value of $\frac{1}{2}m_2u_2^2$, then at the same temperature by hypothesis

$$\tfrac{1}{2}m_1u_1^2 = \tfrac{1}{2}m_2u_2^2. \tag{1.16}$$

But if these two kinds of gas at this common temperature also occupy equal volumes V at equal pressures P, then by (1.4)

$$\tfrac{1}{3}N_1 m_1 u_1^2 = \tfrac{1}{3}N_2 m_2 u_2^2 . \tag{1.17}$$

Division of (1.17) by (1.16) and elimination of common factors yields Avogadro's statement:

$$N_1(T, P, V) = N_2(T, P, V), \tag{1.18}$$

where $N_i(T, P, V)$ is the number of molecules of type i that exist in the volume V at the temperature T at the pressure P.

Since equal volumes of hydrogen and chlorine at the same temperature and pressure unite to yield two volumes of hydrogen chloride, and since every molecule of hydrogen chloride contains hydrogen and chlorine, it is necessary that elemental hydrogen and chlorine each contain an even number of atoms per molecule. Avogadro indeed forced and clarified this distinction between molecule and atom. However, since one volume of oxygen unites with hydrogen to give two volumes of water at the same temperature and pressure as the reactants, and since every water molecule contains oxygen, elemental gaseous oxygen must also contain an even number of atoms per molecule. It has been found that two, the simplest even number, adequately explains all the gaseous reactions of oxygen and leads to no other inconsistencies. Accordingly, if the smallest chemical weight of oxygen is the atomic weight of 16, then the smallest physical weight of gaseous oxygen is the molecular weight of 32.

Exactly 32 grams of pure gaseous oxygen occupy 22.394 l at 0.00°C at a pressure of one atm. At lower pressures, where intermolecular interactions become less and less important, the measured volumes (when corrected by Boyle's law to the volume that would be occupied at one atm) increase gradually. The limit at zero pressure is 22.4140 l. This is the volume that exactly 32 grams of oxygen would occupy at 0.00°C at one atm if intermolecular forces were negligible. This is the volume that would be occupied by one gram-molecular weight of any gas at 0.00°C at one atm if it behaved ideally. By various methods the number of molecules in this volume has been found to be 0.60238×10^{24} under standard conditions. Appropriately, this is called *Avogadro's number N*.

Molecular weights are assigned to gases by direct or indirect comparison to the standard of 32 for oxygen. Because sulfur dioxide is twice as dense as oxygen at the same temperature and pressure, its molecular weight is 64. Because helium is one-eighth as dense, its molecular weight is 4. A molecular weight is perhaps most simply considered as the weight in grams of a pure gas that would occupy 22.4140 l at 0.00°C at one atm if intermolecular forces were negligible. Measurements made under other conditions can be corrected to these standard conditions through the ideal gas law (1.12) generalized to allow for any number n of gram-moles:

$$PV = nRT . \qquad (1.19)$$

The proportionality constant R assumes a definite universal value through oxygen.[1]

$$R = \frac{PV}{nT}$$

$$= \frac{(1.00000 \text{ atm}) \times (22.4140 \text{ l})}{(1.00000 \text{ g mole}) \times (273.160°\text{K})}$$

$$= 0.0820544 \text{ l atm mole}^{-1} \text{ deg}^{-1} . \qquad (1.20)$$

There are several methods of determining the molecular weight M of a substance that can be vaporized. The most direct method is to weigh the amount g of gas that occupies a vessel of volume V at a pressure P and temperature T. Since the effects of the buoyancy of air and adsorption of gases like water on the surfaces of large glass vessels are noticeable, it is common to use an identical glass vessel as a tare in order to minimize such possible errors. Since the molecular weight M is the mass g of gas per mole, it follows from (1.19) that

$$M = \frac{g}{n}$$

$$= \frac{gRT}{PV}. \qquad (1.21)$$

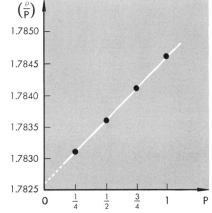

Fig. 1.4. *Density of Argon as a Function of Pressure (0.00°C).*

Very exact values of M can be found by determining the value of the function (g/PV) for various pressures at the constant temperature T. At low pressures and a constant temperature, (g/PV) or (ρ/P) is a linear function of pressure P. Extrapolation from finite low pressures to zero pressure by means of a straight line as in Figure 1.4 yields a value of (g/PV) or (ρ/P) at zero pressure where intermolecular forces are nil and all gases are perfect. Then,

$$M = RT \lim_{P \to 0} \left(\frac{g}{PV} \right). \qquad (1.22)$$

Example 1.3. Experimentally observed densities of argon at 0.00°C are listed in the accompanying table and values of (ρ/P) in grams per liter per atmosphere are plotted as a function of pressure in Figure 1.4. What is the atomic weight of argon if each molecule contains one atom?

Density ρ (g l⁻¹)	Pressure P (atm)
1.7846	1.0000
1.3381	0.7500
0.8918	0.5000
0.44578	0.2500

The values of (ρ/P) are 1.7846, 1.7841, 1.7836 and 1.7831 g l⁻¹ atm⁻¹. By Figure 1.4, extrapolation yields

$$\lim_{P \to 0} \left(\frac{\rho}{P}\right) = \lim_{P \to 0} \left(\frac{g}{PV}\right) = 1.7826 \text{ g l}^{-1} \text{ atm}^{-1}.$$

Then, by (1.22),

$$M = 0.0820544 \times 273.160 \times 1.7826 = 39.955 \text{ g mole}^{-1}.$$

If each molecule contains one atom, the atomic weight is 39.955.

The vapor density of a substance that is a liquid or solid at ordinary temperatures and pressures yields in a similar way a molecular weight of the substance as it exists in the gaseous state. A direct way of measuring vapor density is to add the condensed substance to a rigid vessel with a narrow neck, immerse all but the narrow neck in a thermostat at a temperature high enough that the substance vaporizes at room pressure. If enough of the condensed material was added at the start, the vessel will have been swept clean of air upon complete vaporization of the substance. When no more condensed material remains, the vessel is sealed off at the known laboratory pressure and known thermostat temperature. Weighing the cooled sealed vessel and subsequent calibration of its volume by weighing it empty and filled with water yield all the variables on the right of (1.21).

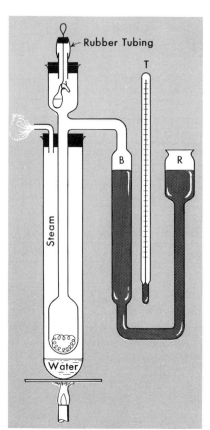

The Victor Meyer method of estimating the molecular weight of a volatile liquid or solid is somewhat less direct. Figure 1.5 is a schematic diagram of one of many modifications of the apparatus. A jacket containing steam provides a thermostat at about 100°C. A small sealed vial containing about 0.002 mole of liquid weighed accurately is suspended in the cool zone of the closed constant-volume system. When a stationary state is achieved in which part of the closed system is at about 100°C and the remainder is at room temperature, the mercury levels in the gas burette B and reservoir R are leveled and the reading on the burette is recorded. The barometric pressure of the laboratory is also recorded. The hook on which the sealed vial is hung can be moved vertically into the tube without admitting air to the system by stretching the rubber joint at the top. Such a vertical movement jams the vial into the tube and causes it to break. The bulb falls into glass wool in the hot zone and the liquid vaporizes slowly as the vial warms. Warm air, displaced into the cool

Fig. 1.5. *A Modification of Victor Meyer Apparatus.*

zone, cools and forces already cool air on into the burette. After complete vaporization and before the vapors have diffused out of the hot zone, the reading of the gas burette is once again taken with leveled mercury levels, and the barometric pressure is noted in the laboratory. A volume of cool air at room temperature and pressure has been measured in place of an equal volume of hot vapors at about 100°C at room pressure. Because the same hot volume must exist at beginning and end, and because the increase in volume is measured in the cool zone, the appropriate temperature for use in (1.21) is the temperature T of the laboratory. However, the molecular weight found is that characteristic of the liquid's vapors at about 100°C. The temperature of the thermostat should be about 20°C greater than the boiling point of the liquid in order to minimize deviations from ideal gas behavior.

Example 1.4. A Victor Meyer glass vial weighed 5.014 g empty. Filled with a pure saturated organic liquid containing only carbon, fluorine, and chlorine, the sealed vial weighed 5.284 g. The vial was broken in a vessel that was jacketed by a bath of water that boiled at 99.8°C. The initial mercury level in the gas burette was 10.46 ml, and the final level was 46.22 ml. The barometric pressure was constant at 754.6 mm Hg, and the temperature of the laboratory was 23.2°C. If the compound contained 57% by weight chlorine, determine (a) its molecular weight as it exists at 99.8°C, and (b) its molecular formula.

The increase in volume in the cool part of the closed system was $46.22 - 10.46 = 35.76$ ml. The amount of liquid vaporized was $5.284 - 5.014 = 0.270$ g. The approximate molecular weight is, then,

$$M = \frac{gRT}{PV} \tag{1.21}$$

$$= \frac{0.270 \times 0.08205 \times 296.4}{\left(\dfrac{754.6}{760.0}\right) \times 0.03576} = 185 .$$

The general formula of a saturated compound of this sort is $C_nF_xCl_y$, where $x + y = 2n + 2$. But since 57% of the compound is chlorine,

$$y \approx \frac{0.57 \times 185}{35.5} = 2.97 \approx 3 .$$

Hence, since

$$M = 12.01n + 19.00x + 35.46 \times 3$$

and

$$x = 2n - 1 ,$$

it follows that

$$185 \approx 12n + 19(2n - 1) + 106.5$$
$$97.5 \approx 50n$$
$$n = 2$$
$$x = 2n - 1$$
$$= 3 .$$

The molecular formula is $C_2F_3Cl_3$, and its exact molecular weight is

$$M = 12.01 \times 2 + 19.00 \times 3 + 35.46 \times 3 = 187.40 .$$

1.4   Equations of State of a Real Gas

The perfect gas law fails to describe the behavior of a real gas for two reasons. It takes no account of the actual volume of the molecules and it ignores the attractive energies that cause any real gas to condense as a liquid or solid. The perfect gas law is adequate when the volume occupied by the molecules themselves is a very small part of the volume of the gas and when the kinetic energy of the molecules is great relative to attractive intermolecular energies.

When the unoccupied volume is not great relative to the very volume of the molecules, the compressibility of a gas is less than expected because the unoccupied volume is significantly less than the apparent volume of the gas. If b is the volume proper to 1 mole of molecules, then the unoccupied volume of n moles with an apparent total volume V is $(V - nb)$.   This unoccupied volume $(V - nb)$ is the volume that can be lost by compression.

The feeble intermolecular attraction that culminates at low temperatures in condensation extends over a distance of several molecular diameters. When the average distance between collisions is also several diameters in magnitude, each molecule has a lower energy than might be expected because it tends to be held by its neighbors in a favorable position.   In other words, in addition to kinetic energy it exhibits potential energy.   Compared to an ideal gas, its energy is low, and thus its impacts on the walls of its container are less violent than those of an ideal gas.

In 1873, van der Waals proposed as the equation of state of a real gas

$$\left(P + \frac{an^2}{V^2}\right)(V - nb) = nRT .\tag{1.23}$$

In (1.23), P, V, n, R, and T have their usual meaning as in (1.19), and a and b are empirical constants.   Although b represents the real volume of 1 mole of molecules themselves, it is actually somewhat greater than the molar volume of the liquid.   The constant a is a proportionality constant linking a "pressure-that-might-have-been" to the number of collisions, all of which are considered as attractive.   The number of collisions suffered by a molecule in entering an occupied vessel is proportional to the number of target molecules per unit volume.   But if all molecules act also as missiles, the number of collisions is proportional not only to the number of target molecules per unit volume but also to the number of missile molecules per unit volume.   In other words, the number of collisions is proportional to $(n/V)^2$.   Thus originates the pressure that might have been.

There are for real gases two other simple equations of state that involve just two arbitrary constants.   The first of these, due to Berthelot and resembling (1.23) somewhat, is (1.24), where again the symbols have their usual significance and where a and b are empirical constants characteristic of a gas.

$$\left(P + \frac{an^2}{TV^2}\right)(V - nb) = nRT .\tag{1.24}$$

The last of these common two-constant equations, that of Dieterici, is (1.25).

$$(Pe^{an/VRT})(V - nb) = nRT .\tag{1.25}$$

All three of these equations have the general form of the perfect gas law, but the volume is the unoccupied volume and the ideal pressure is replaced by two parts: the observed pressure P and a pseudopressure (that might have been) that is attributed to intermolecular attractions.

All three of these equations can be expressed approximately in the common form (1.26), called the *virial* (Latin: *force*) *equation of state*.

$$\frac{PV}{nRT} = 1 + \frac{nB}{V} + \frac{n^2C}{V^2} + \cdots ,\tag{1.26}$$

where B is called the *second virial coefficient*, C the *third*, and so on. Generally, the third and succeeding terms are negligible. According to van der Waals' equation (1.23),

$$PV + \frac{an^2}{V} - Pnb - \frac{abn^3}{V^2} = nRT ;$$

whence
$$\frac{PV}{nRT} = 1 + \frac{Pb}{RT} - \frac{an}{VRT} + \frac{abn^2}{V^2RT}$$

$$= 1 + \frac{b}{RT}\left(\frac{nRT}{V - nb} - \frac{an^2}{V^2}\right) - \frac{an}{VRT} + \frac{abn^2}{V^2RT}$$

$$= 1 + \frac{nb}{V}\left(1 - \frac{nb}{V}\right)^{-1} - \frac{an}{VRT}$$

$$= 1 + \frac{nb}{V}\left[1 + \frac{nb}{V} + \left(\frac{nb}{V}\right)^2 + \cdots\right] - \frac{an}{VRT}$$

$$= 1 + \frac{n}{V}\left(b - \frac{a}{RT}\right) + \frac{n^2}{V^2}(b^2) + \cdots .$$

By comparison with (1.26) it is clear that for the van der Waals' equation,

$$\left.\begin{array}{c} B = b - \dfrac{a}{RT} \\[2mm] C = b^2 . \end{array}\right\}\tag{1.27}$$

and

Sometimes it is convenient to express the virial equation as a power series in P, as in (1.28).

$$PV = nRT + nBP + \cdots .\tag{1.28}$$

In this form B has the same value as in (1.26), but the third virial coefficients of (1.28) and (1.26) would differ. Thus, a second approximate form of (1.23) is (1.29).

$$PV = nRT + n\left(b - \frac{a}{RT}\right)P.\tag{1.29}$$

Table 1.1. *Virial Coefficients of Nitrogen**

$$PV = A\left(1 + \frac{B}{V} + \frac{C}{V^2} + \cdots\right)$$

(P in atm; V = 1.00000 at 0°C at P = 1.00000 atm)

τ (°C)	A	$B \times 10^3$	$C \times 10^6$
400	2.46522	+1.04930	2.2523
300	2.09903	+0.92142	1.7599
200	1.73283	+0.68491	2.0487
150	1.54973	+0.51457	2.1797
100	1.36662	+0.27400	2.5627
50	1.18368	−0.01150	2.5954
0	1.00045	−0.46137	3.3371
−50	0.81735	−1.17733	4.0822
−100	0.63425	−2.31462	4.2354

Similarly, Berthelot's equation (1.24) yields

$$\left. \begin{aligned} B &= b - \frac{a}{RT^2} \\ C &= b^2. \end{aligned} \right\} \quad (1.30)$$

and

Finally, expansion of $e^{-an/VRT}$ as a power series yields for Dieterici's equation (1.25) the values

$$\left. \begin{aligned} B &= b - \frac{a}{RT} \\ C &= b^2 - \frac{ab}{RT} + \frac{a^2}{2R^2T^2}. \end{aligned} \right\} \quad (1.31)$$

and

The values of a and b for a substance differ for each equation; the second virial coefficient B has the dimensions of volume per mole and is a function of the temperature. At high temperatures it is greater than zero, but as the temperature decreases B decreases continuously and eventually becomes less than zero. The temperature at which B is zero is called the *Boyle temperature*. For van der Waals' or Dieterici's equations, the Boyle temperature T_B is, by (1.27) or (1.31) for $B = 0$,

$$T_B = \frac{a}{bR}. \quad (1.32)$$

Table 1.1 lists the observed values of virial coefficients of N_2 for several temperatures; and in Table 1.2 are listed for several gases values of the constants a and b of the van der Waals' equation (1.23). The value of T_B calculated for N_2 from Table 1.2 is 426°K, somewhat greater than the data of Table 1.1 require.

Table 1.2. *van der Waals Constants†*

GAS	a (liter^2 atm mole^{-2})	b (liter mole^{-1})
H_2	0.245	0.0266
N_2	1.348	0.0386
O_2	1.360	0.0317
CH_4	2.263	0.0428
CO_2	3.61	0.0428
Cl_2	6.48	0.0562
CCl_4	19.52	0.1267
C_2H_2	4.41	0.0515
C_2H_4	4.49	0.0573
C_2H_6	5.44	0.0643
CO	1.456	0.0395
HCl	3.67	0.0408
n-C_5H_{12}	18.8	0.145
n-C_6H_{14}	24.5	0.174
n-C_7H_{16}	31.0	0.206
NH_3	4.20	0.0374
H_2O	5.42	0.0302
C_2H_5OH	12.0	0.0840

Example 1.5. Ten moles ethane were confined in a vessel of volume 4.86 l at 300°K. Predict the pressure of gaseous ethane under these conditions with the use of the equation of state (a) of the perfect gas, and (b) of van der Waals ($a = 5.44$ l^2 atm mole^{-2}, $b = 64.3$ ml mole^{-1}). The observed value [Sage, B. H., D. C. Webster, and W. N. Lacey, *Ind. Eng. Chem.*, **29**, 658 (1937)] is 34.0 atm.

(a) By the perfect gas law (1.19), since $V = 4.86$ l and $T = 300$°K and $n = 10.00$ moles, it follows that

$$P = \frac{nRT}{V} = \frac{10.00 \times 0.08205 \times 300}{4.86} = 50.7 \text{ atm.}$$

* Holborn and Otto, *Zs. fur Physik.*, **30**, 320 (1924), as quoted in *Int. Crit. Tables, III*, p. 19.
† Calculated by the methods of Section 1.5 from values of T_c and P_c of Table 1.3.

(b) By van der Waals' equation (1.23),

$$P = \frac{nRT}{V - nb} - \frac{an^2}{V^2} = \frac{10.00 \times 0.08205 \times 300}{4.86 - 10.0 \times 0.0643} - \frac{5.44 \times 10.0^2}{4.86^2}$$

$$= 58.4 - 23.0 = 35.4 \text{ atm.}$$

Since the volume actually occupied by the molecules of ethane constitutes an appreciable part of the 4.86 l and since this 0.643 l is incompressible, the pressure on this account might have been 58.4 atm, even greater than the 50.7 atm expected of a perfect gas of point molecules. However, because of intermolecular attractions, this value of 58.4 is decreased to only 35.4 atm, which is close to the observed pressure of 34.0 atm.

1.5 Principle of Corresponding States

Because the perfect gas equation of state is inadequate when temperatures, volumes, and pressures approach values where condensation is possible, modified equations of state such as those of the preceding section have been developed. The regularity of nature would suggest that, at least for chemically similar substances, there should be a common functional form of their equations of state. It is the purpose of this section to study the extent to which one function can represent the behavior of many substances.

Figure 1.6 illustrates the typical behavior of dense gases. Each curve is called an *isotherm* and represents the observed pressure P of a fixed amount of a pure fluid as a function of its volume V at constant temperature. At high temperatures, the curves resemble those of Figure 1.2, which illustrates Boyle's law. At intermediate temperatures, the curves are no longer hyperbolas $PV = k_B$ because of deviations from ideal behavior. Still, the pressure decreases continuously at constant temperature as the volume increases. At low temperatures, there is a range of volumes in which the pressure of the system is constant at constant temperature. In these circumstances, the volume is occupied

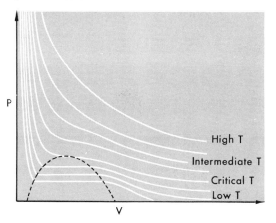

Fig. 1.6. *Typical Behavior of Fluids in the Region of the Critical State.*

by liquid and gas and the constant pressure (the horizontal portions of the isotherms) is the vapor pressure of the fluid. If the figure is drawn for 1 mole of the substance, the ends of these horizontal isotherms define the volumes of 1 mole of liquid and gas. In other words, in the dome-shaped region, liquid and gaseous states coexist; the boundaries of the dome-shaped region mark the limits of pressure and temperature under which liquid and gas coexist at equilibrium.

The *critical temperature* of a substance is that temperature at which liquid and vapor become so similar that they can no longer be distinguished as individuals. The indexes of refraction, densities, and molar volumes of the two phases become identical in the critical state. The critical state is at the very top of the dome-shaped region where liquid and gaseous molar volumes become equal. The isotherm that goes through this point is the *critical isotherm*. The pressure at the top of the dome-shaped region is the *critical pressure*, and the *critical state* is the state of matter at the critical temperature, volume, and pressure.

At the critical state, the slope of the critical isotherm is zero. That is, at the critical state and even within the dome-shaped region, the pressure does not depend upon the volume of the system at constant temperature. A small change in volume ΔV would not cause a change in pressure ΔP. Mathematically, with the subscript to indicate explicitly that the temperature is constant along an isotherm,

$$\lim_{\Delta V \to 0} \left(\frac{\Delta P}{\Delta V} \right)_T = \left(\frac{\partial P}{\partial V} \right)_T = 0. \tag{1.33}$$

The expression (1.33) is zero because ΔP is zero within the dome-shaped region of Figure 1.6.

The critical isotherm is distinguished from those at lower temperatures in that its slope increases continuously to zero at the critical point and then decreases continuously once again. That is, the slope reaches a maximum value of zero at the critical state. Mathematically, when the slope $(\partial P)/\partial V)_T$ is a maximum, the rate of change of the slope with respect to changes in volume is zero. Hence, at the critical point

$$\frac{\partial}{\partial V} \left(\frac{\partial P}{\partial V} \right)_T = \left(\frac{\partial^2 P}{\partial V^2} \right)_T = 0. \tag{1.34}$$

Equation (1.34) is true also within the dome-shaped area, but the points at which the slope becomes zero do not coincide and the value of zero is not attained continuously.

The two conditions (1.33) and (1.34) serve to define the critical state. As conditions upon an equation of state that is meant to describe a substance in its fluid state, (1.33) and (1.34) serve to fix the two parameters a and b of the equations of state of van der Waals, Dieterici, or Berthelot. Since these equations are dimensionally homogeneous (that is, yield values of their variables with correct units), it is possible to eliminate the constants a and b through (1.33) and (1.34) and to express the equations in terms of reduced variables that are dimensionless. The reduced pressure P_r is the ratio of pressure P to the critical pressure P_c; the reduced temperature T_r is the ratio of the temperature T to the critical temperature T_c; and the reduced volume V_r is the ratio of volume V to the critical volume V_c. The principle of corre-

sponding states says that for a group of similar substances there is one functional form of the equation of state of the form

$$P_r = f(V_r, T_r) .$$ (1.35)

In the neighborhood of the critical state, Dieterici's equation (1.25) is the best of the three 2-constant equations discussed. It is transformed into reduced form similar to (1.35) in the following way. By (1.25),

$$P = \left(\frac{nRT}{V - nb}\right) e^{-an/VRT} .$$ (1.36)

In order to satisfy (1.33) and (1.34) it is necessary to take the first and second derivatives of P with respect to V when $T, n, R, a,$ and b are constant.

$$\left(\frac{\partial P}{\partial V}\right)_T = P\left(\frac{an}{V^2 RT} - \frac{1}{V - nb}\right) .$$ (1.37)

At the critical state, (1.33) requires

$$0 = \frac{anP_c}{V_c^2 RT_c} - \frac{P_c}{V_c - nb} .$$ (1.38)

That is,

$$a = \frac{V_c^2 RT_c}{n(V_c - nb)} .$$ (1.39)

Calculation of the second partial derivative begins with (1.37). By use of (1.37) as needed, the result is

$$\left(\frac{\partial^2 P}{\partial V^2}\right)_T = -\frac{2Pan}{V^3 RT} + \frac{P}{(V - nb)^2} + \left(\frac{an}{V^2 RT} - \frac{1}{V - nb}\right)^2 P .$$

Accordingly, at the critical point, by (1.34),

$$0 = P_c\left[\left(\frac{an}{V_c^2 RT_c} - \frac{1}{V_c - nb}\right)^2 - \frac{2an}{V_c^3 RT_c} + \frac{1}{(V_c - nb)^2}\right] .$$

Use of (1.38) leads to considerable simplification, and, as a result,

$$0 = -\frac{2an}{V_c^3 RT_c} + \frac{1}{(V_c - nb)^2} .$$

That is,

$$a = \frac{V_c^3 RT_c}{2n(V_c - nb)^2} .$$ (1.40)

Equations (1.39) and (1.40) are simultaneous equations that fix the values of a and b in terms of the critical values of pressure P_c, of volume V_c, and of temperature T_c. Division of (1.40) by (1.39) yields (1.41).

$$1 = \frac{V_c}{2(V_c - nb)}$$

$$2V_c - 2nb = V_c$$

$$b = \frac{V_c}{2n} \cdot \tag{1.41}$$

Use of (1.41) in (1.39) yields Equation (1.42) for a as a function of T_c; that is,

$$a = \frac{(2nb)^2 RT_c}{n(2nb - nb)} = \frac{4n^2 b^2 RT_c}{n^2 b} \cdot$$

By (1.41) this becomes

$$a = \frac{2V_c RT_c}{n} \cdot \tag{1.42}$$

Application of (1.36) at the critical point with account of (1.41) and (1.42) yields the relation of a and b to P_c.

$$P_c = \left(\frac{nRT_c}{V_c - nb}\right) e^{-an/V_c RT_c}$$

$$= \left[\frac{nR\left(\dfrac{a}{4bR}\right)}{2nb - nb}\right] e^{-an/2nbR(a/4bR)}$$

$$= \frac{a}{4b^2 e^2} \cdot \tag{1.43}$$

Any two of the three equations (1.41), (1.42), and (1.43) are sufficient for the evaluation of a and b in terms of the critical constants. Since Dieterici's equation is not perfect, the values of a and b depend somewhat upon which two of the three critical constants, P_c, V_c, and T_c, are chosen.

If a and b are eliminated from (1.41), (1.42), and (1.43) there results a relation that should, in view of the principle of corresponding states, apply to all substances. Upon substitution of (1.41) and (1.42) into (1.43),

$$P_c = \frac{2V_c RT_c}{n4\left(\dfrac{V_c}{2n}\right)^2 e^2}$$

$$\frac{P_c V_c}{nRT_c} = \frac{2}{e^2} = 0.2707. \tag{1.44}$$

Table 1.3. *Observed Values of the Compressibility Factor at the Critical State**

SUBSTANCE	P_c (atm)	V_c (ml mole^{-1})	T_c (°K)	$\dfrac{P_c V_c}{RT_c}$	GENERAL CHARACTERISTICS OF FLUID
He	2.261	57.8	5.23	0.305	Nonpolar; slightly polarizable
Ne †	25.9	41.7	44.5	0.296	
Ar	48.0	75.3	150.7	0.292	
Kr ‡	54.1	92.1	209.4	0.290	
Xe	58.2	113.8	289.8	0.279	
H_2	12.8	65.0	33.2	0.306	
N_2 †	33.5	90.1	126.1	0.292	
O_2	50.1	74.4	154.8	0.293	
CH_4	45.8	99.4	191.1	0.290	
CO_2	72.9	94.9	304.3	0.277	
Cl_2	76.1	123.8	417.	0.275	Nonpolar; polarizable
CS_2	78.	173.	552.	0.298	
CCl_4	45.0	262.	556.3	0.258	
C_2H_2	61.6	113.	309.2	0.272	
C_2H_4	50.6	134.	282.8	0.292	
C_2H_6 §	48.7	141.7	305.7	0.275	
C_6H_6	48.6	260.	562.	0.274	
SO_3	83.8	126.5	491.4	0.263	
CO ‡	34.5	93.2	133.0	0.295	Polar; slightly polarizable
HCl	81.6	86.0	324.6	0.263	
N_2O	71.7	96.2	309.7	0.271	
CH_3Cl	65.9	143.0	416.3	0.276	Polar; polarizable
SO_2	77.8	123.8	430.7	0.273	
CH_3COCH_3	46.6	213.	508.5	0.238	
n-C_5H_{12}	33.3	310.3	469.8	0.268	
n-C_6H_{14}	29.9	367.5	507.9	0.264	
n-C_7H_{16}	27.0	428.	543.2	0.259	
C_6H_5F	44.6	271.2	559.8	0.263	
C_6H_5Cl	44.6	308.0	632.4	0.265	
NH_3	111.3	72.9	405.5	0.244	Hydrogen-bonded
H_2O	219.5	58.8	647.6	0.243	
CH_3OH	78.5	117.7	513.2	0.220	
C_2H_5OH	63.0	167.2	516.	0.249	

* Data calculated from Lange's *Handbook of Chemistry*. New York: McGraw-Hill Book Co., Inc., 1956, pp. 1439-52, 1473 unless noted otherwise.
†Hirschfelder, J. O., C. F. Curtiss, and R. B. Bird, *Molecular Theory of Gases and Liquids.* New York: John Wiley and Sons, Inc., 1954, p. 245.
‡ Guggenheim, E. A., *Thermodynamics.* Amsterdam: North-Holland Publ. Co., 1957, p. 167.
§ Sage, B. H., D. C. Webster, and W. N. Lacey, *Ind. Eng. Chem.*, **29**, 658 (1937).

Similar development of the equations of van der Waals and of Berthelot yield (1.45), which is analogous to (1.44).

$$\frac{P_c V_c}{nRT_c} = \frac{3}{8} = 0.3750. \tag{1.45}$$

Values of the left-hand members of (1.44) and (1.45) for various fluids, as calculated from observed critical constants, are listed in Table 1.3 for five general kinds of fluid. On this criterion, Dieterici's equation must be adjudged superior to the others. Fluids with small (slightly polarizable) symmetrical (nonpolar) molecules have critical state compressibility factors close to 0.29. Polarity or polarizability almost always lowers this value to about 0.26 or 0.27, while hydrogen-bonding so dominates intermolecular attractions that very low values result for water and similar substances. More thorough discussions of the applicability of the principle of corresponding states are given elsewhere.[2]

Dieterici's equation is transformed into the form (1.35) with reduced dimensionless variables by elimination of a and b through (1.41) and (1.42) and division by (1.44).

$$(Pe^{an/VRT})(V - nb) = nRT \tag{1.25}$$

$$(Pe^{2V_c RT_c n/nVRT}) \left[V - n \left(\frac{V_c}{2n} \right) \right] = nRT$$

$$(Pe^{2/V_r T_r}) \left(V - \frac{V_c}{2} \right) = nRT$$

$$\left(\frac{P}{P_c} \right) (e^{2/V_r T_r}) \left(\frac{V}{V_c} - \frac{1}{2} \right) = \left(\frac{T}{T_c} \right) \left(\frac{e^2}{2} \right)$$

$$P_r e^{2/V_r T_r} (V_r - \tfrac{1}{2}) = \frac{e^2}{2} T_r , \tag{1.46}$$

where

$$P_r = \frac{P}{P_c}, \qquad V_r = \frac{V}{V_c}, \qquad T_r = \frac{T}{T_c} .$$

The analogous transformations to reduced variables of the equations of van der Waals and Berthelot are left as exercises for the student.

Example 1.6. With Dieterici's equation of state, predict the pressure of gaseous ethane when 10.0 moles are confined in a vessel of volume 4.86 l at 300°K. Critical constants of ethane are listed in Table 1.3.

By (1.41),

$$b = \frac{0.1417}{2} = 0.0708 \text{ l mole}^{-1}.$$

By (1.42),

$$a = 2 \times 0.1417 \times 0.08205 \times 305.7 = 7.11 \text{ liter}^2 \text{ atm mole}^{-2}.$$

If $V = 4.86$ and $T = 300$ and $n = 10.0$, then (1.25) yields

$$P = \left(\frac{nRT}{V - nb}\right) e^{-an/VRT}$$

$$= \left(\frac{10.0 \times 0.08205 \times 300}{4.86 - 10.0 \times 0.0708}\right) e^{-7.11 \times 10.0/(4.86 \times 0.08205 \times 300)}$$

$$= 59.3e^{-0.594} = 32.7 \text{ atm}.$$

This value of 32.7 atm differs from the observed value of 34.0 atm by 1.3 atm, while the equation of van der Waals predicted a value in Example 1.5 that was 1.4 atm too high. (If the van der Waals constants a and b had been calculated from V_c and T_c as the Dieterici constants were in this example, the van der Waals equation would have predicted 39.2 atm.)

1.6 Various Equations of State

As the number of parameters like a and b of the two-constant equations of state is increased, more and more accurate equations are possible. Indeed, Hougen and Watson[3] have published charts in which the compressibility factor z is graphed as an empirical function of reduced pressure and reduced temperature; that is,

$$z(P_r, T_r) = \frac{PV}{nRT}. \tag{1.47}$$

This is in the spirit of the principle of corresponding states, but is also tacit admission that a definite functional form is inadequate over large ranges of pressure and temperature.

A second equation due to Berthelot is (1.48).

$$\frac{PV}{nRT} = 1 + \frac{9R}{128}\left(\frac{P}{P_c}\right)\left(\frac{T_c}{T}\right)\left(1 - \frac{6T_c^2}{T^2}\right). \tag{1.48}$$

The symbols have their usual meaning in (1.48), which finds its greatest use in making small corrections to ideal behavior at pressures of the order of a few atmospheres. It finds use, for example, in the Victor Meyer method of determining molecular weight.

By far the best empirical equation is that of Beattie and Bridgeman,[4] (1.49), wherein the volume V is for 1 mole.

$$PV^2 = RT\left(1 - \frac{c}{VT^3}\right)\left(V + B_0 - \frac{bB_0}{V}\right) - A_0\left(1 - \frac{a}{V}\right). \tag{1.49}$$

The five constants characteristic of several gases are listed in Table 1.4. This equation is accurate up to about 250 atm.

B. KINETIC THEORY

1.7 Molecular Velocity

When Equation (1.4) is applied to exactly 1 gram-mole of gas, N is equal to Avogadro's number and RT may be substituted for PV because of (1.12). Then,

$$RT = \tfrac{1}{3}Nmu^2$$

$$u = \sqrt{\frac{3RT}{Nm}}.$$

But Nm is the mass of 1 gram-mole of gas, or M. Hence,

$$u = \sqrt{\frac{3RT}{M}}. \tag{1.50}$$

This value of u differs from zero because it is really the square root of the average value of u^2. The average value of the velocity itself is zero since movement is equally likely and equally large in all directions.

In order to obtain a numerical value of the root mean square velocity u, R must be expressed in units more suitable than liter-atmospheres per mole-degree. The standard atmosphere is defined as 1.013250×10^6 dynes cm^{-2}. This represents the force exerted by a column of mercury 76.0000 cm in length and one cm^2 in cross-section at 0°C when accelerated by gravity by 980.665 $cm\ sec^{-1}\ sec^{-1}$. Since exactly 1 l is equivalent to 1000.027 cc, it follows that

$$R = 0.0820544\ \text{l atm mole}^{-1}\ \text{deg}^{-1}$$
$$= 82.0544\ \text{ml atm mole}^{-1}\ \text{deg}^{-1}$$
$$= 82.0567\ \text{cm}^3\ \text{atm mole}^{-1}\ \text{deg}^{-1}$$
$$= 82.0567 \times 1.013250 \times 10^6\ \text{dyne cm mole}^{-1}\ \text{deg}^{-1}$$
$$= 8.31439 \times 10^7\ \text{ergs mole}^{-1}\ \text{deg}^{-1} \tag{1.51}$$
$$= 8.31439\ \text{joules mole}^{-1}\ \text{deg}^{-1}. \tag{1.52}$$

Table 1.4. *Beattie-Bridgeman Constants [Equation (1.49)]**

GAS	$A_0 \times 10^4$	$a \times 10^4$	$B_0 \times 10^4$	$b \times 10^4$	$c \times 10^{-4}$
H_2	1975	−50.6	209.6	−435.9	0.504
N_2	13445	261.7	504.6	−69.1	4.20
O_2	14911	256.2	462.4	42.08	4.80
NH_3	23930	1703.1	341.5	1911.2	476.87
CH_4	22769	185.5	558.7	−158.70	12.83
CO_2	50065	713.2	1047.6	723.5	66.0
$n\text{-}C_5H_{12}$	282600	1509.9	3940.0	1396.0	400.00

* From H. S. Taylor and S. Glasstone, *A Treatise on Physical Chemistry*, Vol. II. Copyright 1951 D. Van Nostrand Company, Inc., Princeton, N. J.

It is common also to express R in calories per mole per degree. Since 1 cal is defined as equivalent to 4.184000 absolute joules, it follows that

$$R = \frac{8.31439}{4.184000}$$

$$= 1.98719 \text{ cal mole}^{-1} \text{ deg}^{-1}. \tag{1.53}$$

These values are listed in Appendix C.

When R is expressed in ergs per mole per degree, (1.50) yields the velocity u in cgs units, centimeters per second. That (1.50) is dimensionally correct is verified thus:

$$\frac{\text{cm}}{\text{sec}} = \sqrt{\frac{(\text{ergs mole}^{-1} \text{ deg}^{-1}) \times \text{deg}}{\text{grams mole}^{-1}}} = \sqrt{\frac{\text{gram cm}^2 \text{ sec}^{-2}}{\text{gram}}}.$$

Example 1.7. Calculate and tabulate the root mean square velocities of H_2, N_2, and SF_6 at 0°C and at 100°C.

The molecular weights M of H_2, N_2, and SF_6 are 2.016, 28.02, and 146.1. By (1.50), at 0.0°C

$$u = \sqrt{\frac{3 \times 8.314 \times 10^7 \times 273.2}{M}} = \sqrt{\frac{681.4 \times 10^8}{M}}.$$

At 100.0°C,

$$u = \sqrt{\frac{930.8 \times 10^8}{M}}.$$

SUBSTANCE	M	ROOT MEAN SQUARE VELOCITY (cm sec^{-1} × 10^{-4})	
		0.0°C	100.°0C
H_2	2.016	18.38	21.49
N_2	28.02	4.931	5.764
SF_6	146.1	2.160	2.524

The tabulated values result upon substitution of values of M into these equations for u.

1.8 Probability Distribution of Velocities

Even if all molecules in a given sample of a pure gas had velocities exactly equal in absolute magnitude but differing in direction so that the gas as a whole would not move or behave nonisotropically, this extraordinary state would soon be modified by collisions. In a head-on collision, in which the motion of two spheres is along the line between their centers at impact, there is an interchange of velocities if the collision is elastic and the masses of the two bodies are equal. For example, if a moving sphere collides head-on and elastically with another sphere at rest, the moving sphere comes to rest and the one struck moves off with the velocity of the first. As viewed from one of these identical spheres, the process is like the bouncing of a ball on a fixed surface of infinite inertia. As viewed from a system of coordinates moving with half the velocity of the moving sphere, this process would be a head-on collision of two identical spheres each moving at half speed toward each other. After impact, they separate at the same rate but in the directions from which they first approached the impact.

When trajectories are in the same plane, similar statements apply to components of velocity. An example is provided in the collision of two identical spheres each with the same kinetic energy, in which one retires from the collision with all their kinetic energy to leave the other at rest. Suppose that a sphere collides elastically with another that is proceeding in the same plane at right angles to its path. If their trajectories are in the same plane and if the collision occurs at the very instant that the center of the second sphere lies along the projected trajectory of the first identical sphere, the first sphere will stop and the second will possess not only all its own original velocity but will have gained all the velocity of the first sphere. These two equal perpendicular velocity components would add as vectors and the second sphere would proceed at a 45° angle with a velocity of magnitude $\sqrt{2}$ times that of either sphere before impact. In this collision, linear momentum and kinetic energy are conserved and the first sphere is stopped while the kinetic energy of the other is doubled. Other types of collision would be expected to effect a lesser transfer of energy. Thus a system of particles with uniform velocities would rapidly achieve a range of velocities from zero to large values that might rarely result from several reinforcing glancing blows.

Let $\rho(v)$ be the number of particles with vector velocities that differ only infinitesimally from the velocity v.[5] In a three-dimensional velocity space in which each axis is a component of velocity, $\rho(v)$ is a density of particles. The total number N of particles would then be merely the sum of the numbers of particles with all possible velocities; hence,

$$N = \int_{-\infty}^{\infty} \int_{-\infty}^{\infty} \int_{-\infty}^{\infty} \rho(v)\, dv_x\, dv_y\, dv_z \,, \tag{1.54}$$

where $dv_x\, dv_y\, dv_z$ is the infinitesimal element of volume in velocity-space and where $\rho(v)\, dv_x\, dv_y\, dv_z$ is the number of molecules in that element. Because of the huge numbers of molecules involved, $\rho(v)$ is reasonably continuous if the volume element $dv_x\, dv_y\, dv_z$ is thought of as very small but not really infinitesimal. The value of dv_x would then represent the limit of accuracy with which the x-component of velocity could be specified, and the volume element $dv_x\, dv_y\, dv_z$ would enclose a number of molecules so large that on the average fluctuations from $\rho(v)$ would be small compared to $\rho(v)$.

The functional form of $\rho(v)$ is readily derived from a consideration of a collision process. Suppose that two molecules, each of mass m, had velocities v_1' and v_2' before collision and velocities v_1'' and v_2'' after collision. Since mechanical energy is conserved in elastic collisions, the kinetic energy of the system of two particles is unchanged by the collision so that

$$\tfrac{1}{2}mv_1'^2 + \tfrac{1}{2}mv_2'^2 = \tfrac{1}{2}mv_1''^2 + \tfrac{1}{2}mv_2''^2 \,.$$

That is,

$$v_1'^2 + v_2'^2 = v_1''^2 + v_2''^2 \,. \tag{1.55}$$

The number of times a collision of this kind occurs is proportional to the product of the numbers of molecules $\rho(v)\, dv$ of the specified velocity v that are present in the same region dv. At equilibrium, all molecular processes proceed forward and backward at the same rate so that in the absence of interference by other molecules or the walls,

$$\rho(v_1')\rho(v_2') = \rho(v_1'')\rho(v_2'') . \tag{1.56}$$

The only function $\rho(v)$ that satisfies both (1.55) and (1.56) simultaneously is (1.57).[6]

$$\rho(v) = Ae^{-av^2} . \tag{1.57}$$

The form of the right-hand member of (1.57) does not depend upon the direction or sign of the velocity. Since a gas is isotropic, this result is not unexpected. If $N(v)\, dv$ is the number of molecules with *scalar* velocity between v and $v + dv$, then, as in (1.54), the sum of the numbers of molecules of all scalar velocities v is the total number N:

$$N = \int_0^\infty N(v)\, dv . \tag{1.58}$$

$N(v)\, dv$ is, in fact, the number of molecules in a spherical shell of volume $4\pi v^2\, dv$ in velocity space. It follows, then, that

$$N(v)\, dv = 4\pi v^2 \rho(v)\, dv . \tag{1.59}$$

Equation (1.58) imposes a restriction upon the values of A and a. By (1.57), (1.58), and (1.59),

$$N = \int_0^\infty 4\pi v^2 \rho(v)\, dv = \int_0^\infty 4\pi v^2 Ae^{-av^2}\, dv = 4\pi A \int_0^\infty v^2 e^{-av^2}\, dv$$

$$= 4\pi A \int_0^\infty \left(\frac{x}{a}\right)^{1/2} e^{-x} \frac{dx}{2a} \qquad \begin{cases} x = av^2 \\ dx = 2av\, dv \end{cases}$$

$$= \frac{2\pi A}{a^{3/2}} \int_0^\infty x^{3/2-1} e^{-x}\, dx$$

$$= \frac{2\pi A}{a^{3/2}} \, \Gamma\left(\frac{3}{2}\right) = \frac{2\pi A}{a^{3/2}}\left(\frac{\sqrt{\pi}}{2}\right) .$$

Hence, $A = \left(\dfrac{a}{\pi}\right)^{3/2} N.$ \hfill (1.60)

The integral that occurred in evaluating (1.60) is of considerable importance in chemistry and physics. It is called the *gamma function* $\Gamma(n)$, where

$$\Gamma(n) = \int_0^\infty x^{n-1} e^{-x}\, dx , \qquad (n > 0) . \tag{1.61}$$

Direct definite integration yields $\Gamma(1)$ thus:

$$\Gamma(1) = \int_0^\infty x^0 e^{-x} \, dx = - \int_0^\infty e^{-x} \, d(-x)$$

$$= \left[-e^{-x} \right]_{x=0}^{x=\infty} = - \left(e^{-\infty} - e^0 \right) = 1 \ . \tag{1.62}$$

Some of the other fundamental properties of the gamma function are given in (1.63) and (1.64).[7]

$$\Gamma(\tfrac{1}{2}) = \sqrt{\pi} \ , \tag{1.63}$$

and for all values of n except negative integers,

$$\Gamma(n + 1) = n\Gamma(n) \ . \tag{1.64}$$

With (1.64) and the value of $\Gamma(n)$ for $1 < n < 2$ as it is presented in tables of integrals, any value of $\Gamma(n)$ can be evaluated, excepting of course for n equal to negative integers.

These properties of the gamma function are required in evaluating a in (1.57). The total energy of the system is given by (1.1) and (1.11),

$$E = \tfrac{1}{2}Nmu^2 = \tfrac{3}{2}RT \ , \tag{1.1} \ (1.11)$$

where the value of u is chosen so that the average energy of one molecule is $\tfrac{1}{2}mu^2$. The energy of a molecule is actually $\tfrac{1}{2}mv^2$ at any instant, and the total energy of the system is the sum of the various energies of all the molecules. The number of molecules with scalar velocity v is, by (1.57), (1.59), and (1.60),

$$N(v) \, dv = \left(\frac{a}{\pi} \right)^{3/2} 4\pi N v^2 e^{-av^2} \, dv \ . \tag{1.65}$$

Since this is the number of molecules with velocity v, their energy is $\tfrac{1}{2}mv^2 N(v) \, dv$. The total energy E of the system is, then, the sum for all velocities.

$$E = \int_0^\infty (\tfrac{1}{2}mv^2) N(v) \, dv \tag{1.66}$$

$$= \frac{m}{2} \left(\frac{a}{\pi} \right)^{3/2} 4\pi N \int_0^\infty v^4 e^{-av^2} \, dv$$

$$= 2\pi Nm \left(\frac{a}{\pi} \right)^{3/2} \int_0^\infty \left(\frac{x}{a} \right)^{3/2} e^{-x} \frac{dx}{2a} \qquad \begin{cases} x = av^2 \\ dx = 2av \, dv \end{cases}$$

$$= \frac{Nm}{a\sqrt{\pi}} \Gamma\left(\frac{5}{2} \right) = \frac{Nm}{a\sqrt{\pi}} \left(\frac{3}{2} \right)\left(\frac{1}{2} \right)\sqrt{\pi} = \frac{3Nm}{4a} \ ;$$

but
$$E = \frac{3RT}{2}, \tag{1.2}$$

hence,
$$a = \frac{Nm}{2RT}. \tag{1.67}$$

In terms of the Boltzmann constant k, where $R = kN$, Equations (1.65) and (1.67) yield (1.68) as the final form of the Maxwell-Boltzmann distribution law:

$$N(v) = 4\pi N \left(\frac{m}{2\pi kT}\right)^{3/2} v^2 e^{-mv^2/2kT}. \tag{1.68}$$

The Maxwell-Boltzmann distribution law can be expressed in terms of energy E. If $N(E)$ is the number of molecules with energy between E and $E + dE$, then

$$N(E)\, dE = N(v)\, dv. \tag{1.69}$$

Since
$$E = \tfrac{1}{2}Nmv^2$$

and
$$dE = Nmv\, dv,$$

it follows from (1.68) and (1.69) that

$$N(E) = N(v) \frac{dv}{dE}$$

$$= 4\pi N \left(\frac{m}{2\pi kT}\right)^{3/2} v^2 e^{-E/RT} \left(\frac{1}{Nmv}\right)$$

$$= \frac{2N}{\sqrt{\pi RT}} \left(\frac{E}{RT}\right)^{1/2} e^{-E/RT}. \tag{1.70}$$

The probability that a molecule has an energy only infinitesimally different from E is, then,

$$P(E) = \frac{N(E)}{N}$$

$$= \frac{2}{\sqrt{\pi RT}} \left(\frac{E}{RT}\right)^{1/2} e^{-E/RT}. \tag{1.71}$$

In Figure 1.7, the function $(\sqrt{\pi RT}/2)P(E)$ is plotted as a function of $(E/RT)^{1/2}$. The exponential dependence upon (E/RT) is characteristic of the Boltzmann distribution.

Average values of the mechanical properties of the system of molecules can be calculated by means of the Maxwell-Boltzmann distribution (1.68).

27

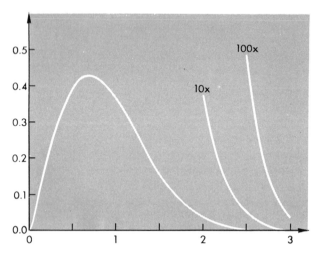

Fig. 1.7. *Maxwell-Boltzmann Distribution.*

Ordinate: $\left(\dfrac{\sqrt{\pi RT}}{2}\right) P(E)$; *abscissa:* $\left(\dfrac{E}{RT}\right)^{1/2}$.

In the evaluation of a in (1.57), the total energy of all N molecules was calculated by (1.66)

$$E = \int_0^\infty (\tfrac{1}{2}mv^2) N(v) \, dv . \qquad (1.66)$$

The average energy per molecule is then

$$\bar{\epsilon} = \frac{E}{N} = \frac{1}{N} \int_0^\infty (\tfrac{1}{2}mv^2) N(v) \, dv . \qquad (1.72)$$

Equation (1.72) is of the usual form for determining average values given the probability distribution function $\phi(v)$. In (1.72),

$$\phi(v) = \frac{N(v)}{N} . \qquad (1.73)$$

The function $\phi(v)$ is the probability that any one of the N molecules will have the velocity v within the infinitesimal uncertainty $\tfrac{1}{2} \, dv$.

The casting of dice illustrates the idea of probabilities. The probability that a prescribed face of a die, say the face labeled three, shall be face-up after an unbiased throw is $\tfrac{1}{6}$, for only one of the six faces is so labeled and each of the six faces is equally likely if the die is true. The average value per throw after many throws of a die is the sum of the numbers on the upturned faces divided by the number of throws. One-sixth of the throws are expected to exhibit each of the possible numbers. Accordingly, in the long run, the average value per throw is

$$\tfrac{1}{6}(1) + \tfrac{1}{6}(2) + \tfrac{1}{6}(3) + \tfrac{1}{6}(4) + \tfrac{1}{6}(5) + \tfrac{1}{6}(6) .$$

Each of these terms is called the *expected value* of its corresponding face. Each expected value is nothing more than the probability of success times the reward for success. The average value is just the sum of the expected values.

Similarly, the average value of a function $f(v)$ is the sum, for all possible values of v, of the expected value of $f(v)$, namely, $f(v)\phi(v)$. If $\overline{f(v)}$ is this average value, and if v can assume all positive values and zero,

$$\overline{f(v)} = \int_0^\infty f(v)\phi(v) \, dv . \qquad (1.74)$$

In (1.72), $f(v)$ was the energy $\tfrac{1}{2}mv^2$. If $f(v)$ is unity, (1.74) represents the number of molecules expected when one sample is withdrawn; that is,

$$1 = \int_0^\infty \phi(v) \, dv . \qquad (1.75)$$

Equation (1.75) follows from (1.58) or (1.74), and is called the *normalization condition* on $\phi(v)$ for it makes the sum of the probabilities unity.

Example 1.8. Calculate the average velocity and most probable velocity of a molecule and compare the results with the root mean square velocity u.

By (1.74), the average value of v is, when $f(v) = v$,

$$\bar{v} = \int_0^\infty v\phi(v)\, dv$$

$$= \frac{1}{N} \int_0^\infty vN(v)\, dv \qquad \text{[by (1.73)]}$$

$$= \frac{1}{N} \int_0^\infty v 4\pi N \left(\frac{m}{2\pi kT}\right)^{3/2} v^2 e^{-mv^2/2kT}\, dv \qquad \text{[by (1.68)]}$$

$$= 4\pi \left(\frac{m}{2\pi kT}\right)^{3/2} \int_0^\infty v^3 e^{-mv^2/2kT}\, dv$$

$$= \frac{2}{\sqrt{\pi}} \left(\frac{2kT}{m}\right)^{1/2} \int_0^\infty x e^{-x}\, dx \quad \left\{ \begin{array}{l} x = \dfrac{mv^2}{2kT} \\[2mm] dx = 2\left(\dfrac{m}{2kT}\right) v\, dv \end{array} \right.$$

$$= \left(\frac{8kT}{\pi m}\right)^{1/2} \Gamma(2) \qquad \text{[by (1.61)]}$$

$$= \left(\frac{8kT}{\pi m}\right)^{1/2} \qquad \text{[by (1.62) and (1.64)]}$$

Similarly, since $u = \sqrt{\bar{v^2}} = \sqrt{u^2}$, it follows that

$$u^2 = \int_0^\infty v^2 \phi(v)\, dv$$

$$= \frac{1}{N} \int_0^\infty v^2 4\pi N \left(\frac{m}{2\pi kT}\right)^{3/2} v^2 e^{-mv^2/2kT}\, dv$$

$$= 4\pi \left(\frac{m}{2\pi kT}\right)^{3/2} \int_0^\infty v^4 e^{-mv^2/2kT}\, dv$$

$$= \frac{2}{\sqrt{\pi}} \left(\frac{2kT}{m}\right) \int_0^\infty x^{3/2} e^{-x}\, dx \qquad \left(x = \frac{mv^2}{2kT}\right)$$

$$= \frac{2}{\sqrt{\pi}} \left(\frac{2kT}{m}\right) \Gamma\left(\frac{5}{2}\right) = \frac{2}{\sqrt{\pi}} \left(\frac{2kT}{m}\right) \left(\frac{3}{2}\right) \Gamma\left(\frac{3}{2}\right)$$

$$= \frac{2}{\sqrt{\pi}} \left(\frac{2kT}{m}\right) \left(\frac{3}{2}\right) \left(\frac{1}{2}\right) \sqrt{\pi} = \frac{3kT}{m},$$

which agrees with (1.1) and (1.2). It follows, therefore, that

$$\frac{\bar{v}}{u} = \frac{\left(\dfrac{8kT}{\pi m}\right)^{1/2}}{\left(\dfrac{3kT}{m}\right)^{1/2}} = \left(\frac{8}{3\pi}\right)^{1/2};$$

so that u is 8.5% greater than $\bar{v}$.

The most probable value of v is that value v_m for which $N(v)$ is a maximum. The maximum value of $N(v)$ occurs when

$$\frac{dN(v)}{dv} = 0.$$

From (1.68), this condition becomes:

$$4\pi N \left(\frac{m}{2\pi kT}\right)^{3/2} \frac{d}{dv}\left(v^2 e^{-mv^2/2kT}\right) = 0$$

$$v^2 \frac{d}{dv}\left(e^{-mv^2/2kT}\right) + e^{-mv^2/2kT} \frac{d}{dv}\left(v^2\right) = 0.$$

$$-\frac{mv_m^3}{kT} + 2v_m = 0$$

$$v_m = \left(\frac{2kT}{m}\right)^{1/2}.$$

From the results above,

$$\frac{v_m}{u} = \frac{\left(\dfrac{2kT}{m}\right)^{1/2}}{\left(\dfrac{3kT}{m}\right)^{1/2}} = \left(\frac{2}{3}\right)^{1/2}.$$

Like $\bar{v}$, v_m is less than u but of the same order of magnitude.

1.9 Mean Free Path

The mean free path of a molecule is the average distance it moves between collisions. A rigorous calculation of this characteristic distance for rigid spheres is straightforward but tedious. Since the boundaries of real molecules are somewhat ill-defined and, in fact, depend upon the method of measurement or definition, the following approximate derivation[8] seems suitable because it is simple and yields the correct order of magnitude and correct functional form.

Suppose that molecules of kind 1 have a radius r_1 and that molecules of kind 2 have a radius r_2. If the molecules are rigid, the distance between centers at impact is $r_1 + r_2$. Whenever their centers approach to the distance $r_1 + r_2$ a collision occurs. It is convenient, then, to picture the collision as occurring when a point molecule comes within a distance of $r_1 + r_2$ of another molecule that is assigned an effective radius of $r_1 + r_2$.

Suppose that the point molecules are projectiles fired into a gas of molecules with radii $r_1 + r_2$. The number of point molecules dN lost by collision on penetrating a distance dx into the target gas is proportional to dx and to the number of point molecules N that are fired at the target. That is,

$$dN = -kN \, dx \, . \tag{1.76}$$

The negative sign accounts for the fact that N decreases as x, the depth of penetration, increases. The proportionality constant k is positive and is a function of the target. Equation (1.76) is readily integrated:

$$\int \frac{dN}{N} = -k \int dx$$

$$\ln N = -kx + C \, . \tag{1.77}$$

The constant of integration C is evaluated by letting N_0 be the number of point molecules that enter the target gas at $x = 0$. Substitution of these values in (1.77) yields

$$\ln N_0 = -k \times 0 + C. \tag{1.78}$$

Hence, by (1.77),

$$\ln N = -kx + \ln N_0$$

$$N = N_0 e^{-kx} \, . \tag{1.79}$$

The same result might have been reached by definite integration of (1.76) thus:

$$\int_{N_0}^{N} \frac{dN'}{N'} = -k \int_0^x dx'$$

$$\ln \left(\frac{N}{N_0} \right) = -kx$$

$$N = N_0 e^{-kx} \, . \tag{1.79}$$

The average distance l traversed by a point molecule is the sum of the expected values of x; that is, it is the sum of the distances x times the fraction of molecules dN/N_0 that penetrate to the depth x. Hence, upon summation over all molecules N_0,

$$l = \int_0^{N_0} x \, \frac{dN}{N_0} \cdot \tag{1.80}$$

Equation (1.79) yields

$$dN = -kN_0 e^{-kx} \, dx \, . \tag{1.81}$$

Since all molecules are absorbed after passing through a target of infinite thickness, $N = 0$ at $x = \infty$. But since $N = N_0$ at $x = 0$, it follows from (1.80) and (1.81) that

$$l = \int_{\infty}^{0} -kxe^{-kx}\,dx .$$ (1.82)

Interchanging the limits of the definite integral is equivalent to reversing the sense of the summation, and this involves a negative sign. Hence,

$$l = \int_{0}^{\infty} kxe^{-kx}\,dx$$

$$= \frac{1}{k} \int_{0}^{\infty} ye^{-y}\,dy, \qquad (y = kx)$$

$$= \frac{1}{k}\,\Gamma(2)$$

$$= \frac{1}{k}\cdot$$ (1.83)

The proportionality constant k is a characteristic of the target gases. According to (1.76), it is the fraction of molecules dN/N that collide in the distance dx. As such, it is the ratio of the total area of N_2 target molecules, each of area $\pi(r_1 + r_2)^2$, to the cross-sectional area in which they are seen by the approaching point molecules. If this cross-sectional area be unit area, if N_2 molecules exist in the volume V, and if possible overlaps are ignored,

$$k = \pi(r_1 + r_2)^2\,\frac{N_2}{V}\cdot$$ (1.84)

It follows, therefore, from (1.83) and (1.84) that

$$l = \frac{V}{\pi\sigma^2 N},$$ (1.85)

where a distance σ characteristic of the molecules is substituted for $(r_1 + r_2)$, and where the subscript on N is ignored. When an appropriate average over all angles is calculated and when account is taken of the Maxwell-Boltzmann distribution in velocities, the correct formula for mean free path l is (1.86).

$$l = \frac{V}{\sqrt{2}\pi\sigma^2 N}\cdot$$ (1.86)

In view of the real indefiniteness of σ, the mean effective collision distance, this factor of $\sqrt{2}$ is almost negligible. Since $PV = NkT$, (1.86) becomes

$$l = \frac{kT}{\sqrt{2}\pi\sigma^2 P}\cdot$$ (1.87)

Table 1.5 lists some values of l at 27°C at several pressures when $\sigma = \sqrt{10} \times 10^{-8}$ cm. In order to assure swift pumping speeds, vacuum apparatus is built with large tubing; in tubing of a small bore, a molecule might bounce between walls and progress along the tubing only very slowly at very low pressures because the mean free path is long and collisions between molecules are infrequent relative to their numbers at atmospheric pressure.

Table 1.5. *Mean Free Path at* 27°C

$$(\sigma^2 = 10 \times 10^{-16} \text{ cm}^2)$$

P (mm Hg)	P (atm)	l (cm)
1.00×10^{-6}	1.32×10^{-9}	6990.
1.00×10^{-3}	1.32×10^{-6}	6.99
1.00	1.32×10^{-3}	6.99×10^{-3}
760.	1.00	9.20×10^{-6}

1.10 Collisions

The frequency of collisions Z_1 suffered by one molecule is its mean velocity $\bar{v}$ divided by the average distance between collisions, namely, its mean free path l. The mean velocity $\bar{v}$ was found in Example 1.8 to be

$$\bar{v} = \left(\frac{8kT}{\pi m}\right)^{1/2}. \tag{1.88}$$

From this and (1.86),

$$Z_1 = \left(\frac{8kT}{\pi m}\right)^{1/2}\left(\frac{\sqrt{2}\pi\sigma^2 N}{V}\right)$$

$$= 4\sigma^2\left(\frac{N}{V}\right)\left(\frac{\pi kT}{m}\right)^{1/2}. \tag{1.89}$$

Because there are (N/V) molecules per unit volume capable of undergoing collision, the frequency of collisions per unit volume might be expected to be just $Z_1 N/V$. However, in order to avoid counting each of these bimolecular collisions twice, the frequency Z_2 of bimolecular collisions per unit volume is only half as great. Accordingly,

$$Z_2 = \tfrac{1}{2}\left(\frac{Z_1 N}{V}\right)$$

$$= 2\sigma^2\left(\frac{N}{V}\right)^2\left(\frac{\pi kT}{m}\right)^{1/2} \tag{1.90}$$

$$= 2\sigma^2\left(\frac{N}{V}\right)^2\left(\frac{\pi RT}{M}\right)^{1/2}. \tag{1.91}$$

When the colliding molecules differ, the time rate $Z_2(1, 2)$ of collisions between unlike molecules of types 1 and 2 per unit volume is

$$Z_2(1, 2) = \tfrac{1}{4}\left(\frac{N_1}{V}\right)\left(\frac{N_2}{V}\right)(\sigma_1^2 + \sigma_2^2)\left(\frac{8\pi RT}{M_{1,2}}\right)^{1/2}, \tag{1.92}$$

33

where N_1 and N_2 are the numbers of types 1 and 2 in the volume V, where σ_1 and σ_2 are their collision diameters, and where the reduced molecular weight $M_{1,2}$ is related to the individual molecular weights M_1 and M_2 by (1.93).

$$M_{1,2} = \frac{M_1 M_2}{M_1 + M_2}. \tag{1.93}$$

The bimolecular collisions discussed above were conceived as definite events characterizable as collisions between rigid spheres of definite size. Any real collision of real molecules is less definite. At distances of several Angstroms there is generally a weak attraction between molecules, and only at much smaller distances does a strong repulsion gradually dominate the interaction. The characteristic collision diameter σ represents a kind of average distance of interaction. As soon as the molecules are thought of as deformable, or as soon as any bimolecular collision endures for a finite time, there is a possibility of a triple collision. A triple collision is conceived as a collision of a third molecule with two others that are actually colliding. The ratio of the number of triple collisions to the number of double collisions would then appear to be in the ratio of the collision diameter to the mean free path; that is,

$$\frac{Z_3}{Z_2} = \frac{\sigma}{l}. \tag{1.94}$$

Even at 1 atm where l is about 10^{-5} cm, triple collisions represent less than 1% of the collisions in a gas.

Example 1.9. Calculate the total number of bimolecular collisions in 1 sec in 1 ml pure He and pure N_2 at $300°K$ at 1 atm. Assume that σ of He is 2×10^{-8} cm and that σ of N_2 is 4×10^{-8} cm.

At $P = 1$ and $T = 300$,

$$\left(\frac{N}{V}\right) = \frac{P}{RT} \times 6.02 \times 10^{23} = \frac{1.00 \times 6.02 \times 10^{23}}{82.05 \times 300}$$

$$= 2.45 \times 10^{19} \text{ molecules ml}^{-1}.$$

By (1.91), since $M_{\text{He}} = 4.00$,

$$Z_2(\text{He}) = 2 \times (2 \times 10^{-8})^2 \times (2.45 \times 10^{19})^2 \left(\frac{\pi \times 8.314 \times 10^7 \times 300}{4.00}\right)^{1/2}$$

$$= 7 \times 10^{28} \text{ collisions sec}^{-1} \text{ ml}^{-1}.$$

Similarly, for N_2,

$$Z_2(N_2) = 2 \times (4 \times 10^{-8})^2 \times (2.45 \times 10^{19})^2 \left(\frac{\pi \times 8.314 \times 10^7 \times 300}{28.0}\right)^{1/2}$$

$$= 10 \times 10^{28} \text{ collisions sec}^{-1} \text{ ml}^{-1}.$$

1.11 Viscosity of Gases

Viscosity is a measure of a fluid's resistance to flow quite apart from its inertia. Viscosity measures the steady-state transfer of momentum due to a difference in velocities within the fluid. If the flow pattern involves parallel layers flowing past each other at differing velocities, the flow is called *laminar*. The force F required to maintain a difference in velocity dv between layers of area $\mathcal{A}$ distant from each other by a distance dz is given by (1.95).

$$F = \eta\, \mathcal{A}\, \frac{dv}{dz}. \tag{1.95}$$

The proportionality constant η is called the *coefficient of viscosity*. In the cgs system, when F is measured in dynes, $\mathcal{A}$ in cm², and the gradient of velocity dv/dz in sec^{-1}, the dimensions of η are gram cm^{-1} sec^{-1}, or *poises*. The value of η is the force in dynes required to maintain a difference in velocity of laminar flow of one cm sec^{-1} for layers separated by one cm and joined by an area of one cm².

Suppose that, in addition to its momentum due to random motion, the average momentum per molecule in a steady state of laminar flow is mv_0 at the level $z = 0$. The flow is imagined to be in the x-y-plane. At the height z the momentum per molecule is mv, where the velocity vector v is parallel to but greater than v_0. If the rate of change of velocity with respect to distance along the z-axis is uniform, dv/dz is constant. The momentum at the height z is given by (1.96), the beginning of a Taylor's series expansion about $z = 0$.

$$mv = mv_0 + z\, \frac{d(mv)}{dz}$$

$$= mv_0 + zm\, \frac{dv}{dz}. \tag{1.96}$$

In addition to the parallel translational velocities v_0 and v, the molecules possess the usual randomly oriented velocities characteristic of a gas. Because these random movements can transfer a molecule along the z-axis, there is an exchange of momentum among neighboring levels. On the average, only one-third of the molecules are effective in changing momentum along the z-axis; this is equivalent to resolving the random velocities into components along the three axes and to ignoring the x- and y-components. For this one-third of all molecules, the average distance along the z-axis between collisions is the mean free path l and the average distance moved per unit time is $\bar{v}$, the mean random velocity. The average volume swept out per unit time is $\bar{v}\mathcal{A}$, where $\mathcal{A}$ is the area perpendicular to the z-axis. If there is a total of N molecules in the volume V, the effective number that proceed through the area $\mathcal{A}$ per unit time in both directions along the z-axis is $(N/3)(\bar{v}\mathcal{A}/V)$. The force F required to maintain the difference in flow velocities is the average time rate of transfer of momentum due to these movements of molecules along the z-axis. Since the transfer is effected by collisions that occur on the average a distance l along the z-axis, if $z = l$ in (1.96),

$$F = \left(\frac{N}{3}\right)\left(\frac{\bar{v}\alpha}{V}\right)(mv - mv_0) = \left(\frac{N\bar{v}\alpha}{3V}\right)\left(lm\frac{dv}{dz}\right) = \left(\frac{N\bar{v}lm}{3V}\right)\alpha\left(\frac{dv}{dz}\right).$$

On comparison with (1.95) it is evident that

$$\eta = \frac{N\bar{v}lm}{3V}. \tag{1.97}$$

Simplification of (1.97) with the values of l and $\bar{v}$ provided by (1.86) and (1.88) yields the final result.

$$\eta = \frac{Nm}{3V}\left(\frac{V}{\sqrt{2\pi\sigma^2 N}}\right)\left(\frac{8kT}{\pi m}\right)^{1/2}$$

$$= \left(\frac{2}{3\pi}\right)\frac{\sqrt{\pi mkT}}{\pi\sigma^2}. \tag{1.98}$$

More careful calculation with account of the Maxwell-Boltzmann distribution of velocities and their dependence upon direction yields (1.99) in place of (1.98).[9]

$$\eta = \left(\frac{5}{16}\right)\frac{\sqrt{\pi mkT}}{\pi\sigma^2}. \tag{1.99}$$

When Maxwell first deduced that viscosity depended only upon temperature and not upon density or pressure, experiments were immediately begun to test this remarkable result of the kinetic theory. The observed slight dependences on pressure can be attributed to nonideal behavior of the gases. The fact that η is proportional to a power of T somewhat greater than one-half is attributable to a dependence of σ^2 upon temperature through long-range attractive forces. For He, Ar, and N_2,[10] observed and calculated values of η agree within about 20–25% from 100°K to 500°K.

Example 1.10. Calculate the viscosity of N_2 at 300°K. Assume that $\sigma = 4 \times 10^{-8}$ cm.

Since (1.99) is to be used, values of m and k are required. If N is Avogadro's number,

$$m = \frac{M}{N} = \frac{28.02}{0.6024 \times 10^{24}} = 46.51 \times 10^{-24}$$

and

$$k = \frac{R}{N} = \frac{8.314 \times 10^7}{0.6024 \times 10^{24}} = 1.380 \times 10^{-16}.$$

By (1.99),

$$\eta = \left(\frac{5}{16}\right)\frac{\sqrt{\pi \times 46.51 \times 10^{-24} \times 1.380 \times 10^{-16} \times 3.00 \times 10^{2}}}{\pi \times 4^{2} \times 10^{-16}}$$

$$= 1.53 \times 10^{-4} \text{ poise.}$$

The observed value is 1.66×10^{-4} poise.

1.12 The Most Probable Distribution of Energies[10]

The mechanical behavior of a body obeying the laws of classical mechanics is defined for all past and future time if at any instant its velocity and position are specified and if the differential equation of motion is given. A similar statement can be made of an assembly of bodies that interact in given ways, say, by collision or through connecting springs. Once the positions and momenta (that is, positions, masses, and velocities) of the bodies of the system are specified at any instant, all future and past behavior can be calculated through the equation of motion.

In a system of N identical simple bodies, it would be necessary to specify $3N$ position coordinates (x, y, and z) and $3N$ momentum coordinates (the components of linear momentum: p_x, p_y, and p_z). Of these $6N$ coordinates, some are commonly classed as intramolecular coordinates when the so-called molecules are not simple. Such internal coordinates are then referred to axes fixed to the molecule with their origin at the center of mass. For example, in a system of diatomic molecules, it is generally convenient to specify five coordinates of position (x, y, z, and two angles that specify the direction of the axis) and to leave the sixth position coordinate as an internal molecular coordinate, namely, the interatomic distance. A nonlinear molecule of r atoms would have $3r - 6$ internal position coordinates (the six others being x, y, z coordinates of the center of mass and three angles describing the orientation of the molecule relative to axes fixed to the system's container) and $3r - 6$ internal momentum coordinates (the six others being the linear momenta p_x, p_y, p_z of the center of mass and three angular momenta about three mutually perpendicular axes of rotation).

Regardless of the way in which coordinates are chosen, there are always just $6N$ coordinates of position and momentum required for exact specification of the mechanical behavior of a system of N bodies obeying the laws of classical mechanics. By analogy with three-dimensional space, it is said that a point in a space of these $6N$ dimensions specifies the dynamical state of the system at any instant. The point moves with time as momenta and positions of the bodies of the system change. Since many different dynamical states cannot be distinguished from each other on the basis of the few observable macroscopic variables that are suitable averages of the mechanical properties of the system, many different points in such a $6N$-dimensional space would correspond to the same macroscopic state. For statistical reasons this $6N$-dimensional space, which is called the γ-phase space, is populated with an ensemble (or collection) of systems, each of which is represented by a point and could have mechanical properties in accord with the same macroscopic state of the system. Because immense numbers of systems (points) are involved, there is a reasonably continuous density of points in γ-phase space. If the macroscopic state is specified by the energy E of the system, there is a region or volume δv_γ in γ-phase space with systems of energies between E and $E + \delta E$, where δE is a small variation or uncertainty in energy.

For each complex molecule in each system there is, similarly, a μ-phase space of $6r$ dimensions. If all molecules are alike, there are $n = N/r$ molecules in each system. Just as a point in γ-phase space specifies the mechanical state of a system of N bodies, a point in μ-phase space specifies the mechanical state of one molecule of r atoms. The element of volume δv_μ in μ-phase space specifies all $6r$ dynamical variables within a certain small range of values. As long as the molecules do not interact with each other, the state of the system of N atoms is correctly described by the n elements of volume δv_μ for the molecules of the system. That is, the range of variables δv_γ in γ-phase space is the product of the n factors $\delta v_\mu^{(i)}$ which give the approximate position of molecule i in its μ-phase space.

At any instant, the number n is in fact so large for systems of physical interest that many molecules will have approximately the same dynamical state and thus will exist in corresponding regions δv_μ of their own μ-spaces. If n_i is the number of molecules in corresponding $\delta v_\mu^{(i)}$, there are $n_i!$ ways of redistributing these molecules without in any way affecting the condition of the system or its macroscopic state. Such redistributions of identical molecules in identical states will, however, be described by different regions δv_γ in γ-phase space because molecules really have been interchanged. The number G of different regions δv_γ of equal size in γ-phase space with n_i molecules in the various elements $\delta v_\mu^{(i)}$ is

$$G = \frac{n!}{n_1! n_2! \cdots n_i! \cdots}. \tag{1.100}$$

Here G is just the number of ways of distributing n distinguishable objects among groups labeled i, with n_i in group i.

Since it can be shown that regions δv_γ of equal size are equally likely to be occupied by the system of energy from E to $E + \delta E$ if the system is in a state of macroscopic equilibrium, G in (1.100) is proportional to the probability P that the system does in fact have the dynamical state assumed. Hence, if C is the constant of proportionality,

$$P = \frac{n!}{n_1! n_2! \cdots n_i! \cdots} \times C. \tag{1.101}$$

With (1.101) as the starting point, it is possible to derive the most probable distribution of molecules among the molecular states i.

The most probable value of P is its maximum value. By analogy with the requirement that the derivative be zero at a maximum or minimum, the condition that P be an extremum is that the variation δP be zero.

$$\delta P = 0 . \tag{1.102}$$

It is more convenient to maximize the logarithm of P because the Stirling approximation for factorials of large numbers then permits considerable mathematical simplification. According to the Stirling approximation, for large n

$$n! \approx \left(\frac{n}{e}\right)^n \sqrt{2\pi n} . \tag{1.103}$$

That is,

$$\ln (n!) \approx n \ln n - n + \tfrac{1}{2} \ln (2\pi n) . \tag{1.104}$$

When n is large, $\ln n \ll n$ so that

$$\ln (n!) \approx n \ln n - n . \tag{1.105}$$

From (1.101) and (1.105) it follows that

$$\begin{aligned}
\ln P &= \ln C + \ln (n!) - \ln (n_1!) - \ln (n_2!) - \cdots - \ln (n_i!) - \cdots \\
&= \ln C + \ln (n!) - \sum_i \ln (n_i!) \\
&= \ln C + n \ln n - n - \sum_i n_i \ln n_i + \sum_i n_i .
\end{aligned}$$

But the total number n of molecules is just the sum of the numbers n_i in the various regions $\delta v_\mu^{(i)}$ of the μ-phase spaces; that is,

$$n = \sum_i n_i . \tag{1.106}$$

It follows, therefore, that

$$\ln P = \ln C + n \ln n - \sum_i n_i \ln n_i . \tag{1.107}$$

The condition (1.102) then is

$$\delta(\ln C + n \ln n - \sum_i n_i \ln n_i) = 0 .$$

The variations may be treated as first differentials so that by the usual methods of calculus

$$\delta n \ln n + n \left(\frac{\delta n}{n}\right) - \sum_i \left[\delta n_i \ln n_i + n_i \left(\frac{\delta n_i}{n_i}\right)\right] = 0$$

$$\delta n \ln n + \delta n - \sum_i \delta n_i \ln n_i - \sum_i \delta n_i = 0 . \tag{1.108}$$

This maximum is achieved subject to two conditions: (1) that the total energy E of the system be constant within $\frac{1}{2}(\delta E)$; and (2) that the total number n of molecules be constant. With (1.106), this second condition is

$$\delta n = \sum_i \delta n_i = 0 . \tag{1.109}$$

Use of (1.109) simplifies (1.108) thus:

$$\sum_i \delta n_i \ln n_i = 0 . \tag{1.110}$$

The first condition requires that $\delta E = 0$. If ϵ_i is the energy of one molecule in group i, then the total energy E of the system is the sum of the energies of the molecules in the several groups i, and

$$E = \sum_i \epsilon_i n_i . \tag{1.111}$$

If E is constant,

$$\delta E = \sum_i \epsilon_i \delta n_i = 0 . \tag{1.112}$$

Equations (1.109), (1.110), and (1.112) must be satisfied simultaneously to maximize P or $\ln P$ under these two conditions.

Lagrange's method of undetermined multipliers permits the three equations to be united by the use of two undetermined multipliers α and β, each to be expressed later in terms of known quantities by the use of (1.106) and (1.111). Multiplication of (1.109) by α and (1.112) by β and summation with (1.110) yields (1.113), the condition for a maximum in $\ln P$.

$$\sum_i \delta n_i \, (\ln n_i + \alpha + \beta \epsilon_i) = 0 . \tag{1.113}$$

Since δn_i for each region in μ-phase space is arbitrary, (1.113) is satisfied only if

$$\ln n_i + \alpha + \beta \epsilon_i = 0 .$$

Whence,

$$n_i = e^{-\alpha - \beta \epsilon_i} . \tag{1.114}$$

The value of n_i given by (1.114) is the most probable number of molecules in group i subject to the conditions that the total energy E and total number of molecules n of the system be constant. This Boltzmann distribution law (1.114) holds for a system in a macroscopically steady condition.

Equation (1.106) imposes a condition upon α and β in (1.114) in the following way.

$$n = \sum_j n_j . \tag{1.106}$$

By (1.114),

$$n = \sum_j e^{-\alpha} e^{-\beta \epsilon_j} = e^{-\alpha} \sum_j e^{-\beta \epsilon_j} .$$

Therefore,

$$e^{-\alpha} = \frac{n}{\sum_j e^{-\beta \epsilon_j}} \cdot \qquad (1.115)$$

Similarly, Equation (1.111) fixes β thus:

$$E = \sum_i \epsilon_i n_i . \qquad (1.111)$$

By (1.114),

$$E = \sum_i \epsilon_i e^{-\alpha} e^{-\beta \epsilon_i} .$$

By (1.115),

$$E = \left[\frac{n}{\sum_j e^{-\beta \epsilon_j}} \right] \sum_i \epsilon_i e^{-\beta \epsilon_i} .$$

If $\bar{\epsilon}$ is the average energy per molecule, it follows at once that

$$\bar{\epsilon} = \frac{E}{n} = \frac{\sum_i \epsilon_i e^{-\beta \epsilon_i}}{\sum_j e^{-\beta \epsilon_j}} . \qquad (1.116)$$

Equation (1.116) resembles (1.74) in that the factors of the form

$$\frac{e^{-\beta \epsilon_i}}{\sum_j e^{-\beta \epsilon_j}}$$

represent normalized discrete probabilities (n_i/n) of the energy ϵ_i. The summation upon i replaces the integration throughout the range of the variable v in (1.74), and $f(v)$ in (1.74) is replaced by ϵ_i in (1.116). By methods analogous to those of Section 1.8, it would be found that

$$\beta = \frac{1}{kT} \cdot \qquad (1.117)$$

In (1.117), k is the Boltzmann constant and T is the absolute temperature.

1.13 Equipartition of Energy[10]

From Equations (1.114), (1.115), and (1.117) is obtained the Boltzmann distribution in its most general form (1.118).

$$n_i = \frac{n e^{-\epsilon_i/kT}}{\sum_j e^{-\epsilon_j/kT}} \cdot \qquad (1.118)$$

Out of a fixed number n of molecules in a state of steady macroscopic energy, n_i is the number with the energy ϵ_i when the temperature of the system is T.

The summation upon j in (1.118) is over all possible states of energy. When the energies ϵ_j are represented as functions of the position and momentum coordinates, the summation is most conveniently performed as an integration of the form:

$$\int_{-\infty}^{\infty} \int_{-\infty}^{\infty} e^{-\epsilon/kT} \, dp \, dq \,,$$

where $dp \, dq$ represents the product of all the differential elements of momentum and position coordinates in γ-phase space.

In order to verify that Equation (1.117) is a true correlation between the statistical temperature β and the usual macroscopic property called temperature, imagine that the thermometer measuring T is a perfect gas of non-interacting particles each of energy

$$\epsilon = \tfrac{1}{2}mv^2 = \frac{m}{2}\left(v_x^2 + v_y^2 + v_z^2\right) . \tag{1.119}$$

Since $p_x = mv_x$, $p_y = mv_y$, and $p_z = mv_z$,

$$\epsilon = \frac{p^2}{2m} = \frac{1}{2m}\left(p_x^2 + p_y^2 + p_z^2\right) . \tag{1.120}$$

The average energy $\bar{\epsilon}$ per particle is then, by the calculus-analogue of (1.116),

$$\bar{\epsilon} = \frac{\displaystyle\int_{-\infty}^{\infty} \int_{-\infty}^{\infty} \left(\frac{p^2}{2m}\right) e^{-p^2/2mkT} \, dp \, dq}{\displaystyle\int_{-\infty}^{\infty} \int_{-\infty}^{\infty} e^{-p^2/2mkT} \, dp \, dq} .$$

Integration over all position coordinates yields

$$\bar{\epsilon} = \frac{\displaystyle\int_{-\infty}^{\infty} \left(\frac{p^2}{2m}\right) e^{-p^2/2mkT} \, dp}{\displaystyle\int_{-\infty}^{\infty} e^{-p^2/2mkT} \, dp} . \tag{1.121}$$

By (1.120),

$$\bar{\epsilon} = \frac{\dfrac{1}{2m} \displaystyle\int_{-\infty}^{\infty} \int_{-\infty}^{\infty} \int_{-\infty}^{\infty} (p_x^2 + p_y^2 + p_z^2) \exp\left(-\frac{p_x^2 + p_y^2 + p_z^2}{2mkT}\right) dp_x \, dp_y \, dp_z}{\displaystyle\int_{-\infty}^{\infty} \int_{-\infty}^{\infty} \int_{-\infty}^{\infty} \exp\left(-\frac{p_x^2 + p_y^2 + p_z^2}{2mkT}\right) dp_x \, dp_y \, dp_z} .$$

But this denominator is just the cube of the integrals

$$\int_{-\infty}^{\infty} e^{-p_x^2/2mkT}\, dp_x = \int_{-\infty}^{\infty} e^{-p_y^2/2mkT}\, dp_y = \int_{-\infty}^{\infty} e^{-p_z^2/2mkT}\, dp_z\,,$$

while the numerator is the sum of three integrals of the form

$$\frac{1}{2m}\int_{-\infty}^{\infty} p_x^2 e^{-p_x^2/2mkT}\, dp_x \int_{-\infty}^{\infty} e^{-p_y^2/2mkT}\, dp_y \int_{-\infty}^{\infty} e^{-p_z^2/2mkT}\, dp_z\,.$$

Hence,

$$\bar{\epsilon} = \left(\frac{3}{2m}\right)\frac{\displaystyle\int_{-\infty}^{\infty} p_x^2 e^{-p_x^2/2mkT}\, dp_x}{\displaystyle\int_{-\infty}^{\infty} e^{-p_x^2/2mkT}\, dp_x}\,.$$

Since the functions $\exp(-p^2/2mkT)$ and $p^2\exp(-p^2/2mkT)$ do not change sign as p changes sign, the integrals from $-\infty$ to $+\infty$ are equal to twice those from 0 to $+\infty$ and

$$\bar{\epsilon} = \left(\frac{3}{2m}\right)\frac{\displaystyle\int_{0}^{\infty} p_x^2 e^{-p_x^2/2mkT}\, dp_x}{\displaystyle\int_{0}^{\infty} e^{-p_x^2/2mkT}\, dp_x}\,.$$

With the substitution $w = p_x^2/2mkT$, this becomes

$$\bar{\epsilon} = \left(\frac{3}{2m}\right)\frac{\dfrac{(2mkT)^{3/2}}{2}\displaystyle\int_{0}^{\infty} w^{1/2}e^{-w}\, dw}{\dfrac{(2mkT)^{1/2}}{2}\displaystyle\int_{0}^{\infty} w^{-1/2}e^{-w}\, dw}$$

$$= 3kT\,\frac{\Gamma\left(\tfrac{3}{2}\right)}{\Gamma\left(\tfrac{1}{2}\right)}$$

$$= \frac{3kT}{2}\,. \tag{1.122}$$

The value assigned to β by (1.117) is thus justified, because (1.122) states for the average energy per molecule what (1.11) states for the average energy of N molecules. From the method of calculation of $\bar{\epsilon}$, it is clear that $\tfrac{1}{2}kT$ is the energy associated with each component of momentum.

Consider a system in which the energy of each atom is given by (1.123).

$$\epsilon = \frac{p^2}{2m} + \frac{bq^2}{2} = \frac{1}{2m}(p_x^2 + p_y^2 + p_z^2) + \frac{b}{2}(x^2 + y^2 + z^2)\,. \tag{1.123}$$

The energy consists of two parts, kinetic and potential. The potential energy, due to displacements x, y, and z against a restoring force proportional to these displacements, follows Hooke's law ($F_x = -bx$ and so on). The kinetic energy terms will again contribute the energy $3kT/2$ as for a free particle. And so do the potential energy terms! This comes about in the following way. By (1.116),

$$\bar{\epsilon} = \frac{\displaystyle\int_{-\infty}^{\infty}\int_{-\infty}^{\infty} \epsilon e^{-\epsilon/kT}\, dp\, dq}{\displaystyle\int_{-\infty}^{\infty}\int_{-\infty}^{\infty} e^{-\epsilon/kT}\, dp\, dq}$$

$$= \frac{\displaystyle\int_{-\infty}^{\infty}\int_{-\infty}^{\infty} \left(\frac{p^2}{2m}\right) e^{-p^2/2mkT} e^{-bq^2/2kT}\, dp\, dq + \int_{-\infty}^{\infty}\int_{-\infty}^{\infty} \left(\frac{bq^2}{2}\right) e^{-bq^2/2kT} e^{-p^2/2mkT}\, dq\, dp}{\displaystyle\int_{-\infty}^{\infty} e^{-p^2/2mkT}\, dp \int_{-\infty}^{\infty} e^{-bq^2/2kT}\, dq}$$

$$= \frac{\displaystyle\int_{-\infty}^{\infty} \left(\frac{p^2}{2m}\right) e^{-p^2/2mkT}\, dp}{\displaystyle\int_{-\infty}^{\infty} e^{-p^2/2mkT}\, dp} + \frac{\displaystyle\int_{-\infty}^{\infty} \left(\frac{bq^2}{2}\right) e^{-bq^2/2kT}\, dq}{\displaystyle\int_{-\infty}^{\infty} e^{-bq^2/2kT}\, dq}.$$

But these two terms are like (1.121) if $(1/m)$ replaces b in the second term. Since the value of (1.121) is independent of m, this second term is like the first in having the value $3kT/2$. And for similar reasons, each additive term in the energy that involves the square of a momentum or position coordinate contributes the average energy $\frac{1}{2}kT$. Although more general and sophisticated statements of the principle of equipartition of energy have been made,[11] this is the meaning of the principle of equipartition of energy: The average energy due to each coordinate that contributes a quadratic term to the total molecular energy is $kT/2$, regardless of the kind of coordinate.

Example 1.11. Calculate the increase in energy per degree rise in temperature for a substance containing N atoms each bound to its equilibrium position by forces that are proportional to the displacement from equilibrium.

The mean energy E of the system of N atoms is N times as great as for one atom, and the energy of one such atom is given by (1.123). Hence,

$$E = \frac{N}{2m}(p_x^2 + p_y^2 + p_z^2) + \frac{Nb}{2}(x^2 + y^2 + z^2).$$

Since this expression involves three quadratic terms in momenta and three in positions, there are six contributions of $\frac{1}{2}kT$ per atom. Hence,

$$E = 6N\left(\frac{kT}{2}\right) = 3NkT.$$

The increase in energy per degree is then $dE/dT = 3Nk$.

If N is Avogadro's number, this rate is $3R$, or 6.0 cal mole^{-1} deg^{-1}. This is essentially the law of Dulong and Petit.

Example 1.12. Estimate the increase in energy per degree for 1 mole of a gas consisting of rigid nonlinear polyatomic molecules.

All the energy of the system is kinetic. The translational kinetic energy is of the form $1/2m(p_x^2 + p_y^2 + p_z^2)$. The rotational kinetic energy, as expressed in terms of moments of inertia I and angular velocities ω, is of the form

$$\tfrac{1}{2}(I_x\omega_x^2 + I_y\omega_y^2 + I_z\omega_z^2) .$$

Since there are, in all, six quadratic terms, the total energy E is

$$E = 6N \left(\frac{kT}{2}\right) = 3RT .$$

Whence, $dE/dT = 3R = 6.0$ cal mole^{-1} deg^{-1}.

1.14 Dipole Orientation in an Electrostatic Field

The principle of the equipartition of energy is a rather general application of the Boltzmann distribution; a somewhat more specialized application describes the extent to which an electric field tends to orient electrically unsymmetrical molecules of a gas. A very intense field may ionize the gas, and by accelerating ions and electrons produce by bombardment many more ions until a gaseous discharge occurs. If the field is not intense enough to transform or destroy molecules, however, it tends merely to orient electrically unsymmetrical molecules so that a part of a molecule that is preponderantly negative in charge tends toward the positive pole of the external electric field while the positively charged part of a molecule tends toward the negative pole. Because the molecule is neutral it does not migrate, and because it is continually bombarded by other molecules its alignment in the field is far from perfect.

In a symmetrical molecule like Ne or N_2 the external electric field may actually induce a movement of charges within the molecule so as to effect a separation of charge proportional to the strength of the field. Unsymmetrical molecules like HCl and CH_3Cl, however, present to the field a permanent separation of centers of positive and negative charge. The product of the distance of separation l and the amount of charge ze (z is the effective number of electronic charges e of magnitude 4.80223×10^{-10} e.s.u.) is the dipole moment. It is a vector directed from the center of negative charge to the center of positive charge. Its magnitude is μ_0, where

$$\mu_0 = zel . \qquad (1.124)$$

In this treatment, μ_0 shall be assumed to be independent of the electrostatic field.

Because the molecule as a whole is uncharged, there is no force acting on it as a whole and its energy is independent of the position of its center of mass in

45

the field. The molecule's orientation in the field is, however, influenced by the field. Let the angle from the direction of the field $\mathbf{E}$ to the vector dipole moment be θ, with $\theta = 0$ when alignment is ideal and the energy of the dipole in the field is a minimum. Then the potential energy of the dipole for any orientation is $V(\theta)$, where

$$V(\theta) = -\mu_0 \mathbf{E} \cos \theta . \tag{1.125}$$

Here $V(\theta)$ is energy in excess of the kinetic energy enjoyed by each molecule.

Just as the Boltzmann distribution (1.118) specifies the distribution of molecules according to their kinetic energies, it similarly specifies their numbers according to their potential energies $V(\theta)$ relative to their energies in the absence of the field. Since the component of the dipole moment in the direction of the field is $\mu_0 \cos \theta$, the average value of the dipole moment is the sum of the components $\mu_0 \cos \theta$ for all molecules divided by the total number of molecules. This is the same as the sum of the expected values of the function $\mu_0 \cos \theta$ for all possible angles. In spherical coordinates, where the element of volume dq is $r^2 \sin \theta \, d\theta \, d\phi \, dr$, the average value of μ_0 is then

$$\bar{\mu}_0 = \frac{\displaystyle\int_0^R \int_0^{2\pi} \int_0^{\pi} \mu_0 \cos \theta e^{-(-\mu_0 \mathbf{E} \cos \theta)/kT} r^2 \sin \theta \, d\theta \, d\phi \, dr}{\displaystyle\int_0^R \int_0^{2\pi} \int_0^{\pi} e^{-(-\mu_0 \mathbf{E} \cos \theta)/kT} r^2 \sin \theta \, d\theta \, d\phi \, dr} .$$

The limits for the integration on r are such as to enclose the gas that composes the system; the limits on ϕ are such as to include all angles of rotation about the direction of the field, from $\phi = 0$ to $\phi = 2\pi$; the limits on θ proceed from perfect alignment at $\theta = 0$ to the least favorable alignment at $\theta = \pi$. The integrations over ϕ and r in numerator and denominator cancel, and

$$\bar{\mu}_0 = \frac{\displaystyle\int_0^{\pi} \mu_0 \cos \theta e^{\mu_0 \mathbf{E} \cos \theta/kT} \sin \theta \, d\theta}{\displaystyle\int_0^{\pi} e^{\mu_0 \mathbf{E} \cos \theta/kT} \sin \theta \, d\theta} . \tag{1.126}$$

The appearance of these integrals is simplified by transformation to the convenient variable

$$x = \left(\frac{\mu_0 \mathbf{E}}{kT}\right) \cos \theta .$$

Since μ_0, $\mathbf{E}$, k, and T are independent of θ, by the rules of calculus

$$dx = \left(\frac{\mu_0 \mathbf{E}}{kT}\right)(-\sin \theta \, d\theta) .$$

When $\theta = 0$, $x = (\mu_0 E/kT)$ and when $\theta = \pi$, $x = -(\mu_0 E/kT)$. Hence,

$$\bar{\mu}_0 = \frac{\mu_0 \left(\dfrac{kT}{\mu_0 E}\right)^2 \displaystyle\int_{(\mu_0 E/kT)}^{-(\mu_0 E/kT)} x e^x \, dx}{\left(\dfrac{kT}{\mu_0 E}\right) \displaystyle\int_{(\mu_0 E/kT)}^{-(\mu_0 E/kT)} e^x \, dx}. \tag{1.127}$$

But $\quad \int x e^x \, dx = \int x \, d(e^x) = x e^x - \int e^x \, dx = x e^x - e^x + C$.

Accordingly, (1.127) becomes

$$\bar{\mu}_0 = \mu_0 \left(\frac{kT}{\mu_0 E}\right) \frac{\left[x e^x - e^x \right]_{\substack{x = \left(\frac{\mu_0 E}{kT}\right)}}^{\substack{x = -\left(\frac{\mu_0 E}{kT}\right)}}}{\left[e^x \right]_{\substack{x = \left(\frac{\mu_0 E}{kT}\right)}}^{\substack{x = -\left(\frac{\mu_0 E}{kT}\right)}}}$$

$$= \mu_0 \left(\frac{kT}{\mu_0 E}\right) \frac{\left[-\left(\frac{\mu_0 E}{kT}\right) e^{-\mu_0 E/kT} - e^{-\mu_0 E/kT} \right] - \left[\left(\frac{\mu_0 E}{kT}\right) e^{\mu_0 E/kT} - e^{\mu_0 E/kT} \right]}{\left[e^{-\mu_0 E/kT} - e^{\mu_0 E/kT} \right]}$$

$$= \mu_0 \left(\frac{e^{\mu_0 E/kT} + e^{-\mu_0 E/kT}}{e^{\mu_0 E/kT} - e^{-\mu_0 E/kT}} - \frac{kT}{\mu_0 E}\right)$$

$$= \mu_0 \left[\coth\left(\frac{\mu_0 E}{kT}\right) - \frac{1}{\left(\frac{\mu_0 E}{kT}\right)} \right] \tag{1.128}$$

$$= \mu_0 L(y) . \quad \left(y = \frac{\mu_0 E}{kT} \right) \tag{1.129}$$

Of importance in the theory of paramagnetism as well as for the orientation of electric dipoles is the function $L(y)$, called the *Langevin function*, where

$$L(y) = \coth y - \frac{1}{y}. \tag{1.130}$$

Since molecular dimensions are of the order of 10^{-8} cm and since ze is of the order of 5×10^{-10} e.s.u., dipole moments are of the order of 5×10^{-18} cm $\times$ e.s.u. The usual field E is less than 3000 volts cm^{-1}, or 10 electrostatic volts cm^{-1}. At room temperature, kT is about 4×10^{-14} ergs

47

molecule^{-1}. Thus it happens that

$$y = \frac{\mu_0 E}{kT} \approx \frac{5 \times 10^{-18} \times 10}{4 \times 10^{-14}} \approx 10^{-3}\ .$$

Since $L(y)$ is required only for values of y much less than unity, it is convenient to expand $L(y)$ as a rapidly convergent power series in y. The result is (1.131).

$$L(y) = \frac{y}{3}\left(1 - \frac{y^2}{15} + \cdots\right). \tag{1.131}$$

Since only the first term is of importance, by (1.129) and (1.131),

$$\bar{\mu}_0 = \frac{\mu_0^2 E}{3kT}. \tag{1.132}$$

In addition to this average dipole moment $\bar{\mu}_0$, there is in gases composed of symmetrical or unsymmetrical molecules an electric moment induced by the electric field. This induced moment μ_i exists only when the field exists and is proportional to the field intensity E.

$$\mu_i = \alpha E\ . \tag{1.133}$$

The proportionality constant α is the polarizability of the molecule. The induced moment is attributed to an electronic polarization in which the field displaces electrons relative to nucleuses and to an atomic polarization in which the field deforms the molecule by moving atoms relative to others in the same molecule. Although the value of α depends upon the direction within the molecule, a mean value averaged over all angles is adequate for fluids. Since these induced and orientational moments are almost independent, the total average moment $\bar{\mu}$ per molecule is then, by (1.132) and (1.133),

$$\bar{\mu} = \left(\alpha + \frac{\mu_0^2}{3kT}\right)E\ . \tag{1.134}$$

For a gas of N molecules in a volume V, the polarization P per unit volume is then

$$P = \frac{N}{V}\left(\alpha + \frac{\mu_0^2}{3kT}\right)E\ . \tag{1.135}$$

Since the dielectric constant κ is related to the electric field strength E and the polarization P by the relation

$$\frac{\kappa - 1}{4\pi} = \frac{P}{E}, \tag{1.136}$$

it follows from (1.135) that

$$\kappa - 1 = 4\pi\left(\frac{N}{V}\right)\left(\alpha + \frac{\mu_0^2}{3kT}\right). \tag{1.137}$$

Equation (1.137) is the Debye equation for the dielectric constant of gases as a function of temperature. It applies to gases that are so dilute that intermolecular forces that would tend to cause molecules to influence the orientation of their neighbors are negligible. When the neighboring molecules do exert an effect upon the orientation of a molecule, the molecule finds itself in a kind of average local field $\mathbf{E}_{local}$, where

$$\mathbf{E}_{local} = \mathbf{E} + \tfrac{4}{3}\pi\mathbf{P} . \tag{1.138}$$

Here $\mathbf{E}_{local}$ is the field in the center of a spherical cavity in a polarized dielectric. Since it is this local field that is effective in inducing an electrical moment μ_i and in orienting the permanent moment μ_0, it follows from (1.134) and (1.135) that

$$\mathbf{P} = \left(\frac{N}{V}\right)\left(\alpha + \frac{\mu_0^2}{3kT}\right)\left(\mathbf{E} + \frac{4}{3}\pi\mathbf{P}\right) ; \tag{1.139}$$

whence

$$1 = \left(\frac{N}{V}\right)\left(\alpha + \frac{\mu_0^2}{3kT}\right)\left(\frac{\mathbf{E}}{\mathbf{P}} + \frac{4}{3}\pi\right) .$$

By (1.136),

$$1 = \left(\frac{N}{V}\right)\left(\alpha + \frac{\mu_0^2}{3kT}\right)\left(\frac{4\pi}{\kappa - 1} + \frac{4\pi}{3}\right)$$

$$= \left(\frac{N}{V}\right)\left(\alpha + \frac{\mu_0^2}{3kT}\right)\left(\frac{4\pi}{3}\right)\left(\frac{3}{\kappa - 1} + 1\right) ;$$

whence

$$\frac{\kappa - 1}{\kappa + 2} = \frac{4}{3}\pi \left(\frac{N}{V}\right)\left(\alpha + \frac{\mu_0^2}{3kT}\right) . \tag{1.140}$$

Equation (1.140) is a second form of the Debye equation (1.137), and it reduces to (1.137) for dilute gases because their dielectric constants are essentially unity.

The molar polarization $\mathcal{P}_M$ of a substance is defined by (1.141), where V_M is the molar volume of the substance.

$$\mathcal{P}_M = V_M \left(\frac{\kappa - 1}{\kappa + 2}\right) . \tag{1.141}$$

When the local field approximation is valid, as it is in gases (and in dilute liquid solutions of polar substances in nonpolar solvents), $\mathcal{P}_M$ is almost independent of density. Pure nonpolar liquids yield the same value of $\mathcal{P}_M$ as they exhibit as gases. Here $\mathcal{P}_M$ is not expected to be the same for gaseous and condensed phases of polar substances, for the local field approximation fails because of preferred positions in the liquid and solid. From (1.140), for those substances for which the local field approximation is valid, $\mathscr{P}_M$ depends upon the temperature as in (1.142), where N is Avogadro's number.

$$\mathscr{P}_M = \frac{4}{3}\pi N\left(\alpha + \frac{\mu_0^2}{3kT}\right). \tag{1.142}$$

Measurement of the dielectric constant κ at two or more temperatures allows a calculation of α and μ_0. If $\mathscr{P}_M$ is independent of temperature, as it is for nonpolar substances, μ_0 is zero. The dipole moment is important in valence theory. Moreover, with α and μ_0 known, (1.140) or (1.142) permits a calculation of κ at any density and temperature for which the local field is a valid approximation.

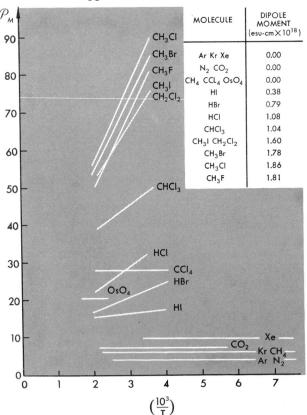

MOLECULE	DIPOLE MOMENT (esu-cm $\times 10^{18}$)
Ar Kr Xe	0.00
N_2 CO_2	0.00
CH_4 CCl_4 OsO_4	0.00
HI	0.38
HBr	0.79
HCl	1.08
$CHCl_3$	1.04
CH_3I CH_2Cl_2	1.60
CH_3Br	1.78
CH_3Cl	1.86
CH_3F	1.81

Fig. 1.8. *Molar Polarization* $(\mathscr{P}_M)$ *as a Function of Reciprocal Temperature* $(T)^*$.

The dielectric constant is usually measured by measuring the capacitance of a condenser in an alternating electric field. The ratio of its capacitance filled with fluid to the capacitance evacuated is κ. The varying electric field must be of a low enough frequency that the molecules can rotate with the field. Radio frequencies of the order of 10^8 cycles per second are satisfactory. At higher frequencies the orientational term containing μ_0 gradually decreases in importance because molecules are unable to rotate fast enough to keep pace with a field that alternates faster than about 10^{10} times per second. For frequencies from 10^{10} to 10^{12} cycles per second, atomic and electronic polarizations contribute to $\mathscr{P}_M$; but beyond 10^{12} cycles into the visible and ultraviolet regions of the electromagnetic spectrum, atomic movements that result in atomic polarizations are too slow to keep pace with the field. Fortunately, the atomic polarization of a substance is a small fraction (often about 5%) of the induced polarization. It is therefore possible to estimate the induced polarization from measurements with visible light (see

* Data from Landolt-Bornstein, *Zahlenwerte und Funktionen . . .*, *I Band, 3. Teil*, Springer-Verlag, Berlin (1951), pp. 386 *et seq.* and pp. 514–7.

Section 2.20). Figure 1.8 exhibits the dependence of $\mathcal{P}_M$ on temperature at radio frequencies for several simple molecules. In addition to the obvious increases in $\mathcal{P}_M$ due to a dipole moment, Fig. 1.8 illustrates how $\mathcal{P}_M$ increases as the number of electrons in a molecule increases. The molar polarizations of the rare gases increase from Ar at 4.12 through Kr at 6.26 to Xe at 10.09. For Ne and He, $\mathcal{P}_M$ is 1.00 and 0.54 cc, respectively. However, due mainly to the great attraction of the highly positive osmium nucleus for its inner electrons, the molar polarization of OsO_4 with its 108 electrons is less than that of CCl_4 which has only 80 electrons.

Example 1.13. The molar polarizations $\mathcal{P}_M$ of gaseous H_2O at 1 atm at several temperatures are listed below [Hurdis, E. C. and C. P. Smyth, *J. Am. Chem. Soc.*, **64**, 2829 (1942)]. From these data: (a) calculate the dipole moment μ_0 of gaseous H_2O; (b) calculate the moment associated with an OH bond if the angle subtended by the bonds in H_2O is 105°; and (c) estimate the ionic character of the OH bond in H_2O if the OH bonds in H_2O are each 0.957 Å in length.

$\mathcal{P}_M$ (cc)	57.4	53.5	50.1	46.8	43.1
T (°K)	384.3	420.1	444.7	484.1	522.0

(a) In Figure 1.9, $\mathcal{P}_M$ is plotted as a function of the reciprocal of absolute temperature. The slope of the best straight line is 2.08×10^4 cc × deg. This value is equal to the coefficient of T^{-1} in (1.142) so that

$$2.08 \times 10^4 = \frac{4}{3}\pi N \left(\frac{\mu_0^2}{3k}\right) ;$$

whence,

$$\mu_0 = \sqrt{\frac{9k \times 2.08 \times 10^4}{4\pi N}}$$

$$= \sqrt{\frac{9 \times 1.380 \times 10^{-16} \times 2.08 \times 10^4}{4 \times \pi \times 0.6024 \times 10^{24}}}$$

$$= 1.85 \times 10^{-18} \text{ e.s.u.} \times \text{cm} .$$

(b) The molecule of H_2O is planar. The component of the bond moment μ_{OH} along the axis of the molecule is

$$\mu_{OH} \cos\left(\frac{105°}{2}\right) = \mu_{OH} \cos(52.50°) .$$

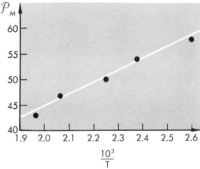

Fig. 1.9. *Molar Polarization* $(\mathcal{P}_M)$ *of Gaseous Water as a Function of Reciprocal Temperature* (T).

Since two bonds contribute to the molecular moment of 1.85×10^{-18} e.s.u. × cm,

$$1.85 \times 10^{-18} \text{ e.s.u.} \times \text{cm} = 2\mu_{OH} \cos(52.50°)$$
$$\mu_{OH} = 1.52 \times 10^{-18} \text{ e.s.u.} \times \text{cm} .$$

The bond moment is thus 1.52×10^{-18} e.s.u. × cm.

(c) By (1.124), the fractional charge z separated by 0.957×10^{-8} cm is

$$z = \frac{\mu}{el} = \frac{1.52 \times 10^{-18}}{4.80 \times 10^{-10} \times 0.957 \times 10^{-8}} = 0.33 .$$

Each OH bond is thus expected to have one-third ionic character. (Since the unshared pairs of electrons on the oxygen atom may contribute to the moment of the molecule and since the OH bonds may interact, this result must not be taken too seriously.)

Example 1.14. Landolt-Bornstein, *Zahlenwerte und Funktionen* (Berlin: Verlag Julius Springer, 1951, Band I., 3, Teil, pp. 386 *et seq.* and pp. 514–517) list many atomic and electronic molar polarizations and many dipole moments. For NH_3, the dipole moment is reported to be about 1.44×10^{-18} e.s.u. $\times$ cm and the atomic and electronic molar polarizations total about 6.0 cc. Calculate the dielectric constant of NH_3 at $\frac{1}{2}$ atm at 0°C if NH_3 is a perfect gas. By (1.142),

$$\mathcal{P}_M = \frac{4}{3}\pi N\alpha + \frac{4}{3}\pi N\left(\frac{\mu_0^2}{3kT}\right)$$

$$= 6.0 + \frac{4}{3}\pi \times 6.024 \times 10^{23}\left(\frac{1.44^2 \times 10^{-36}}{3 \times 1.38 \times 10^{-16} \times 273}\right)$$

$$= 6.0 + 46.2 = 52.2 \text{ cc.}$$

Since the molar volume under these conditions is 44.8 l, namely, twice the standard molar volume, by (1.141)

$$\frac{\kappa - 1}{\kappa + 2} = \frac{\mathcal{P}_M}{V_M} = \frac{52.2}{44.8 \times 10^3} = 1.165 \times 10^{-3}$$

$$\kappa - 1 = 0.001165\kappa + 0.00233$$

$$\kappa = \frac{1.00233}{0.99883} = 1.00350 .$$

1.15 Kinetic Theory of Colloids

The kinetic theory of matter can perhaps be traced to the philosophical theories of the Greeks, who were preoccupied with explaining change in a world in which some things were clearly rather permanent. Nevertheless, as a scientific theory with an experimental basis it began with Kronig and Clausius in about 1857. Others, including Maxwell, Kelvin, and Boltzmann, developed the kinetic theory greatly; but as a theory that had a true foundation in reality it was not accepted universally until Perrin, beginning in 1908, had performed his classic experiments on colloids.

Colloidal particles range in size from about 10–1000 angstroms. On the basis of modern knowledge of atomic and molecular structure, one colloidal particle may contain from a few hundred to a few billion atoms. Although such particles are smaller than the wavelength of light and thus are not visible directly, they can be viewed by the light that they scatter, just as a particle of dust can be seen readily in a beam of sunlight. The continual random movements of colloidal particles, first noticed in 1827 by Robert Brown as he studied pollen grains suspended in water, are attributed to bombardment of the colloidal particle (considered as a huge molecule) by the molecules of the dispersing medium. Throughout his researches, Perrin assumed that a colloidal particle would behave like a molecule as regards all its mechanical properties. Direct observation of molecular properties by means of a suitable microscope was then possible.

One of the experiments that exhibits Perrin's methods was his determination of Avogadro's number from the equilibrium distribution of colloidal particles in a gravitational field. The gravitational potential energy ϵ of a spherical particle of density ρ and radius r at a height z when suspended in a fluid of density ρ_0 is

$$\epsilon = (\tfrac{4}{3}\pi r^3)(\rho - \rho_0)gz. \tag{1.143}$$

This value of ϵ is just the work required to lift the mass $(\tfrac{4}{3}\pi r^3)(\rho - \rho_0)$ to the height z. If n_0 is the number of colloidal particles at $z = 0$, since ϵ is zero at $z = 0$, it follows from (1.118) that

$$n_0 = \frac{n}{\sum_j e^{-\epsilon_j/kT}}. \tag{1.144}$$

At the height z where the number of colloidal particles is n_z,

$$n_z = \frac{ne^{-\epsilon/kT}}{\sum_j e^{-\epsilon_j/kT}}. \tag{1.145}$$

Division of (1.144) by (1.145) yields

$$\frac{n_0}{n_z} = e^{\epsilon/kT}. \tag{1.146}$$

That is, by (1.143)

$$\ln\left(\frac{n_0}{n_z}\right) = \frac{\tfrac{4}{3}\pi r^3(\rho - \rho_0)gz}{kT}. \tag{1.147}$$

Since $R = Nk$, where N is Avogadro's number, it follows from (1.147) that

$$N = \frac{RT}{(\tfrac{4}{3}\pi r^3)(\rho - \rho_0)gz}\ln\left(\frac{n_0}{n_z}\right). \tag{1.148}$$

By standard and straightforward methods, Perrin was able to measure the densities ρ and ρ_0. Perrin was also able to prepare colloidal particles of gamboge and mastic that were spherical and of uniform size. He determined their size by three methods, two of which involved actual counting of the number of spherical particles in a known mass of particles. Finally, counting and averaging the numbers of particles suspended at levels separated by a distance z at the temperature T yielded a value of the right-hand member of (1.148). The values of N found from experiments at various temperatures in various dispersing media were about 7×10^{23}. The agreement of this method of evaluating Avogadro's number with many other methods, some not at all related to the kinetic theory, was accepted as proof of the validity of Perrin's assumption that the particles of colloid behaved like molecules. It was accepted also as proof in support of the kinetic theory.

REFERENCES

Fowler, R. G. and D. I. Meyer, *Physics for Engineers and Scientists.* Boston, Mass.: Allyn and Bacon, Inc., 1958.

Guggenheim, E. A., *Thermodynamics, an Advanced Treatment for Chemists and Physicists.* Amsterdam: North-Holland Publishing Co., 1957.

Hirschfelder, J. O., C. F. Curtiss, and R. B. Bird, *Molecular Theory of Gases and Liquids.* New York: John Wiley & Sons, Inc., 1954.

Mayer, J. E. and M. G. Mayer, *Statistical Mechanics.* New York: John Wiley & Sons, Inc., 1940.

Tolman, R. C., *The Principles of Statistical Mechanics.* New York: Oxford University Press, 1938.

PROBLEMS

1. Calculate in ergs the kinetic energy of a neon molecule with a velocity of 5×10^4 cm sec $^{-1}$.
Answer: 4.19×10^{-14} erg.

2. Explain with the aid of a mathematical equation how the constant-volume hydrogen thermometer works. The observables are two pressure measurements, one of which is taken at a standard temperature.

3. How many molecules are there per cubic centimeter of a perfect gas at a pressure of 1.0×10^{-6} mm Hg at $27°C$?
Answer: 3.2×10^{10} molecules.

4. Evaluate the gas constant R in English units.

5. If 40.0 l N_2 at $27°C$ at 0.900 atm were cooled to $4°C$ at 1.000 atm:
(a) How many gram-moles of N_2 were present?
(b) What was the final volume of the N_2?

6. What is the density of gaseous ethyl chloride (C_2H_5Cl) at $50°C$ at 2.20 atm?

7. What is the pressure of gaseous HCl at $-40°C$ if its density is 8.00 g l^{-1}?
Answer: 4.20 atm (perfect gas); 4.06 atm (van der Waals).

8. Exactly 10 l NH_3 at $0°C$ were compressed to a volume of 7.50 l at $100°C$. If the initial pressure was 1.00×10^{-3} atm, what was the final pressure?

9. What is the volume of 10.0 g gaseous H_2 at $27°C$ at 3.32 atm? Of 10.0 g SO_2 under the same conditions? Use the perfect gas law and the equation of Dieterici for each gas.

10. Transform the equation of van der Waals to reduced form.

11. Calculate the mean free path of pure gaseous Cl_2 at standard conditions if $\sigma = 3 \times 10^{-8}$ cm. Repeat for H_2 if $\sigma = 3 \times 10^{-8}$ cm.

12. Calculate the numbers of double and triple collisions in N_2 at $27°C$ and at $1000°C$ at 0.500 atm.
Answer: $(27°C)$ $Z_2 = 2.5 \times 10^{28}$ sec^{-1} ml^{-1}; $Z_3 = 8.8 \times 10^{25}$ sec^{-1} ml^{-1}.

13. Calculate the viscosity of steam at $150°C$ if $\sigma = 5 \times 10^{-8}$ cm.

14.   Calculate the total average kinetic energy of a rigid oxygen molecule at equilibrium with the surrounding gas at a temperature such that it has a root mean square velocity of 5×10^4 cm sec^{-1}.

15.   Calculate in ergs the kinetic energy of 1 l of a perfect monatomic gas at 1 atm.
Answer: 1.52×10^9 ergs.

16.)   It takes 75 sec for a certain amount of a gas of molecular weight 28 to effuse from a certain tiny hole.   Under similar conditions it takes another gas 120 sec. What is the molecular weight of the second gas?   What if the second gas were impure?

17.   At what temperature will SO_3 have the same average velocity as that of N_2 at 0°C?

18.   Small amounts of gaseous NH_3 and gaseous HCl were released simultaneously at the ends of an 80-cm tube of stagnant air.   At what point does NH_4Cl form?

19.   At 100°C, 1.83 g of a pure volatile organic compound with empirical formula CH_2 occupies a volume of 1.90 l at 0.691 atm.   What is the formula of the hydrocarbon? *Answer:* C_3H_6.

20.   The best vacuum pump can generate a vacuum of about 1×10^{-9} mm Hg. At room temperature, about how many molecules are there per milliliter at this pressure?   What is the order of magnitude of the mean free path?

21.   What is the density of steam at 140°C at 3.22 atm if steam is: (a) A perfect gas? (b) A van der Waals gas?   (c) A Dieterici gas?

22.   Calculate the pressure expected of two moles of gaseous CO_2 at 27°C when confined in a volume of 4.00 l if the equation of state is that of: (a) A perfect gas. (b) A van der Waals gas.
Answer: (a) 12.3 atm; (b) 11.7 atm.

23.   By means of an almost linear graph, determine the Boyle temperature of N_2 from the data of Table 1.1.

24.   Calculate the pressure of 50.000 g N_2 in a five-liter container at −50°C by use of the virial equation and data of Table 1.1.
Answer: 6.4764 atm.

25.   For several fixed temperatures, indicate graphically how PV for a van der Waals gas depends upon P when: (a) $a = 0$. (b) $b = 0$. (c) $a = b = 0$.

26.)   Calculate the compressibility coefficient β of SO_2 at 1 atm at 25°C from Dieterici's equation of state if

$$\beta = -\frac{1}{V}\left(\frac{\partial V}{\partial P}\right)_T.$$

27.   Compare the pressures predicted by the Dieterici and Beattie-Bridgeman equations for one mole CH_4 at −60°C at a density of 0.200 g ml^{-1}.

28.   Find an expression for the distance to which half of any set of gaseous molecules at thermal equilibrium move before suffering a second collision.

29.   A few hundred miles above the surface of the earth there are about 10^8 molecules ml^{-1} and the temperature may be as high as 1000°K.   At such heights estimate the mean free path of a molecule and the number of double collisions per cubic mile for molecules with molecular weights of the order of 10.

30.   The viscosity of H_2 at 300°C is 140×10^{-6} poise (cgs unit).   Calculate σ^2 for H_2. *Answer:* 6.49×10^{-16} cm^2.

31. The viscosities of gases often vary as a power of T slightly greater than one-half. If all this extraordinary variation is attributed to variations in σ, and in the spirit of the equations of state discussed, suggest how σ or σ^2 may vary with T.

32. Estimate the increase in energy per degree rise in temperature for 1 mole of a diatomic gas if the molecules are: (a) Rigid. (b) Almost rigid. (c) Weakly bonded.

33. Calculate the dipole moment of nitromethane (CH_3NO_2) from the data below [C. P. Smyth and K. B. McAlpine, *J. Am. Chem. Soc.*, **56**, 1697 (1934)].

$T(°K)$	339.0	380.7	400.8	435.1	448.8	493.2	494.1
$\mathcal{P}_M(ml)$	231.5	208.5	198.6	185.0	179.6	164.9	164.6

Answer: 3.44×10^{-18} e.s.u. cm.

34. Calculate the dipole moments of CH_3Br and CH_3I from the data below [C. P. Smyth and K. B. McAlpine, *J. Chem. Phys.*, **2**, 499 (1934)]. Predict the dipole moments of CBr_3I and CI_3Br if all bond angles are tetrahedral.

CH₃Br		CH₃I	
$T(°K)$	$P_M(ml)$	$T(°K)$	$P_M(ml)$
306.2	79.60	304.7	71.82
309.1	78.85	313.4	70.15
330.8	74.40	345.9	65.3
368.0	68.40	398.6	59.4
405.9	63.85	446.7	55.5
		494.4	51.8

35. With the Boltzmann distribution develop an equation for the isothermal dependence of density of a perfect gas upon altitude in a gravitational field.
Answer: $\rho = \rho_0 e^{-Mgz/RT}$.

---

36. Calculate the relative rates of effusion of He and CH_4 through the same pinhole at the same temperature if the pressure of CH_4 is four times that of He.
Answer: Rates equal.

37. What is the coefficient of expansion α of a perfect gas at $500°K$?

$$\alpha = \frac{1}{V}\left(\frac{\partial V}{\partial T}\right)_P.$$

38. Exactly 1 g of a metal was oxidized to form 1.629 g of a pure volatile oxide of the metal. This volatile oxide had a vapor density of about 1.08 g l⁻¹ at 100°C at 0.200 atm. From these data, calculate:
(a) The equivalent weight of the metal.
(b) The molecular weight of the volatile oxide.
(c) The formula of the volatile oxide.
(d) The *exact* atomic weight of the metal.
Answer: RuO_4.

39. Repeat Problem 38 if exactly 1 g of metal yielded 1.337 g oxide with vapor density of 1.65 g l⁻¹ at 100°C at 0.200 atm.

40. Exactly 1 g of element X was burned in air to form 2.29 g pure volatile oxide that occupied 2070 ml at 550°C at 200 mm Hg.
(a) What is the molecular weight of the oxide?
(b) If one molecule contains four atoms of X, what is the atomic weight of X?

41. A Victor Meyer vial weighed 4.332 g empty. When filled with a pure liquid containing about 74.0% by weight fluorine, the sealed vial weighed 4.786 g. As in the usual procedure, the vial was broken in a vessel that was jacketed by a boiling water bath at 99.8°C. The volume of air displaced was measured over mercury at 27°C at 745 mm Hg; it occupied 44.6 ml. If the liquid contains only two elements, determine:
(a) Its molecular weight as it exists at 99.8°C.
(b) Possible chemical formulas of the fluoride.

42. Show that van der Waals' b must be greater than the actual molar volume.

43. Calculate the pressures predicted for two moles ethylene (C_2H_4) confined in a volume of 1.400 l at -20°C. (The vapor pressure of ethylene at -20°C is 24.8 atm.) *Answer:* 23.2 atm (van der Waals).

44. Criticize the statement: At its Boyle temperature, each gas follows Boyle's law exactly.

45. Can a van der Waals gas with $a = 0$ be liquefied? Is the equation $P(V - nb) = nRT$ suitable near the critical point? Explain mathematically.

46. By Berthelot's equation of Section 1.6, calculate the density of SO_2 at 25°C at several pressures less than 1 atm.

47. Calculate the root mean square velocities, mean velocities, and most probable velocities of O_2 and CO_2 at 37°C. Compare and discuss biological implications.

48. Calculate average values of p, p^2, p^3, and p^4, where p is linear momentum of a gas molecule.

49. In a system of molecules at equilibrium at temperature T, calculate the fraction that have energies in excess of $10RT$.

Answer: $4/\sqrt{\pi} \int_{\sqrt{10}}^{\infty} y^2 e^{-y^2} \, dy$.

50. Estimate the increase in energy per degree rise in temperature for:
(a) One mole of a gas consisting of rigid linear polyatomic molecules.
(b) One mole of a solid containing rigid nonlinear polyatomic molecules if each molecule is free to rotate and if each molecule is bound to its position in the solid by forces that are proportional to the displacement from its equilibrium position.

51. In terms of the Boltzmann energy distribution, what meaning has a negative absolute temperature? Is this hotter or colder than ordinary temperatures? *Answer:* Hotter.

52. The molar polarization $\mathcal{P}_M$ of cis-dichloroethylene at 301.5°K is 93.13 cc and at 427.0°K is 71.42 cc [A. A. Maryott, M. E. Hobbs, and P. M. Gross, *J. Am. Chem. Soc.*, **63**, 661 (1941)].
(a) Calculate the dipole moment of cis-dichloroethylene.
(b) Predict the dipole moment of planar trans-dichloroethylene.
(c) Calculate the visible index of refraction of liquid cis- or trans-dichloroethylene if the density of each is about 1.28 g ml^{-1} and if the atomic polarization $\mathcal{P}_A$ is about 10% of the induced polazriation $\mathcal{P}_D$.

53. Latex particles with densities of 1.21 g cm^{-3} and with average diameters of 4000 A were colloidally dispersed in water. When equilibrium with respect to sedimentation had been achieved at 20°C, the average number of colloidal particles seen in the field of the microscope was halved for a vertical rise of 0.00360 cm. From these data calculate Avogadro's number. *Answer:* 7×10^{23}.

FOOTNOTES

1. See Appendix C.

2. See, for example, Hirschfelder, J. O., C. F. Curtiss, and R. B. Bird, *Molecular Theory of Gases and Liquids*. New York: John Wiley & Sons, Inc., 1954, p. 235 *et seq.* Or see Guggenheim, E. A., *Thermodynamics*. Amsterdam: North-Holland Publishing Co., 1957, p. 165 *et seq.*

3. Hougen, O. A. and K. M. Watson, *Chemical Process Principles*. New York: John Wiley & Sons, Inc., 1947, Part II.

4. Beattie, J. A. and O. C. Bridgeman, *Journal of the American Chemical Society*, **49** (1927), 1665.

5. Mayer, J. E. and M. G. Mayer, *Statistical Mechanics*. New York: John Wiley & Sons, Inc., 1940, p. 6 *et seq.*

6. See, for example, Mayer, J. E. and M. G. Mayer, *Statistical Mechanics*. New York: John Wiley & Sons, Inc., 1940, pp. 10-12.

7. A very lucid explanation is given by Woods, F. S., *Advanced Calculus*. Boston, Mass.: Ginn & Co., 1934, p. 164 *et seq.*

8. Mayer, J. E. and M. G. Mayer, *Statistical Mechanics*. New York: John Wiley & Sons, Inc., 1940, pp. 18-21.

9. Hirschfelder, J. O., C. F. Curtiss, and R. B. Bird, *Molecular Theory of Gases and Liquids*. New York: John Wiley & Sons, Inc., 1954, pp. 13-15.

10. The development of this section follows closely several parts of Chapter IV of Tolman, R. C., *The Principles of Statistical Mechanics*. New York: Oxford University Press, 1938.

11. Tolman, R. C., *The Principles of Statistical Mechanics*. New York: Oxford University Press, 1938, p. 95 *et seq.*

2 / STRUCTURES OF

CONDENSED PHASES

A. GENERAL ASPECTS

2.1 Law of Rational Indexes

Whereas the gaseous state of matter is simple because of its disorder and randomness, the solid state of matter is simple because of its order and regularity. While disorder leads to homogeneity, order leads to inhomogeneity.

The clearest manifestation of order and inhomogeneity in crystalline substances is in the perfection and regularity of the faces of individual crystals. The particular form of a crystal depends upon the conditions of growth. Precipitation from a slightly supersaturated solution or a very slowly cooling melt allows all naturally occurring faces to grow. If the growing crystal is completely bathed in a homogeneous environment, its growth generally proceeds in such a way as to develop highly symmetrical crystals like those of Figure 2.1. However, if precipitation alters the concentration near a face or if all faces of a growing crystal are not bathed in the solution or melt, perhaps because the crystal rests on the bottom of its container, then imperfect crystals are expected. Sometimes rapid growth in a melt or greatly supersaturated solution may allow quickly growing faces to develop so fast that they disappear. For example, if the octahedral faces of Figure 2.1(f) were to grow more rapidly than the cubic faces, (f) would become (d), and finally (a). Thus, the observed faces are usually the most slowly growing ones, but minerals often grow so slowly and from solutions that are so very slightly supersaturated that many faces are developed. Traces of impurities such as dyes often greatly modify the relative rates of growth of various faces and thus lead to unusual crystalline forms.[1]

Although the perfection of crystals of a substance is variable, the angles between the normals to the various faces are characteristic and distinctive features of a substance. Identification of a crystalline species depends in part upon measurements of the interfacial angles. With large crystals a contact goniometer may be used to measure these angles, but for tiny crystals a reflection goniometer is used. A beam of light is reflected from a face as from a mirror in order to measure the angles between faces. From the interfacial angles it is possible to derive a set of crystallographic axes that describe the crystal. The law of rational indexes says: *For any crystalline species there is a set of axes in terms of which all naturally occurring faces have reciprocal intercepts proportional to small integers (hkl).*

The three axes appropriate to the description of the crystalline species of Figure 2.1 are mutually perpendicular to one another and are of equal length. Each face, if extended sufficiently, would cut each axis. Each face of the cube cuts one axis at a distance a from the origin and cuts the other two cubic axes at an infinite distance.

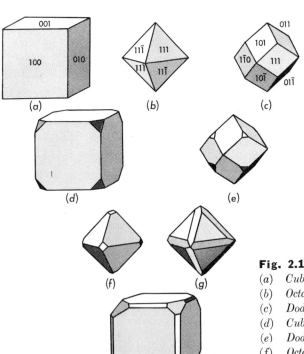

Fig. 2.1. *Some Crystalline Habits.*

(a) *Cube [NaCl, PbS, Cu₂O]*

(b) *Octahedron [Au, NaCl, Cu₂O, MgAl₂O₄, Fe₃O₄]*

(c) *Dodecahedron [Cu₂O, Fe₃O₄]*

(d) *Cube and Octahedron [KCl, PbS]*

(e) *Dodecahedron and Octahedron [Fe₃O₄]*

(f) *Octahedron and Cube [PbS, Cu₂O]*

(g) *Octahedron and Dodecahedron [MgAl₂O₄]*

(h) *Cube-Octahedron-Dodecahedron [Cu₂O]*

The reciprocal intercepts are a^{-1}, 0, and 0 in terms of this set of axes. If the proportionality constant be a, then the small integers are (100). If the positive sense of the first axis is outward from the figure and if the positive senses of the second and third axes are to the right and upward, then the front face of the cube is (100). Similarly, the right-hand face is (010) and the top face is (001). Because they intercept the negative axes, the back, left-hand, and bottom faces are ($\bar{1}$00), (0$\bar{1}$0), and (00$\bar{1}$), respectively, where the symbol $\bar{1}$ means *minus unity*. The indexes appropriate to the visible faces of the other simple crystals of Figure 2.1 are inscribed on the various faces. The (111) face of the octahedron is so labeled because it intercepts each of the axes at $+a$. The (110) face of the dodecahedron intercepts the first two axes at $+a$ and the third axis at infinity. The actual magnitude of the proportionality constant a is not established by the interfacial angles. Rather, all that can be said is that the (111) face cuts all three axes at the same distance from the origin.

The set of axes described above is not the only choice that leads to small integers. If axes rotated by $\pi/4$ about the vertical had been chosen, (111) of (b) would have been (101), (100) and (010) of (a) would have been (1$\bar{1}$0) and (110), and so on. The set chosen originally is, however, the simplest set of many possible choices. It is seldom necessary to choose integers greater than 5 regardless of the complexity of the crystalline development. The integers (hkl) are called the *Miller indexes of a face*. They define the orientation of a face or plane relative to the three noncoplanar axes fixed in the crystal. These axes may be of any length and may be inclined at any angle. When several sets that yield small integers

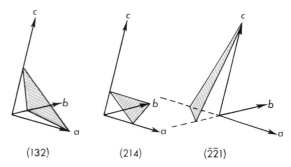

(132) (214) ($\bar{2}\bar{2}$1)

Fig. 2.2. *Examples of Miller Indexes.*

are at hand, that set which most fully describes the symmetry of the crystals is chosen. Several examples of Miller indexes of planes are described in Figure 2.2, the order of the axes being a, b, c.

2.2 Lattices

A lattice is a mathematical construct for describing the order of a structure. In 1782 Abbe Haüy advanced the hypothesis that crystals are built by the ordered arrangement of simple units. To him is also due the credit for the law of rational indexes. By the end of the nineteenth century, mathematicians had exhausted the possibilities of building orderly geometrical arrangements in three-dimensional space.

A lattice is an infinite set of points repeated regularly throughout space. In one dimension, a set of points that are repeated at a distance a along a line is a one-dimensional lattice. A line of identical equally spaced telephone poles provides a simple example of a structure based on such a lattice. The characteristics of such a lattice are that each lattice point is identical with any other lattice point and that the distance between any two lattice points is an integral multiple of the distance a. The various lattice sites are occupied by congruent figures that may or may not be points. Movement by an integral multiple of the primitive translation a leads inevitably to a corresponding position on a congruent figure at the final position. The figure that is repeated endlessly throughout space is the *motif* of the lattice. The motif of a line of equally distant identical telephone poles is one such pole. But if the poles were painted alternately red and green, the motif would be a pair of poles and the primitive translation would be twice as great as it was when the poles were not distinguished by color.

In two dimensions, a lattice is an infinite set of points recurring regularly in a plane. A field of identical cornstalks provides a homely example of a structure based upon such a lattice. Two translations that are not parallel fix the positions of all lattice sites. The directions taken by the two translations must, however, be specified just as their lengths are specified. Since a vector is a mathematical quantity having magnitude and direction, such a two-dimensional lattice is appropriately described by two vectors. Some of the many possible choices of two such vectors for a particular lattice are indicated in Figure 2.3. In fact, the choices of Figure 2.3 are a few of the many ways in which a primitive pair of vectors may be chosen for the lattice, a primitive pair being a pair that includes only one lattice site in its parallelogram, namely, that at the origin. A primitive pair is found systematically by choosing a between two successive sites along a line of sites and then choosing b as the vector from the tail of a to any point in one of the closest lines of sites parallel to a. The region included by the parallelogram that could be generated from primitive pairs of vectors is called the *primitive unit cell of the lattice*. The primitive unit cell of a one-dimensional lattice is just the vector that links successive identical points on the line in one dimension.

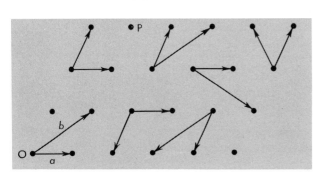

Fig. 2.3. *Some Primitive Vector-Pairs.*

As with the one-dimensional lattice, the two-dimensional lattice is a mathematical device for finding equivalent positions in a structure composed of regularly repeated congruent figures. If a and b are the two primitive vectors of the lattice, then a movement by

$$r = ua + vb, \qquad (2.1)$$

such that u and v are integers, would lead to an equivalent position on a congruent figure. For example, to achieve point P from point O in Figure 2.3, $u = -2$ and $v = 3$. A beetle that was moved by r while napping could not distinguish his new ear of corn or its stalk from the one he occupied before he was spirited through his field.

The familiar lines of cornstalks in a field are lines that have certain Miller indexes (hk) once a pair of vectors has been chosen for the planar lattice. Figure 2.4 illustrates the assignment of indexes. Lines labeled (10) do not intersect b; (11) intersects a and b with equal frequency; and so on. A study of the rows of this figure shows that lattice sites generally become more and more distant along the rows as the indexes increase and that the distance between parallel rows generally decreases as the indexes increase.

A three-dimensional lattice has lattice sites that are repeated regularly throughout three dimensions. Three noncoplanar primitive vectors a, b, and c that describe such a lattice can be found by an extension of the method in two dimensions. First, let the distance between two adjacent lattice sites be the primitive vector a. Extension of this line yields lattice sites along the line at ua, where u is an integer. Second, choose a plane containing this line and any lattice site not on the line, and in this plane find the primitive

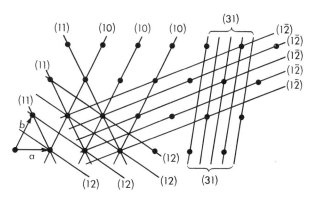

Fig. 2.4. *Indexes of Some Rows in a Planar Lattice.*

vector b as in a two-dimensional lattice. Third, find an equivalent parallel plane that is as near to the plane of a and b as is any other such plane. A vector c from any lattice site of one plane to a lattice site in such an immediately adjacent parallel plane is the third noncoplanar vector c of the triple of primitive vectors a, b, and c. This triple, of course, may not be the simplest possible choice of primitive vectors.

Any movement r between equivalent points in this three-dimensional lattice is then

$$r = ua + vb + wc, \qquad (2.2)$$

where u, v, and w are integers that each range from $-\infty$ to $+\infty$. Indeed, the lattice can be generated from a point by letting u, v, and w assume all integral values. As a mathematical construct designed to label equivalent positions in a structure, the lattice is infinite in extent while the structure is bounded by the finiteness of the number of its elements.

63

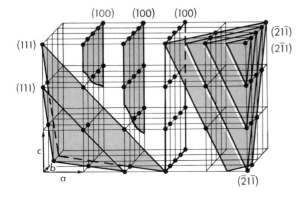

Fig. 2.5. *Some Indexed Planes.*

Plane faces such as those developed by crystals are indexed by integers (hkl). These are the same integers called Miller indexes. The requirement of the law of rational indexes that these integers be small means that planes that develop naturally in crystals have a high surface density of lattice sites, just as in a two-dimensional lattice rows having small indexes generally have more sites per unit length than rows with large indexes. Figure 2.5 illustrates the indexing of a few planes in a three-dimensional lattice.

2.3 Fourteen Space Lattices

There are 14 different ways of arranging lattice points in three-dimensional space. These 14 ways were first described by Bravais in 1850 and are called the *Bravais lattices.* The axes chosen for these lattices display the full symmetry of the structures that they describe. Figure 2.6 exhibits for each of these 14 Bravais lattices its unit cell, the smallest part of the lattice that is repeated throughout space in order to generate the whole lattice.

The lattices are classified according to the seven crystal systems (cubic, tetragonal, orthorhombic, hexagonal, trigonal, monoclinic, and triclinic) and according to the number and kind of lattice sites in the unit cell. Primitive unit cells are labeled P and contain only one lattice site at the origin. The position of this site is described as 000, the three zeros indicating

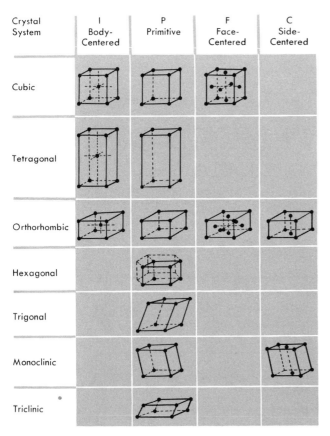

Crystal System	I Body-Centered	P Primitive	F Face-Centered	C Side-Centered
Cubic				
Tetragonal				
Orthorhombic				
Hexagonal				
Trigonal				
Monoclinic				
Triclinic				

Fig. 2.6. *Bravais Lattices. The* a *axis proceeds to the right;* b, *to the rear; and* c, *upwards from the origin at the lower front left.*

that the site is not displaced from the origin along a, b, or c. More than the minimum number of lattice sites is shown in Figure 2.6 in order to show the symmetry of the unit cells. In each P cell, the seven additional lattice points not at 000 in the cells shown are in fact at 000 in the seven cells that are immediately above, to the right of, and behind the cell shown.

Nonprimitive unit cells are labeled I, F, and C, and are chosen as nonprimitive in order to match the full symmetry of the lattice. Body-centered unit cells, labeled I from the German *innenzentriertes Gitter*, contain two lattice sites per unit cell, one at the origin 000 and one at the position $\frac{1}{2}\frac{1}{2}\frac{1}{2}$ displaced from the origin by $\frac{1}{2}a + \frac{1}{2}b + \frac{1}{2}c$. Face-centered lattices are labeled F and contain, besides the site at 000, three more sites in the centers of the faces at displacements from the origin $\frac{1}{2}a + \frac{1}{2}b$, $\frac{1}{2}a + \frac{1}{2}c$, and $\frac{1}{2}b + \frac{1}{2}c$. In terms of fractional displacements along the vectors that describe the unit cells, these four sites per unit cell of a face-centered lattice are at 000, $\frac{1}{2}\frac{1}{2}0$, $\frac{1}{2}0\frac{1}{2}$, and $0\frac{1}{2}\frac{1}{2}$. Side-centered lattices in which the (001) face, the one intersecting only c, is the only face centered, are labeled C. Such C cells contain two sites per unit cell, one at 000 and another at $\frac{1}{2}\frac{1}{2}0$. [If the (100) face were centered, the lattice would be labeled A; if (010), B.]

The I, F, and C lattices that appear to be missing from Figure 2.6 may not really be lattices, or may, in fact, be equivalent to one of the 14 lattices already set forth. A cubic C lattice is not a cubic lattice because centering the C face would make the C-axis different from the a- and b-axes and would thus lead to tetragonal symmetry. On the other hand, a tetragonal C lattice can be described more simply in terms of a primitive lattice based on axes rotated by $\pi/4$ relative to those used to describe the C unit cell, as Figure 2.7 explains.

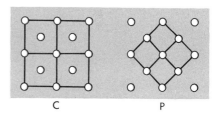

Fig. 2.7. *The (001) Face of Four Unit Cells of Tetragonal* C *and* P *Lattices and Their Equivalence.*

Table 2.1 lists the parameters that must be specified in order to define the size and shape of a unit cell in any of the seven crystal systems. The length of the edge of the cubic unit cell is the only variable that must be specified in the cubic system. Less symmetrical systems require the specification of more variables than just the scale of size. For example, three different cell lengths must be specified in the orthorhombic system. The triclinic system has so little symmetry that all six parameters, three lengths and three interaxial angles, must be specified in order to fix the size and shape of the unit cell.

Table 2.1 also lists the symmetry characteristic of a crystal system and the parameters that are fixed by this symmetry. The symmetry operations that are listed are rotations. If rotation by $2\pi/n$ about an axis leads to an arrangement identical to that which existed before rotation, the element of symmetry that exists is called an n-fold axis. Only one-, two-, three-, four-, and sixfold axes are allowed in lattices; five-, seven-, eight-, and higherfold axes are forbidden by the repetition that is the essence of a lattice. The four

Table 2.1. *Symmetry and Parameters of Crystal Systems.*

CRYSTAL SYSTEM	CHARACTERISTIC SYMMETRY	PARAMETERS[a] FIXED BY SYMMETRY	PARAMETERS[a] TO BE SPECIFIED
Cubic	Four threefold axes perpendicular to (111), $(\bar{1}11)$, $(\bar{1}\bar{1}1)$, $(1\bar{1}1)$	$a = b = c$ $\alpha = \beta = \gamma = \dfrac{\pi}{2}$	a
Tetragonal	One fourfold axis perpendicular to (001)	$a = b$ $\alpha = \beta = \gamma = \dfrac{\pi}{2}$	$a;\ c$
Orthorhombic	Three mutually perpendicular twofold axes	$\alpha = \beta = \gamma = \dfrac{\pi}{2}$	$c < a < b$
Hexagonal	One sixfold axis perpendicular to (001)	$a = b$ $\alpha = \beta = \dfrac{\pi}{2}$ $\gamma = \dfrac{2\pi}{3}$	$a;\ c$
Trigonal	One threefold axis perpendicular to (111)	$a = b = c$ $\alpha = \beta = \gamma$	a α
Monoclinic	One twofold axis perpendicular to (010)	$\alpha = \gamma = \dfrac{\pi}{2}$	$c < a;\ b$ $\beta > \dfrac{\pi}{2}$
Triclinic	Onefold axes	None	$c < a < b$ α, β, γ

[a] The values of a, b, and c are the magnitudes of the vectors $\mathbf{a}$, $\mathbf{b}$, and $\mathbf{c}$. The angle α is the angle between $\mathbf{b}$ and $\mathbf{c}$; β, between $\mathbf{a}$ and $\mathbf{c}$; γ, between $\mathbf{a}$ and $\mathbf{b}$.

threefold axes characteristic of the cubic system transform the a-, b-, and c-axes into each other. For example, rotation by $2\pi/3 = 120°$ around the axis perpendicular to (111) transforms $\mathbf{a}$ into $\mathbf{b}$, $\mathbf{b}$ into $\mathbf{c}$, and $\mathbf{c}$ into $\mathbf{a}$. The triangular faces of the octahedron in Figure 2.1 clearly show the effect and character of these four axes of rotation. The fourfold axis of the tetragonal system transforms $\mathbf{a}$ into $\mathbf{b}$ and $\mathbf{b}$ into $-\mathbf{a}$ if applied once; if applied three more times, both axes would return to their initial position. However, each rotation by $2\pi/4$ would lead to a configuration that could not be distinguished from others of the series.

Certain kinds of symmetry operations leave at least one point in space unmoved. Reflection of left hand into right hand across a plane halfway between them leaves all points in the plane of reflection unmoved; rotation about an axis leaves points on the axis unmoved; rotation followed by reflection in a plane perpendicular to the axis of rotation leaves one point unmoved. On the other hand, other kinds of symmetry operations transform similar figures into each other by translations in space coupled with rotations and reflections. A screw rotation is a rotation followed (or preceded) by a translation parallel to the axis of rotation; a gliding reflection is a reflection followed (or preceded) by a translation parallel to the plane of reflection. There are in all just 230 space groups that combine all possible space operations of three-dimensional lattices. The mathematicians Fedorov and Schoenflies derived these 230 space groups in 1890. There are 32 crystallographic point groups that combine all the elements of symmetry allowed at a lattice point into a group of operations that leave at least one point in space invariant. For molecules free of a lattice, many more point groups are possible and observed. For the student who cares to pursue this fascinating study further, a list of carefully selected references is given in the footnotes.[2]

2.4 Powder Diffraction Equation

Although the electron microscope has revealed to "direct" observation the regular stacking of huge virus molecules into a lattice, no one has actually seen how ions, atoms, and small molecules are arranged in lattices. Information about the positions and sizes of atoms, ions, and molecules has come through the interpretation of the interference patterns caused when X rays with wavelengths of the same order of magnitude as atomic sizes are diffracted from the lattice as from a diffraction grating. At the suggestion of von Laue, Friedrich and Knipping examined several crystalline and amorphous substances and found for the crystalline ones the interference phenomena expected by von Laue. The Braggs at once undertook similar work in England when these results were published in 1912, and within a year had determined the structures of NaCl, KCl, diamond, ZnS, CaF_2, and others. The success of the Braggs, father and son, was due in part to their recognition of the X-ray patterns as the results of diffraction and to their simple mathematical formulation of the spectra.

The interaction of X radiation with a crystal is conceived as a reflection of radiation from one of the many sets of planes that exist in a three-dimensional lattice. Suppose that a set of such planes separated by the distance d is viewed edge-on as in Figure 2.8. Reflection of a beam of X radiation is said to occur when the angle θ between the incident beam and the planes equals the angle θ between the planes and the reflected beam. The reflected beam can have an intensity greater than zero only when the difference in path length along two reflected rays from the wavefront at I to that at R is an integral number n of wavelengths λ. Otherwise, the interference that occurs because of the many reflecting planes is complete and the intensity is zero

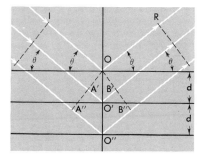

Fig. 2.8. *Bragg Reflection of X Radiation.*

in the reflected wave. If OA' and OB' are perpendicular to the ray that is reflected at O, this difference in path length is $A'O' + O'B'$. Since the sides of the angles $A'OO'$ and $B'OO'$ are perpendicular to the sides of the angles θ, both angles are equal to θ; whence it follows at once from the definition of the sine that in the right triangles $O'OA'$ and $O'OB'$,

$$O'A' = O'B' = d \sin \theta .$$

Since the difference in path length $(A'O' + O'B')$ must equal $n\lambda$ for reinforcement of the reflected radiation, it follows that

$$n\lambda = 2d \sin \theta . \qquad (2.3)$$

For the plane through O'', the path difference is $2n\lambda$ and is equal to $2(2d \sin \theta)$, again yielding (2.3). Equation (2.3) is the famous Bragg equation. It can also be derived very elegantly by vector methods.[3]

Provided the wavelength λ is small enough relative to the spacing d between lattice planes, several values of n, the order of the reflection, are possible for $0 \leqslant \theta \leqslant \pi/2$, the allowed range of θ. Figure 2.9 shows three orders of reflection from planes separated by d. The order n can be suppressed altogether from the Bragg equation by a transformation that is equivalent to imagining the existence of fictitious planes parallel to the real Bragg planes. Division of the Bragg equation (2.3) by n yields (2.4).

$$\lambda = 2 \left(\frac{d}{n}\right) \sin \theta . \qquad (2.4)$$

This has the same form as the Bragg equation in first order; but between the real planes, which are populated with lattice sites and separated by the distance d, there are $(n - 1)$ new imaginary planes that divide the distance d into n equal parts of length (d/n).

The form of (2.4) is convenient because the value of (d/n) can be calculated very simply from the indexes (hkl) when these indexes are any three integers. True Miller indexes are always taken to be relatively prime. But if the indexes are not relatively prime and thus contain a common factor, it happens that this common factor is n, the order of the reflection. It can be shown geometrically for a lattice in which $\alpha = \beta = \gamma = \pi/2$ that the interplanar spacing d_{hkl} depends upon the triple of integers (hkl) in the simple manner of (2.5).

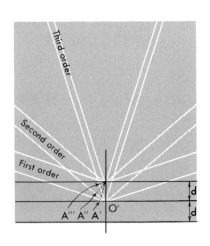

Fig. 2.9. *Bragg Reflection in Three Orders.*
$\lambda = 2(A'O'); \ 2\lambda = 2(A''O');$
$3\lambda = 2(A'''O')$

$$\frac{1}{d_{hkl}^2} = \frac{h^2}{a^2} + \frac{k^2}{b^2} + \frac{l^2}{c^2} . \qquad (2.5)$$

When h, k, and l are referred to axes of a primitive unit cell, d_{hkl} is the distance d between real planes of lattice sites only if h, k, and l are true Miller indexes, relatively prime. If h, k, and l contain a common factor n, (2.5) yields $d_{hkl} = d/n$, where d is the distance between planes really populated by lattice sites. Equation (2.4) then reads simply

$$\lambda = 2d_{hkl} \sin \theta \, . \tag{2.6}$$

Equation (2.6) is generally more convenient than (2.3). In Figure 2.10, real planes are shown as solid lines and imaginary planes are shown as dashed lines. In second order, $2\lambda = 2(A'O') = 4(A''O'')$. In pseudo-first-order reflection from both kinds of plane, $\lambda = 2(A''O'') = 2(d/2) \sin \theta$.

If h, k, and l are referred to axes of nonprimitive unit cells and contain a common factor n [e.g., $n = 2$ for (200)], planes that might be expected to be imaginary on the basis of this discussion may really be populated by lattice sites. For example, all (200) planes in either body-centered or face-centered cubic lattices are in fact equally populated by lattice sites. Section 2.6 discusses the effect this has on the intensities of reflections.

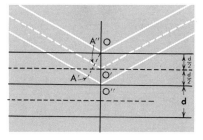

Fig. 2.10. *Bragg Reflection from Fictitious Planes. Real planes are solid lines; fictitious planes are dashed lines. In the second order,* $2\lambda = 2(A'O') = 4(A''O'')$; *hence,* $\lambda = 2(A''O'')$.

The interplanar spacings in lattices in which α, β, or γ differs from $\pi/2$ depend upon the indexes (hkl) and lattice parameters in somewhat more complicated ways.[4] Since all lattices except monoclinic and triclinic can be referred to mutually perpendicular axes, albeit less than the best axes in the hexagonal and trigonal cases, Equation (2.5) will suffice.

2.5 Recording Diffraction Patterns

As a qualitative and quantitative analytical method, X-ray diffraction provides several advantages over chemical methods. Without destroying the sample, analysis by X-ray powder diffraction examines small samples so as to reveal the size, shape, and perfection of crystals, their identity, and the relative amounts of several crystalline substances in mixtures. It reveals these things swiftly and often with great accuracy.

An X-ray diffraction pattern can be recorded in several ways. Early investigators like the Braggs used large spectrometers containing ionization chambers that held gases like SO_2. Reflected X radiation that entered the ionization chamber through slits would ionize the gas according to its intensity and wavelength, and the degree of ionization was measured electrically. From the very beginning until now, X radiation has been recorded photographically, for the degree of blackening of a negative is directly proportional to the intensity of X radiation of any given wavelength. Modern X-ray apparatus available commercially records X-ray spectra photographically or by means of Geiger counters, proportional counters, scintillation crystals and photo-multiplier tubes, or other means.

The angles at which the diffracted X rays emerge from the crystals are measured in various kinds of spectrometers. Each type of spectrometer produces a diffraction pattern of reflections that is useful for answering a particular question about the nature and structure of the sample. The two spectrometers whose operation is most easily understood are the Bragg spectrometer of Figure 2.11 and the powder camera of Figure 2.12. In the Bragg spectrometer, X radiation that is almost monochromatic originates in an X-ray tube at X and is collimated by slits S into a beam of almost parallel rays that meet the reflecting planes of the crystal at an angle θ. The crystal C is mounted on a table that rotates through an angle θ while the ionization chamber or counter R, which receives the radiation through the slits S', rotates through an angle 2θ. The table and counter may be geared to rotate together or may be rotated independently. Reflections are recorded only when (2.6) is satisfied.

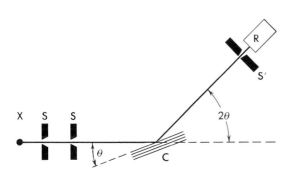

Fig. 2.11. *Top Schematic View of Bragg Spectrometer.*

In a powder camera, almost monochromatic X radiation from X is collimated by slots S and falls on a sample C that contains many small crystals oriented at random. The sample is generally rotated in order to assure that the orientation of the crystals appears random relative to the X-ray beam. As the sample C rotates, various of its crystals assume just the right angle θ for reflection and several diffracted beams are recorded at $R, R', R'', \cdots$ on a strip of photographic film P that is pressed tightly inside the cylindrical camera. The X radiation that is not diffracted is caught in a beam trap T to prevent its fogging the film. The film is mounted unsymmetrically to facilitate corrections for film expansion and contraction when the positions of the reflections R, R', R'' are measured from the developed negative. Fig-

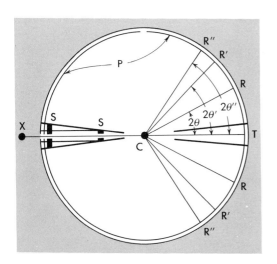

Fig. 2.12. *Top Schematic View of Powder Camera.*

ure 2.13 shows X-ray spectra of Cu, Al, W, NaCl, CaO, CsCl, CaF₂, and diamond. If the X-ray wavelength is also known, Equation (2.6) yields at once the values of d_{hkl} characteristic of the sample C.

A Bragg spectrometer like that of Figure 2.11 will record powder diffraction patterns if a sample of randomly oriented powdered crystals is placed at C. In fact, instruments are available commercially that automatically record the intensities as R rotates twice as fast as C. Thus X-ray diffraction has become a routine tool of the analytical chemist.

2.6 Extinct Reflections

The intensity of X radiation in a diffracted beam relative to that of the incident beam is

$$KF^2 p \left(\frac{1 + \cos^2 2\theta}{\sin^2 \theta \cos \theta} \right) e^{-\delta^2 s^2/2} . \quad (2.7)$$

In (2.7), K is a proportionality constant that depends upon the number of unit cells per unit volume, upon the mass and charge of the electron, upon the wavelength of X radiation, upon the length of the arc produced on the photograph or upon the length of the slits S_2, upon the volume of the sample that can reflect, upon the velocity of light, upon the radius

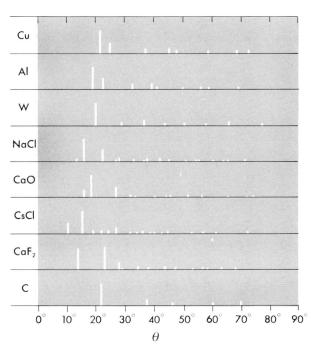

Fig. 2.13. *X-ray Spectra of Cu, Al, W, NaCl, CaO, CsCl, CaF₂, and Diamond ($\lambda = 1.541$ A).*[*]

of the camera, upon the degree to which the sample absorbs the X rays, and upon the characteristics of the recording process. The factor

$$\left(\frac{1 + \cos^2 2\theta}{\sin^2 \theta \cos \theta} \right)$$

takes account of the polarization of the X rays and of the fact that the angle of the cone that describes the diffracted beam permits more radiation to fall on the recording device when θ is near 0 or $\pi/2$ than it does when θ is near $\pi/4$. The factor $\exp (-\delta^2 s^2/2)$ is called the *temperature factor* because it accounts for the decrease in intensity due to lattice vibrations; δ^2 is the mean square

[*] Calculated from *Standard X-ray Diffraction Powder Patterns*, National Bureau of Standards Circular 539, U. S. Government Printing Office, Washington 25, D. C. (1953): Volume I by H. E. Swanson and E. Tatge; Volume II by H. E. Swanson and R. K. Fuyat.

displacement of the elements of the structure and $s = (4\pi \sin \theta)/\lambda$. The factor p in (2.7) is the multiplicity of the reflection (hkl); it is the number of equivalent planes that have the same value of d_{hkl}. For example, in a cubic crystal, $p = 24$ for (230) because the 2 and 3 may be positive or negative and the order of indexes is unimportant in determining d_{hkl} by (2.5) because $a = b = c$. With four independent choices for sign $(2 \times 2 \times 1)$, three independent choices for the first index $(2, 3,$ or $0)$, two remaining choices for the second index, and no free choice for the third, $p = (2 \times 2 \times 1) \times 3 \times 2 \times 1 = 24$.

The factor of (2.7) that is of real interest is F, the structure factor. Only F depends upon the arrangement of the elements of the structure. For a reflection indexed (hkl),

$$F(hkl) = \sum_i f_i e^{-2\pi i(hx_i + ky_i + lz_i)} . \tag{2.8}$$

The summation upon i proceeds over all atoms in the unit cell. The atomic scattering factor f_i depends upon the scattering variable $s = (4\pi \sin \theta)/\lambda$ because each atom is not a point and thus yields diffracted radiation that is more and more out of phase as θ increases. At small θ or s, however, f_i is equal to the number of electrons per atom or ion, for it is the electrons that scatter or reflect the X rays. The value of f_i decreases continuously and in a theoretically predictable manner as s increases.

In (2.8), h, k, and l are the indexes of the reflection and x_i, y_i, and z_i are the fractional displacements of atom i along a, b, and c. If lattice sites are occupied by single atoms, x_i, y_i, and z_i are zero in P lattices, assume the values 000 and $\frac{1}{2}\frac{1}{2}\frac{1}{2}$ in I lattices, assume the values 000 and $\frac{1}{2}\frac{1}{2}0$ in C lattices, and assume the values 000, $\frac{1}{2}\frac{1}{2}0$, $\frac{1}{2}0\frac{1}{2}$, and $0\frac{1}{2}\frac{1}{2}$ in F lattices. In P lattices, $F = \sum_i f_i$ for all possible integral triples (h, k, l); that is, all reflections are allowed in a primitive lattice. However, in nonprimitive lattices, certain combinations of (hkl) yield $F = 0$ and lead to what are called *extinct reflections:* reflections of zero intensity because of the nature of the lattice. The three simplest extinction laws are derived below.

In a C lattice that contains one atom with a scattering factor f at each lattice site (000 and $\frac{1}{2}\frac{1}{2}0$), (2.8) provides the following condition upon h and k when F is zero and the reflection is extinct.

$$F = fe^{-2\pi i(0+0+0)} + fe^{-2\pi i[(h/2)+(k/2)+0]}$$

$$0 = f[1 + e^{-\pi i(h+k)}]$$

$$e^{-\pi i(h+k)} = -1$$

$$h + k = 2m + 1, \qquad (m = 0, \pm 1, \pm 2, \cdots) .$$

That is, when $(h + k)$ is odd, F is zero and the reflection is extinct. Allowed (nonzero) reflections are possible only when $(h + k)$ is even. This rule applies in general, for each atom of a complex at each lattice site could have been chosen as the reference atom at 000 and $\frac{1}{2}\frac{1}{2}0$.

In an exactly analogous way, for F lattices, the condition upon the indexes when F is zero is

$$0 = f\left[1 + e^{-\pi i(h+k)} + e^{-\pi i(h+l)} + e^{-\pi i(k+l)}\right].$$

This condition is satisfied when $(h + k)$, $(h + l)$, or $(k + l)$ is odd. For example, for (211), $(h + k)$ and $(h + l)$ are odd but $(k + l)$ is even, and

$$F = f[1 + e^{-\pi i(2+1)} + e^{-\pi i(2+1)} + e^{-\pi i(1+1)}]$$
$$= f(1 + 2e^{-3\pi i} + e^{-2\pi i}) = f[1 + 2(-1) + 1] = 0.$$

Since F is not necessarily zero when $(h + k)$, $(h + l)$, and $(k + l)$ are even, it follows that if $h, k,$ and l are all even or all odd, a reflection is possible.

For I lattices, which have lattice sites at 000 and $\frac{1}{2}\frac{1}{2}\frac{1}{2}$, the condition upon the indexes when F is zero is

$$0 = f\left[1 + e^{-\pi i(h+k+l)}\right].$$

This condition is satisfied when $(h + k + l)$ is odd. Thus, for an I lattice, (211) is allowed but (111) is extinct.

The process of finding lattice parameters and indexes (hkl) for the diffraction lines of a powder photograph or for the diffraction spots due to reflections from single crystals is called *indexing*. Standard methods are available for indexing patterns of the simpler lattice types.[5] Indexing with respect to the correct unit cell generally makes evident systematic extinctions such as those derived above for C, F, and I lattices. Distinguishing F and I cubic lattice is quite simple, as shown by Table 2.2, which lists all possible integer triples the sum of whose squares is less than 26.

Diffraction patterns of tetragonal and orthorhombic structures obey the same extinction rules as cubic structures. However, because the axes are not all equal, many more reflections are possible. For example, in an orthorhombic lattice, a (220) reflection will occur at an angle that differs from that of a (202) reflection because the values of d_{220} and d_{202} differ. The planes (202), (20$\bar{2}$), ($\bar{2}$02), and ($\bar{2}$0$\bar{2}$) will, of course, reflect at the same angle and yield a multiplicity p of 4 for (202).

Table 2.2. *Indexes of Cubic Crystals*

INDEXES (hkl)	$(h^2 + k^2 + l^2)^a$	LATTICE TYPE THAT ALLOWS REFLECTION
100	1	P
110	2	P I
111	3	P F
200	4	P F I
210	5	P
211	6	P I
220	8	P F I
300, 221	9	P
310	10	P I
311	11	P F
222	12	P F I
320	13	P
321	14	P I
400	16	P F I
410, 322	17	P
411, 330	18	P I
331	19	P F
420	20	P F I
421	21	P
332	22	P I
422	24	P F I
500, 430	25	P

^{a} When $h, k, l, m,$ and n are integers, the following is impossible: $h^2 + k^2 + l^2 = (7 + 8m) 4^n$.

Example 2.1. At 20°C, elemental silver reflects X radiation of wavelength 1.5418 A at $\theta = 19.076°$, $22.171°$, $32.256°$, $38.743°$, $40.816°$, $49.004°$, and so on. These are the only reflections observed at angles less than 50°. Determine the kind and size of the cubic unit cell of silver metal from these data.

The Bragg equation (2.6) yields six values of d_{hkl} from the wavelength $\lambda = 1.5418$ A and the six Bragg angles according to the relation:

$$d_{hkl} = \frac{\lambda}{2 \sin \theta}.$$

For example, if $\theta = 19.076°$,

$$d_{hkl} = \frac{1.5418}{2 \times \sin 19.076°} = \frac{1.5418}{2 \times 0.32682} = 2.3588 \text{ A}.$$

The six spacings calculated in this way are listed in the accompanying table.

θ	d_{hkl} (A)	IF BODY-CENTERED		IF FACE-CENTERED	
		(hkl)	a (A)	(hkl)	a (A)
19.076°	2.3588	110	3.3358	111	4.0855
22.171°	2.0428	200	4.0856	200	4.0856
32.256°	1.4444	211	3.5382	220	4.0855
38.743°	1.2318	220	3.4840	311	4.0855
40.816°	1.1794	310	3.7296	222	4.0855
49.004°	1.0214	222	3.5382	400	4.0856

Since it is given that silver crystallizes in the cubic system, it must be possible to calculate these six spacings from six triples of integers (the indexes) and just one parameter, the length of the edge of the cubic unit cell. Since P cubic lattices having only one atom per unit cell have not been observed, the possibility that more than one atom is associated with each lattice site is ignored and only I and F cubic lattices need be investigated. The first six allowed sets of indexes listed in Table 2.2 are assigned to these spacings and values of a, the length of the cell edge, as calculated from (2.5) are also listed. For example, for the (220) reflection if the lattice is F,

$$\frac{1}{d_{220}^2} = \frac{2^2}{a^2} + \frac{2^2}{a^2} + \frac{0}{a^2}$$

$$\frac{1}{1.4444^2} = \frac{8}{a^2}$$

$$a = 1.4444\sqrt{8} = 4.0855 \text{ A}.$$

It is clear from the values of a that the unit cell is face-centered and that $a = 4.086$ A. A body-centered cubic unit cell cannot explain the observed reflections in terms of its sole parameter a.

2.7 Calculation of Density

The *density* of a substance is the ratio of its mass to its volume. A knowledge of the lattice type and unit-cell dimensions and a knowledge of the mass associated with each lattice site permits a calculation of density because the large visible crystal is merely an ordered repetition of unit cells. Imperfect crystals with voids or vacant lattice sites would of course exhibit densities lower than expected.

The mass per lattice site is the molecular or formula weight M of matter associated with a site divided by Avogadro's number N. The amount of matter per unit cell is the mass per lattice site (M/N) times the number Z of lattice sites per unit cell. In P lattices, $Z = 1$; in C- and I-type lattices, $Z = 2$; and in F-type lattices, $Z = 4$. If v is the volume of the unit cell, the calculated density is, then,

$$\rho = \frac{ZM}{Nv}. \qquad (2.9)$$

The volume of a cubic unit cell is a^3; of a tetragonal unit cell, a^2c; of an orthorhombic unit cell, abc; and so on.

Example 2.2. Calculate the density of silver at 20°C if it crystallizes in a face-centered cubic lattice with one atom per lattice site and a unit cell that is 4.086 A in length.

There are four lattice sites per unit cell: 000, $\frac{1}{2}\frac{1}{2}0$, $\frac{1}{2}0\frac{1}{2}$, $0\frac{1}{2}\frac{1}{2}$. At each site there is one silver atom. Since the atomic weight of silver is 107.88, the density is

$$\rho = \frac{ZM}{Nv}$$

$$= \frac{4 \times 107.88}{0.6024 \times 10^{24} \times 4.086^3 \times 10^{-24}}$$

$$= 10.501 \text{ g cm}^{-3}.$$

Equation (2.9) permits the calculation of any one of its five variables from a knowledge of the other four. Long before absolute wavelengths of X rays were established by diffraction from ruled gratings, the Braggs used (2.9) to fix the wavelength of their X rays. Barlow and Pope had proposed several hypothetical structures for NaCl. When the Braggs found by their experiments that one of these proposed structures was true, it was a simple matter to calculate v from (2.9) by assuming that Z was four, as required for the proposed structure. Since M, N, and ρ were known, the value of a was at once fixed through v. Then, through the Bragg equation, λ was fixed and thus the scale of all dimensions determined by X-ray diffraction was fixed.

Now that the wavelengths of X radiation are known independently of (2.9), this equation is commonly used to determine Z or M. It has also been used to fix the value of Avogadro's number, but crystalline imperfections limit its use for the determination of N.

Example 2.3. Tobacco seed globulin has a density of 1.287 g cm^{-3} and crystallizes in a face-centered cubic unit cell with $a = 123$ A (Donnay, J. D. H., and W. Nowacki,

Crystal Data. Geological Society of America 1954). Calculate the molecular weight of tobacco seed globulin.

By (2.9), $\quad M = \dfrac{\rho N v}{Z} = \dfrac{1.287 \times 0.6024 \times 10^{24} \times 123^3 \times 10^{-24}}{4} = 3.60 \times 10^5$.

B. CRYSTALLINE STRUCTURES

2.8 Body-Centered Cubic Structures

Twenty metallic elements crystallize in the body-centered cubic structure, some only at temperatures well removed from room temperature. In this type of structure, one atom occupies a lattice site and has eight equivalent nearest neighbors. Besides these eight, each atom has six other neighbors that are only slightly farther away along the directions of the cubic axes.

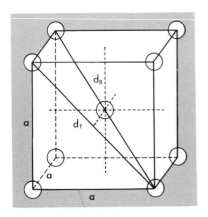

Distances between atoms in structures having all angles between axes equal to right angles are readily calculated by the Pythagorean theorem. Consider the body-centered cubic structure of Figure 2.14. In the plane of the front face, the theorem of Pythagoras says that the length a of the edge of the unit cell is related to the length d_F of the face diagonal by the relation

$$d_F^2 = a^2 + a^2 . \tag{2.10}$$

That is,

$$d_F = \sqrt{2}a . \tag{2.11}$$

Fig. 2.14. *Body-Centered Cubic Unit Cell.*

The third axis perpendicular to the front plane is perpendicular to all lines in that plane; therefore, it is perpendicular to the face diagonal d_F. The lines labeled d_F and d_B in Figure 2.14 then form two of the three sides of a right triangle in which, according to Pythagoras,

$$d_B^2 = a^2 + d_F^2 . \tag{2.12}$$

On elimination of d_F^2 through (2.10), the length d_B of the body diagonal of the cube is related to a thus:

$$d_B^2 = a^2 + a^2 + a^2 = 3a^2 ,$$

or $\qquad\qquad d_B = \sqrt{3}a . \tag{2.13}$

Thus, although the shortest distance between atoms along lines parallel to the cubic axes is a, the shortest distance between atoms is $d_B/2$, or $\sqrt{3}a/2$.

If the atoms of a body-centered structure be conceived as spheres, knowledge of the size of the unit cell not only fixes the radius of the atom as $\sqrt{3}a/4$ but also fixes the fraction of the total volume that actually is occupied by the spheres. Each unit cell has a total volume of a^3 and contains two spheres, each of volume $4\pi r^3/3$. Since $r = \sqrt{3}a/4$, it follows at once that the ratio of occupied to total volume is

$$\frac{2\left(\frac{4}{3}\pi r^3\right)}{a^3} = \frac{\frac{8}{3}\pi\left(\frac{\sqrt{3}}{4}a\right)^3}{a^3} = \frac{\pi\sqrt{3}}{8} = 0.680. \qquad (2.14)$$

Only about 68% of the volume is actually occupied by identical spheres packed according to a body-centered cubic lattice.

Unit cell dimensions of some elements that crystallize with the body-centered cubic structure are listed in Table 2.3. Note the accuracy that has been attained for tungsten. Indeed, accurate measurement of unit cell dimensions at various temperatures is a method of evaluating the coefficient of expansion. This method is particularly valuable for polycrystalline substances because in noncubic systems the coefficient of expansion differs in different crystallographic directions.

There are many structures based upon a body-centered cubic lattice that have more than one atom at each lattice site: alloys, oxides, nitrides, sulfides, and so on. Among the organic compounds which have a whole molecule at each lattice site in a body-centered cubic lattice are hexa-methylenetetramine and tetramethylorthothiocarbonate III.

2.9 Face-Centered Cubic Structures

Twenty-six elements crystallize with one atom at each lattice site of a face-centered cubic lattice. Each atom in a face-centered cubic structure has 12 equivalent nearest neighbors. The 12 atoms closest to the atom at the origin in Figure 2.15 are at the centers of the 12 faces that meet at

* Data from Wyckoff, R. W. G., *Crystal Structures.* New York: Interscience Publishers, Inc., 1948-, Vol. I, Chapter II, Table II, 4.

Table 2.3. *Dimensions of Body-Centered Cubic Unit Cells**

ELEMENT	TEMPERATURE (°C)	DIMENSION (a) A
Cr	25	2.8839
α-Fe	25	2.8665
β-Fe	800	2.91
δ-Fe	1425	2.94
K	−150	5.21
Na	20	4.2906
Ta	25	3.3058
V		3.040
W	25	3.16469

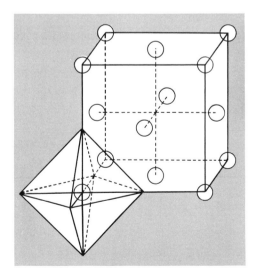

Fig. 2.15. *Face-Centered Cubic Unit Cell with the Twelve Planar Faces that Meet at a Point.*

the origin. The same environment obtains at all lattice points, for each could have been chosen as origin.

Since the length of a face diagonal is $\sqrt{2}a$, as in (2.11), the distance between nearest neighbors is $\sqrt{2}a/2$. If the atoms be thought of as rigid spheres in contact, their radii are $\sqrt{2}a/4$. Since there are four lattice sites per unit cell, the ratio of the volume of these four spheres to the volume of the unit cell is

$$\frac{4\left(\dfrac{4}{3}\pi r^3\right)}{a^3} = \frac{\dfrac{16\pi}{3}\left(\dfrac{\sqrt{2}a}{4}\right)^3}{a^3} = \frac{\sqrt{2}\pi}{6} = 0.741 .\tag{2.15}$$

About 74% of the volume is actually occupied by identical spheres packed according to a face-centered cubic lattice. The proof that this is the closest possible packing of identical rigid spheres is presented in the next section. Table 2.4 lists the dimensions of the unit cells of some elements that crystallize in a face-centered cubic structure.

Table 2.4. *Dimensions of Face-Centered Cubic Unit Cells**

ELEMENT	TEMPERATURE (°C)	DIMENSION (a) A
Ag		4.0862
Au	25	4.07864
Ca		5.576
Cu	18	3.61496
γ-Fe	22	3.5910
Ni	25	3.52387

Substances that crystallize in a structure based on the face-centered cubic lattice and have more than one atom per lattice site are quite common: halides of group I elements; sulfides, selenides, and tellurides of group II elements; phosphides and arsenides of group III elements; perchlorates; methane; alloys; ferricyanides and related species; diamond; many ionic oxides; and many other types of substances. Of these, the structures of NaCl, CaF_2 and ZnS are described in detail below.

Example 2.4. Calculate the radius of a silver atom as it exists in elemental silver. Since $a = 4.086$ A, the length of a face diagonal is $\sqrt{4.086^2 + 4.086^2}$, or 5.778 A. The radius of a silver atom is just one-fourth this face diagonal, namely 1.444 A.

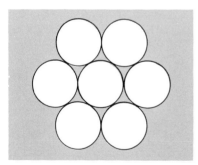

Fig. 2.16. *Close-Packing in a Plane.*

2.10 Hexagonal Close-Packed Structures

If identical coins or golf balls are arranged as closely as possible around each other in a plane, each unit of the planar array that results has six nearest neighbors arranged as in Figure 2.16. The sixfold rotation axis characteristic of the hexagonal system is at once evident. This type of array can be extended indefinitely in all directions with each unit's assuming a role identical to any other unit.

* Data from Wyckoff, R. W. G., *Crystal Structures*. New York: Interscience Publishers, Inc., 1948-, Vol. I, Chapter II, Table II, 2.

A planar array of close-packed spheres becomes a three-dimensional close-packed array by the addition of layers above (and below) the first layer. Among each triplet of spheres in a layer there is a hollow into which a fourth sphere can nestle, as a cannon ball does among three that support it in display. Once this first sphere of the new layer is set in place, all others in its layer naturally fall into place in similar hollows in the layer below. This newly created second layer is also close-packed; it is shown shaded in Figure 2.17.

A third layer can be added to the second just as the second was added to the first. A twofold choice of hollow now exists; either the initial layer can be repeated as the third layer as in Figure 2.17(a), or a third layer [black in Figure 2.17(b)] can be generated over the hollows in the first layer that were never populated when the second layer was added. Both types of array are close-packed because each is built of close-packed layers that fit into each other as four cannon balls do when stacked for display. Yet the two arrays differ in the third layer as a trigonal prism differs from a trigonal antiprism in Figure 2.18.

These two types of close packing are often described as ABABABA ⋯ for type (a) and ABCABC-ABCA ⋯ for type (b). In each sequence a letter indicates a layer that is close-packed in its own plane. Each such layer is close-packed relative to adjacent layers but differs from them in that superposition requires more than just a translation perpendicular to the layers. The first two layers, which differ, are AB. The two choices (a) or (b) for the third layer lead to A, which is directly above the first layer atom for atom, or to C, which is directly above neither A nor B.

The sequence ABABABA ⋯ in which every other layer is repeated is hexagonal close packing. That the sequence ABCABCABCA ⋯ is cubic close packing or face-centered cubic is explained in Figures 2.19 and 2.20. (In these figures, the spheres have been contracted without displacement of their centers in order that all can be seen.) Removal of a corner sphere from a face-centered cubic unit cell exposes its hollow among three (at face centers) and a close-

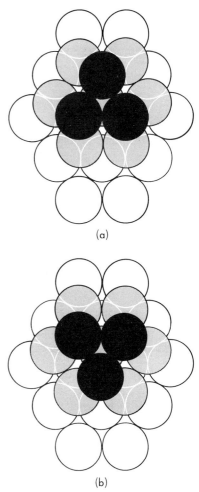

(a)

(b)

Fig. 2.17. *Close-Packed Layers of Identical Close-Packed Spheres.*

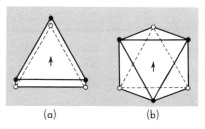

(a)   (b)

Fig. 2.18. *Trigonal Prism and Antiprism Viewed Almost Along Threefold Axes.*

packed layer parallel to a (111) face. Removal of these six exposes another layer that is also close-packed. This last exposed layer in Figure 2.19(c) is one of the eight faces of the trigonal antiprism of Figure 2.18(b). Figure 2.20 illustrates the orientation and size of this trigonal antiprism (which is really an octahedron) as it exists in eight face-centered cubic unit cells. Each edge of the octahedron has halfway along it a sphere from the center of a unit-cell face. Spheres occupy all its corners and its center. A plane through the center and parallel to any of the octahedral faces has six spheres close-packed around the central sphere as in Figure 2.16.

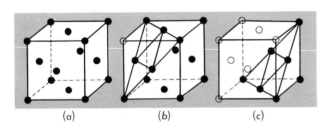

Fig. 2.19. *Close-Packed Layers in Face-Centered Cubic Structure.*

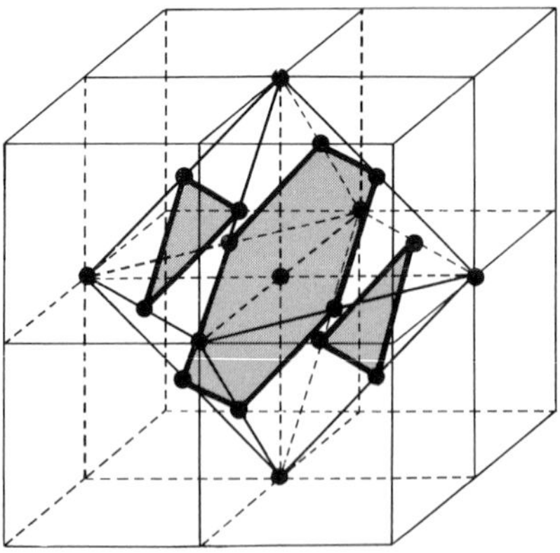

Fig. 2.20. *Close-Packed Layers in Face-Centered Cubic Unit Cells.*

Although it should be intuitively obvious that the fraction of the volume actually occupied by spheres in hexagonal close-packing is the same as for a face-centered cubic array of spheres, the straightforward but tedious geometrical exercise of proving this is now given. Two quantities must be found in terms of the radius of the identical spheres: the area of the hexagonal base of the prism of Figure 2.21 and its altitude c. The altitude is just twice the distance from the center of a sphere to the plane of the three that are in contact with it. This distance ($c/2$) is readily found by reference to a face-centered cubic lattice with unit cell length a. In such a lattice, the distance between close-packed layers is one-third of the body diagonal, or $\sqrt{3}a/3$, and the radius of the close-packed spheres is one-fourth of the face diagonal, or $\sqrt{2}a/4$. That is,

$$\frac{c}{2} = \frac{\sqrt{3}a}{3} \tag{2.16}$$

and

$$r = \frac{\sqrt{2}a}{4}. \tag{2.17}$$

Elimination of a yields

$$c = \frac{2\sqrt{3}}{3}\, a$$

$$= \frac{2\sqrt{3}}{3} \times \frac{4r}{\sqrt{2}}$$

$$= \frac{8}{\sqrt{6}}\, r \,. \tag{2.18}$$

The hexagonal base consists of six equilateral triangles each with side $2r$. Since the altitude of each of these triangles is $\sqrt{3}r$, the area of each triangle is $\frac{1}{2}(\sqrt{3}r)(2r)$, and the area of the hexagonal base is $6\sqrt{3}r^2$. The volume of the prism of Figure 2.21 is, then, $24\sqrt{2}r^3$.

The hexagonal prism contains several spheres. The three in the B layer are wholly within the prism. One of the two at the centers of the bases is to be ascribed to the prism. And of the 12 at the corners, two are to be ascribed to the prism shown because only one-sixth of each is within the prism. There are, then, effectively six spheres per prism. The fraction of the volume of the prism actually occupied by the spheres is thus

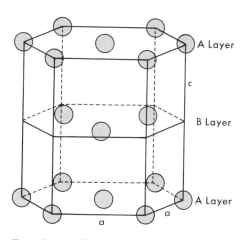

Fig. 2.21. *Hexagonal Close-Packing.*

$$\frac{6\left(\frac{4}{3}\pi r^3\right)}{24\sqrt{2}r^3} = \frac{\sqrt{2}\pi}{6} = 0.741 \,. \tag{2.19}$$

This is the same value found for a face-centered cubic structure of identical spheres. Both are close-packed.

Table 2.5 lists the dimensions of the unit cells of some elements that crystallize in a lattice that is at least approximately hexagonal close-packing. Ideally, for a nonprimitive cell like the hexagonal prism of Figure 2.21, the ratio of the altitude c to the edge of the hexagonal cell a is, by virtue of the discussion above and (2.18),

$$\frac{c}{a} = \frac{8r/\sqrt{6}}{2r} = \frac{2\sqrt{6}}{3} = 1.63299\cdots \,. \tag{2.20}$$

Table 2.5. *Dimensions of Hexagaonal Unit Cells of Elements**

ELEMENT	TEMPERATURE (°C)	a (A)	c (A)
Ca	450.	3.98	6.52
Cd	26.	2.97887	5.61765
Cr		2.722	4.427
Mg	25.	3.20927	5.21033
Zn	25.	2.6648	4.9467

*Data from Wyckoff, R. W. G., *Crystal Structures.* New York: Interscience Publishers, Inc., 1948-, Vol. I, Chapter II, Table II, 3.

Some of the elements listed in Table 2.5 deviate from this ideal axial ratio because bonds to neighbors in adjacent layers differ in strength and length from those to neighbors in the same layer.

2.11 Structures Based on Close-Packed Species

Identical spheres can be close-packed in only two ways, cubic and hexagonal, if each sphere of such an array is to exist in an environment identical to those of all other spheres. There are, however, many different close-packed arrays in which the environments of spheres may differ. The arrangement ABACABAC ⋯ is close-packed; but the spheres in the A layers are in a cubic environment because immediately adjacent layers differ, while spheres in the B or C layers are in a hexagonal environment, immediately adjacent layers being both A. Many other close-packed arrays are possible. Indeed, the sequence of layers of types A, B, and C in elemental cobalt is random.

Whether or not a particular complex structure is considered to be based upon close-packing depends upon the degree of perfection expected in the close-packing and also upon the view taken of the structure. Many complex halides, oxides, hydroxides, and sulfides are very simply described in terms of approximately close-packed anions with smaller cations in the voids. These cations generally disturb the packing because they do not quite fit into the interstices. It frequently happens that such disturbance is small and that the close-packed array is obvious in its general nature. Sometimes the relation to close-packing is unexpected: SnI_4, WCl_6, and UCl_6 can be thought of as close-packed halogen atoms with metal atoms arranged in just the right way so that individual molecules are preserved. The volatility, compressibility, and low melting points of these substances indicate that the crystals consist of molecules rather than ions. Sometimes the relation to close-packing is somewhat artificial: NaCl, ZnS, CaF_2, and TiO_2 can be considered to be based upon close packing of Cl^-, S^{--}, Ca^{++}, or O^{--}. Except perhaps for TiO_2, these simple types of crystal are better described in other terms, as in succeeding sections.

The inert gases are not the only molecular crystals that consist of close-packed molecules. Crystalline HCl, HBr, HI, H_2S, H_2Se, NH_3, CH_4, SiH_4, and H_2 are approximately close-packed. In these structures, the molecules are generally freely rotating. These substances also exhibit at very low temperatures crystalline species in which rotation is restricted or absent.

Like the metallic elements, many alloys are best described in terms of close-packed atoms. Many carbides, nitrides, and hydrides are described very simply as solutions of N, C, and H atoms in the voids of cubic close-packed metallic atoms. But most important of all are the oxide systems. More than 90% of the volume of the lithosphere consists of oxide ions.[7] Most of these oxides are silicates and are described very simply as close-packed oxide ions containing ions of Si, Al, Fe, Mg, Ca, Na, K, Ti, H, and so forth. In order to understand these three important classes —— alloys, interstititial solutions, and oxides —— it is necessary to investigate the kinds, sizes, and numbers of voids in close-packed arrays; for it is in these voids that the small atoms or ions are considered to reside.

There are three kinds of void. The smallest is among three touching spheres and is in their plane. Figure 2.22 illustrates this trigonal void. The largest sphere of radius r_+ that can be inserted among three identical touching spheres of radius r_- is found thus. The centers of the three large spheres are at the corners of an equilateral triangle of side $2r_-$. The distance from the center of this triangle to a corner, $r_+ + r_-$, is the hypotenuse of a small right triangle with a side r_-. The third side of this small right triangle is $(r_+ + r_-)/2$ because it is opposite an angle of $\pi/6$. By the Pythagorean theorem, in this small triangle it follows that

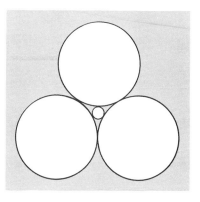

Fig. 2.22. *Trigonal Void Among Close-Packed Spheres.*

$$(r_+ + r_-)^2 = \left(\frac{r_+ + r_-}{2}\right)^2 + r_-^2 ,$$

whence
$$3(r_+ + r_-)^2 = 4r_-^2$$

$$r_+ + r_- = \frac{2r_-}{\sqrt{3}}$$

$$\frac{r_+}{r_-} = \frac{2\sqrt{3} - 3}{3} = 0.1547 . \tag{2.21}$$

Only B^{+3} ion appears to occupy this type of void among oxide ions, and even then its coordination may be influenced by bonding that is covalent rather than ionic.

A somewhat larger void exists at the center of a tetrahedron whose corners are the centers of four identical touching spheres. This tetrahedral void exists among four cannon balls stacked for display. Between two close-packed layers there are two sets of such tetrahedral voids: one set is below the spheres of the upper layer in the hollows of triples of spheres in the lower layer; the second set is above the spheres of the lower layer under the hollows of triples of spheres in the upper layer. Since each of these two sets has one tetrahedral void per sphere per layer, there are twice as many voids of this kind as there are close-packed spheres.

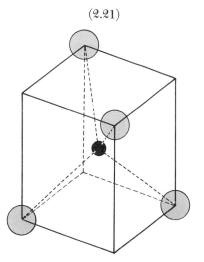

Fig. 2.23. *Tetrahedral Void Among Close-Packed Spheres.*

The size of a tetrahedral void is readily found with the aid of Figure 2.23, in which large spheres of radius r_- are imagined to be shrunk in order that the void can be seen. A face diagonal of the cube of Figure 2.23 is $2r_-$ and its body diagonal is $\sqrt{3/2}$ times as long. In terms of r_- and r_+, the radius of the largest sphere that can exist in a tetrahedral void, this body diagonal is $2(r_+ + r_-)$. Hence,

$$2(r_+ + r_-) = \sqrt{\frac{3}{2}}\,(2r_-)$$

$$\frac{r_+}{r_-} = \sqrt{\frac{3}{2}} - 1 = 0.2247 . \qquad (2.22)$$

Since the oxide ion has a radius of about 1.40A, it would appear that ions of radius of about 0.32A are the largest that such a void could accommodate. Actually, however, larger ions fill such voids because expansion attendant upon entry of ions with radii greater than 0.32A relieves the coulombic repulsions between oxide ions. Ions of Li, Be, B, and Si, and sometimes of Al and Ge, can be accommodated in tetrahedral voids among close-packed oxide ions.

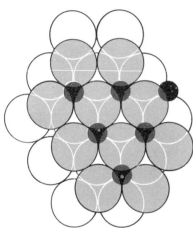

Fig. 2.24. *Octahedral Voids Among Close-Packed Spheres.*

The largest void in close-packed identical spheres is octahedral, so called because the polyhedron that has its corners at the centers of the spheres that define the void is an octahedron. The center of this void is halfway between adjacent layers and is equally distant from three adjacent spheres in each layer. In Figure 2.24, which contains two close-packed layers, octahedral voids are indicated with dots. From their arrangement over the third type of position (C if the layers shown are A and B), it is clear that the number of octahedral positions equals the number of close-packed spheres. The radius r_+ of the largest sphere that can be inserted into these octahedral voids without disturbing the close-packed spheres of radius r_- is readily calculated by reference to Figure 2.25. In this figure, the spheres are in cubic close-packing. The centers of octahedral voids occur at the center of the cube and at the centers of the cell edges. Since r_- equals $\sqrt{2}/4$ times the cell edge, and since the cell edge equals $2(r_+ + r_-)$, it follows that

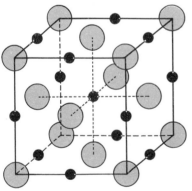

Fig. 2.25. *Octahedral Voids in Cubic Close-Packing of Spheres.*

$$\frac{r_+}{r_-} = \sqrt{2} - 1 = 0.4142 . \qquad (2.23)$$

The largest cation that can fit among close-packed oxide ions each of radius 1.40A is therefore 0.58A. Cations with radii less than 0.58A occupy tetrahedral positions because in so doing they cause the oxide ion array to expand, electrical repulsions among oxide ions thus being relieved. Cations with radii greater than 0.58A occupy octahedral positions among oxide ions. [It will be shown in Section 2.14 that when (r_+/r_-) exceeds $\sqrt{3} - 1$, eight or more anions can pack around one cation. Hence, octahedral voids in close-packed oxide ions are occupied by cations with radii from 0.58A to 1.02A.] Some ions that prefer octahedral voids among oxide ions are Al^{+3}, Fe^{+2}, Fe^{+3}, Mg^{+2}, Ca^{+2}, Na^+, Ti^{+4}, and, in fact, most ions of the transition elements.

Silicates can be thought of as close-packed arrays of oxide, hydroxide, and fluoride ions. The hydroxide and fluoride ions are almost the same size as the oxide ion. Silicon, with an ionic radius of about 0.40A, always assumes a tetrahedral position. Although aluminum prefers an octahedral position, it may sometimes assume a tetrahedral position. Monovalent and divalent ions like Na^+, K^+, Mg^{+2}, Ca^{+2}, Fe^{+2}, and so on are present in numbers sufficient to render the whole assembly of ions electrically neutral. The enormous number of ways of packing anions and cations is matched by the great variety of known silicate minerals and synthetic silicates.

Besides the silicates, the three most important types of oxide have the structures characteristic of spinel, ilmenite, and perovskite. Important features of these types of mineral are listed in Table 2.6. From the formulas it is obvious that only part of the voids is filled. The examples listed have

Table 2.6. *Characteristics of Important Types of Oxide*

| | NAME OF TYPE | | |
CHARACTERISTIC	SPINEL	ILMENITE	PEROVSKITE
Formula	$MgAl_2O_4$	$FeTiO_3$	$CaTiO_3$
General Formula	AB_2O_4	ABO_3	ABO_3
Type of Close-Packing	Cubic	Slightly Distorted Hexagonal	Cubic
Close-Packed Species	O^{--} (or S^{--})	O^{--}	A; O^{--} (or F^-)
Species in Tetrahedral Voids	A	none	none
Species in Octahedral Voids	B	A, B	B
Examples	$FeAl_2O_4$	$CoTiO_3$	$BaCeO_3$
	$ZnAl_2O_4$	$MgTiO_3$	$BaThO_3$
	$FeCr_2O_4$	Cr_2O_3	$LaFeO_3$
	$TiCo_2O_4$	$\alpha\text{-}Al_2O_3$	$NaWO_3$
	VMg_2O_4	$\alpha\text{-}Fe_2O_3$	$RbCaF_3$
	$MoAg_2O_4$		
	WNa_2O_4		
	Fe_3O_4		
	$MnIn_2S_4$		
	Ni_3S_4		

been chosen from among the 85 or more known spinels, the 14 substances known to be like ilmenite, and the 175 substances known to have structures like that of perovskite. Most of these perovskite-like structures are slightly distorted cubic structures. For example, $BaTiO_3$ is like perovskite, but is trigonal below $-80°C$, orthorhombic from $-80°C$ to $0°C$, tetragonal from $0°C$ to $120°C$, and cubic above $120°C$. These changes in symmetry are associated with its ferroelectric properties. Or again, $KMgF_3$ is monoclinic with cell edges of 8.02A and β equal to about $91°$.[6] The structure of $CaTiO_3$ itself is not quite the ideal cubic structure of perovskite in Figure 2.26. An interesting and lucid explanation of the natures of these three kinds of oxide is given by Wells.[7]

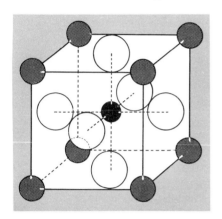

Fig. 2.26. *Ideal Perovskite Structure, ABO_3. (A at 000; B at $\frac{1}{2}\frac{1}{2}\frac{1}{2}$; oxide at $\frac{1}{2}\frac{1}{2}0$, $0\frac{1}{2}\frac{1}{2}$, $\frac{1}{2}0\frac{1}{2}$).*

2.12 Lattice Imperfections

As a mathematical device for fixing equivalent positions, a lattice is an idealization never achieved by a structure. Impurities, vibrations, loose electrons generated by the absorption of radiation, and other similar imperfections are unavoidable. But beyond these obvious kinds of imperfection there are various ways in which the stacking of structural units can be imperfect. The influence of these defects upon mechanical, electrical, and other physical properties is profound but cannot be discussed adequately here or even in several books. It is enough, then, to note their existence and general nature.

There are two ways in which the arrangement of ions can be defective or imperfect.

1. A *Frenkel defect* is a misplaced ion, generally a cation held interstitially in a region that would otherwise be a perfect array of ions. For every interstitial ion of this kind there is also a vacant ion site.

2. A *Schottky defect* is a vacant ion site. Both anions and cations are missing from what might have been a perfect structure. The ions from the vacated sites are considered to be moved to the surface of the crystal.

When cations and anions are about the same size, Frenkel defects are difficult to form because there is not enough room for interstitial ions. However, as in AgCl and AgBr, when the cation is much smaller than the anion, repulsive forces that result from squeezing a cation into a "wrong" position are moderate. Moreover, the small cation can polarize the large anions' electrons and thus tend from ionic bonding toward covalent bonding and increased stability. In the alkali halides, particularly the chlorides and fluorides, the ions are almost the same size and are only moderately polarizable, as shown by modest dielectric constants. In these substances Schottky defects are possible, the energy requirement being about 25 kcal mole^{-1} of defect-sites. Defects of these two kinds may be present at one in fifty possible sites near the melting point of some crystals, but generally only about one in a million possible sites is vacant.[8] Frenkel defects are generally 100 or more times rarer than Schottky defects. It is worth noting, also, that a substance seldom shows both types of defect since the conditions that favor one type render the other energetically unfavorable.

A second kind of imperfection in stacking of structural units is common in alloys of the types AB and A_3B. These are prone to a disordering phenomenon in which metal atoms can be arranged regularly but without distinction between atoms of kind A and those of kind B. There are about 40 alloys of the type AB (e.g., CuZn, AgCd, AuMg, MgTl, ZnCe) in which the disordered structure appears to be body-centered cubic. On annealing, however, the distinction between the two kinds of atom leads to an ordered structure like that shown in Figure 2.27. There, kind A is at 000 and kind B is at $\frac{1}{2}\frac{1}{2}\frac{1}{2}$, and the lattice is no longer body-centered because these two lattice sites are no longer equivalent. In alloys of the type A_3B (e.g., Cu_3Au, Ni_3Fe), the disordered state has both types of atoms arranged in a face-centered cubic structure. In the ordered state, atoms of kind A take the positions at the centers of faces and atoms of kind B take the positions at the cube corners, as in Figure 2.28. This kind of ordering process involves anomalies in heat capacity and evident changes in other physical properties, such as electrical conductivity.

Certain oxides, among them γ-Al_2O_3 and γ-Fe_2O_3, which seemingly ought to be ideal substances in view of their simple formulas, are in a way similar to disordered alloy structures. Their oxide ions are packed as in spinels, with

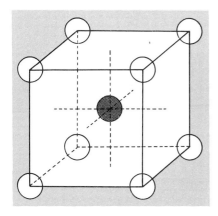

Fig. 2.27. *Cubic Unit Cell of Ordered Alloy AB.*

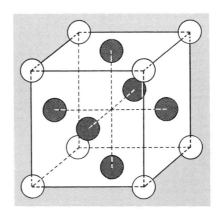

Fig. 2.28. *Cubic Unit Cell of Ordered Alloy A_3B.*

the usual 32 oxide ions per unit cell. The 64/3 cations that accompany these 32 anions occupy tetrahedral and octahedral positions at random. Many sites that would be occupied in a spinel are vacant and the vacancies are unorganized.

Still another aspect of crystalline perfection is concerned with defects of the order of hundreds of angstroms in size. These occur in all kinds of crystal and have marked influence particularly on the mechanical properties of a crystal. A truly perfect crystal should have X-ray intensities that are proportional to F, the structure factor, and not to F^2 as in (2.7). Proportionality to F is indeed exhibited by perfect diamonds and selected crystals of CaF_2. The dependence upon F^2 observed for most crystals led Darwin to postulate that most real crystals consist of a mosaic of perfect domains about 10^3 A on a side. These domains are not quite perfectly aligned and so reflect X rays over a small range of angles, generally several hundred seconds. Reflection from planes of a perfect crystal is not additive in the same way as from a mosaic crystal. In a perfect crystal, a reflected ray emerges at an angle such that it can be re-reflected from the inner side of the planes that first caused its reflection. Multiple reflections and reduced intensity are the result.

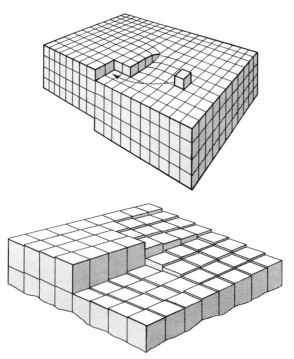

Fig. 2.29. *End of a Screw Dislocation.**

A more definite description of dislocations classifies them as *screw* and *edge*. Suppose that a path is followed from atom to atom or from ion to ion in a real crystal. If this path returns upon itself, it is called a *Burgers circuit.* If the same path in the lattice that typifies the structure does not return upon itself so that the beginning and end do not lie on the same atom, as they did in the real crystal, then the Burgers circuit encloses one or more dislocations. The vector that completes the closed circuit in the lattice is the *Burgers vector.* It measures the magnitude of the dislocation.

If the Burgers vector is parallel to the line that locates the dislocation, it is called a *screw dislocation.* The shortest screw dislocation is analogous to the vertical movement of a helical (sometimes ineptly called spiral) staircase that rises by one step per revolution. The end of such a dislocation

* Reproduced from W. T. Read, Jr., *Dislocations in Crystals*, New York: McGraw-Hill Book Co., Inc., 1953, Figures 10.3 and 10.4.

is shown in Figure 2.29. The dislocation line is perpendicular to the upper face. Far from this line, the structure looks almost ideal: all planes are approximately parallel and correctly spaced.

On the other hand, if the Burgers vector is perpendicular to the dislocation line, it is an *edge dislocation*. The simplest edge dislocation is an incomplete plane of atoms or ions interleaved between two normal planes. It is analogous to a book mark between the pages of a book. On one side of the dislocation line, the planes separate to make room for the extra layer; on the other side, there is a compression due to the intruding layer.

In general, a dislocation is part screw and part edge. In a well-annealed crystal, dislocations are about 10^4 A apart, but cold-working moves them about, increases their numbers, and complicates their interrelationships so that their separations may become about 10^2 A. Cold-working may lead to about 10^{12} dislocations cm^{-2}, while a good natural ionic crystal may have less than 10^8 dislocations cm^{-2}.

The screw dislocation is particularly important for the growth of a crystalline face. It always presents an edge one or a few atoms high. At this edge continued growth is easy. In view of the variety of imperfections that are possible, it is indeed startling that the very growth of the faces that tell much about the symmetry and order of a crystal really depends upon a dislocation.

2.13 NaCl Structure

One of the simplest and most common structural types is that of NaCl. Hydrides, halides, cyanides, and hydrosulfides of the alkali metals; oxides, sulfides, selenides, and tellurides of divalent metals, especially the alkaline earths; and many nitrides and carbides have this structure. Figure 2.25 shows the unit cell of this structural type. Except for the iodides, it is best not to classify the NaCl structure as close-packed anions with an equal number of cations in octahedral voids. The reasons are that the anions generally do not touch, and that such a view does little to simplify study of the structure.

Table 2.7 lists unit cell dimensions of a few of the 100 or more substances known to have this simple structure. The simplicity of this arrangement has inspired much theoretical discussion

Table 2.7. *Dimensions of Cubic Unit Cells of Substances Like NaCl*[*]

SUBSTANCE	TEMPERATURE (°C)	DIMENSION (a) (A)
NaCl	18°C	5.63978
NaCl	26°C	5.64056
KF		5.347
KCl	25°C	6.29294
KBr	25°C	6.6000
KI	25°C	7.06555
CaO		4.8105
CdO	27°C	4.6953
MnO	26°C	4.4448
$Fe_{0.944}O$[a]		4.3010
$Fe_{0.912}O$[a]		4.2816
VN		4.128
LaN		5.295
UN		4.880
TiC		4.3186
VC		4.182
KCN	25°C	6.527

[a] A. F. Wells, *Structural Inorganic Chemistry*. New York: Oxford University Press, 1950, p.382.

[*] Data from Wyckoff, R. W. G., *Crystal Structures*. New York: Interscience Publishers, Inc., 1948-, Vol. I, Chapter II, Table III, 2, unless noted otherwise.

of this kind of structure.[9]   A few remarks on ionic radii are perhaps in order in this regard.

A glance at Figure 2.25 reveals that the distance between unlike ions is one-half the length of the cell edge.   If the anions were either all in contact or all not in contact, regular differences in interionic distance would be obvious. The comparisons made of anion-cation distances in LiF, LiI, RbF, and RbI in Table 2.8 belie such a hope.   The reason for the discrepancies is that in all halides of lithium except LiF, the halide ions are in direct contact.   The lithium ion thus lies loose in its octahedral void among close-packed anions.   But if the iodide ions in Li are close-packed, their radii are then equal to $\sqrt{2}/4$ times the length of the face-centered cubic unit cell. In 1920, Landé proposed this simple method of calculating the radius of an iodide ion and thus of apportioning to anion and cation their proper shares of the interionic distance.   The radius calculated for iodide in this way is 2.13 A.   A more commonly accepted value calculated in another way is 2.16 A.

Table 2.8.   *Interionic Distances in Some Alkali Halides**

ANION CATION	Fluoride	Iodide	DIFFERENCE
Lithium	2.01 A	3.02 A	1.01 A
Rubidium	2.82 A	3.66 A	0.84 A
DIFFERENCE	0.81 A	0.64 A	ANION CATION

With a value of the radius of iodide ion, simple subtraction from 3.66 A for the $Rb^+ - I^-$ distance yields a rubidium ion radius of 1.50 A.   Next, from the $Rb^+ - F^-$ distance of 2.82 A and the value of 1.50 A for Rb^+, the fluoride ion's radius is expected to be 1.32 A.   When such calculations are done systematically for all the alkali halides having the NaCl arrangement, it is clear that radii are not quite additive.   Various adjustments with theoretical bases can be made, however, that yield agreement to within about 0.001 A.[9]

An example of the difficulties involved is shown in LiF, for which the observed interionic distance is somewhat large.   This expansion is attributed to double repulsion, for the radius ratio is so close to the critical $\sqrt{2} - 1$ of Equation (2.23) that both anions and cations are almost in contact.   Each repels its own kind vigorously.

The salient feature of the NaCl structure is that each ion is surrounded octahedrally by six of the opposite kind.   The coordination number is said to be 6.

2.14   CsCl Structure

As the ratio of cation radius to anion radius increases, it at last becomes possible to fit more than six anions around a cation without undue anion-anion

* Pauling, L., *The Nature of the Chemical Bond*.   Ithaca, N. Y.: Cornell University Press, 1960, p. 520.

repulsion. A common structural type exhibiting a coordination number of 8 for both ions is the structure of CsCl, shown in Figure 2.27. Although at first sight this structure seems to be based upon a body-centered lattice, the lattice is really primitive because the ion at $\frac{1}{2}\frac{1}{2}\frac{1}{2}$ differs from that at 000. Each ion is surrounded by eight nearest neighbors of the other kind arranged at the corners of a cube.

The largest cation of radius r_+ that can just fit into the void among eight anions of radius r_- is readily found. If anions touch,

$$2r_- = a ,$$

where a is the edge of the cubic unit cell. But the shortest distance between unlike ions, $r_+ + r_-$, is one-half the body diagonal; hence,

$$r_+ + r_- = \frac{\sqrt{3}a}{2}.$$

Elimination of a yields

$$\frac{r_+}{r_-} = \sqrt{3} - 1 = 0.7321 . \qquad (2.24)$$

Table 2.9. *Dimensions of Cubic Unit Cells of Substances Like* CsCl*

SUBSTANCE	DIMENSION (a) (Å)
CsCl	4.110
CsBr	4.29
CsI	4.562
TlCl	3.8340
TlBr	3.97
TlI	4.198
NH₄Cl	3.866
CuZn	2.945
AgCd	3.33
AgZn	3.156
AlNi	2.881

This ratio marks the theoretical limit of stability between the NaCl and CsCl structures.

About 15 ionic substances and about 35 alloys exhibit this structure. Dimensions of the cubic unit cells of a few of these substances are listed in Table 2.9. Halides of rubidium can be transformed from the NaCl- to CsCl-structure under pressures of several thousands of atmospheres.

2.15 CaF₂ and TiO₂ Structures

The NaCl- and CsCl-types of structure are limited to substances with formulas containing two atoms that differ. Next in order of increasing complexity are substances with formulas containing three atoms, two of which are like. The two most common structural types of this kind are fluorite (CaF₂) and rutile (TiO₂).

The fluorite lattice is shown in Figure 2.30.

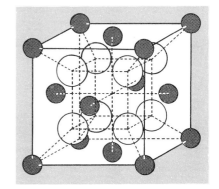

Fig. 2.30. *CaF₂.*

Calcium ions are located in a face-centered cubic lattice and fluoride ions fill all the tetrahedral voids. As a result, each fluoride ion is surrounded by four

* Data from Wyckoff, R. W. G., *Crystal Structures*. New York: Interscience Publishers, Inc., 1948-, Vol. I, Chapter III, Tables III, 7, 8.

equally distant calcium ions and each calcium ion is surrounded by eight fluoride ions located at the corners of a cube. As for CsCl-like structures, the anions would touch if r_+/r_- were less than $\sqrt{3} - 1$. In compounds of this type, r_+ is greater than $(\sqrt{3} - 1)r_-$. Because the cations are generally smaller than the anions, it is best not to belabor the seeming close packing of cations.

Table 2.10. *Dimensions of Cubic Unit Cells of Substances Like* CaF_2*

SUBSTANCE	DIMENSION (a) (A)
CaF_2	5.451
SrF_2	5.784
BaF_2	6.187
PbF_2	5.942
ThO_2	5.59
UO_2	5.47
$SiMg_2$	6.39
$SnMg_2$	6.765
K_2O	6.436

The substances that are known to crystallize with this structure are: about ten fluorides of metals having rather large divalent ions; about 15 oxides of metals having rather large quadrivalent ions; about ten oxyfluorides of trivalent metals; a few chlorides, nitrides, and complex fluorides; about 15 alloys; oxides, sulfides, selenides, and tellurides of the alkali metals in which the roles of cation and anion are interchanged from their roles in CaF_2; and a few other types of substance. Unit cell dimensions of a few of these substances are listed in Table 2.10.

When the radius ratio of cation to anion falls below $\sqrt{3} - 1$, octahedral coordination is favored. About 14 oxides of tetravalent metals and about seven fluorides of divalent metals are known to crystallize with the structure characteristic of TiO_2. In this structure, anions are almost close-packed and half the octahedral voids are occupied by cations. The following are some of the substances that crystallize in the tetragonal structure of this kind: MgF_2, NiF_2, ZnF_2, MnO_2 (if it exists), PbO_2, SnO_2, and TiO_2.

2.16 ZnS Structures

Two types of lattice that form the basis of ionic and covalent crystals are those of sphalerite and wurtzite, the cubic and hexagonal forms of ZnS. Sphalerite is based upon a face-centered cubic lattice in which zinc atoms are at 000, $\frac{1}{2}\frac{1}{2}0$, $\frac{1}{2}0\frac{1}{2}$, $0\frac{1}{2}\frac{1}{2}$, and sulfur atoms are in half the tetrahedral voids. The tetrahedral voids containing sulfur are at $\frac{1}{4}\frac{1}{4}\frac{1}{4}$, $\frac{3}{4}\frac{3}{4}\frac{1}{4}$, $\frac{3}{4}\frac{1}{4}\frac{3}{4}$, $\frac{1}{4}\frac{3}{4}\frac{3}{4}$. The unit cell contains four atoms of each kind and each atom is surrounded tetrahedrally by four atoms of the opposite kind. If the bonding is viewed as covalent, as it must be in substances like diamond (which exhibits this structure without distinction between atoms), then the bonding is similar to that found in organic molecules. On the other hand, if the bonding is viewed as ionic, then the structure is viewed as close-packed sulfide ions containing zinc ions in half the tetrahedral voids. Wurtzite is related to sphalerite as hexagonal close packing is to cubic. Both forms of ZnS can be viewed as close-packed arrays of sulfide ions with zinc ions in half the tetrahedral voids.

* Data from Wyckoff, R. W. G., *Crystal Structures.* New York: Interscience Publishers, Inc., 1948-, Vol. I, Chapter IV, Table IV, 2.

Substances that crystallize in this kind of structure are the fourth family elements (C, Si, Ge, Sn) and compounds containing one atom from each of the families arranged symmetrically with respect to the fourth. That is, Ge, GaAs, ZnSe, and CuBr each exist in a crystalline form of this kind.

Sets of covalent or ionic radii for all the substances of this kind are very simply derived from the observed interatomic distances. Predicted and observed distances agree within about 0.02 A. Values of this kind as derived by Pauling and Huggins are listed in Table 2.11. The interatomic distances r predicted from this table are related to the edge a of the cubic unit cell by the Pythagorean theorem thus:

$$r^2 = \left(\frac{a}{4}\right)^2 + \left(\frac{a}{4}\right)^2 + \left(\frac{a}{4}\right)^2 = \frac{3a^2}{16}$$

$$r = \frac{\sqrt{3}}{4} a . \qquad (2.25)$$

Table 2.11. *Tetrahedral Covalent Radii* (A)*

		Be	B	C	N	O	F
		1.06	0.88	0.77	0.70	0.66	0.64
		Mg	Al	Si	P	S	Cl
		1.40	1.26	1.17	1.10	1.04	0.99
Cu	Zn	Ga	Ge	As	Se	Br	
1.35	1.31	1.26	1.22	1.18	1.14	1.11	
Ag	Cd	In	Sn	Sb	Te	I	
1.52	1.48	1.44	1.40	1.36	1.32	1.28	
Hg							
1.48							

2.17 Layer Structures

Many chlorides, bromides, and iodides of divalent and trivalent metals crystallize in a structure based upon close packing of halide ions. Since the number of octahedral voids equals the number of close-packed spheres, not all the available octahedral voids are occupied by cations in crystals of dihalides and trihalides. If the vacancies demanded by electroneutrality are organized into planes parallel to the close packed layers, the structure that results for a substance like CdI$_2$ (or CdCl$_2$) has a cross section like Figure 2.31. The structural unit is a plane sandwich of cations in octahedral voids between close-packed layers of halide ions. The halide ions of adjacent layers fit in the usual ways into the hollows among three ions on the outer surfaces of such a sandwich. There are, however, no cations between sandwiches; the anions are in an unsymmetrical environment.

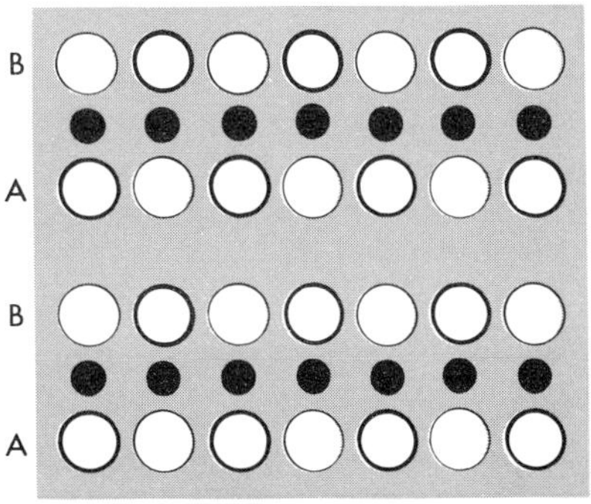

Because there are many, many ways of close packing spheres, there are many potential ways in which dihalides can crystallize in structures built of such two-dimensional networks. In the CdI$_2$ type of structure, the halide ions are in hexagonal close packing, ABABAB$\cdots$. In the CdCl$_2$ type, the close packing is cubic,

Fig. 2.31. *Layers of* MX_2. (*The X ions are in hexagonal close-packing.*)

* Pauling, L., *The Nature of the Chemical Bond*. Ithaca, N. Y.: Cornell University Press, 1960, p. 246.

ABCABC $\cdots$. In general, diiodides, dibromides, and dihydroxides of divalent transition elements crystallize like CdI_2, while dichlorides of the same elements crystallize like $CdCl_2$. Several disulfides, diselenides, and ditellurides of quadrivalent Co, Ni, Pd, Pt, Ti, Zr, and Sn also are like CdI_2 in having anions almost hexagonally close-packed.

The compounds WS_2 and MoS_2 differ from the previous structures in the environment about W or Mo. The sulfur atoms are arranged as in a trigonal prism about the metal atom instead of being arranged octahedrally (see Figure 2.18). The contacts between sulfur atoms in different sandwiches remain close packed, as do the arrangements of sulfur atoms in their own close-packed layers.

Certain kinds of silicate minerals, the swelling clays and mica-like silicates, form layer structures in analogous ways. Aluminum and silicon ions bind two or more close-packed layers of oxide ions into a complex that extends indefinitely in two dimensions. Monovalent and divalent ions may bind these layer-like complexes. Cleavage occurs between such complexes and absorption of water, glycerol, or other small molecules between such layers causes swelling in a direction perpendicular to the layers. Identification of clays by X-ray diffraction generally requires that such swelling be controlled by replacing H_2O with ethylene glycol or glycerol.

A final example of a layer structure is graphite. Each layer is a polynuclear aromatic condensed ring system that extends indefinitely in all directions in its own plane. Each ring is a hexagon of carbon atoms, each of which has three nearest neighbors at a distance of 1.42 A. The distance between carbon atoms in benzene is 1.39 A, and in polynuclear aromatic hydrocarbons like naphthalene, anthracene, and phenanthrene, carbon-carbon distances range from about 1.38 A to 1.42 A.

Adjacent layers are stacked so that half their atoms are directly above or below atoms of the adjacent layers. The other half of the atoms are directly over or under the centers of hexagons of adjacent layers. The distance between layers is 3.35 A, the great length indicating only weak interlayer forces. Graphite is very easily cleaved by separation of these layers, and most expansion due to a rise in temperature occurs in a direction perpendicular to the layers. The lubricating properties of graphite are attributed to absorption of molecules between the layers, and its electrical conductivity to mobility of electrons within a layer.

In ordinary graphite, every other layer is an exact repetition; the packing of layers is ABABAB $\cdots$. A second, rare type of graphite exhibits layer packing of the type ABCABC $\cdots$. Pyrolyzed organic substances, such as the "coke" deposited on silica-alumina cracking catalysts, may consist of similar layers. A layer of this kind is essentially a huge polynuclear aromatic hydrocarbon having hydrogen atoms on its periphery and extending about 30 A in its plane. The coke consists of several layers stacked parallel, but with random orientation relative to adjacent layers.

C. LIQUIDS

2.18 Noncrystalline Structures

Solids are generally distinguished from liquids by their rigidity. Both solids and liquids have their own volume, but a solid does not conform to the shape of its container. Glass apparently should be classed as a solid at room temperature. However, glass does not exhibit a crystalline habit of well-developed faces, cannot be cleaved like most crystals, and displays a rather indistinct X-ray diffraction pattern that lacks the well-defined rings so typical of metals, salts, and minerals. Moreover, as a glass forms on cooling, there is no discontinuity in density, index of refraction, or viscosity. Rather, the viscosity rises continuously to about 10^{25} poise at room temperature; this viscosity is so great that the substance is apparently a solid. Because the X-ray diffraction pattern of glass is obviously like the diffraction patterns of substances that are free-flowing liquids, glass must indeed be a liquid by structure.

The characteristic feature of crystalline structures is their lattice-like order. When this kind of regularity extends for only 5 or even 10 A, structures lose their crystallinity. While long-range order may be gone, generally the short-range order involving nearest and next-to-nearest neighbors remains, with little modification, what it might have been if crystallization had occurred.

Crystallization almost always is accompanied by a discontinuous and marked decrease in volume at the freezing point T_f. This kind of change is shown in the lowest curve of Figure 2.32. In the absence of suitable crystal nucleuses, a liquid can be cooled to a temperature below T_f. Such a liquid is supercooled and is not the most stable state of aggregation at that temperature. When suitable crystallization nucleuses do not exist or develop, con-

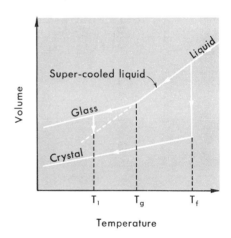

Fig. 2.32. *Comparison of Glassy and Crystalline States.**

tinued cooling may lead to such an increase in viscosity that the structure is effectively frozen in a configuration characteristic of the liquid at a temperature such as T_g. The substance is a glass that contracts in its own characteristic way on further cooling. At fixed temperatures somewhat below T_g, as at T_1, a glass may contract slowly and achieve a volume on the extrapolated curve for the supercooled liquid. Such stabilization is slow and requires ever longer times as the temperature decreases.

There are two general types of substance that can form glasses.[10] Substances whose liquids consist of long molecules that become inextricably

* After G. O. Jones, *Glass.* London: Methuen and Co., Ltd., 1956, p. 2.

entangled form glasses because rearrangement to crystalline order would require breaking many covalent bonds. Organic polymers and plastic sulfur are of this kind. The second class of glass-former is the substance that has directed covalent bonds and crystallizes in an open structure. The open structure results from a low coordination number and the fixed directions taken by this small number of bonds. The simplest substances of this second class are SiO_2 and H_2O. Glassy H_2O forms, however, only on extremely rapid cooling or upon condensation at about $-100°C$. More generally, oxides of B, Si, Ge, P, and As can form glasses. Substitution of cations with lower charge usually reduces the viscosity of such oxides, but crystallization or devitrification may still be slow because the degree of organization required for nucleation usually increases as such cations are added. Alcohols, glycols, and other hydroxy substances also form glasses and supercool easily.

The structure of liquids and glasses is aptly described in terms of a radial distribution function. Because there is no unique or preferred direction in a liquid or glass, this radial distribution function depends only on the distance r from any point chosen as origin. It describes the density of matter averaged both in space and time. The number of atoms between r and $r + dr$ is taken to be $4\pi r^2 \rho(r)\, dr$, where $\rho(r)$ is the density of atoms and $4\pi r^2\, dr$ is the infinitesimal volume between spheres of radii r and $r + dr$. Here $4\pi r^2 \rho(r)$ can be calculated directly from the indistinct X-ray diffraction pattern characteristic of liquids.[10]

Far from the origin, $\rho(r)$ fluctuates less and less from the average value of the number of atoms per unit volume of sample. If $\rho(r)$ is constant, the amount of scattering matter at the large distance r is proportional to r^2. Instead of numbers of atoms, the X-ray data yield numbers of electrons between r and $r + dr$ because the X rays are diffracted by electrons. The radial distribution function $4\pi r^2 \rho(r)\, dr$ for vitreous SiO_2 is presented in Figure 2.33. This curve is the sum of the probability densities of electrons at various distances from either an oxygen atom or a silicon atom. The upward sweep is caused by the r^2-dependence. Peaks, which represent most likely distances, occur at 1.62 A, 2.65 A, and so on. The distance 1.62 A is characteristic of

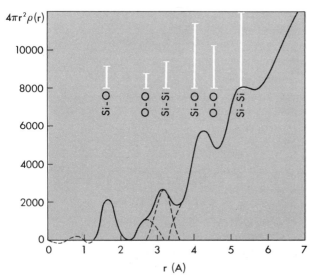

Fig. 2.33. *Probability Distribution of Interatomic Distances in Vitreous Silica.**

* B. E. Warren, H. Krutter, and O. Morningstar, *J. Amer. Ceramic Soc.* **19**, 202 (1936).

the Si-O bond, and 2.65 A is to 1.62 A as the distance between corners of a tetrahedron is to the distance from a corner to its center. This and all other features are interpreted in terms of a structure in which each silicon atom is surrounded tetrahedrally by four oxygen atoms, each of which is bonded to two silicon atoms. That is, the structure may be imagined to consist of SiO_4 tetrahedra linked at their corners by oxygen atoms common to two tetrahedra. The various distances in cristobalite, to which vitreous silica devitrifies, are shown with their relative importance at the top of Figure 2.33. The correspondence is excellent. The difference in the structures of vitreous silica and cristobalite is in the long-range order of the latter. Silica gel is similar to vitreous silica in its short-range order, but the diffraction pattern of silica gel indicates that there are large discontinuities and voids in its structure. Vitreous silica, however, is a continuous structure in which the SiO_4 tetrahedra form one vast and continuously linked network.

Ice I, tridymite (a crystalline species of SiO_2), and wurtzite (a form of ZnS) are similar to each other in structure. The oxygen atoms of H_2O and the Si atoms of tridymite are in positions like those of Zn or S. Thus, each O in ice and each Si in tridymite is surrounded tetrahedrally by four other atoms of the same kind. There is one oxygen atom midway between each pair of adjacent silicon atoms in tridymite, and in ice there is one hydrogen atom between each pair of adjacent oxygen atoms. Each proton has two positions available to it along the line between oxygens.[11] In either position it is bonded covalently to one oxygen and electrostatically by a hydrogen-bond to the other oxygen. The covalent bond is about 0.99 A long, and the hydrogen-bond extends the remainder of the 2.76 A between oxygens. The arrangement of protons among their positions is random except that any particular oxygen almost always has just two hydrogens bonded covalently to it. The crystal is a loosely arranged array of molecules of the formula H_2O.

Liquid water resembles ice in the general arrangement of hydrogens and oxygens. There are, however, somewhat less than four oxygen atoms arranged tetrahedrally around any one oxygen. That is, water is a broken-down ice structure in which hydrogen-bonds are continually broken and remade. Water is, however, denser than ice because, as the temperature rises, the molecules tend to approach a close-packed arrangement. X-ray diffraction has shown that atoms in liquid Hg and liquid Na exist in an environment that is approximately close-packed. While short-range order calls for about 12 nearest neighbors, random movements so loosen the close packing that long-range order is absent.

2.19   Surface Tension

At the boundary of a phase, atoms and molecules exist in an unsymmetrical environment. Even if the boundary of the phase is not defined within a distance about the size of an atom, the number of atoms or molecules of a given kind changes rapidly in a direction perpendicular to the surface. Attractive forces of the van der Waals type or stronger tend to increase the number of favorable contacts within a substance. Quite naturally, this leads to a stable state in which there is a minimum of exposed surface area. Thus, spilled mercury collects in droplets that appear from above to be round, and droplets of water on an oily surface are round and tend to unite as mercury droplets do. In field-free space, mercury, water, and all fluids would agglomerate in a spherical shape because a sphere has a minimum exposed surface area for a given volume. It is just as though a confining membrane composed of surface atoms and molecules were stretched taut about the droplets. Like fluids, which cannot support a shear stress, solids also tend to minimize their exposed area, but their rigidity prevents their taking a spherical shape.

It is common experience, however, that water may not collect as mercury does. If molecules of water are adsorbed on a surface because attractive forces between water and surface are stronger than attractive forces among water molecules, then the water is said to *wet* the surface.

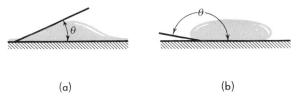

(a)   (b)

Fig. 2.34. *Contact Angle θ: Wetting* (a) *and Non-Wetting* (b).

It tends to spread out over the surface in a thin film. Thus, water wets sugar, cotton, clean glass, or a clean metallic surface. The degree to which a surface is wetted is shown by the angle between the surface and the pseudo-membrane that seems to surround a droplet on the surface. This angle θ is shown for wetting and nonwetting in Figure 2.34. Figure 2.34(a) is typical of water on clean glass, while (b) is typical of mercury on glass or water on teflon. Attraction between unlike phases decreases as θ increases.

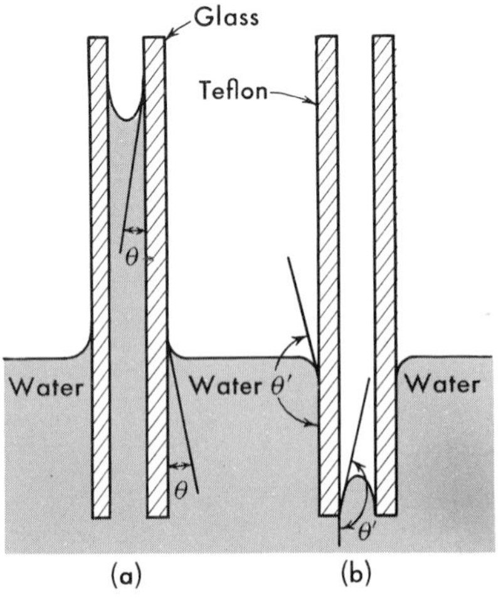

Of the several ways of measuring surface tension, the macroscopic measure of attractive forces between like molecules, the simplest is the capillary rise method. Inserting a tube of fine bore into a liquid causes the liquid level within the tube to rise or fall. If the liquid wets the interior surface of the tube, the level rises [Figure 2.35(a)]; if not, it falls [Figure 2.35(b)]. At equilibrium, a compromise is effected. The tendency for the liquid to wet the tube is balanced by the reluctance of the liquid to flow upward against gravity. Similarly, if the liquid does not wet the tube, the tendency for the liquid to avoid contact with the tube is tempered by the need to depress the surface of the liquid against gravity.

Fig. 2.35. *Capillary Rise Method of Determining Surface Tension: Wetting* (a) *and Non-Wetting* (b).

The surface tension γ of a liquid is the energy required to generate unit area of surface. While γ is a property of the liquid, its effective value in contact with another phase is $-\gamma \cos \theta$. When a liquid rises to a height z in a tube of radius r, the extra energy of the liquid due to its contact with the area $2\pi rz$ of the tube is $-2\pi rz\gamma \cos \theta$. The negative sign indicates that the adsorption and rise decrease the surface energy of the liquid. On the other hand, such a rise, however advantageous in leading to a lower energy through attraction of unlike phases, requires energy to elevate the liquid. This gravitational energy is the product of the volume $\pi r^2 z$ of liquid, its density ρ, the acceleration of gravity g, and the average height $z/2$ to which it rises. That is, the energy required to lift a mass $\pi r^2 z' \rho$ to a height ranging from 0 to z is

$$\int_0^z \pi r^2 z' \rho g \, dz' = \frac{\pi r^2 z^2 \rho g}{2}.$$

The energy E of the liquid due to both surface and gravitational influences is, then,

$$E = \frac{\pi r^2 z^2 \rho g}{2} - 2\pi rz\gamma \cos \theta . \tag{2.26}$$

At equilibrium, the energy is minimized by adjustment of z; hence,

$$\frac{dE}{dz} = \pi r^2 \rho g z - 2\pi r\gamma \cos \theta = 0 ; \tag{2.27}$$

whence,
$$\gamma = \frac{r\rho g z}{2 \cos \theta}. \tag{2.28}$$

Although (2.28) was derived for $z > 0$ and $\theta < \pi/2$, it holds equally well when $\theta > \pi/2$, for then $z < 0$. A small correction to the volume of liquid because its free surface is not a plane has been neglected. Moreover, ρ represents the density of the liquid relative to the phase above. If ρ_1 is the true density of liquid and ρ_0 is the density of the phase above, ρ should be replaced by $(\rho_1 - \rho_0)$.

Example 2.5. Distilled water rose to a height of 4.96 cm at 20°C in a certain capillary tube. The density of water at 20°C is 0.9982 g cm^{-3}. The same tube, when filled with mercury of density 13.55 g cm^{-3}, contained 38.3 mg cm^{-1} of tube length. Calculate the surface tension of water if the angle of contact is zero.

Since the volume of a tube of length 1.000 cm is πr^2, it follows that

$$38.3 \times 10^{-3} = 13.55 \times \pi r^2$$

$$r = 0.0300 \text{ cm}.$$

Then, by (2.28), since $\cos \theta = 1$,

$$\gamma = \frac{3.00 \times 10^{-2} \times 0.9982 \times 980.7 \times 4.96}{2} = 72.8 \text{ ergs cm}^{-2} .$$

The surface tension of a liquid decreases continuously as the temperature rises until, at the critical point, the liquid and gaseous phases no longer differ

The surface energy of a mole of liquid is expected to be proportional to $\gamma(M/\rho)^{2/3}$, for (M/ρ) is the volume of a mole and $(M/\rho)^{2/3}$ is thus proportional to its surface area. It has been found that the rate of change of the function $\gamma(M/\rho)^{2/3}$ with respect to temperature is constant. That is, with a negative sign to indicate that the function decreases with temperature,

$$\frac{d\left[\gamma\left(\dfrac{M}{\rho}\right)^{2/3}\right]}{dT} = -k .\tag{2.29}$$

Definite integration of (2.29) between a state at temperature T with surface tension γ and the critical state at temperature T_c where $\gamma = 0$ relative to gas yields (2.30).

$$\int_{\gamma'=0}^{\gamma'=\gamma} d\left[\gamma'\left(\frac{M}{\rho}\right)^{2/3}\right] = -\int_{T_c}^{T} k\,dT'$$

$$\gamma\left(\frac{M}{\rho}\right)^{2/3} = k(T_c - T) .\tag{2.30}$$

Observed data for unassociated liquids fit (2.31), the Ramsay-Shields equation, better than (2.30).

$$\gamma\left(\frac{M}{\rho}\right)^{2/3} = 2.1(T_c - T - 6) .\tag{2.31}$$

The value $k = 2.1$ is for the cgs system and is accurate generally within 10% for liquids like hydrocarbons and their halogen derivatives, ethers, and esters. Values of k for liquids containing hydrogen bonds are generally much less than 2.1 and vary with the temperature.

2.20 Molar Refraction and Polarization

The index of refraction of a substance is the ratio of the phase velocity of light in a vacuum, $c = 2.998 \times 10^{10}$ cm sec^{-1}, to the phase velocity of light in the substance. In noncubic crystals, the index of refraction depends upon the direction of a ray of light relative to the crystallographic axes; but in cubic crystals and most liquids, the index of refraction is the same in any direction. An absolute index of refraction is usually more difficult to measure than a relative one. A relative index of refraction is the ratio of phase velocities of light in two different optical media. If n_{Li} is the absolute index of refraction of medium i, then the relative index of refraction n_L is given by (2.32).

$$n_L = \frac{n_{L2}}{n_{L1}} = \frac{\left(\dfrac{c}{u_2}\right)}{\left(\dfrac{c}{u_1}\right)} = \frac{u_1}{u_2} .\tag{2.32}$$

Here, u_i is the phase velocity of light in medium i. If n_L is measured in air, u_1 is the velocity of light in air. Or if medium 1 is a vacuum, then $u_1 = c$ and (2.32) yields the absolute index of refraction of medium 2.

Snell's law relates the indexes of refraction of two media and the angles between a ray of light that passes from one medium to another and the normal to their optical interface. Figure 2.36 illustrates the passage of a beam of light from a medium where the velocity of light is u_1 to a medium where it is u_2. The angle of incidence is ϕ_1; the angle of refraction is ϕ_2. At a wave front such as $O'A'$ or OA, the light in medium 1 is in phase. Because $u_2 < u_1$, a wave originating at O reaches B when the wave from A reaches P; so the light along BP is also in phase, as it is later at $B'P'$.

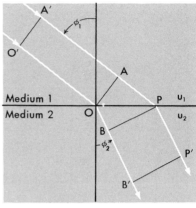

Fig. 2.36. *Index of Refraction and Angles of Incidence ϕ_1 and Refraction ϕ_2.*

Angle $POA = \phi_1$ and angle $OPB = \phi_2$. Since triangles OAP and OBP are right triangles with a common side OP,

$$OP = \frac{AP}{\sin \phi_1} = \frac{OB}{\sin \phi_2} ; \qquad (2.33)$$

but

$$\frac{AP}{OB} = \frac{u_1}{u_2}. \qquad (2.34)$$

Uniting (2.33) and (2.34) yields

$$\frac{u_1}{u_2} = \frac{\sin \phi_1}{\sin \phi_2}. \qquad (2.35)$$

By (2.32), this becomes Snell's law, (2.36).

$$\frac{n_{L2}}{n_{L1}} = \frac{\sin \phi_1}{\sin \phi_2}$$

$$n_{L1} \sin \phi_1 = n_{L2} \sin \phi_2 . \qquad (2.36)$$

If a beam of light comes to an interface where its phase velocity would increase, as in going from medium 2 to medium 1 in Figure 2.36, total reflection may occur at the interface. No beam will enter medium 1 if ϕ_1 would exceed $\pi/2$. That is, by (2.36), total reflection occurs when $\phi_2 > \phi_c$, where $\sin \phi_1 = 1$ and

$$\sin \phi_c = \frac{n_{L1}}{n_{L2}} = \frac{1}{n_L} ; \qquad (n_L > 1) . \qquad (2.37)$$

The Abbe refractometer measures the index of refraction of a liquid by measuring ϕ_c. This type of refractometer is diagrammed in Figure 2.37. Diffuse light enters the film of liquid of index n_{L1} through the roughened surface of the lower prism. This diffuse light enters the upper prism of index n_{L2} at an angle of incidence ϕ_1 less than $\pi/2$. As a result, ϕ_2 is less than or equal to ϕ_c and there is formed a dark edge marking the angle at which total reflection would occur for the interface of upper prism of known n_{L2} and liquid of unknown n_{L1}. The edge separating light from dark is brought to bear on cross hairs in a fixed viewer by moving the prism assembly. A pointer attached to the movable prism assembly indicates the value of n_{L1} on a fixed scale calibrated to read index of refraction directly.

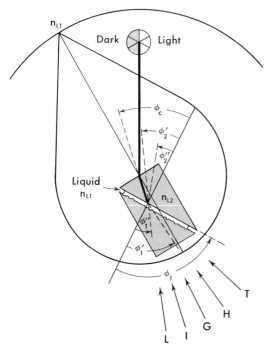

Fig. 2.37. *Diagram of Abbe Refractometer.*

According to Maxwell's electromagnetic theory of radiation, the dielectric constant κ_i and the magnetic permeability μ_i are related to the absolute index of refraction n_{L_i} of substance i by (2.38).

$$\kappa_i \mu_i = n_{Li}^2 . \qquad (2.38)$$

Since μ_i differs from unity by 10^{-4} or less for substances that are not ferro-magnetic, in general

$$\kappa = n_L^2 . \qquad (2.39)$$

By analogy with the molar polarization $\mathcal{P}_M$ of a substance, where

$$\mathcal{P}_M = V_M \left(\frac{\kappa - 1}{\kappa + 2} \right) , \qquad (1.141)$$

the molar refraction R_M of a substance is defined as

$$R_M = V_M \left(\frac{n_L^2 - 1}{n_L^2 + 2} \right) . \qquad (2.40)$$

As explained near the end of Section 1.14, if n_L^2 is found for visible light, R_M includes polarization terms attributable only to electronic movement. At the high frequencies characteristic of light, atoms and molecules are too massive to move rapidly enough to stay in phase with light radiation. Thus, if κ is the low-frequency dielectric constant of a substance, $\mathcal{P}_M$ exceeds R_M by the orientational and induced polarization characteristic of the substance. For light of infinite wavelength and frequency approaching zero, R_M equals $\mathcal{P}_M$. Now R_M for a liquid generally differs from R_M for a gas by only a few per cent in the visible region. Because the index of refraction of a liquid is easily measured, R_M is usually found for the liquid.

Example 2.6. Estimate the dipole moment of water from the facts that its molar polarization at 20°C is, by Example 1.13, 74.2 cc and that its index of refraction at 20°C is 1.333. The density of water at 20°C is 0.9982 g cm^{-3}.

By (2.40),

$$R_M = \left(\frac{1.333^2 - 1}{1.333^2 + 2}\right) \frac{18.02}{0.9982} = 3.72 \text{ cc} .$$

With neglect of atomic and induced polarization, by (1.142),

$$\frac{4}{3}\pi N\left(\frac{\mu_0}{3kT}\right)^2 = \mathcal{P}_M - R_M .$$

$$\mu_0^2 = \frac{9kT}{4\pi N}(\mathcal{P}_M - R_M)$$

$$= \frac{9 \times 8.314 \times 10^7 \times 293}{4 \times \pi \times (6.024 \times 10^{23})^2}(74.2 - 3.7)$$

$$= 3.39 \times 10^{-36}$$

$$\mu_0 = 1.84 \times 10^{-18} \text{ cm} \times \text{e.s.u.}$$

If a molecule is conceived as an electrically conducting sphere, then R_M for radiation of very long wavelength and almost zero frequency is the molar volume of the substance. Since spherical molecules and ions lack a dipole moment, $R_M = \mathcal{P}_M$ and molar refraction as determined in visible light is useful in estimating sizes of molecules and ions. With $\mu_0 = 0$, (1.142) yields

$$\mathcal{P}_M = \tfrac{4}{3}\pi N\alpha = \tfrac{4}{3}\pi Nr^3 , \qquad (2.41)$$

where r is the radius of the molecule or ion. Several values of the polarizabilities of molecules and ions are listed in Table 2.12. The polarizability of a body is a measure of the tightness with which its electrons are held. As the number of electrons or their distance from the nucleus increases, the polarizability increases. Wasastjerna used the fact that polarizability is proportional to ionic volume to divide observed interionic distances in the alkali halides into two parts, a cation and an anion radius.

Example 2.7. From its polarizability, estimate the size of an atom of argon. The radius observed in the cubic close-packed crystal is 1.92 Å.

From Table 2.12, $\alpha = 1.66 \times 10^{-24}$ cm^3. Hence, by (2.41),

$$r = \sqrt[3]{1.66 \times 10^{-24}} = 1.18 \text{ Å} .$$

Table 2.12. *Polarizabilities of Spherical Species**

($\alpha \times 10^{24}$ cc)

H$^-$	He	Li$^+$	Be^{++}
10.18	0.20	0.03	0.008
O^{--}	F$^-$	Ne	Na$^+$	Mg^{++}
2.74	0.96	0.40	0.19	0.10
S^{--}	Cl$^-$	Ar	K$^+$	Ca^{++}
8.94	3.60	1.66	0.89	0.55
Se^{--}	Br$^-$	Kr	Rb$^+$	Sr^{++}
11.4	5.0	2.54	1.50	1.02
Te^{--}	I$^-$	Xe	Cs$^+$	Ba^{++}
16.1	7.60	4.15	2.60	1.86

* Pauling, L., *Proc. Roy. Soc.*, **A114**, 191 (1927); Fajans, K., *Zs. phys. Chem.*, **B24**, 103 (1934); Fajans, K., and G. Joos, *Zs. Phys.*, **23**, 1 (1924).

Example 2.8. From data in Table 2.12, calculate the index of refraction of KCl. The observed value is 1.490, and the density of KCl is 1.989 g cm^{-3}.

For 1 mole KCl, the molar refraction is the sum of the molar polarizabilities; hence,

$$R_M = \tfrac{4}{3}\pi N[\alpha(K^+) + \alpha(Cl^-)]$$
$$= \tfrac{4}{3}\pi(0.6024 \times 10^{24})[(0.89 + 3.60) \times 10^{-24}]$$
$$= 11.34 \text{ cm}^3 .$$

But by (2.40),

$$R_M = \frac{M}{\rho}\left(\frac{n_L^2 - 1}{n_L^2 + 2}\right)$$

$$11.34 = \frac{74.56}{1.989}\left(\frac{n_L^2 - 1}{n_L^2 + 2}\right)$$

$$0.3045 = \frac{n_L^2 - 1}{n_L^2 + 2}$$

$$\frac{1.6090}{0.6955} = n_L^2$$

$$n_L = 1.521 .$$

The observed value is lower than the calculated value because the ions polarize each other in the solid and thus results a general tightening of the electronic structure, particularly that of the anion.

Example 2.9. The observed lattice constant of KCl is 6.291 A at 20°C. With the aid of polarizabilities from Table 2.12, calculate the radii of K^+ and Cl^-.

The ratio of the radii is equal to the cube root of the ratio of their polarizabilities; hence,

$$\frac{r_-}{r_+} = \sqrt[3]{\frac{3.60}{0.89}} = 1.594 ;$$

but

$$r_+ + r_- = 3.146 \text{ A} .$$

Hence,

$$r_+ + 1.594r_+ = 3.146 \text{ A}$$

$$r_+ = \frac{3.146 \text{ A}}{2.594} = 1.212 \text{ A}$$

$$r_- = 3.146 - 1.212 = 1.934 \text{ A} .$$

The commonly accepted values are $r_+ = 1.33$ A and $r_- = 1.80$ A .

Molar refraction is sometimes used to establish the chemical structure of a molecule with known M, ρ, and n_L, where R_M is an additive property and a constitutive property. That is, its magnitude depends upon the number of atoms or bonds and upon their arrangement or kind. For details, the student is referred elsewhere.[12]

2.21 Optical Activity

Some crystals and molecules can rotate the plane of plane-polarized light that passes through them. A molecule (or a crystal considered as a very great molecule) is optically active in this way if translation and rotation in space cannot lead to superposition of it on its mirror image. Mirror images are related as left hand is to right, the mirror plane being midway between facing hands. The two forms that cannot be superposed are called *dextro-* and *levo-rotary,* and are identical in every way except in the arrangement in space of equivalent chemical groupings.

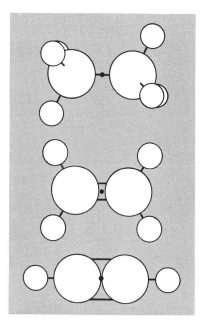

Any molecule or crystal that exhibits a rotation-inversion axis as part of its own symmetry cannot be optically active. A onefold rotation-inversion involves a rotation by 360° followed by movement of all atoms from $+x$, $+y$, $+z$ to $-x$, $-y$, $-z$. It is nothing else than a center of inversion. If a symmetry operation transforms the molecule into a configuration that is indistinguishable from the original one, the molecule is said to possess the *element of symmetry.* Many molecules including H_2, N_2, C_2H_4, and SF_6 possess a center of inversion. The staggered form of C_2H_6, shown with C_2H_2 and C_2H_4 in Figure 2.38, contains a center of inversion midway between the carbon atoms. Ethene is planar and ethyne is linear.

A twofold rotation-inversion axis involves a rotation by 360°/2 followed by inversion. A rotation by 180° around the z-axis transforms x, y, z into $-x$, $-y$, z; subsequent inversion yields x, y, $-z$. Accordingly, a twofold rotation-inversion is equivalent to reflection across a mirror plane in the x-y-plane, for

Fig. 2.38. *Centers of Inversion in Ethane, Ethene, and Ethyne.*

the net change is x, y, z to x, y, $-z$. Similarly, an n-fold rotation inversion involves rotation by 360°/n followed by inversion. Since most situations of interest involve rotation-inversion axes that contain mirror planes or centers of inversion as subgroups, the usual guide to optical activity is this: Optical activity is possible in a molecule that has neither a mirror plane nor a center of inversion. There are, however, exceptions to this last statement.[13]

The simplest type of optically active molecule would be SbFClBr or NHDT, an isotopically substituted NH_3. Here SbX_3 and NH_3 are pyramidal in form. The two forms of optically active ammonia are shown in Figure 2.39. They are related to each other by reflection in a mirror plane and no rotation or movement in space can turn

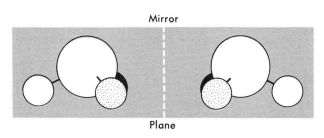

Mirror

Plane

Fig. 2.39. *Optically Active Ammonia.*

them so that the two forms can be superposed. Ordinary ammonia (NH₃) or NH₂D is not optically active because each has a vertical mirror plane. Reflection in such a plane interchanges protons, which are indistinguishable from one another. Planar BFClBr, however, is not optically active because, by a rotation about an axis in the plane of the molecule, two forms that appear to be mirror images can in fact be superposed. Indeed, because the molecule is planar, its plane is a mirror plane, the twofold rotation inversion axis being perpendicular to the plane of the molecule.

Optical activity almost always results from an asymmetric carbon atom, a carbon holding four unlike groups. Thus, there exist two forms of CHFClBr. Every optically active site presents two possibilities, a left- and a right-hand form. As a result, a sugar containing four asymmetric carbon atoms will have 2^4 isomers.

The angle α_R through which the plane of polarization is rotated by an optically active substance or its solution is proportional to the concentration of the optically active substance and to the length of the optical path. If the length of the optical path is l decimeters and if g grams of the substance are in V milliliters of fluid (solution or pure liquid or gas), then

$$\alpha_R = [\alpha_R]_T^\lambda \frac{lg}{V}. \tag{2.42}$$

The proportionality constant $[\alpha_R]_T^\lambda$ is the specific rotation. It varies with the wavelength of light and the temperature, is almost independent of concentration, and is a characteristic of the optically active species. Equation (2.42) provides a simple, rapid, accurate, and nondestructive means of analysis that is used routinely in the sugar industry. Table 2.13 lists specific rotations of a few substances dissolved in water. When the plane of polarization is rotated to the right on proceeding in the direction of the light, the angle of rotation is positive; to the left, negative.

Table 2.13. *Specific Rotations in Aqueous Solution*[*]

SUBSTANCE	TEMPERATURE	SPECIFIC ROTATION[a]	(Na D)
Dextrose (d-glucose)	20°C	$+52.5 + 0.025d$	$(1 < d < 18)$
Levulose (d-fructose)	25°C	$-88.5 - 0.145d$	$(2.6 < d < 18.6)$
Sucrose	20°C	$+66.412 + 0.01267d - 0.000376d^2$	$(0 < d < 50)$
Nicotine	20°C	-77	$(1 < d < 16)$

[a] d = grams per 100 g solution.

* *Handbook of Chemistry and Physics.* Cleveland, O.: Chemical Rubber Publishing Co., 1958-1959, p. 2811.

Example 2.10. Calculate the angle of rotation caused by a solution containing 10.0 g sucrose in 90.0 g water at 20°C when the sodium D line is used and when the optical path is 20.00 cm in length.

The density of such a solution is 1.038 g ml^{-1}; hence,

$$\frac{g}{V} = \frac{10.0}{\left(\dfrac{100}{1.038}\right)} = 0.1038 \text{ g ml}^{-1}.$$

From Table 2.13, for $d = 10$,

$$[\alpha_R]_T^\lambda = 66.412 + 0.127 - 0.038 = 66.501.$$

Finally, by (2.42),

$$\alpha_R = 66.501 \times 2.000 \times 0.1038 = 13.81°.$$

2.22 Viscosity

A force is required to maintain a steady laminar flow in a fluid because flow requires molecules to assume positions in which intermolecular forces are not the most favorable. Because molecules migrate randomly, their paths take them between regions of different flow rates. In thus moving perpendicular to the direction of flow, they must be accelerated or decelerated. The continuous force that maintains flow is

$$F = \eta \mathcal{A} \frac{dv}{dz},\tag{1.95}$$

where η is the coefficient of viscosity, a proportionality constant linking force F, contact area $\mathcal{A}$, and velocity gradient dv/dz.

Gases exhibit viscosity because each molecule has a mass that resists acceleration and a collisional cross section that allows collisions. The viscosity of a gas increases with the square root of the temperature because the rate of movement perpendicular to the direction of flow increases with $\sqrt{T}$.

In a liquid, displacement perpendicular to the direction of flow is severely limited because of the high density. Although the reason for viscosity, namely, a change of momentum between adjacent layers, remains the same for gas and liquid, the intermolecular forces so dominate flow in liquids that η depends upon T in a different and more marked way. In liquids in general,

$$\ln \eta = \frac{A}{RT} + B,\tag{2.43}$$

where B is an empirical constant and A represents an energy of viscous flow due to breaking of bonds or unfavorable intermolecular contacts during flow. In silica-based glasses, A is of the order of 40 kcal mole^{-1}; in water, it is about 4 kcal mole^{-1}. Silica-based glasses have viscosities of the order of 10^{25} dyne sec cm^{-2} at room temperature. The viscosities of several liquids at 20°C are listed in Table 2.14.

The rate of flow of an incompressible fluid is given by Poiseuille's law (2.44).

$$\frac{dV}{dt} = \frac{\pi \Delta P r^4}{8l\eta},$$

(2.44)

where ΔP is the pressure drop in a pipe of radius r and length l. This law gives the volume of liquid that flows per unit time when the flow is laminar or streamline.

When a viscous fluid is forced rapidly past a small object or through a narrow pipe, the flow may become turbulent. Turbulent flow is characterized by a complicated flow pattern, with eddies and vortices, and a fluctuating flow rate at any particular point. It results when the dimensionless Reynolds number R_N exceeds a critical value between 10^3 and 10^4.

$$R_N = \frac{\rho v a}{\eta}.$$

(2.45)

Table 2.14. *Viscosities of Liquids* (20°C)*

SUBSTANCE	η (dyne-sec cm^{-2})
Benzene	0.00647
Ethanol	0.011943
Glycerol	10.690
Heptane	0.004163
Mercury	0.01547
Water	0.01002

In (2.45), ρ and v are density and velocity, η is the coefficient of viscosity, and a is the dimension of an object in the flow or the diameter of the pipe. Turbulent flow seldom occurs or continues when R_N is less than 10^3, and always results when R_N exceeds 10^4. Whether or not flow is turbulent for values between 10^3 and 10^4 often depends upon the preparation of the system.[14]

Viscosities are readily compared in an Ostwald viscometer, a device with fixed values of l, r, and V. The pressure drop ΔP is proportional to the density of the liquid tested because the difference in levels during flow is held almost constant. Thus, in such a device, if t_i is the time for the fixed volume of fluid of density ρ_i and viscosity η_i to flow between reservoirs, it follows from (2.44) that

$$\frac{\eta_1}{\eta_2} = \frac{t_1 \rho_1}{t_2 \rho_2}.$$

(2.46)

Example 2.11. At 20°C, pure water with an absolute viscosity of 0.01009 dyne sec cm^{-2} required 102.2 sec to flow through the capillary of an Ostwald viscometer. At 20°C, toluene required 68.9 sec. If the densities of water and toluene are 0.998 and 0.866 g cm^{-3}, what is the viscosity of toluene?

By (2.46), if species 1 is toluene,

$$\eta_1 = \eta_2 \left(\frac{t_1 \rho_1}{t_2 \rho_2}\right) = 0.01009 \left(\frac{68.9 \times 0.866}{102.2 \times 0.998}\right) = 0.00590 \text{ dyne sec cm}^{-2}.$$

* Lange's *Handbook of Chemistry.* New York: McGraw-Hill Book Co., Inc., 1956, pp. 1657-62.

2.23 Critical Temperature and Structure

At the critical point, two coexistent fluid phases become so alike in physical properties such as density and index of refraction that they become one fluid phase. Although the critical temperature of a substance is of great use in practical and theoretical studies, only about 300 critical temperatures are known. They are difficult to measure even when the substance investigated is stable at its critical temperature. In 1890, Guldberg stated an empirical rule that the absolute critical temperature of a substance is about one and one-half times its absolute boiling point at 1 atm. When substances are suitably classified, the relations of boiling point and critical temperature can be refined beyond the simple rule of Guldberg. This has been done by Marschner and Beverly.[15]

For elements, hydrides, and halides, the observed ratios of critical temperature T_c to normal boiling point T_b follow (2.47).

$$\frac{T_c}{T_b} = K . \tag{2.47}$$

Marschner and Beverly report that for the 20 elements for which data are available, K is 1.72 and all values agree within 3% except for Hg and He. For the hydrides HF, HCl, HBr, HI, H_2O, H_2S, H_2Se, NH_3, N_2H_4, CH_4, and SiH_4, K is also 1.72 within 3%. For polyhalides of B, C, Si, Ge, and Sn, K is 1.53, again within 3%. Methyl, ethyl, and phenyl monohalides are well represented by K equals 1.66, 1.58, and 1.56.

A somewhat more complicated empirical relationship between critical temperature T_c and normal boiling point T_b has been found by Marschner and Beverly for ten homologous orgainc series. The members of each series differ by a multiple of CH_2. For them,

$$\frac{(1000/T_b) - 1}{(1000/T_c) - 1} = K . \tag{2.48}$$

Values of K for (2.48) are listed in Table 2.15 for ten kinds of organic compound. Branched and unbranched isomers behave alike, but data for molecules with rings suggest that shape is important.

The general conclusions drawn from this study of critical temperatures are that the shape of the molecule determines the value of K and the mass of the molecule determines its position along the line (2.47) or (2.48) that fits its class. Expressing T_c and T_b in these ways clearly shows these influences at work and thus helps to dispel a bit of the mystery that still surrounds the liquid and critical states.

Table 2.15. *Marschner-Beverly Constants*

HOMOLOGOUS SERIES	K (2.48)
Alkanes	1.980
Alkenes	2.009
Alkynes	2.097
Alkyl benzenes	2.343
Alkanols	1.924
Alkyl ethers	2.160
Akanoic acids	2.189
Alkyl esters	2.074
Alkyl amines	2.033
Alkyl nitriles	2.220

REFERENCES

Barrett, C. S., *Structure of Metals*. New York: McGraw-Hill Book Co., Inc., 1952.

Buerger, M. J., *X-ray Crystallography*. New York: John Wiley & Sons, Inc., 1942.

Bunn, C. W., *Chemical Crystallography*. New York: Oxford University Press, 1946.

Donnay, J. D. H., and W. Nowacki, *Crystal Data*. New York: The Geological Society of America. Memoir 60 of The Geological Society of America, 1954.

Garner, W. E., ed., *Chemistry of the Solid State*. London: Butterworth's Scientific Publications, 1955.

Glasstone, S., *Textbook of Physical Chemistry*. New York: D. Van Nostrand Co., Inc., 1946.

James, R. W., *The Crystalline State, Volume II, The Optical Principles of the Diffraction of X-rays*. London: George Bell & Sons, Ltd., 1950.

Jones, G. O., *Glass*. London: Methuen & Co., Ltd., 1956.

Kittel, C., *Introduction to Solid State Physics*. New York: John Wiley & Sons, Inc., 1953.

Pauling, L., *The Nature of the Chemical Bond*. Ithaca, N. Y.: Cornell University Press, 1960.

Syrkin, Y. K., and M. E. Dyatkina, *Structure of Molecules and the Chemical Bond* (tr. by M. A. Partridge and D. O. Jordan). London: Butterworth's Scientific Publications, 1950.

Wells, A. F., *Structural Inorganic Chemistry*. New York: Oxford University Press. 1950.

Wyckoff, R. W. G., *Crystal Structures*. New York: Interscience Publishers, Inc., 1948-

PROBLEMS

1. Obtain crystals of NaCl, I_2, alum, K_2SO_4, and other substances that seem interesting. Note the general regularity and symmetry of the crystals.

2. Precipitate NaCl from its saturated solution:
(a) By slow evaporation.
(b) By adding concentrated HCl swiftly.
(c) Containing about 10% dissolved urea by slow evaporation.
Note differences in the crystals of NaCl.

3. Account for the following:
(a) Petrification of wood, etc.
(b) Growth of stalagmites and stalactites.
(c) Conchoidal fracture of glass.
(d) Easy deformability of annealed copper as contrasted to cold-worked copper.

4. Distinguish between lattice and structure, with a large automobile parking lot as example.

5. Show that face-centered tetragonal is really body-centered tetragonal.

6. Draw a face-centered cubic unit cell, and outline in it a primitive unit cell. Repeat for a body-centered cubic lattice.

7. Justify Equation (2.5) for a few particular triples (hkl) and also in general by means of analytic geometry.

8. A sample of iridium had its first ($h00$) reflection at $\theta = 23.7°$, its first ($hh0$) reflection at $34.7°$, and its first (hhh) reflection at $20.4°$ with radiation of wavelength 1.542 A.   Calculate the lattice type, dimension of the cubic unit cell, and the density of iridium if there is one atom per lattice site.
Answer: F.C.C. $a = 3.84$ A; $\rho = 22.6$ g cm^{-3}.

9. Metallic vanadium, with a density of 6.02 g cm^{-3}, diffracts X radiation of wavelength 0.710 A so that the first ($h00$) reflection is at $\theta = 13.5°$, the first ($hh0$) reflection is at $\theta = 9.50°$, and the first (hhh) reflection is at $\theta = 23.9°$.   From these data and the atomic weight, and if there is one atom per lattice site, find:
(a)   The kind and size of the cubic unit cell.
(b)   The distance of closest approach of V atoms.
(c)   Avogadro's number.
(d)   The angles at which the next reflections of the types above will occur.

10. Calculate the density of europium metal, which crystallizes with one atom at each lattice site in a body-centered cubic lattice with $a_0 = 4.58$ A.

11. Determine the location and size of the largest sphere that can exist among identical spheres in a body-centered cubic structure without disturbing that structure.
Answer: 0.291 at $(\frac{1}{2}\frac{1}{4}0)$.

12. Determine the densities of KCl and KBr with data from Table 2.7.
Answer: 1.9866 g cm^{-3}; 2.7489 g cm^{-3}.

13. Calculate the coefficient of linear expansion of NaCl at room temperature from data of Table 2.7.

14. Calculate the densities of TlCl and AlNi with data from Table 2.9.

15. What is the ratio of the heights attained by each of two pure liquids in a certain capillary tube wetted by each if their densities are equal but their surface tensions differ by a factor of two?   What if one liquid did not wet the tube?

16. The surface tension of water at 20°C is 72.75 dyne cm^{-1}.   How high will a column of water rise in a capillary tube with a radius of 0.00500 cm?
Answer: 29.7 cm.

17. The indexes of refraction, densities, and molecular weights of cyclohexane and 1, 4-dioxane are, respectively: 1.428 and 1.423; 0.779 g cm^{-3} and 1.032 g cm^{-3}; 84.2 and 88.1.   Calculate the molar refraction equivalents of CH$_2$ and of O in an ether.

18. Why don't cis- and trans- 1, 2-dichloroethylene rotate the plane of plane polarized light?
Answer: Each has mirror plane.

19. If it takes 50.0 sec for benzene to flow through a capillary tube at fixed pressure, how long will it take heptane to do so under similar conditions?
Answer: 32.2 sec.

20. From their normal boiling points estimate the critical temperatures of all pentanes.

---

21. Find the interfacial angles of an octahedron and a dodecahedron.   (A scalar product of vectors eases the calculation.)
Answer: (octahedron) 70.53°; 109.48°; 180°.

22. Give examples of lattice-like arrangements from everyday experience of one-, two-, and three-dimensional structures.

23. Give the results of rotation of a cubic crystal by $2\pi/3$ around the perpendicular to: (a) $(1\,\bar{1}\,\bar{1})$. (b) $(\bar{1}\,1\,1)$.

24. Show that a primitive hexagonal lattice can be described as an end-centered orthorhombic lattice, and find a restriction upon the orthorhombic axial lengths.

25. By a drawing, show several choices of a monoclinic unit cell for the same set of lattice points.

26. Why must the X radiation used in powder photography be almost monochromatic?

27. Metallic molybdenum has a density of 10.22 g cm^{-3}. From a powder photograph of Mo taken with X radiation of wavelength 0.711 A, the first $(h00)$ reflection occurred at $\theta = 13.1°$, the first $(hh0)$ reflection occured at $\theta = 9.2°$, and the first (hhh) reflection occurred at $\theta = 23.1°$. From these data, if there is one atom per lattice site, calculate:
(a) The type and size of cubic unit cell.
(b) The distance of closest approach of Mo atoms.
(c) Avogadro's number.
(d) The angle θ at which the (211) reflection should occur.

28. When niobium metal diffracts X radiation of wavelength 1.542 A, the first $(h00)$ reflection lies at $2\theta = 55.64°$, the first $(hh0)$ reflection lies at $2\theta = 38.54°$, and the first (hhh) reflection lies at $2\theta = 108.10°$. The metal is cubic, has a density of 8.57 g cm^{-3}, and has a specific heat of 0.065 cal g^{-1} deg^{-1}. In one of its oxides, the equivalent weight of the metal is 18.54. From only these data, calculate Avogadro's number if there is one atom per lattice site.

29. At 89°K, krypton exists in a cubic lattice with density of 3.00 g cm^{-3}. The first three X-ray reflections occur at $\theta = 13.54°$, 15.68°, and 22.46° when the wavelength is 1.542 A. From gas density measurements the atomic weight of krypton is known to be 83.8. Calculate the type and size of the cubic unit cell and the diameter of a krypton atom.

30. Calculate for a face-centered lattice containing one atom with atomic scattering factor f at each lattice site the structure factors $F(hkl)$ as follows:
(a) $F(000)$. (b) $F(100)$. (c) F(110). (d) $F(111)$. (e) $F(200)$. (f) $F(210)$. (g) $F(211)$. (h) $F(220)$.
Answer: (a)(d)(e)(h) $F = 4f$; otherwise, $F = 0$.

31. Repeat Problem 30 for a body-centered lattice.

32. What is the multiplicity of:
(a) $(h00)$ in the cubic system.
(b) $(hk0)$ in the orthorhombic system.

33. What is the ratio of atomic radii of a metal that has the same density in body-centered cubic and face-centered cubic structures?
Answer: 1.0287.

34. Calculate the squares of the structure factors of NaCl for these reflections: (100), (200), (300), (111), (222), (333). Assume $f(Na^+) = 10$ and $f(Cl^-) = 18$.

35. Calculate the densities of sphalerite and wurtzite, two forms of ZnS, from the data of Table 2.11.
Answer: 4.04 g cm^{-3}.

36. Are the sulfide ions of WS_2 and MoS_2 all close-packed? Explain.

37. Compare the layers of $CdCl_2$ to those of NaCl.

38. Calculate the density of ice. Calculate the density of water if it consisted of spherical, close-packed molecules H_2O with radii of 1.75 A.
Answer: 0.924 g cm^{-3}, 0.99 g cm^{-3}.

39. At 20°C, ethanol rises 5.21 cm in a capillary tube with diameter 0.0220 cm. The density of ethanol at 20°C is 0.789 g cm^{-3}. What is its surface tension?

40. What is the surface tension of methanol at 40°C if it rises to a height of 6.88 cm in a capillary tube of internal radius 0.00800 cm? The density of methanol at this temperature is 0.774 g cm^{-3}.

41. Predict the angle of rotation of plane-polarized Na D light due to passage through 2.00 decimeters of aqueous solution at 20°C if 100.0 g of solution of density 1.03 g ml^{-1} contains:
(a) Ten g d-glucose.
(b) Eight g d-glucose and 2.0 g l-glucose.

42. Explain the presence or absence of optical activity in:
(a) The several pentanols.
(b) Glycine ($HOOCCH_2NH_2$).
(c) Lactic acid ($HOOCCHOHCH_3$).
(d) The several dichlorocyclopropanes.
(e) $K_3Co(C_2O_4)_3$.

43. At about what velocity (linear and volume) does the flow of water at 20°C change from laminar to turbulent in a pipe with internal diameter of one in.?
Answer: 4 cm sec^{-1}; 20 cm^3 sec^{-1}.

44. By the method of Cailletet-Mathias, the critical volume of a substance can be found by extrapolating the average density of liquid and saturated vapor linearly as a function of temperature to the critical temperature. Find the critical molar volume of oxygen at its critical temperature of -118.4°C. [Data from Lange's *Handbook of Chemistry.* New York: McGraw-Hill Book Co., Inc., 1956, pp. 1448–9.]

Temperature (°C)	Liquid Density (g cm^{-3})	Gaseous Density (g cm^{-3})
-210.4	1.2746	8.65×10^{-5}
-182.0	1.1415	4.90×10^{-3}
-154.5	0.9758	0.0385
-140.2	0.8742	0.0805
-129.9	0.7781	0.1320
-123.3	0.6779	0.2022
-120.4	0.6032	0.2701

45. By the method of Hakala (R. W. Hakala, *Chem. & Eng. News*, March 16, 1959, pp. 43-4), find the critical molar volume of oxygen by plotting mean density of liquid D and saturated vapor d against the function $(D - d)^{10/3}$ and extrapolating linearly to $D = d$. Use the data of Problem 44.

46. In the cubic system, what is the angle between these pairs of faces? (110) and (111); (100) and (210).
Answer: 35.3°; 26.6°.

47. Draw a portion of a planar rectangular lattice and inscribe lines with indexes (2, 1), (4, 2), (3, 0), (2, 1) after defining axes.

48. Show that monoclinic B lattice is monoclinic C lattice.

113

49. Metallic aluminum, with one atom per lattice site and a density of 2.70 g cm^{-3} at 25°C, exhibits its first four X-ray reflections at θ = 19.25°, 22.38°, 32.58°, and 39.15°. If the wavelength of radiation is 1.542 A, determine:
(a) The type and size of cubic unit cell.
(b) The atomic weight of Al.
(c) The distance between closest Al atoms.
(d) The angle θ at which (400) reflection occurs.

50. Show that the (222) reflection of CaF$_2$ is weak. Describe the intensities of X radiation of wavelengths λ and 2λ as reflected from the (111) face of a single crystal of CaF$_2$.

51. The (200) reflection of metallic lithium at −183°C is at θ = 26.272° when the wavelength of X rays is 1.5418 A. At 20°C, the same reflection is at 26.062°. Calculate the coefficient of linear expansion of Li. Must the wavelength of X rays be known?
Answer: 3.7 × 10^{-5} deg^{-1}.

52. Solid solutions of copper and nickel have cubic lattice constants that vary linearly with the mole fraction. Predict the density of a solid solution with a mole fraction of Cu of 0.750 (that is, three Cu for every one Ni).
Answer: 8.929 g cm^{-3}.

53. Find the relative radius of a sphere situated among eight identical spheres arranged in a square Archimedean antiprism. The eight spheres are in contact with each other and the central one.

54. FeO has the NaCl structure with cation vacancies, and γ-Fe$_2$O$_3$ has the spinel structure with cation vacancies. Discuss the oxidation of FeO to Fe$_3$O$_4$ to γ-Fe$_2$O$_3$ as a continuous process. (See A. F. Wells, *Structural Inorganic Chemistry*, New York: Oxford University Press, 1950, pp. 381-2.)

55. If Frenkel defects in a certain crystal are about 1000 times rarer than Schottky defects, and if each type could have been generated, what is the order or magnitude of the energy difference of these two types of defect?
Answer: 7RT.

56. If the lattice constants of Fe$_x$O vary linearly with composition, calculate the size of the cubic unit cell of FeO. Calculate the densities of Fe$_{0.912}$O and FeO and compare the values. See Table 2.7 for data.

57. The Si−O bond distance in vitreous silica is 1.62 A. If the Si−O−Si bond angle is π and if the O−Si−O bond angles are all tetrahedral, calculate the three other well-defined bond distances in vitreous silica. Compare the result with Figure 2.33. Can the peak at 5.2 A be explained in terms of a ring of tetrahedra?
Answer: 2.64 A; 3.24 A; 4.08 A.

58. Calculate the extraordinary pressure within a spherical droplet because of surface tension by equating the infinitesimal increase in surface energy to the infinitesimal expansion work that accompanies growth of the droplet.

59. With the aid of Figure 1.8 estimate the indexes of refraction of gaseous CCl$_4$ and CHCl$_3$ at standard conditions for wavelengths in the visible, infrared, and radio-frequency ranges.

60. From the data of Hurdis and Smyth in Example 1.13, find the polarizability of H$_2$O. Compare this value with the polarizability of the oxide ion and justify the difference quantitatively in terms of electronic structure. Predict the polarizability of HBr.

61. Methyl propionate boils at 80°C at 1.00 atm. The density of the liquid at 80°C is 0.841 g cm^{-3}; at 10.00 atm in equilibrium with vapor at 172°C, the liquid density is 0.700 g cm^{-3}. [Lange's *Handbook of Chemistry*, McGraw-Hill Book Co., Inc., N. Y. (1956), p. 1448.] By Hakala's method, estimate the critical density of methyl propionate. The observed value at 257.4°C is 0.3124 g cm^{-3}.

62. Rutile (a form of TiO$_2$) is tetragonal with $a = 4.49$ Å and $c = 2.89$ Å. Titanium atoms lie at (000) and $(\frac{1}{2}\frac{1}{2}\frac{1}{2})$, and oxygen atoms lie at: (0.31, 0.31, 0); (0.81, 0.19, 0.50); (0.69, 0.69, 0); and (0.19, 0.81, 0.50). [R. W. G. Wyckoff, *Crystal Structures*, Interscience Publishers, Inc., New York, (1948-) Vol I, Chapter IV.]
(a) Draw a sketch of the unit cell with its atoms.
(b) Calculate the density of rutile.
(c) Determine the coordination number of Ti.
(d) Find the average Ti−O distance.

63. Index the spectra of Figure 2.13 and determine the sizes of the unit cells.

FOOTNOTES

1. Buckley, H. E., *Crystal Growth*. New York: John Wiley & Sons, Inc., 1951.

2. (a) Herzberg, G., *Molecular Spectra and Molecular Structure, Volume II, Infrared and Raman Spectra*. Princeton, N. J.: D. Van Nostrand Co., Inc., 1945, Introduction. (b) Margenau, H. and G. M. Murphy, *The Mathematics of Physics and Chemistry*. Princeton, N. J.: D. Van Nostrand Co., Inc., chapter on group theory in late editions. (c) Phillips, F. C., *Crystallography*. New York: Longmans, Green & Co., Inc., 1956. (d) Henry, N. F. M., and K. Lonsdale, eds., *International Tables for X-ray Crystallography, Volume I, Symmetry Groups*. Birmingham, England: The Kynoch Press, 1952.

3. James, R. W., *The Crystalline State, Volume II, The Optical Principles of the Diffraction of X-rays*. London: George Bell & Sons, Ltd., 1950, pp. 2-3.

4. See, for example, Buerger, M. J., *X-ray Crystallography*. New York: John Wiley & Sons, Inc., 1942, p. 103.

5. See, for example, Bunn, C. W., *Chemical Crystallography*. New York: Oxford University Press, 1946.

6. Ludekens, W. L. W. and A. J. E. Welch, *Acta Crystallographica*, 5, 841, 1952.

7. Wells, A. F., *Structural Inorganic Chemistry*. New York: Oxford University Press, 1950, pp. 570, 375-85.

8. Stone, F. S., *The Chemistry of the Solid State*, ed. W. E. Garner. London: Butterworth's Scientific Publications, 1955, pp. 20-25.

9. See, for example, Pauling, L., *The Nature of the Chemical Bond*. Ithaca, N. Y.: Cornell University Press, 1960, Chapter 13.

10. Jones, G. O., *Glass*. London: Methuen & Co., Ltd., 1956, p. 23 *et seq*, and pp. 38-45.

11. See, for example, Pauling, L., *The Nature of the Chemical Bond*. Ithaca, N. Y.: Cornell University Press, 1960, p. 464 *et seq*.

12.   See, for example, Glasstone, S., *Textbook of Physical Chemistry*.   Princeton, N. J.:   D. Van Nostrand Co., Inc., 1946, pp. 528-38.   See also Syrkin, Y. K. and M. E. Dyatkina, *Structure of Molecules and the Chemical Bond*.   Translated by M. A. Partridge and D. O. Jordan.   New York: Interscience Publishers, Inc., 1950, pp. 197-204.

13.   Wells, A. F., *Structural Inorganic Chemistry*.   New York: Oxford University Press, 1950, pp. 207-10.   Also Bunn, C. W., *Chemical Crystallography*.   New York: Oxford University Press, 1945, p. 88.

14.   Fowler, R. G., and D. I. Meyer, *Physics for Engineers and Scientists*.   Boston: Allyn and Bacon, Inc., 1958, pp. 239-40.

15.   Marschner, R. F., and J. B. Beverly, *Journal of Chemical Education*, 33, 604 (1956).

3 / FIRST LAW OF

THERMODYNAMICS

A. THE FIRST LAW

3.1 Definitions

Thermodynamics is the exact mathematical science that describes the inter-relationships of heat and mechanical energy. The kinetic theory and statistical mechanics describe how the mechanics of molecules and atoms and other tiny bits of matter is responsible for seemingly continuous and homogeneous behavior. Observed as a whole, myriads of such bits of matter exhibit steady average properties. Thermodynamics describes transformations of matter and energy when the atomistic constitution of matter can be ignored. The mechanical energy of thermodynamics may be closely related to the mechanical energy of the elementary bits of matter, but thermodynamics treats of matter as a continuum that displays thermal and mechanical properties on a visible or molar basis.

That part of the physical universe that is under study is the *system;* everything else in the universe constitutes the *surroundings.* A *closed system* cannot exchange matter with the surroundings, but an *open system* can. If a system cannot exchange matter or energy of any kind with its surroundings, it is called an *isolated system*. Because there is no barrier to gravitation a perfectly isolated system is impossible, but the influence of gravity is often negligible. The boundary of a closed system must be unpenetrated by matter, while the boundary of an isolated system is not crossed by flow of matter, heat, radiation, or other forms of energy, and is not displaced against a force. These definitions require that mass and energy be conserved separately. In this nonrelativistic view of the universe, mass and energy are not interconvertible; each is itself conserved in any change.

The *state of a system* is defined when a certain number of properties of the system are specified. The properties chosen are ordinarily *intensive properties*, that is, properties that do not depend upon the amount of matter in the system. When two systems have each of their several intensive properties alike, they are said to be *in the same state*. For example, the temperature and pressure of a gas are intensive properties, for each can be measured whether 1 mole or 1000 moles are in the system. The pressure and temperature in two systems containing different amounts of matter can be equal and are in no way restricted or determined by the amount of matter in each. Similarly, the mole fractions of all the molecular species present and the index of refraction of a mixture would be classed as intensive properties, but volume or mass would not.

If in a system the intensive properties like density and pressure are continuous functions of position, then the system is said to be *homogeneous;* if they are discontinuous, then *inhomogeneous* or *heterogeneous*. The distinction *continuous or discontinuous* depends upon the scale of measurement. For thermodynamics, the scale is the wavelength of visible light: if a body looks to be continuous even under the best optical microscope, it is taken to be continuous on the macroscopic scale. Water and oil ordinarily form two phases; that is, there is a region rich in water where the density and elemental composition correspond closely to the values for water, and there is another region where the intensive properties correspond closely to those for oil. At the interface between the two liquid phases various intensive properties appear discontinuous to the eye, but on a molecular scale the apparent discontinuity is perhaps a thin layer of very rapidly changing molecular population. Exactly which intensive thermodynamic properties are to be specified is often a matter of experimental convenience. However, the number of such independent properties that must be specified in any set of circumstances in order to fix the state of the system is a matter that can be answered by thermodynamics, namely, by the phase rule.

As a system changes from an initial well-defined state, wherein enough intensive properties are specified to fix the state of the system, to a final well-defined state, the various intensive properties assume intermediate values. Sometimes these intermediate values are ill defined. Generally, however, in this simple treatment of thermodynamics, the process or path by which such a change is effected will be sufficiently well defined to permit calculation of required thermodynamic functions. *Equilibrium thermodynamics*, the kind to be discussed here, is not concerned with the effects of time or the difficulties associated with such ill-defined intermediate states. Thermodynamics does assume, as experience readily verifies, that of all possible processes some come to equilibrium in a finite time while others do not.

Many kinds of *process, path,* or *change* are possible. A *reversible process* is a series of equilibrium states. A system is in a state of thermodynamic *equilibrium* if its intensive properties are independent of time and if there are no currents of matter or energy within the system or at its boundaries. Another way of defining a reversible process is to say that the process can be stopped or reversed by infinitesimal changes in the variables that control the state of the system. Squeezing a rubber ball slowly and within its elastic limits is reversible, but squeezing a tube of toothpaste usually is not. In a *cyclic process,* like a game of golf, the initial and final states of the system are the same, at the clubhouse. An *isothermal process* proceeds at constant temperature, as in a thermostat; an *isobaric process* proceeds at constant pressure, as open to the atmosphere in a laboratory in a short time; an *adiabatic process* proceeds without exchange of heat energy between system and surroundings, as in a thermos bottle. Other kinds of process shall be met from time to time.

Energy is commonly defined in mechanics as the ability to do work. In the absence of heat, this definition is adequate, but it will eventually become clear, especially after discussion of heat engines and the second law of thermodynamics, that this definition of energy is not generally adequate. The units of energy are, however, fixed by the laws of classical mechanics. In the cgs system, the unit of energy is the *erg*, the amount of work performed by a force of one dyne acting through a distance of one cm. A *dyne* is that force which imparts, by Newton's second law of mechanics, to a mass of one g an acceleration of one cm sec^{-2}. In the mks system, the unit of energy is the *joule*, the amount of work performed by a force of one newton acting through a distance of one m. A *newton* is that force which imparts to a mass of one kg an acceleration of one m sec^{-2}. The unit of heat energy is the *thermochemical calorie* and is defined as equal to 4.18400 joules. This corresponds closely with the amount of energy required to increase the temperature of one g water by one degree centigrade.

Energy exists in two forms. *Kinetic energy* is energy possessed by a body by virtue of its motion. *Potential energy* is energy possessed by a body by virtue of its position in a field of force. If the field of force be a stretched spring, the potential energy is mechanical; if the attraction of the earth, gravitational; if the attraction of unlike electrical charges, electrical; if the tendency towards minimizing exposed area, surface potential energy; if the attraction of atoms toward a more stable configuration, chemical potential energy.

3.2 Work

Work is defined as the product of the distance by which a body is moved and of the component of force along the direction of movement. It is a scalar quantity with the units of energy. Work done on a system by the surroundings is energy gained by the system by virtue of the movement of its parts by an external force.

The infinitesimal work dw done on a body of mass m as it is lifted vertically against the force of gravity is the product of the infinitesimal vertical distance dz and the force mg that is exerted on the body to lift it.

$$dw = mg \, dz \, . \tag{3.1}$$

As the height z increases, the amount of work increases and is proportional to the mass m and the acceleration of gravity g.

Work done in a gravitational field is performed in one dimension, vertically. Work can be done in increasing the exposed surface of a phase. The force that must be overcome is the force that tends to maximize the contacts among parts of one phase and minimize the contacts among different phases. The proportionality factor between the work dw done on a system and the increase in area $d\mathcal{Q}$ effected by the work is called the *surface tension* or *surface energy* γ.

$$dw = \gamma \, d\mathcal{Q} \, . \tag{3.2}$$

As the area of the system increases by the amount $d\mathcal{Q}$, a positive amount of work dw must be done on the system. In order that (3.2) be dimensionally homogeneous, γ is given the units of force per unit length or energy per unit area.

Work done in three dimensions involves changes in volume. A positive amount of work done on a system will decrease its volume; that is, $+dw$ is the infinitesimal work done on a system as its volume changes by $-dV$.

$$dw = -P \, dV \, . \tag{3.3}$$

The quantity P in (3.3), with the dimensions of force per unit area, is the pressure exerted by the surroundings on the system as the expansion or compression work is performed. In fluid systems, this pressure P is a uniform normal pressure; work done in deforming or compressing solids requires more complicated mathematical treatment that cannot be undertaken here.

The infinitesimal electric work done in generating a charge of dQ at a potential $\mathcal{E}$ or in moving a charge dQ through a potential difference $\mathcal{E}$ is

$$dw = + \, \mathcal{E} \, dQ \, . \tag{3.4}$$

The convention on the signs of $\mathcal{E}$ and Q (Chapter 7) requires the positive sign. If $\mathcal{E}$ is measured in volts and dQ in coulombs, then dw is the number of joules of electric work energy that is done on the system.

Although work can be performed under circumstances other than those described above, the gravitational, surface, volume, and electrical kinds of work described by Equations (3.1) to (3.4) are sufficient for chemical thermodynamics. It is a matter of experience that when only pressure-volume work is performed, the work done on the system by the surroundings is equal in magnitude but opposite in sign to the work done by the system on the surroundings. The laws of hydraulics also assure that in a reversible process the pressure exerted on the system is numerically equal to the pressure exerted by the system. With these things in mind, it is possible to show that work calculated by (3.3) depends upon how the change occurs. That is, the amount of work depends on how the work is done, on the intermediate states, and on the path followed during the process. The initial and final states that exist before and after a process involving work may be the same for several processes, but the amount of work involved in the change is a function of the path followed in the change.

For example, the work done by 1 mole of gas as it changes from a pressure of 10 atm to a pressure of 1 atm at constant temperature depends on how the change in pressure occurs. In fact, the work done on the surroundings by the gas can range from none to a definite maximum value. Suppose that the gas expands isothermally from a pressure of 10 atm to a pressure of 1 atm by expansion into an evacuated chamber of just the right size to give a final pressure of 1 atm, or in a second isothermal process by expansion against the essentially constant atmospheric pressure obtaining in a laboratory, or again in a third isothermal process by forcing a piston slowly outward against a constantly diminishing pressure that differs only infinitesimally from the pressure of the gas itself. This third process is reversible, for the expansion could be stopped or reversed by an infinitesimal change in pressure in the surroundings. Since the force against which the displacement occurs is a maximum (for a greater force would stop or reverse the change), the work done by the system in this third process is a maximum.

For the free expansion into a vacuum, the boundary of the surroundings is not displaced if the boundary of the surroundings is chosen to exclude the evacuated space, as is correct. That is, there is no work done by the surroundings on the system, the gas, for the surroundings were unchanged in the process. Nor is it correct to say that the gas did work on itself. Even if there were residual van der Waals attractive forces tending to hold the gas molecules together, there is no work done by the system on the surroundings. There is, of course, energy required to overcome these attractive intermolecular forces, but this energy must be supplied as heat from the surroundings or from the gas itself. For this free expansion, then

$$w_1 = 0 \, . \tag{3.5}$$

For the expansion at a constant pressure of 1 atm P is constant, and, since the work done by the gas is opposite in sign but equal in absolute magnitude to the work done on the system by the surroundings, the work done by the gas in going from a volume V_1 to a volume V_2 is given by (3.6).

$$-w_2 = \int_{V_1}^{V_2} P\,dV = P(V_2 - V_1)$$

$$= (1\text{ atm}) \left(\frac{RT}{1.0\text{ atm}} - \frac{RT}{10.0\text{ atm}} \right)$$

$$= \frac{9}{10} RT . \tag{3.6}$$

For the reversible expansion against a constantly decreasing pressure, P is given by the equation of state of the gas. If the gas is ideal, $PV = RT$ and the work done by the gas is given by (3.7).

$$-w_3 = \int_{V_1}^{V_2} P\,dV = \int_{V_1}^{V_2} \frac{RT}{V}\,dV$$

$$= RT \ln \left(\frac{V_2}{V_1} \right) = RT \ln \left(\frac{P_1}{P_2} \right)$$

$$= RT \ln 10 . \tag{3.7}$$

An alternate way of calculating (3.7) is to find dV as a function of P thus:

$$V = \frac{RT}{P}, \qquad dV = -RT\frac{dP}{P^2}$$

$$-w_3 = \int_{P_1}^{P_2} P\left(-\frac{RT}{P^2} \right) dP = -RT \ln \left(\frac{P_2}{P_1} \right)$$

$$= RT \ln 10 . \tag{3.7}$$

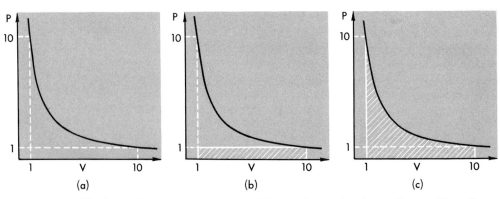

Fig. 3.1. *Work as a Line Integral:* (a) *Free Expansion into a Vacuum* $[P = 0]$; (b) *Expansion at Constant Pressure* $[P = 1]$; (c) *Reversible Isothermal Expansion* $\left[P = \dfrac{k_B}{V} \right]$.

These three different expansion processes between identical pairs of initial and final states illustrate that work is a line integral that depends upon the path of integration. (See Appendix for a discussion of line integrals.) Despite the implications of the notation used, dw is an inexact differential form. That is, there is no function w that depends on the state of the system so that w or the change in w depends merely upon the initial and final states. Rather, w generally depends upon the process and the initial and final states.

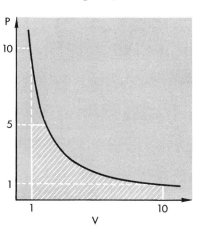

At constant temperature Boyle's law $PV = k_B = RT$ is the equation of state of a fixed amount of a perfect gas. Figure 3.1 shows three hyperbolas of the form $PV = k_B$. The shaded portions are the areas $\int P\, dV$, which by (3.3) are the values of the work done by the system on the surroundings $(-w)$. Although P in (3.3) cannot exceed (k_B/V) for any value of V, it can be less than this value. Figure 3.2 shows a somewhat more complicated expansion, isobaric at $P = 5$ and then reversible. The shaded region is again the work done by the system, somewhat less than the reversible work of

Fig. 3.2. *Isobaric and Reversible Expansion Work at Constant Temperature.*

Figure 3.1(c). In both figures, the expansions occur from the same initial state to the same final state, but the amounts of work differ because the processes differ.

3.3 Functions of State

A thermodynamic system is in a definite and well-defined state if a certain subset of its set of intensive properties is specified. Since these certain intensive properties are the independent variables that determine the state of the system, they become exact differentials in their infinitesimal form. (See Appendix for a discussion of exact and inexact differentials.) Temperature and pressure are two such properties of matter. The change in temperature for a certain change in state is the final value T_2 diminished by the initial value T_1. Thus $\Delta T = T_2 - T_1$. For an infinitesimal change, where ΔT approaches zero as a limit, ΔT becomes dT. Similarly, a finite change in pressure would be $\Delta P = P_2 - P_1$; namely, the final pressure P_2 less the initial pressure P_1. For an infinitesimal process, ΔP becomes dP. In any cyclic process, the values of such independent variables as T or P return to the initial value, and thus the increment of each such variable is zero for the cycle. If the change is accomplished isothermally, the temperature is constant for any small part of the change and $dT = 0$. Similarly, for an isobaric process, $dP = 0$.

Temperature and pressure are functions of state almost by definition because they are ordinarily chosen by the experimenter as the intensive properties that he can control or specify readily. By experience it has been found that the energy of a system is also a function of state. Each well-defined state of matter has its own definite energy. Although this fact concerning energy is part of the first law of thermodynamics, the mathematical implications of this fact are worth discussing in anticipation of the final law. Regardless of how many changes a portion of matter undergoes, when it is returned to its initial state its energy E is found to be the same as it was before the changes. In mathematical language, for any process,

$$\oint dE = 0 . \tag{3.8}$$

As shown in Appendix A, the necessary and sufficient condition that an integral $\int dE$ depend only on the initial and final states is that (3.8) be true, which it is by the first law of thermodynamics. That is, for any process by which state 1 becomes state 2, the change in energy is

$$\Delta E = E_2 - E_1 = \int_{E_1}^{E_2} dE , \tag{3.9}$$

where E_1 is the energy of the initial state and E_2 is the energy of the final state. The unique increase in energy that accompanies any change between the specified terminal states is ΔE. The function E exists and dE is an exact differential. The reference point of zero energy is arbitrary, but this is of little or no importance for it is the increment in energy ΔE that is observable.

An example of energy as a function of state is appropriate here. A person at the Ferry Building in San Francisco can go to the post office in Reno in several ways: by air; by bus on U. S. 40; by car on U. S. 50; by train; by walking. On reaching Reno his potential energy in the gravitational field of the earth is increased for Reno is several thousand feet above sea level. Once arrived, the length or height or difficulty of the passage over the Sierra Nevada is unimportant. The increase in energy is a unique function of initial and final positions. Returning to the initial state at the Ferry Building in San Francisco brings the traveler once again to his initial state and completes a cycle of movement. His energy is what it was at the start, just as though he had not traveled.

3.4 The First Law Stated

When a thermometer, such as a constant-volume hydrogen thermometer, indicates that two separated bodies have the same temperature, it is a matter of experience that no energy is transferred between these two systems if they are placed in thermal contact and if they do not work on each other. On the other hand, if the thermometer had shown a difference in temperature while they were separated, placing the two systems in thermal contact would have allowed a transfer of energy. At the same time, their different initial temperatures would have been observed to approach a single intermediate temperature on achieving equilibrium. As it cools, the hotter body transfers energy to the cooler, which in turn is warmed to a higher temperature. Energy that is transferred from one system to another by virtue of a temperature difference is called *heat*. In terms of the kinetic theory, heat is disorganized molecular and atomic movement, while work is the energy of visibly organized movement that accompanies the forced movement of the boundaries of a system.

The amount of heat transferred is a function of the initial and final temperatures of some standard body, like a certain mass of water, when it absorbs or evolves energy in the form of heat. In particular, 1 calorie of heat is the energy absorbed by 1 gram of water, the standard body, when its temperature increment is 1 centigrade degree. The calorie used in this text has been defined as 4.18400 joules, but in ordinary applications the difference between the two definitions is quite negligible.

The amount of heat absorbed by matter different from that of the standard body, water, is measured by comparing the temperature change observed to the temperature change that the standard body would have suffered on absorbing the same amount of heat. For example, 1 g copper would undergo a temperature change of $10°$ if it absorbed the same amount of heat as 1 g water that suffered a temperature change of $1°$. For a given temperature change, say, $1°$, copper need absorb only one-tenth as much heat as the same amount of water. The extensive factor by which the temperature increment is multiplied to express the heat involved in a certain process is called the *specific heat* or *heat capacity*. Copper has a specific heat of 0.1 cal g^{-1} deg^{-1}. That is, the heat required to increase the temperature of 1 g copper by $1°C$ is one-tenth as much as would have been required to increase the temperature of 1 g water by $1°$. In general, if the temperature is increased from T_1 to T_2, the heat absorbed by n moles of a substance with a molar heat capacity of C is given by (3.10).

$$q = n \int_{T_1}^{T_2} C \, dT \, . \tag{3.10}$$

If the molar heat capacity is independent of temperature, (3.10) becomes (3.11).

$$q = nC \int_{T_1}^{T_2} dT$$
$$= nC \, \Delta T \, . \tag{3.11}$$

While (3.10) and (3.11) are suitable for calculation of heat, the fundamental measurement is a measurement of a temperature increment, either in the standard body or some other body. The temperature of a body is measured by means of an infinitesimal test body that has some obvious property that can be related to the more subtle property called *temperature*. The obvious property may be the volume of a gas at a low constant pressure, or it may be the volume of mercury in a rigid container or the voltage developed by a thermocouple. In any case, the temperature must be a single-valued, continuous, monotonic function of the property to be measured. The volume of 1 g water would not be suitable near 4°C.

The first law of thermodynamics is the law of conservation of energy for the science of thermodynamics. The increase in energy ΔE of a system is equal to the heat q absorbed by the system plus the work w done on the system. In mathematical terms, the first law is given by (3.12).

$$\Delta E = E_2 - E_1 = q + w. \tag{3.12}$$

In its infinitesimal form, provided dq and dw are understood to be inexact differentials, (3.12) reads

$$dE = dq + dw. \tag{3.13}$$

The first part of (3.12), $\Delta E = E_2 - E_1$, implies that E is a function of state, which it is. However, since the work done on a system by the surroundings depends upon the path, heat absorbed by the system from the surroundings also depends upon the path. Like w, q is not a function of state. That is, (3.10) and (3.11) are in general line integrals of inexact differentials, and as such depend upon initial and final states and the process connecting them.

Equation (3.12) can be considered as an alternate definition of heat. If so, heat becomes the energy that is not accounted for in terms of work or the initial and final energy states of the system. Quite often it is easy to evaluate ΔE and w, but quite difficult to calculate the heat absorbed in some process. The first law provides the means of calculating q. That these two definitions of heat are really alike and that the first law is true have been verified experimentally many times. The difference $\Delta E - w$ is always found to be the energy transferred by virtue of a temperature difference. Many texts and thermodynamic treatises state the first law as $\Delta E = q - w$ or $dE = dq - dw$. In these books, w refers to work done *by* the system.

3.5 Processes at Constant Volume

Expansion work due to changes in volume is perhaps the most common form of work in chemical processes. It would be a rare chemical or physical change in which the volume of the final state was identical with the volume of the initial state. Experimentally to achieve a constant volume is perhaps impossible, for even the strongest vessel suffers a slight displacement due to pressure changes within or without. However, for some process in which all work done on the system is pressure-volume work [Equation (3.3)], the first law of thermodynamics [Equations (3.12) and (3.13)] becomes more definite and is given by (3.14) and (3.15).

$$\Delta E = q - \int_{V_1}^{V_2} P \, dV \tag{3.14}$$

$$dE = dq - P \, dV \, . \tag{3.15}$$

In (3.14) and (3.15), P is the uniform normal pressure of the surroundings, and V_1 and V_2 are the initial and final volumes of the system. If the volume V is held constant during the process, dV is everywhere zero, and the increase in energy of the system equals q_V or dq_V, the heat absorbed by the system at constant volume. That is, by (3.14) and (3.15), at constant volume,

$$\Delta E = q_V \tag{3.16}$$

$$dE = dq_V \, . \tag{3.17}$$

Since E is a function of state, q_V is also a function of state. For any process, be it chemical or physical, that involves only pressure-volume work and that is performed at constant volume, ΔE or q_V is the unique increase in energy that accompanies the change.

3.6 Adiabatic Processes

The first law of thermodynamics has been stated as the law of conservation of energy for thermodynamics. Another statement is given by Guggenheim[1] in terms of any process that involves no heat: "The work required to bring a *thermally insulated* system from one completely specified state to a second completely specified state is independent of the source of the work and of the path through which the system passes from the initial to the final state." The process undergone by the thermally insulated system is an adiabatic process; it involves no heat. For an adiabatic process, $q = 0$, and (3.12) becomes (3.18).

$$\Delta E = w \, . \tag{3.18}$$

Similarly, Equation (3.13) becomes (3.19) for an infinitesimal process since $dq = 0$.

$$dE = dw \, . \tag{3.19}$$

Any change that does not involve heat, such as most problems in classical mechanics, is an illustration of an adiabatic process and Equations (3.18) and (3.19). Indeed, these equations are the basis of the definition that energy is the ability to do work.

127

B. SIMPLE APPLICATIONS

3.7 Processes at Constant Pressure

It is very easy to perform experiments at constant pressure. Ordinary apparatus like beakers, furnaces, and burettes is open to the atmosphere of the laboratory. Provided the experiment is completed before the diurnal variation in barometric pressure becomes important, such an experiment can be said to occur in a huge barostat, the atmosphere of the laboratory and earth. It is fitting, therefore, that some thermodynamic function be defined to acknowledge the value of this barostat and its influence on common processes. If only pressure-volume work is involved, the first law [Equation (3.14)] for an isobaric process is restated in (3.20), for P is constant.

$$q_P = \Delta E + \int_{V_1}^{V_2} P \, dV$$

$$= \Delta E + P \, \Delta V \, . \tag{3.20}$$

The subscript on q indicates that q_P is the heat absorbed by the system for a process that occurs at constant pressure.

By definition, the enthalpy H of a system is given by (3.21).

$$H = E + PV \, . \tag{3.21}$$

Since E, P, and V are functions of state, H is also a function of state. That is, changes in enthalpy are independent of the path or process, and dH is an exact differential. Equation (3.20) can be restated thus, since $P = P_1 = P_2$:

$$q_P = \Delta E + P \, \Delta V \tag{3.20}$$

$$= E_2 - E_1 + P(V_2 - V_1)$$

$$= E_2 + P_2 V_2 - E_1 - P_1 V_1 \, .$$

But by (3.21), $$q_P = H_2 - H_1 \, .$$

That is, $$q_P = \Delta H \, . \tag{3.22}$$

Enthalpy is a convenient thermodynamic function for describing thermal effects that accompany isobaric changes, for the increase in enthalpy ΔH is equal to the heat absorbed by the system at constant pressure for changes that involve only expansion work.

For a change that involves a pressure change from P_1 to P_2, a volume change from V_1 to V_2, and an energy change from E_1 to E_2, the increase in enthalpy is given by (3.23).

$$\Delta H = H_2 - H_1 = E_2 + P_2 V_2 - (E_1 + P_1 V_1)$$

$$= E_2 - E_1 + P_2 V_2 - P_1 V_1$$

$$= \Delta E + \Delta(PV) \, . \tag{3.23}$$

Equation (3.23) is perfectly general. For many chemical changes, the magnitude of the $\Delta(PV)$ term is small compared with the ΔH and ΔE terms. Situations in which this is true are illustrated in Example 3.3 and in Section 3.15.

If a particular isobaric change involves work other than pressure-volume work, then recourse to the first law (3.12) and the expression for a change in enthalpy (3.23) leads to (3.24), which relates all the work other than pressure-volume work $w_{\mathrm{non}PV}$ to the enthalpy change ΔH and the heat absorbed by the system q_P.

$$\Delta H = \Delta E + \Delta(PV) \tag{3.23}$$

$$= q_P + w_{PV} + w_{\mathrm{non}PV} + P\,\Delta V \qquad [\text{by } (3.12)]$$

$$= q_P + w_{\mathrm{non}PV}, \tag{3.24}$$

since, by (3.3), $w_{PV} = -\displaystyle\int_{V_1}^{V_2} P\,dV = -P\,\Delta V$. Equation (3.24), which is more general than (3.22), states merely that the increase in enthalpy of a system is equal to the heat absorbed at constant pressure plus all the isobaric work done on the system provided such work is not pressure-volume work.

The determination of the mechanical equivalent of thermal energy is an example of the use of (3.24) when $q_P = 0$. The orderly movement of a paddle-wheel that stirs a thermally insulated fluid into disorganized eddies and vortices increases the enthalpy of the system, the fluid. The amount of energy that enters the system as work is measured by the rise in temperature that results in the fluid. Similarly, the organized movement of electrons that flow in a conductor becomes the disorganized movement of the atoms of the conductor as electric work is transformed into energy that can be measured by a rise in temperature of a fluid in contact with the conductor but thermally insulated from the surroundings.

Example 3.1. Calculate the increase in enthalpy of one mole H_2O when it is changed from ice at 0°C at 0.0060 atm to water vapor at 0°C at 0.0060 atm. The thermal energy necessary to transform one g liquid H_2O to gaseous H_2O at 0°C at 0.0060 atm is 596 cal. The thermal energy to melt one g ice at 0°C at 0.0060 atm is 80 cal.

The problem can be clarified by a diagram.

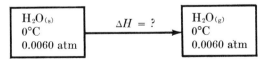

The system is one mole H_2O. The subscripts (s), (l), or (g) indicate the state of aggregation, solid, liquid, or gas. The information that is given can be summarized in a similar way.

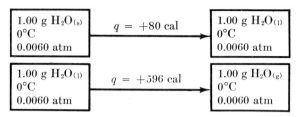

All the processes diagrammed are isothermal ($dT = 0$) and isobaric ($dP = 0$). Since the pressure is constant at 0.0060 atm and since all work is pressure-volume work, the thermal energies are q_P. By Equation (3.22), $q_P = \Delta H$. For 1 mole, the heat of fusion ΔH_f is 18.0×80 cal and the heat of vaporization ΔH_v is 18.0×596 cal. Since H is a function of state, the diagrams can be combined, for the enthalpy of a mole of water does not depend on its previous history as ice, its future state as vapor, or the process by which it was brought to or will leave its liquid state at 0°C at 0.0060 atm.

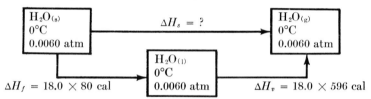

The heat of sublimation ΔH_s is clearly the sum of the enthalpy changes with water as intermediate species. That is, $\Delta H_s = 18.0 \times 80 + 18.0 \times 596$ cal $= 12{,}170$ cal. That this follows from the fact that H is a function of state can be shown mathematically by assigning an absolute molar enthalpy $H_{(s)}$ to ice, $H_{(1)}$ to water, and $H_{(g)}$ to steam. Then,

$$\Delta H_f = H_{(1)} - H_{(s)}, \qquad \Delta H_v = H_{(g)} - H_{(1)}$$
$$\Delta H_s = H_{(g)} - H_{(s)} = H_{(g)} - H_{(1)} + (H_{(1)} - H_{(s)}) = \Delta H_v + \Delta H_f .$$

It is not important how the process by which ice became steam occurred. It might have been irreversible with water existing temporarily at 3°C, but for the change under study, $\Delta H = 12{,}170$ cal. Since ΔH is greater than zero, the enthalpy of steam is greater than that of ice when both steam and ice are at 0°C at 0.0060 atm.

Example 3.2. Calculate the increase in energy ΔE for the condensation of one mole steam at 0°C at 0.0060 atm to water at 0°C at 0.0060 atm. The heat of vaporization of H_2O is 10,730 cal mole⁻¹ at 0°C at 0.0060 atm.

Since vaporization requires that thermal energy be absorbed by the water, condensation must require that water evolve the same amount of energy. For the process $H_2O_{(g)} \rightarrow H_2O_{(1)}$, $\Delta H = q_P = -10{,}730$ cal. The work done on the steam as it condenses at 0°C at 0.0060 atm is given by (3.3).

$$w = -\int_{V_{(g)}}^{V_{(1)}} P \, dV$$
$$= -P(V_{(1)} - V_{(g)})$$
$$= -(0.0060 \text{ atm}) \left[0.018 \text{ l} - \left(22.4 \times \frac{1}{0.0060} \right) \text{l} \right]$$
$$= (22.4 - 0.0060 \times 0.018) \text{ l-atm} = 22.4 \text{ l-atm}$$
$$= 22.4 \times \left(\frac{1.987}{0.08205} \right) \text{cal} = 543 \text{ cal} .$$

By the first law [Equation (3.12)],

$$\Delta E = q + w = -10{,}730 + 543 \text{ cal} = -10{,}187 \text{ cal} .$$

The energy of the liquid is less than that of the vapor since ΔE is less than zero. The same result might have been obtained by (3.23), where the $\Delta(PV)$ term is -543 cal and is dominated by the PV product of the gas phase.

3.8 Heat Capacity

For processes that do not occur at constant temperature it is necessary to account for energy involved in changing the temperature. Indeed, it was the temperature change suffered by a standard body of standard heat capacity that was chosen as the measure of thermal energy transferred. According to (3.10) and (3.11), the heat capacity C is a constant of proportionality with the value

$$C = \frac{dq}{dT} . \tag{3.25}$$

It is customary to let C refer to 1 mole of matter that absorbs the heat.

The thermodynamic definition of C_V, the heat capacity for constant-volume processes, is

$$C_V = \left(\frac{\partial E}{\partial T}\right)_V . \tag{3.26}$$

That this definition is reasonable in view of (3.25) is shown by substitution of (3.25) into the first law (3.15) where all work is expansion work.

$$dE = dq - P \, dV \tag{3.15}$$
$$= C \, dT - P \, dV .$$

If the volume is constant, $dV = 0$ and (3.26) is justified.

Similarly, for processes at constant pressure, the heat capacity C_P is defined as

$$C_P = \left(\frac{\partial H}{\partial T}\right)_P . \tag{3.27}$$

This is reasonable, for by (3.21) $dH = d(E + PV) = dE + P \, dV + V \, dP$. Whence, by (3.15) and (3.25), when only expansion work is involved,

$$dH = dq - P \, dV + P \, dV + V \, dP = dq + V \, dP = C \, dT + V \, dP.$$

If the pressure is constant, $dP = 0$ and (3.27) results, where the subscript P indicates that the pressure is constant.

For finite temperature changes, (3.26) and (3.27) must be integrated.

131

The results are given in (3.28) and (3.29).

$$dE = C_V \, dT, \qquad (dV = 0)$$

$$\int_{E_1}^{E_2} dE = \int_{T_1}^{T_2} C_V \, dT$$

$$\Delta E = \int_{T_1}^{T_2} C_V \, dT, \qquad (dV = 0) \tag{3.28}$$

$$dH = C_P \, dT, \qquad (dP = 0)$$

$$\int_{H_1}^{H_2} dH = \int_{T_1}^{T_2} C_P \, dT$$

$$\Delta H = \int_{T_1}^{T_2} C_P \, dT, \qquad (dP = 0) . \tag{3.29}$$

Example 3.3. Calculate the increases in energy and enthalpy of 1 mole water if its temperature increases from 10°C to 70°C. At constant pressure of 1 atm,

$$\Delta H = \int_{283.16}^{343.16} C_P \, dT = C_P \, \Delta T$$

$$= (18.0 \text{ cal mole}^{-1} \text{ deg}^{-1}) \times (343.16° - 283.16°)$$

$$= 1080 \text{ cal mole}^{-1} .$$

By (3.23),

$$\Delta E = \Delta H - \Delta(PV) = \Delta H - P \, \Delta V$$

$$= 1080 \text{ cal} - \left(\frac{1.987 \text{ cal}}{82.05 \text{ ml atm}} \right) (1.00 \text{ atm}) \left(\frac{18.0 \text{ g}}{0.9778 \text{ g ml}^{-1}} - \frac{18.0 \text{ g}}{0.9997 \text{ g ml}^{-1}} \right)$$

$$= (1080 - 0.00976) \text{ cal} = 1080 \text{ cal} .$$

Here ΔH exceeds ΔE by the small amount of work done by the water if it had expanded isobarically against the atmosphere instead of remaining confined in a closed rigid vessel. For condensed phases, as this problem shows, C_P and C_V are almost identical numerically, as are ΔH and ΔE.

Example 3.4. In determining the thermal equivalent of electric energy, an electric current of 1.00 amp flowed through a conductor with a resistance of 2.00 ohms. The conductor had a specific heat of 0.10 cal g^{-1} deg^{-1} and it weighed one g. The conductor was immersed in 100.0 g pure water, which were in turn held in a vessel with a heat capacity of 5.0 cal deg^{-1}. The vessel and its contents were thermally insulated from the surroundings. The rise in temperature of the system (conductor, water, and vessel) was 2.73°C after the current had flowed 10.0 min. What is the conversion factor between electric work in joules and thermal energy in calories?

By (3.4) and Ohm's law ($\mathcal{E} = \mathcal{I}\mathcal{R}$), the electric work done on the system was

$$w = \int \mathcal{E} \, dQ = \int_0^t \mathcal{E}\mathcal{I} \, dt' = \mathcal{E}\mathcal{I}t = \mathcal{I}^2 \mathcal{R} t$$

$$= (1.00 \text{ amp})^2 \times (2.00 \text{ ohms}) \times (600 \text{ sec}) = 1200 \text{ j} .$$

Since the system was thermally insulated, $q_P = 0$. The increase in enthalpy of the system for this isobaric process is given by (3.29).

$$\Delta H = \int_{T_1}^{T_2} C_P \, dT = C_P \, \Delta T$$

$$= [(0.1 + 100.0 + 5.0) \text{ cal deg}^{-1}] \times [2.73°] = 287 \text{ cal}.$$

By Equation (3.24),

$$\Delta H = q_P + w_{elec}, \qquad 287 \text{ cal} = 0 + 1200 \text{ j}.$$

That is, one calorie is equivalent to 4.18 joules.

3.9 Thermodynamic Properties of a Perfect Gas

When the equation of state of a perfect gas $PV = nRT$ was described in Chapter 1, the temperature scale T was defined in terms of the behavior of a perfect gas. The constant-volume hydrogen gas thermometer is in fact the primary standard of the absolute temperature scale. The second law of thermodynamics will introduce a thermodynamic temperature scale that can be shown to be identical with the perfect gas scale of temperature. The definition of a perfect gas is most aptly put in terms that are consistent with but different from conformity with the perfect gas equation.

A perfect gas must obey Boyle's law and its energy must be independent of its volume at constant temperature. In mathematical terms, a gas is perfect if it conforms to (3.30).

$$\left.\begin{aligned} PV &= f(n,\ T) \\ \left(\frac{\partial E}{\partial V}\right)_T &= 0 \, . \end{aligned}\right\} \tag{3.30}$$

For a specified amount of gas at a specified temperature, $f(n,\ T)$ is a constant. The second criterion was determined experimentally by Gay-Lussac in 1807 and by Joule in 1844. Their system was a compressed gas held in part of a rigid container. When the gas was allowed to expand freely into the unoccupied part of the rigid container, the temperature of the expanding gas decreased and the temperature of the gas streaming into the previously evacuated part of the container increased. When a final uniform temperature of the gas was achieved, it was clear that there was no net transfer of heat between gas and surroundings. The final temperature was the same as the initial temperature; no heat or work was exchanged between system and surroundings. By the first law, since $q = 0$ and $w = 0$,

$$\Delta E = q + w = 0 \, .$$

The experiment showed that the energy of a gas was independent of its volume at constant temperature, and the second criterion is a mathematical statement of this observation.

133

The surroundings used in the early experiments were a water bath that, because of its high heat capacity, could not record by its temperature changes the exchange of slight amounts of thermal energy. Isolation by means of a vacuum and use of thin metal containers does much to refine this type of experiment. Since the Joule-Thomson experiment is quite suitable for noting deviations from ideal behavior in this regard, the matter of experimental elegance is here of small concern. All real gases generally fail to fulfill either or both criteria of (3.30), but often the degree of failure is of little importance.

The energy of a system can be considered to be a function of its composition, volume, and temperature. That is, for a closed system of fixed composition,

$$E = E(V, T) .$$ (3.31)

By the rules of calculus, the differential of E from (3.31) is

$$dE = \left(\frac{\partial E}{\partial T}\right)_V dT + \left(\frac{\partial E}{\partial V}\right)_T dV .$$ (3.32)

But for a perfect gas, the coefficient of dV is zero by (3.30) and the coefficient of dT is C_V, or nC_V if there be n moles in the system. Then (3.32) becomes (3.33).

$$dE = C_V \, dT .$$ (3.33)

By virtue of Equations (3.30) to (3.33), the energy of a fixed amount of a perfect gas is a function only of its temperature. This result was obtained in Chapter 1 by the kinetic theory. Moreover, in any isothermal change, there is no change in the energy of a perfect gas. That is, if $dT = 0$ in (3.33),

$$\left.\begin{aligned} dE &= 0 \\ \Delta E &= 0 \\ E &= E(T) . \end{aligned}\right\}$$ (3.34)

The enthalpy of a perfect gas is also dependent only on its temperature. By (3.30) and (3.34) and the definition of H,

$$H = E + PV = E(T) + f(n, T) = H(T) .$$

Any isothermal change of a perfect gas involves no change in enthalpy if the system is closed. Moreover, the enthalpy of a perfect gas at constant temperature is independent of its pressure. That is, at constant temperature,

$$\left.\begin{aligned} dH &= 0 \\ \Delta H &= 0 \\ H &= H(T) . \end{aligned}\right\}$$ (3.35)

$$\left(\frac{\partial H}{\partial P}\right)_T = 0 .$$ (3.36)

Equations (3.35) and (3.36) are the natural results of and the counterparts of Equations (3.34) and (3.30). Just as E is customarily and conveniently taken as a function of volume and temperature, H is taken as a function of pressure and temperature.

$$H = H(P, T) . \tag{3.37}$$

By the rules of calculus,

$$dH = \left(\frac{\partial H}{\partial T}\right)_P dT + \left(\frac{\partial H}{\partial P}\right)_T dP . \tag{3.38}$$

For any kind of process of a perfect gas, the coefficient of dP in (3.38) is zero and the coefficient of dT is C_P; so that

$$dH = C_P \, dT . \tag{3.39}$$

Equations (3.33) and (3.39) not only are useful for perfect gases but also generally dominate other terms in circumstances where behavior of gases is not quite perfect.

3.10 Heat Capacities of Gases

The heat capacity of a gas at constant pressure exceeds the heat capacity of that gas at constant volume because the gas performs work on its surroundings as it expands at constant pressure. If its volume is held constant, such expansion work by the gas as it is heated is impossible. The difference between C_P and C_V for a perfect gas is easily evaluated from (3.34) and (3.35). By the several definitions of C_P, C_V, and H,

$$
\begin{aligned}
C_P - C_V &= \left(\frac{\partial H}{\partial T}\right)_P - \left(\frac{\partial E}{\partial T}\right)_V \\
&= \left[\frac{\partial}{\partial T}(E + PV)\right]_P - \left(\frac{\partial E}{\partial T}\right)_V \\
&= \frac{dE}{dT} + \left[\frac{\partial}{\partial T}(RT)\right]_P - \frac{dE}{dT},
\end{aligned}
$$

where total derivatives replace partial derivatives since E is a function only of T by (3.34). Accordingly,

$$C_P - C_V = R . \tag{3.40}$$

For any gas, perfect or not, the difference between C_P and C_V is somewhat more complicated. By (3.32), which is true for any substance,

$$dE = \left(\frac{\partial E}{\partial T}\right)_V dT + \left(\frac{\partial E}{\partial V}\right)_T dV . \tag{3.32}$$

135

Division by dT at constant pressure gives

$$\left(\frac{\partial E}{\partial T}\right)_P = \left(\frac{\partial E}{\partial T}\right)_V + \left(\frac{\partial E}{\partial V}\right)_T \left(\frac{\partial V}{\partial T}\right)_P .$$

By definition,

$$C_P - C_V = \left(\frac{\partial H}{\partial T}\right)_P - \left(\frac{\partial E}{\partial T}\right)_V = \left(\frac{\partial E}{\partial T}\right)_P + \left(\frac{\partial (PV)}{\partial T}\right)_P - \left(\frac{\partial E}{\partial T}\right)_V .$$

The first term of the right-hand member is given above; thus

$$C_P - C_V = \left(\frac{\partial E}{\partial V}\right)_T \left(\frac{\partial V}{\partial T}\right)_P + \left(\frac{\partial (PV)}{\partial T}\right)_P = \left[\left(\frac{\partial E}{\partial V}\right)_T + P\right]\left(\frac{\partial V}{\partial T}\right)_P . \quad (3.41)$$

When the value of $(\partial E/\partial V)_T$ is known, (3.41) provides a convenient way to find C_V from C_P and the equation of state, $V = V(P, T)$

Example 3.5. Show that Equation (3.40) is a special case of (3.41).
The equation of state of 1 mole of a perfect gas is $PV = RT$. Substitution in (3.41) and account of (3.30) yield the desired result.

$$C_P - C_V = \left[\left(\frac{\partial E}{\partial V}\right)_T + P\right]\left(\frac{\partial V}{\partial T}\right)_P \qquad (3.41)$$

$$= \left[0 + P\right]\left[\frac{\partial}{\partial T}\left(\frac{RT}{P}\right)\right]_P$$

$$= R . \qquad (3.40)$$

The kinetic theory equation from Chapter 1 explicitly evaluates the energy of a perfect gas as a function of temperature. For 1 mole monatomic gas,

$$E = \frac{3}{2}RT .$$

By Equations (3.26) and (3.40), the molar heat capacities of a perfect monatomic gas are

$$\left. \begin{array}{l} C_V = \left(\frac{\partial E}{\partial T}\right)_V = \frac{3}{2}R \\[2mm] C_P = C_V + R = \frac{5}{2}R . \end{array} \right\} \qquad (3.42)$$

The heat capacities of real gases are in general functions of the absolute temperature, for as the temperature rises the various degrees of freedom within the molecule —— rotations, bendings, vibrations, and electronic changes —— are excited. This excitation requires energy that is added as heat and that therefore appears in the heat capacity. Heat capacities can be calculated by the methods of statistical mechanics, and at high temperatures such calculated heat capacities are often more accurate than observed values. It has long been customary to express the molar heat capacity of a gas empirically as a power series in the temperature, as in (3.43).

$$C_P = C_P^{(0)} + C_P^{(1)} T + C_P^{(2)} T^2 + \cdots . \quad (3.43)$$

The value of C_V can be found from C_P at any temperature by (3.40) or (3.41). Table 3.1 contains the empirically evaluated constants $C_P^{(i)}$ for some common gases.

Table 3.1. *Molar Heat Capacities of Gases at Constant Pressure For Temperatures of* $300°K$ *to* $1500°K$*

$$C_P = C_P^{(0)} + C_P^{(1)} T + C_P^{(2)} T^2 \ (cal \ mole^{-1} \ deg^{-1})$$

GAS	$C_P{}^{(0)}$	$C_P{}^{(1)} \times 10^3$	$C_P{}^{(2)} \times 10^6$
H_2	6.9469	−0.1999	0.4808
O_2	6.0954	3.2533	−1.0171
Cl_2	7.5755	2.4244	−0.9650
Br_2	8.4228	0.9739	−0.3555
N_2	6.4492	1.4125	−0.0807
CO	6.3424	1.8363	−0.2801
HCl	6.7319	0.4325	0.3697
HBr	6.5776	0.9549	0.1581
H_2O	7.1873	2.3733	0.2084
CO_2	6.3957	10.1933	−3.5333
NH_3	6.189	7.887	−0.728
CH_4	3.422	17.845	−4.165
C_3H_8	0.410	64.710	−22.582

Example 3.6. Calculate the heat required to increase the temperature of 1.00 mole gaseous oxygen from 0.0°C to 100.0°C, (a) at constant pressure, and (b) at constant volume. Account for the difference in the heat absorbed in (a) and (b). The heat capacity of O_2 is given in Table 3.1 and O_2 may be assumed to be a perfect gas.

A diagram of the processes follows, where P_i and V_i signify the pressure and volume of the oxygen at state i.

(a) When only pressure-volume work is involved in an isobaric process, Equation (3.22) or (3.24) and Equation (3.29) or (3.39) are applicable.

$$q_P = \Delta H = \int_{T_1}^{T_2} C_P \, dT$$

$$= \int_{T_1}^{T_2} [C_P^{(0)} + C_P^{(1)} T + C_P^{(2)} T^2] \, dT$$

$$= C_P^{(0)} \int_{T_1}^{T_2} dT + C_P^{(1)} \int_{T_1}^{T_2} T \, dT + C_P^{(2)} \int_{T_1}^{T_2} T^2 \, dT$$

$$= C_P^{(0)}(T_2 - T_1) + C_P^{(1)} \left(\frac{T_2^2 - T_1^2}{2} \right) + C_P^{(2)} \left(\frac{T_2^3 - T_1^3}{3} \right)$$

$$= 609.54 + 3.2533 \times 10^{-3} \left(\frac{373.2^2 - 273.2^2}{2} \right) + 1.0171 \times 10^{-6} \left(\frac{373.2^3 - 273.2^3}{3} \right)$$

$$= 609.5 + 105.2 + 10.7 = 725.4 \ cal .$$

* Spencer, H. M. and J. L. Justice, *J. Am. Chem. Soc.*, **56**, 2311 (1934); Spencer, H. M. and G. N. Flannagan, *J. Am. Chem. Soc.*, **64**, 2511 (1942).

(b) Similarly, by Equations (3.16), (3.33), and (3.40),

$$q_V = \Delta E = \int_{T_1}^{T_2} C_V \, dT = \int_{T_1}^{T_2} (C_P - R) \, dT = \Delta H - R(T_2 - T_1)$$

$$= 725.4 - 1.987 \times 100.0 = 526.7 \text{ cal}.$$

More heat is absorbed in the isobaric process than in the process at constant volume because the gas does work as it expands at constant pressure, and this work energy is supplied as heat. The work done by the gas on the surroundings in the process labeled (a) is done at constant pressure P_1, and is calculated thus:

$$-w_P = \int_{V_1}^{V_2} P \, dV = \int_{V_1}^{V_2} P_1 \, dV = P_1(V_2 - V_1)$$

$$= P_1 \left(\frac{RT_2}{P_1} - \frac{RT_1}{P_1} \right) = R(T_2 - T_1) = 1.987 \times 100.0 = 198.7 \text{ cal}.$$

For process (a), then,

$$\Delta E = q + w = q_P + w_P = 725.4 - 198.7 = 526.7 \text{ cal}.$$

Since O_2 is here assumed to be a perfect gas, H and E are functions only of temperature. Since process (c) is isothermal, for it $\Delta H = \Delta E = 0$. For processes (b) and (c), then,

$$\Delta E = \Delta E_{(b)} + \Delta E_{(c)} = 526.7 + 0 = 526.7 \text{ cal}.$$

The same change in energy results for either path that ends at T_2, P_1, and V_2 because the initial and final states are alike and E is a function of state.

It is not possible to calculate the work involved in the process labeled (c), for the process is not specified. The work done by the gas if it had expanded isothermally and reversibly from V_1 to V_2 could be calculated thus:

$$-w = \int_{V_1}^{V_2} P \, dV = RT_2 \int_{V_1}^{V_2} \frac{dV}{V} = RT_2 \ln \left(\frac{V_2}{V_1} \right).$$

But $P_1V_1 = RT_1$ and $P_1V_2 = RT_2$; hence,

$$-w = RT_2 \ln \left(\frac{T_2}{T_1} \right) > 0.$$

Since $\Delta E = 0$ for process (c), heat would have to be absorbed by the gas since

$$q = \Delta E - w = 0 + RT_2 \ln \left(\frac{T_2}{T_1} \right) > 0.$$

If, however, process (c) had been performed irreversibly, less work would have been done by the gas. For example, isothermal expansion into a vacuum could have led to no work, and thus to an adiabatic process since ΔE for process (c) is zero. Since many other processes could be imagined, in the absence of an explicit definition of the process, it is impossible to evaluate the work done by the gas in process (c).

3.11 Reversible Isothermal Work

Although the amount of work involved in a process depends both upon initial and final states and upon the path followed by the process, the qualifications that the work be done reversibly and isothermally so restrict the process as to make such work unique. If the process is reversible, an infinitesimal change in the pressure that causes the process could stop or reverse the process. For a reversible expansion, an infinitesimal increase in the pressure in the surroundings would halt the expansion by which the system works. It is clear, then, that the driving and opposing forces in such a process are everywhere a maximum. Any such work done by the system must also be a maximum. If the pressures on each side of the boundary of the system differ at most by an infinitesimal, they are in the limit equal. It is for this reason that the pressure calculated from the equation of state of the system can be used in place of the pressure exerted by the surroundings.

The specification *isothermal* is not readily explained before development of the second law of thermodynamics. Briefly, such a specification must be made in order to prevent transfer of energy by virtue of a difference in temperature; that is, heat must be avoided. The second law will also clarify the fact that isothermal reversible work is a function of state.

The work done reversibly and isothermally on a system by the surroundings is given by Equation (3.3), which can be stated in the integrated form (3.44).

$$w = -\int_{V_1}^{V_2} P\, dV \, . \tag{3.44}$$

Here V_1 is the initial volume of the system, V_2 is the final volume of the system, and P is the pressure of the system or surroundings as the process occurs. The volume changes of the system are assumed to be equal in magnitude but opposite in sign to the changes in volume of the surroundings. The maximum work done by the system is equal in magnitude but opposite in sign to the work done on the system. That is, the work done by the system is $-w$, where, as above,

$$-w = \int_{V_1}^{V_2} P\, dV \, . \tag{3.44}$$

There are two common ways in which isothermal reversible work can be done. The pressure may vary as the change in volume occurs, or the pressure may remain constant as the volume changes. This latter situation arises in phase changes, as in equilibrium between vapor and a condensed phase at a fixed temperature. The constant pressure is the vapor pressure at the fixed temperature. In (3.44), since the value of P is constant, the integral becomes (3.45).

$$w = -P \int_{V_1}^{V_2} dV = -P\, \Delta V \, . \tag{3.45}$$

It is obvious here that w is a function of state, for P, V_1, and V_2 are themselves functions of state.

A process described by (3.45) might be a condensation. If water vapor at 100°C contains an infinitesimal drop of liquid water, the conditions for equilibrium between liquid and vapor are satisfied. When the pressure exerted on the vapor by the surroundings through a piston is infinitesimally greater than 1 atm, the piston will move inward upon the water vapor and cause it to condense to liquid water at 100°C. The condensation could be stopped or reversed by an infinitesimal decrease in the pressure of the surroundings or an infinitesimal increase in the pressure of the water vapor. This increase in pressure could perhaps be caused by an infinitesimal increase in the temperature of the water. The process is reversible because its direction can be altered by infinitesimal changes in the temperature or pressure. While the weight of the piston, its friction with the cylinder walls, or condensation in a time less than eternity would make the real process irreversible, the essence of the process is not changed when the magnitude of each of these experimental difficulties is imagined to be less and less important. Lighter and lighter alloys could be used in the piston, better and better lubricants and machining could reduce friction, and time is of no concern to equilibrium thermodynamics.

Example 3.7. Calculate the work done on one mole of steam as it is condensed reversibly at 120.0°C.

At 120.0°C, the vapor pressure of water is 1489 mm Hg and the molar volumes of vapor and liquid are 16.07 l and 0.019 l. By (3.45), the work done on the steam is

$$w = -P \, \Delta V = -\left(\frac{1489}{760.0}\right)(0.02 - 16.07) \times \left(\frac{1.987}{0.08206}\right) = 761 \text{ cal}.$$

If 1 mole liquid water is vaporized reversibly at 120.0°C, it would do +761 cal of work on the atmosphere, for reversing the process and worker causes two changes in sign.

If two phases do not coexist at a fixed temperature, the pressure of the system will depend upon its volume. When the system consists of a perfect gas at a constant temperature T, (3.44) is readily evaluated in explicit form for the work done on the system.

$$w = -\int_{V_1}^{V_2} P \, dV = -\int_{V_1}^{V_2} \left(\frac{nRT}{V}\right) dV = -nRT \int_{V_1}^{V_2} \frac{dV}{V}$$

$$= nRT \ln\left(\frac{V_1}{V_2}\right). \tag{3.46a}$$

Since the conditions for Boyle's law obtain, $P_1V_1 = P_2V_2$, and (3.46a) becomes (3.46b).

$$w = nRT \ln\left(\frac{P_2}{P_1}\right). \tag{3.46b}$$

Equations (3.46a) and (3.46b) say that a positive amount of work w must be done on a system if its volume is decreased from V_1 to V_2 or if its pressure is increased from P_1 to P_2. Equation (3.7) and Example 3.6 have anticipated (3.46a) and (3.46b).

Example 3.8. Calculate the minimum work that must be done at 25°C on 2 moles CO_2 to compress them from a volume of 20.0 l to a volume of 1.00 l, when CO_2 is assumed (a) to be a perfect gas; and (b) to follow van der Waals' equation.

If the pressure exerted by the surroundings should momentarily exceed the pressure of the CO_2, the work done by the surroundings would not be a minimum. The excess over the minimum would appear as a shock wave or as kinetic energy of CO_2 molecules and, of course, ultimately as thermal energy. Thus the minimum work, with no wasted energy, is the reversible work at 25°C. (a) By (3.44) or (3.46),

$$w = -\int_{V_1}^{V_2} P\, dV = -nRT \ln\left(\frac{V_2}{V_1}\right) = 2 \times 1.987 \times 298.2 \times 2.303 \times \log_{10}\left(\frac{20.0}{1.00}\right)$$

$$= 3553 \text{ cal}.$$

(b) By (3.44) and van der Waals' equation,

$$w = -\int_{V_1}^{V_2} P\, dV = -\int_{V_1}^{V_2}\left(\frac{nRT}{V-nb} - \frac{an^2}{V^2}\right) dV$$

$$= nRT \ln\left(\frac{V_1 - nb}{V_2 - nb}\right) - an^2\left(\frac{1}{V_2} - \frac{1}{V_1}\right).$$

For CO_2, $a = 3.61 \text{ atm l}^2 \text{ mole}^{-2}$ and $b = 0.0428 \text{ l mole}^{-1}$.

$$w = \left[2 \times 0.08206 \times 298.2 \times 2.303 \times \log_{10}\left(\frac{20.0 - 0.09}{1.00 - 0.09}\right) - 3.61 \times 2^2\left(\frac{20.0 - 1.0}{1.00 \times 20.0}\right)\right]$$

$$= (151.0 - 13.7) \times \frac{1.987}{0.08206} = 3325 \text{ cal}.$$

Less work is done on the CO_2 when the attractive forces between molecules are estimated by van der Waals' equation than when the attractive forces are neglected with use of the perfect gas equation.

C. ADIABATIC PROCESSES

3.12 Adiabatic Processes of a Perfect Gas

In an adiabatic process there is no heat exchanged between system and surroundings: $q = 0$ or $dq = 0$. If the system is assumed to approximate a perfect gas in its behavior, the conditions of Equation (3.30) and their consequences obtain, namely,

$$\left.\begin{array}{c} PV = f(n, T) \\[4pt] \left(\dfrac{\partial E}{\partial V}\right)_T = 0 \end{array}\right\} \tag{3.30}$$

$$\left(\frac{\partial H}{\partial P}\right)_T = 0. \tag{3.36}$$

Use of these equations and the adiabatic condition with the first law provides differential equations from which the adiabatic gas laws can be derived.

By Equations (3.32), (3.30), and (3.26),

$$dE = C_V \, dT \, . \tag{3.33}$$

But for an adiabatic process that involves only pressure-volume work, the first law says $dE = dw = -P \, dV$. Equating the two expressions for dE gives (3.47), which is a suitable differential equation when temperature and volume are the variables specified.

$$C_V \, dT = -P \, dV \, . \tag{3.47}$$

Similarly, when temperature and pressure are the variables specified for an adiabatic process of a perfect gas involving only pressure-volume work, Equations (3.38), (3.36), and (3.27) give (3.48).

$$dH = C_P \, dT \tag{3.39}$$

$$dH = dE + P \, dV + V \, dP = dq - P \, dV + P \, dV + V \, dP = V \, dP \, .$$

That is,

$$C_P \, dT = V \, dP \, . \tag{3.48}$$

When the adiabatic process is reversible, the equation of state of the system can be used in the right of (3.47) or (3.48). The variables are easily separated preparatory to integration when $PV = nRT$, and Equations (3.49) and (3.50) result. By (3.47),

$$C_V \, dT = -P \, dV = -\frac{RT}{V} \, dV$$

$$C_V \frac{dT}{T} = -R \frac{dV}{V} \, .$$

If C_V is independent of temperature, and if V_1 is the volume of the gas at temperature T_1 and V_2 is the volume of the gas at temperature T_2, then (3.47) becomes (3.49).

$$C_V \int_{T_1}^{T_2} \frac{dT}{T} = -R \int_{V_1}^{V_2} \frac{dV}{V}$$

$$C_V \ln \left(\frac{T_2}{T_1} \right) = R \ln \left(\frac{V_1}{V_2} \right) . \tag{3.49a}$$

That is,

$$\frac{C_V}{R} \ln \left(\frac{T_2}{T_1} \right) = \ln \left(\frac{V_1}{V_2} \right)$$

$$V_1 T_1^{(C_V/R)} = V_2 T_2^{(C_V/R)} \, . \tag{3.49b}$$

Similarly, if C_P is independent of temperature, (3.48) becomes (3.50) thus:

$$C_P \, dT = V \, dP = \frac{RT}{P} \, dP, \qquad C_P \frac{dT}{T} = R \frac{dP}{P}$$

$$C_P \int_{T_1}^{T_2} \frac{dT}{T} = R \int_{P_1}^{P_2} \frac{dP}{P}$$

$$C_P \ln \left(\frac{T_2}{T_1}\right) = R \ln \left(\frac{P_2}{P_1}\right). \tag{3.50a}$$

That is, $\qquad P_1 T_2^{(C_P/R)} = P_2 T_1^{(C_P/R)}. \tag{3.50b}$

Equations (3.49) and (3.50) can be transformed in various ways. For such changes it is convenient to define a quantity γ as the ratio of the two heat capacities as in (3.51).

$$\gamma = \frac{C_P}{C_V}. \tag{3.51}$$

The value of γ always exceeds unity. Since $R = C_P - C_V$ by (3.40), $R/C_V = \gamma - 1$. Equation (3.49b) can be rewritten as

$$V_1^{(R/C_V)} T_1 = V_2^{(R/C_V)} T_2.$$

That is, $\qquad T_1 V_1^{\gamma-1} = T_2 V_2^{\gamma-1}. \tag{3.52}$

Elimination of T from (3.52) by the relations $P_1 V_1 = RT_1$ and $P_2 V_2 = RT_2$ that hold at the initial and final states gives (3.53), a common form of the adiabatic perfect gas law.

$$\left(\frac{P_1 V_1}{R}\right) V_1^{\gamma-1} = \left(\frac{P_2 V_2}{R}\right) V_2^{\gamma-1}$$

$$P_1 V_1^{\gamma} = P_2 V_2^{\gamma}. \tag{3.53}$$

Work done on a perfect gas along a reversible adiabatic path is found from (3.3) and (3.53).

$$dw = -P \, dV \tag{3.3}$$

$$w = -\int_{V_1}^{V_2} P \, dV.$$

Since state (2) in (3.53) is any state for the fixed amount of gas, PV^{γ} is a constant; that is, $PV^{\gamma} = C_0.$

143

Then,
$$w = -\int_{V_1}^{V_2} \frac{C_0}{V^\gamma}\, dV = -C_0 \int_{V_1}^{V_2} V^{-\gamma}\, dV$$

$$= -\frac{C_0}{1-\gamma} (V_2^{1-\gamma} - V_1^{1-\gamma})$$

$$= \frac{P_2 V_2 - P_1 V_1}{\gamma - 1} \tag{3.54}$$

$$= \frac{nR(T_2 - T_1)}{\gamma - 1}. \tag{3.55}$$

Equation (3.55) says that T_2 is greater than T_1 if a positive amount of work w is done adiabatically and reversibly on a perfect gas. Conversely, if a perfect gas works reversibly and adiabatically on its surroundings, its temperature will fall, for the work that it does is $-w$ and thus its final temperature T_2 is less than its initial temperature T_1.

Example 3.9. Three moles of a perfect gas with C_V equal to 5.00 cal mole^{-1} deg^{-1} are to be compressed adiabatically and reversibly from a volume of 75.0 l at 1.00 atm to a pressure of 100 atm. Predict (a) the final volume of the gas; (b) the final temperature of the gas; and (c) the work that must be done on the gas to compress it.

Since $C_V = 5.00$, $C_P = 5.00 + R$ by (3.40). Whence,

$$\gamma = \frac{C_P}{C_V} \tag{3.51}$$

$$= \frac{6.99}{5.00} = 1.397$$

(a) Let V_2 = the final volume; by (3.53),

$$1.00 \times 75.0^{1.397} = 100 \times V_2^{1.397}$$

$$\left(\frac{75.0}{V_2}\right)^{1.397} = 100, \qquad \frac{75.0}{V_2} = 27.0, \qquad V_2 = 2.78\ l.$$

(b) Let T_2 = the final temperature; then $P_2 V_2 = nRT_2$ and

$$T_2 = \frac{P_2 V_2}{nR} = \frac{100 \times 2.78}{3.00 \times 0.08206} = 1130°\mathrm{K}.$$

(c) By Equation (3.54),

$$w = \frac{100 \times 2.78 - 1.00 \times 75.0}{1.397 - 1} = \frac{203}{0.397} \times \frac{1.987}{0.08206} = 12{,}400\ \mathrm{cal}.$$

Example 3.10. Three moles of an ideal gas with C_V equal to 5.00 cal mole^{-1} deg^{-1} at an initial pressure of 100 atm at a temperature of 1130°K was suddenly allowed to escape into the atmosphere at a constant pressure of one atm. For this irreversible adiabatic change, calculate ΔE and ΔH.

Since this adiabatic change is irreversible, most of the equations of this section are not applicable. The work done by the gas is $-w$, where by (3.3)

$$-w = \int_{V_1}^{V_2} P\, dV = P\, \Delta V$$

$$= 1.00 \left(\frac{3.00 \times 0.08206 \times T_2}{1.00} - \frac{3.00 \times 0.08206 \times 1130}{100}\right) \times \left(\frac{1.987}{0.08206}\right).$$

For the same change, by (3.33),

$$\Delta E = \int_{T_1}^{T_2} nC_V \, dT = 3.00 \times 5.00 \times (T_2 - 1130) \, .$$

By the first law of thermodynamics, for this adiabatic change, $\Delta E = w$, whence

$$5.00 \, (T_2 - 1130) = -1.99 \left(T_2 - \frac{1130}{100} \right)$$

$$T_2 = 812°\text{K} \, .$$

Hence,

$$\Delta E = w = 3.00 \times 5.00 \times (812 - 1130) = -4770 \text{ cal}$$

$$\Delta H = \Delta E + \Delta(PV) = \Delta E + nR \, \Delta T$$

$$= -4770 + 3.00 \times 1.99 \times (812 - 1130) = -6670 \text{ cal} \, .$$

Although the process occurs at a constant pressure of 1.00 atm, the initial state is not at this pressure. Thus the equation $\Delta H = q_P = 0$ does not apply for this adiabatic change of state. It is worth noting that the work done by the gas in its irreversible isobaric expansion is less than that which it might have performed reversibly, 12,400 cal. As a result, the final state of this example (812°K) differs from the initial state of the preceding example (305°K).

Example 3.11. One mole of methane at 200°C and 10.0 atm expanded adiabatically and reversibly until its temperature was 0°C. If methane is a perfect gas with C_P as given in Table 3.1, calculate (a) the work done by the methane; (b) the final pressure of the methane.

(a) The work done by the methane, $-w$, can be calculated through the first law since the process is adiabatic and ΔE is readily evaluated.

$$-w = -\Delta E \tag{3.18}$$

$$= -\int_{T_1}^{T_2} C_V \, dT = \int_{T_2}^{T_1} (C_P - R) \, dT$$

$$= \int_{273}^{473} (1.435 + 17.845 \times 10^{-3} T - 4.165 \times 10^{-6} T^2) \, dT$$

$$= 1.435 \, (473 - 273) + \frac{17.845 \times 10^{-3}}{2} (473^2 - 273^2)$$

$$- \frac{4.165 \times 10^{-6}}{3} (473^3 - 273^3)$$

$$= 287 + 1331 - 119 = 1499 \text{ cal.}$$

(b) Since C_P is a function of temperature, finding the final pressure must be begun with (3.47) or (3.48).

$$C_P \, dT = V \, dP = \frac{RT}{P} \, dP, \qquad \int_{473}^{273} \frac{C_P \, dT}{T} = R \int_{10}^{P_2} \frac{dP}{P}$$

$$3.422 \ln \left(\frac{273}{473} \right) + 17.845 \times 10^{-3} \, (273 - 473) - \frac{4.165 \times 10^{-6}}{2} (273^2 - 473^2)$$

$$= 1.987 \ln \left(\frac{P_2}{10} \right)$$

$$1.881 + 3.579 - 0.311 = 1.987 \ln \left(\frac{10}{P_2} \right)$$

$$\log \left(\frac{10}{P_2} \right) = 1.125, \qquad P_2 = 0.75 \text{ atm} \, .$$

3.13   Adiabatic Processes of a Real Gas

The salient feature of the previous section of adiabatic processes of a perfect gas was that the energy E or enthalpy H depended only on the temperature. For real gases this is not generally true. Accordingly, in general for real gases, E and H depend on variables other than the temperature, and

$$\left(\frac{\partial E}{\partial V}\right)_T \neq 0 \quad \text{and} \quad \left(\frac{\partial H}{\partial P}\right)_T \neq 0 \, .$$

Until the second law of thermodynamics presents a more suitable independent variable than temperature, it is generally best to speak of temperature and volume as the independent variables for energy, and of temperature and pressure as the independent variables for enthalpy. This is in accord with (3.32) and (3.38).

$$dE = \left(\frac{\partial E}{\partial T}\right)_V dT + \left(\frac{\partial E}{\partial V}\right)_T dV \tag{3.32}$$

$$dH = \left(\frac{\partial H}{\partial T}\right)_P dT + \left(\frac{\partial H}{\partial P}\right)_T dP \, . \tag{3.38}$$

It is the aim of this section to evaluate the coefficients of dV and dP in (3.32) and (3.38).

Let a volume V_1 of gas at a constant pressure P_1 be forced by a piston through a porous barrier or plug that serves merely to establish a pressure difference. As it passes through the barrier, the gas pushes against a piston at a constant pressure P_2 and gradually fills a volume V_2. The work done on the gas is P_1V_1 and the work done by the gas is P_2V_2. The net work done on the gas is then $P_1V_1 - P_2V_2$. If the porous plug and the pistons and cylinders (see Figure 3.3) are very poor conductors of heat, the process can be made essentially adiabatic. It is found experimentally that the final temperature T_2 of a real gas that undergoes this process generally differs from its initial temperature T_1. This means, of course, that $P_1V_1 - P_2V_2$ may not be zero. The change in enthalpy is, however, zero. By (3.23) and the first law

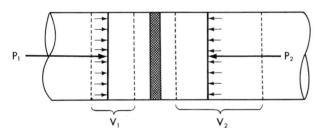

Fig. 3.3.   *Joule-Thomson Porous Plug Experiment.*

$$\Delta H = \Delta E + \Delta(PV) \tag{3.23}$$

$$= q + w + (P_2V_2 - P_1V_1) \, .$$

But $q = 0$ since the process is adiabatic and $w = P_1V_1 - P_2V_2$. By substitution,

$$\Delta H = 0 + (P_1V_1 - P_2V_2) + (P_2V_2 - P_1V_1) = 0 .$$

Since ΔH is zero, the enthalpy of the gas is constant, and $dH = 0$. Equation (3.38) then becomes (3.56).

$$0 = \left(\frac{\partial H}{\partial T}\right)_P dT + \left(\frac{\partial H}{\partial P}\right)_T dP . \tag{3.56}$$

Division of (3.56) by dP gives (3.57),

$$\left(\frac{\partial H}{\partial P}\right)_T = -\mu C_P \tag{3.57}$$

where $C_P = (\partial H/\partial T)_P$ by (3.27) and where the Joule-Thomson coefficient μ is defined by (3.58).

$$\mu = \left(\frac{\partial T}{\partial P}\right)_H . \tag{3.58}$$

The value of μ is given experimentally by the observed change ΔT in temperature caused by the observed change ΔP in pressure when a real gas is allowed to expand adiabatically through the porous plug. Here ΔP is less than zero when the final pressure is less than the initial pressure; if the temperature of the gas decreases then ΔT is also less than zero and μ is greater than zero. The temperature at which μ is zero is called the *inversion temperature*. Above the inversion temperature, μ is less than zero and the expanded gas is warmer than it was initially. Below the inversion temperature, μ is greater than zero and the expanded gas is cooler than it was initially. Use is made of this cooling phenomenon in liquefying gases. It is impossible to liquefy a gas by adiabatic expansion if the initial temperature is above its inversion temperature. The inversion temperature of H_2 is 193°K; of helium, 100°K; of N_2, about 650°K. Inversion temperatures of common gases are generally above room temperature. A few Joule-Thomson coefficients are listed in Table 3.2.

Table 3.2 *Joule-Thomson Coefficients* (μ) *of Common Gases**

GAS	μ (°C atm⁻¹)	TEMPERATURE (°K)
H_2	−0.013	273
H_2	−0.039	373
N_2	+0.333	273
N_2	+0.159	373
O_2	+0.366	273
O_2	+0.193	373

3.14 Liquefaction of Gases by Adiabatic Expansion

A gas below its inversion temperature becomes cooler as its pressure is reduced adiabatically. Commercial processes for the liquefaction of gases use gas

* *International Critical Tables V.* p. 144.

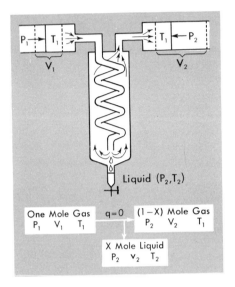

Liquid (P_2, T_2)

One Mole Gas	$q=0$	$(1-X)$ Mole Gas
P_1 V_1 T_1		P_2 V_2 T_1

X Mole Liquid
P_2 v_2 T_2

Fig. 3.4. *Simplified Schematic Diagram of Common Process for Liquefying Gases by Adiabatic Expansion.*

cooled by expansion to lower the temperature of incoming compressed gas until the incoming gas is so cold that part of it liquefies during the expansion. With neglect of the pressure drops and kinetic energy due to flow in such a process, the fraction of incoming high pressure gas that liquefies can be calculated quite easily.

Figure 3.4 is a simplified schematic diagram of the apparatus used in liquefying gases. Let 1 mole of gas at high pressure P_1 and temperature T_1 be delivered to the expansion nozzle through a heat exchanger that allows the expanded gases that flow upward to cool the unexpanded gases that flow downward. The process is adiabatic, for 1 mole of gas, expanded and unexpanded, is the system. When the temperature falls to the boiling point T_2 at the pressure P_2, a fraction X of the gas that issues from the nozzle condenses and a fraction $(1 - X)$ will proceed upward and out of the heat exchanger at a pressure of P_2 and temperature T_1.

As in the Joule-Thomson experiment, the net work done on the system at the constant pressures P_1 and P_2 is

$$w = P_1V_1 - [(1 - X)P_2V_2 + XP_2v_2].$$

By the first law of thermodynamics, since the process is adiabatic,

$$\Delta E = w = P_1V_1 - [(1 - X)P_2V_2 + XP_2v_2].$$

But for the assumed changes of state,

$$\Delta E = (1 - X)E(V_2, T_1) + XE(v_2, T_2) - E(V_1, T_1),$$

where $E(V_2, T_1)$ is the energy of the expanded gas,
where $E(v_2, T_2)$ is the energy of the liquid, and
where $E(V_1, T_1)$ is the energy of the incoming compressed gas.
When these two expressions for ΔE are equated and their terms are rearranged, the following equations result.

$$P_1V_1 - P_2V_2 + X(P_2V_2 - P_2v_2) = E(V_2, T_1) - E(V_1, T_1)$$
$$+ X[E(v_2, T_2) - E(V_2, T_1)]$$

$$[E(V_1, T_1) + P_1V_1] + X[E(V_2, T_1) + P_2V_2] = [E(V_2, T_1) + P_2V_2]$$
$$+ X[E(v_2, T_2) + P_2v_2].$$

But by the definition of enthalpy, the various terms in brackets are identified with enthalpies of the three states of the system; that is, the equations become the following:

$$H(P_1, T_1) + XH(P_2, T_1) = H(P_2, T_1) + XH(P_2, T_2) ,$$

where $H(P_1, T_1)$ is the molar enthalpy of the incoming compressed gas,
where $H(P_2, T_1)$ is the molar enthalpy of the exit gas, and
where $H(P_2, T_2)$ is the molar enthalpy of the liquid.   The fraction X of liquid that is formed is then found by solving for X.

$$X = \frac{H(P_2, T_1) - H(P_1, T_1)}{H(P_2, T_1) - H(P_2, T_2)} . \tag{3.59}$$

The numerator of (3.59) is the change in enthalpy of 1 mole of gas at temperature T_1 when its pressure falls from P_1 to P_2.   The value of this numerator is a function of state and can be evaluated from (3.38) and (3.57) when $dT_1 = 0$.

$$dH = C_P \, dT + \left(\frac{\partial H}{\partial P}\right)_T dP$$

$$= -\mu C_P \, dP \qquad\qquad \text{[by (3.57)]}$$

$$\Delta H = \int_{P_1}^{P_2} (-\mu C_P) \, dP = \int_{P_2}^{P_1} \mu C_P \, dP .$$

The denominator of (3.59) is the change in enthalpy of 1 mole of liquid at temperature T_2 to 1 mole of gas at temperature T_1 when the pressure is constant at P_2.   The value of this denominator can be found by dividing the process into a vaporization at P_2, T_2 and a heating of the gas from T_2 to T_1.

$$\Delta H = H_{(g)}(P_2, T_1) - H_{(l)}(P_2, T_2)$$

$$= H_{(g)}(P_2, T_1) - H_{(g)}(P_2, T_2) + H_{(g)}(P_2, T_2) - H_{(l)}(P_2, T_2)$$

$$= \int_{T_2}^{T_1} C_P \, dT + \Delta H_v .$$

With these evaluations of numerator and denominator, Equation (3.59), which gives the fraction X of gas that condenses in an adiabatic expansion, becomes (3.60).

$$X = \frac{\displaystyle\int_{P_2}^{P_1} \mu C_P \, dP}{\displaystyle\int_{T_2}^{T_1} C_P \, dT + \Delta H_v} . \tag{3.60}$$

149

In (3.60) the value of μ is the value at T_1. With the aid of the second law of thermodynamics, μ can be calculated from the equation of state of the gas. The value of μ may vary with the pressure.

Example 3.12. The molar heat of vaporization of oxygen at its boiling point of $-183°C$ is 1600 cal and its Joule-Thomson coefficient is about 0.30°C atm^{-1}. If the molar heat capacity of oxygen at constant pressure is $7R/2$, estimate the fraction of liquid expected when oxygen gas is allowed to expand adiabatically from a pressure of 100 atm at 0°C to a pressure of 1 atm.

By (3.60),

$$X = \frac{\displaystyle\int_1^{100} 0.30 \times \tfrac{7}{2}R \times dP}{\displaystyle\int_{90}^{273} \tfrac{7}{2}R\, dT + 1600} = \frac{0.30 \times \tfrac{7}{2} \times 1.99 \times (100-1)}{\tfrac{7}{2} \times 1.99 \times 183 + 1600}$$

$$= \frac{207}{1275 + 1600} = 0.072 .$$

For every mole of oxygen pumped in at 100 atm at 0°C, there could be produced 0.072 mole liquid oxygen at its normal boiling point.

D. ISOTHERMAL PROCESSES

3.15 Heat of Reaction

For any change between thermodynamically well defined states there is a unique and definite change in energy or enthalpy, for each of these functions is a function of state. All the examples that have been used to illustrate the calculation of changes in energy or enthalpy have been of the kind that are usually classified as physical changes of state. These included fusion, vaporization, expansion, and so forth. But the illustrations dealt not only with elements but with compounds. If a compound of several elements has a definite state when involved in physical processes, it must also have a definite state in any process, chemical or physical. To its definite state there is to be attributed a definite value of energy and enthalpy, except perhaps for an additive constant that would depend upon the zero of energy chosen.

It is possible to measure the heat evolved or absorbed in a chemical or physical process. If the process occurs at constant pressure, as in a laboratory in open vessels, the heat absorbed by the system in the change would be q_P, and by (3.22) or (3.24) this must equal the increase in enthalpy ΔH if only pressure-volume work is done. That is, in the derivation of (3.22) or (3.24) or in the various definitions of the variables, there is no restriction that would serve to exclude chemical processes from consideration. Similarly, if the chemical change occurred at constant volume, as in a closed rigid vessel, the heat evolved would be q_V or ΔE, as in (3.16). When only condensed phases are involved as reactants and products, the magnitude of the $\Delta(PV)$ term by which ΔH and ΔE differ is often quite negligible compared to the chemical energies ΔH and ΔE. Thus, for reactions involving no gases, ΔH and ΔE are generally almost equal.

When gases do partake in a chemical change, the $\Delta(PV)$ usually leads to a measurable difference between the heats absorbed by the system at constant volume and pressure. By (3.23),

$$\Delta H = \Delta E + \Delta(PV) . \tag{3.23}$$

Each mole of gaseous product will contribute to $\Delta(PV)$ a term

$$P_2 V_2 = n_2 R T_2 .$$

Similarly, each mole of gaseous reactant will contribute a term

$$-P_1 V_1 = -n_1 R T_1 .$$

The values of ΔH and ΔE are customarily quoted for reactants and products at the same temperature; hence, the $\Delta(PV)$ term for the gases involved can be expressed in terms of $\Delta n_{(g)}$, the increase in the number of gas molecules in the reaction, by factoring RT from each PV term. Since the $\Delta(PV)$ term for condensed phases is ordinarily negligible, (3.23) can be restated as (3.61).

$$\Delta H = \Delta E + \Delta n_{(g)} RT . \tag{3.61}$$

The values of ΔH and ΔE for a chemical reaction depend only on the states of the reactants and products. They do not depend upon how the change is effected. Whether or not the change is reversible is of no concern. The values of ΔH and ΔE do not depend on the existence of intermediates that can or cannot be isolated. They do not depend upon the presence or absence of a catalyst, a species which is unchanged in the over-all reaction. They do depend only on the initial and final states of the species that appear in the stoichiometric equation. If the reaction is reversed, the initial and final states are interchanged and ΔH and ΔE change sign. This means that reversing a reaction will require the absorption of just as much heat as is liberated when it proceeds forward. This independence of path is Hess' law.

The value of ΔH or ΔE that is attributed to a particular reaction assumes that the reactants in their specified states are converted completely into the products in their specified states. There are many chemical reactions that do indeed react essentially to completeness. Theoretically, of course, no reaction will go spontaneously to absolute completeness. But even for those reactions which are incomplete at equilibrium, it is possible to calculate the heat that would be absorbed if the reaction began with pure reactants and left no reactants. At one time, the heat of a reaction was considered to be a measure of the completeness of a reaction. This is false, but the explanation must await discussion of free energy and the second law of thermodynamics.

Hess' law is useful in calculating the heat absorbed in reactions that cannot be performed directly in the laboratory because the reaction does not go to completeness or because it produces more than one product. For example, burning graphite in an inadequate supply of oxygen in the hope of producing just carbon monoxide fails because some carbon dioxide is inevitably produced. The heat of the reaction must therefore be calculated by an indirect method, Hess' law. It is possible, however, to burn either graphite or purified carbon monoxide completely to carbon dioxide. For these reactions, values of ΔH with reactants and products at 25°C at one atm from Rossini, F. D., $et\ al.$, $Selected\ Values\ of\ Chemical\ Thermodynamic\ Properties$, Washington, D. C.: Circular 500 of the U. S. National Bureau of Standards, 1952, are given in Equations (3.62) and (3.63).

$$C_{(s)} + O_{2(g)} \rightarrow CO_{2(g)}, \qquad \Delta H = -94.0518 \text{ kcal} \qquad (3.62)$$

$$CO_{(g)} + \tfrac{1}{2} O_{2(g)} \rightarrow CO_{2(g)}, \qquad \Delta H = -67.6361 \text{ kcal} \qquad (3.63)$$

Since (3.62) and (3.63) both proceed to the same final state, gaseous CO_2 at 1 atm, the difference in enthalpies of their initial states can be found by subtraction. It is just as though CO_2 were an intermediate state in the diagram

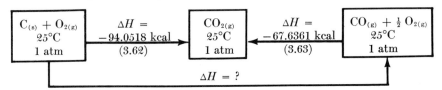

Since ΔH is independent of the path, from the diagram

$$\Delta H - 67.6361 = -94.0518$$

$$\Delta H = -26.4157 \text{ kcal} \qquad (3.64)$$

for the net reaction

$$C_{(s)} + \tfrac{1}{2} O_{2(g)} \rightarrow CO_{(g)} . \qquad (3.64)$$

The same result (3.64) could have been found by treating (3.62) and (3.63) as four algebraic equations and by subtracting the pair labeled (3.63) from the pair labeled (3.62). This is equivalent to reversing (3.63), which of course changes the sign of its ΔH, and proceeding from $C_{(s)}$ and $\tfrac{1}{2} O_{2(g)}$ to $CO_{(g)}$ via $CO_{2(g)}$. The $\tfrac{1}{2} O_{2(g)}$, which is unchanged in the over-all reaction $C_{(s)} + O_{2(g)} \rightarrow CO_{(g)} + \tfrac{1}{2} O_{2(g)}$, can be ignored (that is, subtracted from both sides of the equation) because it is in fact unchanged and thus contributes nothing to ΔH or the reaction.

Example 3.13. When 1 mole $MgSO_{4(s)}$ is dissolved in water at 25°C, 21.8 kcal of heat are evolved. When 1 mole $MgSO_4 \cdot 7 H_2O_{(s)}$ is dissolved in water at 25°C to form the same final solution, 3.3 kcal are absorbed. (Data from Rossini, F. D., *et al.*, Circular 500, N. B. S., 1952.) Calculate ΔH for the reaction:

$$MgSO_{4(s)} + 7\ H_2O_{(l)} \rightarrow MgSO_4 \cdot 7\ H_2O_{(s)}\ .$$

Since the solution of $MgSO_{4(s)}$ liberates heat, it must absorb a negative amount of heat, and thus ΔH is less than zero.

$$MgSO_{4(s)} + (n + 7)\ H_2O_{(l)} \rightarrow Mg^{++}SO_4^{--} \text{ in } (n + 7)\ H_2O_{(l)}, \qquad \Delta H = -21.8\ \text{kcal}\ .$$

Similarly, for the solution of $MgSO_4 \cdot 7\ H_2O_{(s)}$, which involves the absorption of a positive amount of heat,

$$MgSO_4 \cdot 7\ H_2O_{(s)} + n\ H_2O_{(l)} \rightarrow Mg^{++}SO_4^{--} \text{ in } (n + 7)\ H_2O_{(l)}, \qquad \Delta H = +3.3\ \text{kcal}\ .$$

By subtraction, in which the solution is eliminated,

$$MgSO_{4(s)} + 7\ H_2O_{(l)} \rightarrow MgSO_4 \cdot 7\ H_2O_{(s)}, \qquad \Delta H = -21.8 - (+3.3) = -25.1\ \text{kcal}\ .$$

Example 3.14. Calculate the heat of hydrogenation of acetylene to ethylene at constant volume from the following heats of reaction (Rossini, F. D., *et al.*, Circular 500, N. B. S., 1952) at 25°C, in which reactants and products are each at one atm: (a) burning completely one mole $H_{2(g)}$ to liquid water evolves 68.3174 kcal; (b) burning completely one mole acetylene gas to liquid water and gaseous CO_2 evolves 310.615 kcal; (c) burning completely one mole ethylene gas to liquid water and gaseous CO_2 evolves 337.234 kcal.

From the given information:

$$H_{2(g)} + \tfrac{1}{2}\ O_{2(g)} \rightarrow H_2O_{(l)}, \qquad\qquad \Delta H = -68.317\ \text{kcal}$$
$$C_2H_{2(g)} + \tfrac{5}{2}\ O_{2(g)} \rightarrow H_2O_{(l)} + 2\ CO_{2(g)}, \qquad \Delta H = -310.615\ \text{kcal}$$
$$C_2H_{4(g)} + 3\ O_{2(g)} \rightarrow 2\ H_2O_{(l)} + 2\ CO_{2(g)}, \qquad \Delta H = -337.234\ \text{kcal}\ .$$

By subtracting the third pair of equations from the sum of the first two pairs, the result is obtained.

$$C_2H_{2(g)} + H_{2(g)} \rightarrow C_2H_{4(g)}, \qquad \Delta H = -41.698\ \text{kcal}.$$

By (3.61), since $\Delta n_{(g)} = 1 - (1 + 1) = -1$ for the hydrogenation of acetylene,

$$\Delta E = -41.698 - (-1) \times 1.987 \times 298.2 \times 10^{-3} = -41.105\ \text{kcal}\ .$$

More heat is absorbed by the system when acetylene is hydrogenated at constant volume than at constant pressure because ΔE is greater than ΔH. That is, more heat is evolved by the system in the constant-pressure process because the pressure exerted by the surroundings on the system favors the reduction in volume as the reaction occurs.

3.16 Heat of Formation and the Standard State

The 100 or so elements constitute the simplest complete set of independent species from which any chemical compound can be prepared. Since the chemist ordinarily is not interested in separating isotopes or in nuclear reactions, his independent set is comprised of the isotopic mixtures found in nature. On the other hand, a physicist or physical chemist could appropriately choose as his simplest set the several hundred stable isotopes or the 1000 known isotopes, or even the 30-odd fundamental particles, if his interests led him to the separation of stable isotopes, the preparation of radioactively tagged compounds, or the preparations or reactions of nucleuses. The many possible heats of reaction can similarly be catalogued with reference to the energies or enthalpies of the elements as they naturally exist in some standard reference state.

The state of a system is said to be *thermodynamically well defined* if its composition, amount, state of aggregation (solid, liquid, gas, concentrations, surface states, etc.), temperature, and pressure are specified and if positions in and the intensities of fields (electric, magnetic, gravitational, etc.) are also specified. The composition and amount of 1 mole or formula weight of a compound are specified by its chemical formula. Its state of aggregation is commonly noted by a subscript: s for solid; l for liquid; g for gas; aq for infinitely dilute solution in water; and so forth. By common agreement, 25°C is the standard temperature and one atm is the standard pressure. The various fields are absent in the standard state.

By definition, the *standard state* of a liquid or solid element or compound is its stable state of aggregation as a pure substance at equilibrium at one atm at 25°C. The standard state of a gas is similar except that its standard state at 25°C is a hypothetical reference state of unit fugacity that is the same as one atm for perfect gases. (For a solute in dilute solution, the hypothetical ideal state of unit molality, in which the partial molal enthalpy of the solute is the same as its partial molal enthalpy at infinite dilution, is sometimes the standard state of the solute. The meaning of partial molal enthalpy is given in Section 3.18. For ideal solutions, the mole fractions of the several species of a solution are their activities; the standard state of unit activity is the pure substance in such cases.)

The enthalpy of an element in its standard state is zero by definition. The enthalpy of a compound is then referred to the several zeros of enthalpy of its constituent elements. For the reaction by which a compound in a specified state is formed from its elements in their standard states, the increase in enthalpy is called the *heat of formation of the compound* in that state. Enthalpies rather than energies are the basis of this kind of systematization because constant pressure processes are much more common in the ordinary laboratory than are constant volume processes.

The *molar heat of formation* of water is the increase in enthalpy of the reaction that produces 1 mole water from hydrogen and oxygen that are gases in their standard states at one atm at 25°C. If the water is liquid, then the heat of formation is the increase in enthalpy ΔH of the reaction

$$H_{2(g)} + \tfrac{1}{2} O_{2(g)} \rightarrow H_2O_{(l)}, \qquad \Delta H_f^0 = -68.3174 \text{ kcal} . \qquad (3.65)$$

If the water is gaseous, an unstable but well-defined state at 25°C at one atm, the heat of formation is the value of ΔH for the reaction

$$H_{2(g)} + \tfrac{1}{2} O_{2(g)} \rightarrow H_2O_{(g)}, \qquad \Delta H_f^0 = -57.7979 \text{ kcal} . \qquad (3.66)$$

The superscript zero indicates that reactants and products exist in their standard states, and when that state is not the most stable state, as for $H_2O_{(g)}$ in (3.66), it is clearly noted by a subscript or otherwise.

Similarly, the heats of formation of $CO_{(g)}$ and $CO_{2(g)}$ are given in (3.64) and (3.62).

$$C_{(s)} + \tfrac{1}{2} O_{2(g)} \rightarrow CO_{(g)}, \qquad \Delta H_f^0 = -26.4157 \text{ kcal} \qquad (3.64)$$

$$C_{(s)} + O_{2(g)} \rightarrow CO_{2(g)}, \qquad \Delta H_f^0 = -94.0518 \text{ kcal} . \qquad (3.62)$$

The standard state of carbon is graphite, not diamond, for diamond is less stable than graphite under standard conditions and evolves more heat when burned, as shown in (3.67).

$$C_{(s)(diamond)} + O_{2(g)} \rightarrow CO_{2(g)}, \qquad \Delta H^0 = -94.5050 \text{ kcal} . \qquad (3.67)$$

The heat of formation of a compound is often calculated indirectly through the application of Hess' law. For example, graphite and hydrogen do not form ethylene rapidly in significant amounts, yet from the heat of combustion of ethylene its heat of formation can be calculated as follows:

$$C_2H_{4(g)} + 3\,O_{2(g)} \rightarrow 2\,CO_{2(g)} + 2\,H_2O_{(l)}, \qquad \Delta H^0 = -337.234 \text{ kcal} \qquad (3.68)$$

$$2\,H_{2(g)} + O_{2(g)} \rightarrow 2\,H_2O_{(l)}, \qquad 2\,\Delta H_f^0 = 2(-68.317 \text{ kcal}) \qquad (3.65)$$

$$2C_{(s)} + 2\,O_{2(g)} \rightarrow 2\,CO_{2(g)}, \qquad 2\,\Delta H_f^0 = 2(-94.052 \text{ kcal}) . \qquad (3.62)$$

If Equations (3.68) be subtracted from the sums of (3.65) and (3.62), the heat of formation of ethylene is found.

$$2\,C_{(s)} + 2\,H_{2(g)} \rightarrow C_2H_{4(g)} \qquad (3.69)$$

$$\Delta H_f^0 = 2(-68.317) + 2(-94.052) - (-337.234)$$

$$= +12.496 \text{ kcal} . \qquad (3.69)$$

Reversing the calculation would allow the calculation of the heat of combustion, $\Delta H^0 = -337.234$ kcal, of ethylene from the heats of formation of $C_2H_{4(g)}$, $CO_{2(g)}$, and $H_2O_{(l)}$. Similarly, the heat absorbed in any chemical or physical change can be calculated from the heats of formation of the various reactants and products, for the kinds and numbers of atoms are preserved in an ordinary chemical or physical change.

Example 3.15. How much heat is evolved when the thermite reaction occurs?

$$\begin{array}{cccc} Fe_2O_{3(s)} & + \quad 2\,Al_{(s)} & \rightarrow \quad 2\,Fe_{(s)} & + \quad \alpha-Al_2O_{3(s)} \\ \Delta H_f^0 = -196.5 \text{ kcal} & \Delta H_f^0 = 0 & \Delta H_f^0 = 0 & \Delta H_f^0 = -399.1 \text{ kcal} \end{array}$$

$$\Delta H^0 = -399.1 - (-196.5) = -202.6 \text{ kcal} .$$

155

For every formula weight of $Fe_2O_{3(s)}$ that is reduced to 2 $Fe_{(s)}$ at 25°C at 1 atm, 202,600 cal are evolved. If the reaction is really performed, this heat will generally increase the temperature of the products and melt the iron metal.

When dilute ionic solutions are mixed very little heat is evolved or absorbed, for, if interionic attractions and repulsions and dilution effects can be neglected, the final states of the ions do not differ from the initial states. For example, mixing dilute aqueous solutions of KCl and NaF produces no chemical reaction and no heat.

$$K^+_{(aq)} + Cl^-_{(aq)} + Na^+_{(aq)} + F^-_{(aq)} \rightarrow K^+_{(aq)} + F^-_{(aq)} + Na^+_{(aq)} + Cl^-_{(aq)}$$
$$\Delta H^0 = 0 \ . \qquad (3.70)$$

However, when there is a change of state or a chemical reaction, as in dissolution, precipitation, or the production or reaction of slightly ionized substances, then the change in enthalpy is obviously not zero. Example 3.13 contains examples of heats of solution. Perhaps the most fundamental ionic reaction in aqueous solutions is the production of un-ionized water from hydrogen ions and hydroxide ions. When any strong acid reacts in dilute solution with any strong base, about 13,360 cal are evolved for each mole of liquid water produced at 25°C at 1 atm. Equations (3.71) state this fact.

$$H^+_{(aq)} + OH^-_{(aq)} \rightarrow H_2O_{(1)}, \qquad \Delta H^0 = -13.360 \text{ kcal} \ . \qquad (3.71)$$

From this fact and the heat of formation of $H_2O_{(1)}$ it is possible to calculate the sum of the heats of formation of $H^+_{(aq)}$ and $OH^-_{(aq)}$.

$$H_{2(g)} + \tfrac{1}{2} O_{2(g)} \rightarrow H_2O_{(1)}, \qquad \Delta H^0_f = -68.317 \text{ kcal.} \qquad (3.65)$$

From (3.71) and (3.65),

$$H_{2(g)} + \tfrac{1}{2} O_{2(g)} \rightarrow H^+_{(aq)} + OH^-_{(aq)}$$
$$\Delta H^0 = -68.317 - (-13,360) = -54.957 \text{ kcal} \ . \qquad (3.72)$$

By convention, the standard heat of formation of $H^+_{(aq)}$ is taken to be zero. The only heat of formation that is not defined at zero in (3.72) is that of $OH^-_{(aq)}$. Thus (3.72) fixes ΔH^0_f of $OH^-_{(aq)}$ as -54.957 kcal. With these two ions' heats of formation determined, the heat of formation of any other ion can be found from the heats of formation and solution of its pure compound with H^+ or OH^-. For example, ΔH^0_f of $NaOH_{(s)}$ is -101.99 kcal. As n approaches infinity,

$$NaOH_{(s)} (+ n \ H_2O_{(1)}) \rightarrow Na^+_{(aq)} + OH^-_{(aq)}, \qquad \Delta H^0 = -10.25 \text{ kcal.} \qquad (3.73)$$

Since there are equal numbers of moles of water on both sides of (3.73), the two infinities give no net effect and the heat of formation of $Na^+_{(aq)}$ is found thus:

$$-10.25 = \Delta H^0_f [OH^-_{(aq)}] + \Delta H^0_f [Na^+_{(aq)}] - \Delta H^0_f [NaOH_{(s)}]$$
$$= -54.957 + \Delta H^0_f [Na^+_{(aq)}] - (-101.99)$$
$$\Delta H^0_f [Na^+_{(aq)}] = -57.28 \text{ kcal} \ .$$

Similarly, from $NaCl_{(aq)}$ or $HCl_{(aq)}$ the heat of formation of $Cl^-_{(aq)}$ can be found. And so on to all ions. The changes in enthalpy of any ionic reaction can then be found from these ionic heats of formation and the usual heats of formation of compounds by performing similar calculations in reverse.

The heats of formation of about 50 compounds and ions are listed in Table 3.3. The values used in this section and those of Table 3.3 were taken from Rossini, Wagman, Evans, Levine, and Jaffe, *Selected Values of Chemical Thermodynamic Properties;* Washington, D. C.: Circular 500 of the National Bureau of Standards, U. S. Government Printing Office, 1952. Another valuable source of thermodynamic information is Rossini, Pitzer, Taylor, Ebert, Kilpatrick, Beckett, Williams, and Werner, *Selected Values of Properties of Hydrocarbons;* Washington, D. C.: Circular C461 of the National Bureau of Standards, U. S. Government Printing Office, 1947.

Example 3.16. Calculate ΔH^0 for the reaction at 25°C:

$$Ba^{++}_{(aq)} + SO^{--}_{4\,(aq)} \rightarrow BaSO_{4(s)}$$

$$\Delta H^0_f \qquad -128.67 \quad -216.90 \qquad -350.2$$

$$\Delta H^0 = -350.2 - (-128.67 - 216.90) = -4.6 \text{ kcal}.$$

Table 3.3. *Standard Heats of Formation ΔH^0_f of Compounds and Ions at 25°C* (kcal per formula weight)*

SUBSTANCE	ΔH^0_f	SUBSTANCE	ΔH^0_f	SUBSTANCE	ΔH^0_f
$O_{3(g)}$	34.0	$C_{(diamond)}$	0.4532	$Ag_2O_{(s)}$	−7.306
$OH^-_{(aq)}$	−54.957	$CO_{(g)}$	−26.4157	$AgCl_{(s)}$	−30.362
$H_2O_{(g)}$	−57.7979	$CO_{2(g)}$	−94.0518	$AgBr_{(s)}$	−23.78
$H_2O_{(l)}$	−68.3174	$CO_{2(aq)}$	−98.69	$Ag_2CO_{3(s)}$	−120.97
$F^-_{(aq)}$	−78.66	$CO_3^{--}_{(aq)}$	−161.63	$Fe_2O_{3(s)}$	−196.5
$HF_{(g)}$	−64.2	$CH_{4(g)}$	−17.889	$Mn^{++}_{(aq)}$	−52.3
$Cl^-_{(aq)}$	−40.023	$HCO_3^-_{(aq)}$	−165.18	$MnO_{2(s)}$	−124.5
$HCl_{(g)}$	−22.063	$C_2H_{2(g)}$	54.194	$MnO_4^-_{(aq)}$	−123.9
$Br^-_{(aq)}$	−28.90	$C_2H_{4(g)}$	12.496	$\alpha-Al_2O_{3(s)}$	−399.09
$HBr_{(g)}$	−8.66	$C_2H_{6(g)}$	−20.236	$Ba^{++}_{(aq)}$	−128.67
$SO_{2(g)}$	−70.96	$Pb^{++}_{(aq)}$	0.39	$BaCl_{2(s)}$	−205.56
$SO_{3(g)}$	−94.45	$PbSO_{4(s)}$	−219.50	$BaCl_2.H_2O_{(s)}$	−278.4
$SO_4^{--}_{(aq)}$	−216.90	$ZnSO_{4(s)}$	−233.88	$BaCl_2.2 H_2O_{(s)}$	−349.35
$H_2SO_{4(l)}$	−193.91	$ZnSO_4.H_2O_{(s)}$	−310.6	$BaSO_{4(s)}$	−350.2
$NO_{(g)}$	21.600	$ZnSO_4.6 H_2O_{(s)}$	−663.3	$Na^+_{(aq)}$	−57.279
$NO_{2(g)}$	8.091	$ZnSO_4.7 H_2O_{(s)}$	−735.1	$NaOH_{(s)}$	−101.99
$NH_{3(g)}$	−11.04	$Ag^+_{(aq)}$	25.31	$NaCl_{(s)}$	−98.232

*Rossini, F. D., D. D. Wagman, W. H. Evans, S. Levine, and I. Jaffe, *Selected Values of Chemical Thermodynamic Properties.* Washington, D. C.: Circular 500 of the National Bureau of Standards, 1952.

Example 3.17. Calculate the heat evolved when one mole $HCl_{(g)}$ is dissolved in a very large amount of water at 25°C. The change in state is

$$HCl_{(g)} \rightarrow H^+_{(aq)} + Cl^-_{(aq)}$$

$$\Delta H^0_f \qquad -22.063 \quad 0.000 \quad -40.023$$

$$\Delta H^0 = -40.023 - (-22.063) = -17.960 \text{ kcal} .$$

The heat evolved is $-\Delta H^0$, or 17,960 cal.

3.17 Intensive and Extensive Properties

The values of some thermodynamic properties are independent of the amount of matter in the system. The temperature of a mass of water can be taken provided the disturbance due to the heat absorbed or evolved by the thermometer affects the temperature of the water only in a negligible way. But it is of no importance whether 1 cu mile sea water has a temperature of 7.00°C or 1 l sea water has a temperature of 7.00°C. Their temperatures have the same numerical measure and the same value. The same thermometer exhibits the same reading in each. Similarly, if gravitational effects be neglected, the pressure of a gas can be measured anywhere in a large volume of gas at equilibrium and is found to be the same everywhere. Indeed, one measurement of pressure on a small sample of the gas would have yielded the same value for the pressure if the measurement were properly made. Concentrations within a homogeneous region of a system are also independent of the size of the system. Still further properties of this kind are index of refraction, density, and viscosity. This kind of property is called an *intensive property*, and specification of a certain number of intensive properties is sufficient to fix the thermodynamic state of the system.

Another kind of property of a system does depend upon the amount of matter in the system. In fact, the value of the property is directly proportional to the mass of the system or to the number of moles in the system. This kind of property is called an *extensive property*. An extensive property is defined as a property the value of which is of the first degree in masses or moles. For example, volume of a perfect gas is of the first degree in the moles at constant temperature and pressure, for

$$V = \left(\frac{RT}{P}\right) n .$$

Moreover, V is a homogeneous function of first degree in n, for V and n approach zero together. The same sort of remark, *homogeneous of first degree in moles*, applies to the volume of any system and to the energy or enthalpy of a system. The less there is of a chemical like CH_4, the less the enthalpy of this CH_4, and ultimately the less the heat available upon combustion. Some thermodynamic functions still to be defined are extensive properties like E and H.

3.18 Homogeneous Functions

An extensive property is a homogeneous function of first degree in masses or moles and an intensive property, being independent of masses or moles, is a homogeneous function of zero degree in masses or moles. The function $f(x, y, \ldots)$ is said to be a homogeneous function of degree n in $x, y, \ldots$ if

$$f(\lambda x, \lambda y, \cdots) = \lambda^n f(x, y, \cdots) .$$

In particular, for two independent variables, $f(x, y)$ is a homogeneous function of degree n if

$$f(\lambda x, \lambda y) = \lambda^n f(x, y) . \tag{3.74}$$

For example, $x^2 + 4xy + 4y^2$ is homogeneous of the second degree in x and y, for

$$f(x, y) = x^2 + 4xy + 4y^2$$

$$f(\lambda x, \lambda y) = \lambda^2 x^2 + 4\lambda^2 xy + 4\lambda^2 y^2$$

$$= \lambda^2(x^2 + 4xy + 4y^2) = \lambda^2 f(x, y) .$$

Total differentiation with respect to λ transforms (3.74) into (3.75), since $f(\lambda x, \lambda y)$ depends on λ while $f(x, y)$ does not.

$$\frac{df}{d\lambda} = n\lambda^{n-1} f(x, y) . \tag{3.75}$$

Symbolic statement of the operation of taking the derivative of $f(\lambda x, \lambda y)$ is found in (3.76).

$$\frac{df}{d\lambda} = \frac{\partial f}{\partial(\lambda x)} \frac{d(\lambda x)}{d\lambda} + \frac{\partial f}{\partial(\lambda y)} \frac{d(\lambda y)}{d\lambda}$$

$$= x\left[\frac{\partial f}{\partial(\lambda x)}\right] + y\left[\frac{\partial f}{\partial(\lambda y)}\right] . \tag{3.76}$$

By (3.75) and (3.76), for any value of λ,

$$n\lambda^{n-1} f(x, y) = x\left[\frac{\partial f}{\partial(\lambda x)}\right] + y\left[\frac{\partial f}{\partial(\lambda y)}\right] .$$

If $\lambda = 1$,

$$nf(x, y) = x\frac{\partial f}{\partial x} + y\frac{\partial f}{\partial y} . \tag{3.77}$$

Equation (3.77) is Euler's theorem on homogeneous function in its simplest form.[2] The proof for functions of many variables $x, y, z, \ldots$ is quite

159

straightforward. Hence, (3.77) becomes (3.78) when $f(\lambda x,\ \lambda y,\ \lambda z,\ \ldots) = \lambda^n f(x,\ y,\ z,\ \ldots)$.

$$nf(x,\ y,\ z,\ \cdots) = x\frac{\partial f}{\partial x} + y\frac{\partial f}{\partial y} + z\frac{\partial f}{\partial z} + \cdots . \tag{3.78}$$

Euler's theorem is of especial thermodynamic interest when $x,\ y,\ z,\ \ldots$ are moles or grams of the various species in a system and when $n = 1$. For then f is an extensive property like volume, energy, or enthalpy. The partial derivatives in (3.77) and (3.78) are called *partial molar quantities*. For any extensive property V they are given the symbol $\overline{V}_i$, where, by definition, the partial molar quantity is

$$\overline{V}_i = \frac{\partial V}{\partial n_i} = \left(\frac{\partial V}{\partial n_i}\right)_{T,P,n_j} , \qquad (j \neq i) . \tag{3.79}$$

The situation that arises when the system is considered to be composed of two chemical species is mathematically quite tractible. The volumes of various mixtures of alcohol and water, which deviate from the volumes that might be predicted by assuming additivity of volumes, would provide a concrete example of an extensive property V that is some function of the numbers of moles of species 1 and 2. In general, for any extensive property V,

$$V = V(n_1,\ n_2) ,$$

where n_1 is the number of moles of species 1 and n_2 is the number of moles of species 2. By (3.77) and (3.79), if V is indeed an extensive property so that $n = 1$,

$$V = n_1\overline{V}_1 + n_2\overline{V}_2 . \tag{3.80}$$

It is convenient to define a mean molar quantity V_m as in (3.81).

$$V_m = \frac{V}{n_1 + n_2} . \tag{3.81}$$

From (3.80) and (3.81),

$$V_m = \frac{n_1\overline{V}_1 + n_2\overline{V}_2}{n_1 + n_2} = N_1\overline{V}_1 + N_2\overline{V}_2 .$$

But $N_1 + N_2 = 1$; hence,

$$\left.\begin{aligned} V_m &= (1 - N_2)\overline{V}_1 + N_2\overline{V}_2 \\ \frac{\partial V_m}{\partial N_2} &= -\overline{V}_1 + \overline{V}_2 . \end{aligned}\right\} \tag{3.82}$$

Solution of the simultaneous equations (3.82) yields values for the partial molar quantities $\overline{V}_1$ and $\overline{V}_2$.

$$\overline{V}_1 = V_m - N_2\left(\frac{\partial V_m}{\partial N_2}\right) \tag{3.83}$$

$$\overline{V}_2 = V_m + (1 - N_2)\left(\frac{\partial V_m}{\partial N_2}\right). \tag{3.84}$$

The value of V_m and its rate of change with respect to N_2, $\left(\frac{\partial V_m}{\partial N_2}\right)$, can be evaluated analytically, or graphically from a plot of V_m as a function of N_2. The resultant values of $\overline{V}_1$ or $\overline{V}_2$ for the various compositions N_2 represent the changes expected in the extensive property V when 1 mole of one of the species is added to a huge amount of solution of composition N_2. The amount of solution is so large that N_2 is practically the same before and after the addition. From $\overline{V}_1$ and $\overline{V}_2$ the value of V for a mixture of n_1 and n_2 moles can be calculated by (3.80).

A definite example of the use of Equations (3.80) to (3.84) is the calculation of the partial molar volumes of water (species 1) and ethanol (species 2) from the densities of various ethanol-water solutions. The data of Table 3.4 (and Figure 3.5) are drawn from the *International Critical Tables III*, pp. 116–7. Although it is possible to calculate $\overline{V}_1$ and $\overline{V}_2$ from these data very conveniently if grams rather than moles are the independent variables, the partial molar volumes are found here through the use of moles, mole fraction of ethanol N_2, and mean molar volume V_m. Equation (3.83) says that the partial molar volume of water is the value of V_m for the solution at hand less the value of $N_2\left(\frac{\partial V_m}{\partial N_2}\right)$.

But N_2 is the abscissa and $\left(\frac{\partial V_m}{\partial N_2}\right)$ is the slope of the tangent at N_2. In Figure 3.5 the tangent is drawn at $N_2 = 0.610$

The quantity $N_2\left(\frac{\partial V_m}{\partial N_2}\right)$ is just the amount by which V_m at $N_2 = 0.610$ exceeds the ordinate of the tangent at $N_2 = 0$. Thus, the ordinate of the

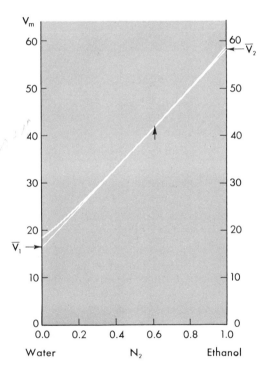

Fig. 3.5. *Mean Molar Volumes V_m of Water-Ethanol Mixtures.*

Table 3.4. *Calculation of Partial Molar Volumes of Water and Ethanol in Their Solutions*

WEIGHT FRACTION OF ETHANOL	DENSITY (25°/4°) (g/ml)	VOLUME OF 100 GRAMS (ml)	MOLES OF SPECIES IN 100 GRAMS		MOLE FRACTION OF ETHANOL N_2	MEAN MOLAR VOLUME V_m	PARTIAL MOLAR VOLUME	
			H_2O	C_2H_5OH			H_2O $\overline{V}_1$	C_2H_5OH $\overline{V}_2$
0.0000	0.99708	100.29	5.5508	0.0000	0.0000	18.068	18.07	
0.1000	0.98043	102.00	4.9957	0.2171	0.0416	19.567	18.10	53.37
0.2000	0.96639	103.48	4.4406	0.4341	0.0890	21.228	18.09	53.33
0.3000	0.95067	105.19	3.8855	0.6512	0.1435	23.187	17.90	54.71
0.4000	0.93148	107.36	3.3305	0.8682	0.2068	25.570	17.62	56.04
0.5000	0.90985	109.91	2.7754	1.0853	0.2810	28.469	17.36	56.86
0.6000	0.88699	112.74	2.2203	1.3024	0.370	32.004	17.12	57.38
0.7000	0.86340	115.82	1.6653	1.5194	0.477	36.368	16.82	57.80
0.8000	0.83911	119.17	1.1102	1.7365	0.610	41.863	16.41	58.13
0.9000	0.81362	122.91	0.5551	1.9535	0.779	48.996	15.62	58.47
1.0000	0.78506	127.38	0.0000	2.1706	1.000	58.684		58.68

tangent at $N_2 = 0$ is $\overline{V}_1$. Similarly, Equation (3.84) says that $(1 - N_2)$ $\left(\dfrac{\partial V_m}{\partial N_2}\right)$ is the amount by which V_m must be increased to give $\overline{V}_2$. And the increase $(1 - N_2)\left(\dfrac{\partial V_m}{\partial N_2}\right)$ is just that increase due to the rise of the tangent line as it proceeds from N_2 to $N_2 = 1$. Thus, $\overline{V}_1$ and $\overline{V}_2$ are the values at $N_2 = 0$ and $N_2 = 1$ of the tangent at N_2. Each value of N_2 has its own tangent and its own values of $\overline{V}_1$ and $\overline{V}_2$. Some values for ethanol-water mixtures are given in Table 3.4.

Example 3.18. Table 3.5 contains the changes in enthalpy attendant upon solution of 1 mole $NaOH_{(s)}$ in n moles water. With the aid of these data, calculate the heat evolved at 25°C when: (a) 1.000 mole $NaOH_{(s)}$ is dissolved in 10.00 moles $H_2O_{(l)}$; (b) 10.00 moles $H_2O_{(l)}$ are added to a solution containing 2.000 moles $NaOH_{(s)}$ in 10.00 moles $H_2O_{(l)}$; (c) 10.00 moles $H_2O_{(l)}$ are added to a huge amount of solution containing 5.00 moles $H_2O_{(l)}$ for every mole of $NaOH_{(s)}$; (d) 1.000 mole $NaOH_{(s)}$ is added to a huge amount of solution containing 5.00 moles $H_2O_{(l)}$ for every mole of $NaOH_{(s)}$.

(a) When one mole $NaOH_{(s)}$ is dissolved in ten moles $H_2O_{(l)}$, the change in state is:

$$NaOH_{(s)} + 10\ H_2O_{(l)} \rightarrow NaOH \text{ in } 10\ H_2O_{(l)},$$

$$\Delta H_f^0 \qquad -101.99 \qquad 10\ \Delta H_{f(H_2O)}^0 \qquad -112.148 + 10\ \Delta H_{f(H_2O)}$$

For the reaction,

$$\Delta H = -112.148 + 10\ \Delta H_{f(H_2O)}^0 - [-101.99 + 10\ \Delta H_{f(H_2O)}^0]$$

$$= -112.148 + 101.99$$

$$= -10.16 \text{ kcal}; 10.16 \text{ kcal of heat are evolved.}$$

Table 3.5. *Heats of Formation of Sodium Hydroxide in* n H_2O *and Heats of Solution of Solid Sodium Hydroxide in* n H_2O* (25°C)

MOLES $H_2O_{(l)}$ n H_2O	ΔH^0_f (KCAL) Na^+OH^- in n $H_2O_{(l)}$	ΔH^0_{sol} (KCAL) $NaOH_{(s)} + n\,H_2O_{(l)} \rightarrow Na^+OH^-$ in n $H_2O_{(l)}$
0	−101.99	0.00
3	−108.894	−6.90
4	−110.219	−8.23
5	−111.015	−9.02
6	−111.520	−9.53
7	−111.836	−9.85
8	−112.011	−10.02
10	−112.148	−10.16
15	−112.228	−10.24
20	−112.235	−10.24
30	−112.203	−10.21
40	−112.175	−10.18
50	−112.154	−10.16
75	−112.123	−10.13
100	−112.108	−10.12
1000	−112.139	−10.15
10000	−112.201	−10.21
50000	−112.220	−10.23
∞	−112.236	−10.25

(b) When ten moles $H_2O_{(l)}$ are added to 2 $NaOH_{(s)}$ in 10 $H_2O_{(l)}$, the change in state is $2[NaOH_{(s)}$ in 5 $H_2O_{(l)}] + 10\,H_2O_{(l)} \rightarrow 2[NaOH_{(s)}$ in 10 $H_2O_{(l)}]$.

$$\Delta H = 2(-112.148) - 2(-111.015) = 2(-1.133) = -2.266 \text{ kcal}.$$

The heat evolved is 2.266 kcal.

(c) When ten moles $H_2O_{(l)}$ are added to an amount of NaOH in 5 $H_2O_{(l)}$ so large that its concentration is practically unchanged by the addition,

$$\Delta H = 10 \times \left(\frac{\partial \Delta H}{\partial n_{H_2O}}\right)_{T,P,n_{NaOH}} = 10\,\overline{\Delta H_2}.$$

Here $\overline{\Delta H_2}$ could be found by finding the slope of ΔH^0_{sol} plotted against n_{H_2O} when $n_{H_2O} = 5.00$, or $\overline{\Delta H_2}$ could be found by the method of intercepts by (3.84). In the region of $n_{H_2O} = 5$, the mean molar heat of solution and the mole fraction of water can be calcualted from Table 3.5; thus:

n $H_2O = n_2$	$N_2 = \dfrac{n_2}{1 + n_2}$	$(\Delta H^0_{sol})_m = \dfrac{\Delta H^0_{sol}}{1 + n_2}$
3	0.750	−1.725
4	0.800	−1.646
5	0.833	−1.503
6	0.857	−1.361
7	0.875	−1.231

* Rossini, F. D., *et al.*, *Selected Values of Chemical Thermodynamic Properties.* Washington, D. C.: Circular 500 of the National Bureau of Standards, U. S. Government Printing Office, 1952.

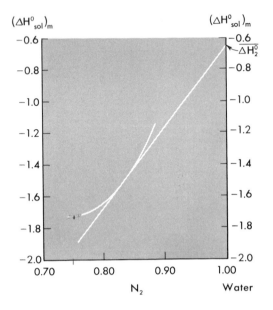

$(\Delta H^0_{sol})_m$

$(\Delta H^0_{sol})_m$

Fig. 3.6. *Mean Molar Heats of Solution of NaOH(s) in Water.*

When the data of the third column are plotted as a function of N_2, Figure 3.6 is obtained. The tangent at $N_2 = 0.833$ leads to an intercept $\overline{\Delta H^0_2}$ at $N_2 = 1$ of -0.64. That is, $\Delta H = 10 \times (-0.64) = -6.40$ kcal. The heat evolved in this change is 6.40 kcal. This exceeds the heat evolved in part (b) because the addition of water is here not supposed to change the concentration.

(d) From part (c) for this solution $\overline{\Delta H^0_2} = -0.64$.

By (3.80),

$$\Delta H^0_{sol} = n_1 \overline{\Delta H^0_1} + n_2 \overline{\Delta H^0_2}$$

$$-9.02 = 1 \times \overline{\Delta H^0_1} + 5\,(-0.64)$$

$$\overline{\Delta H^0_1} = -9.02 + 3.20$$

$$= -5.82 \text{ kcal mole}^{-1} \text{ NaOH}.$$

When $NaOH_{(s)}$ is added to an amount of NaOH in 5 $H_2O_{(l)}$ so large that its concentration is practically unchanged by the addition, 5.82 kcal mole^{-1} are evolved.

E. NONISOTHERMAL PROCESSES

3.19 Changes in Energy and Enthalpy in Physical Processes

The physical processes of interest in this section are restricted to those which accompany a change of temperature, pressure, and volume. For a perfect gas the equation of state $PV = nRT$ says that pressure, volume, and temperature are not all independent variables if the number of moles of gas is fixed. Every substance —— gas, liquid, or solid —— has an equation of state that summarizes the results of simultaneous equilibrium measurement of pressure, volume, and temperature. It is not surprising, then, that (3.31) is quite general and applies to any closed system of definite composition and state of aggregation even though pressure is not listed as a variable.

$$E = E(V, T). \tag{3.31}$$

Similarly, (3.32) is as general as (3.31).

$$dE = \left(\frac{\partial E}{\partial T}\right)_V dT + \left(\frac{\partial E}{\partial V}\right)_T dV. \tag{3.32}$$

Until now there has been no reason to integrate (3.32) in its general form, for the second term has been zero either because the volume was constant or because the system was supposed to be a perfect gas. By (3.26) the coefficient of dT is C_V, the heat capacity at constant volume. With this substitution, (3.32) becomes (3.85).

$$dE = C_V \, dT + \left(\frac{\partial E}{\partial V}\right)_T dV . \tag{3.85}$$

Since the energy E of the system is a function of state, the initial and final states being specified by V and T, the process by which a system changes in volume and temperature from V_1 and T_1 to V_2 and T_2 can for convenience be divided into two processes, one at constant volume and one at constant temperature. The diagram of such a process and its division into simpler processes would look like this.

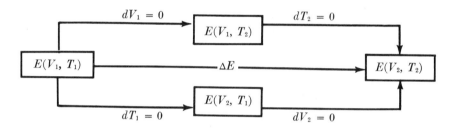

The isothermal process may precede or follow the constant volume process. If it follows, the upper route is followed, and by (3.85),

$$\Delta E = [E(V_1, T_2) - E(V_1, T_1)] + [E(V_2, T_2) - E(V_1, T_2)]$$

$$= \int_{T_1}^{T_2} C_{V_1} \, dT + \int_{V_1}^{V_2} \left(\frac{\partial E}{\partial V}\right)_{T_2} dV . \tag{3.86}$$

If the isothermal process precedes the constant volume process, the value of ΔE will be the same as in (3.86) but the integrals will be different; namely,

$$\Delta E = [E(V_2, T_1) - E(V_1, T_1)] + [E(V_2, T_2) - E(V_2, T_1)]$$

$$= \int_{V_1}^{V_2} \left(\frac{\partial E}{\partial V}\right)_{T_1} dV + \int_{T_1}^{T_2} C_{V_2} \, dT . \tag{3.87}$$

Should a phase change occur at V and T, then the value of ΔE would be calculated according to a more complicated diagram like the following wherein the subscript on E indicates the kind of phase.

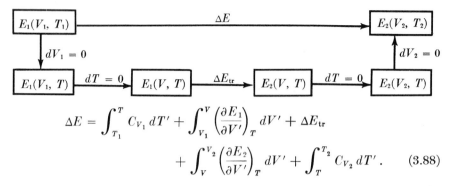

$$\Delta E = \int_{T_1}^{T} C_{V_1} \, dT' + \int_{V_1}^{V} \left(\frac{\partial E_1}{\partial V'}\right)_T dV' + \Delta E_{\text{tr}}$$

$$+ \int_{V}^{V_2} \left(\frac{\partial E_2}{\partial V'}\right)_T dV' + \int_{T}^{T_2} C_{V_2} \, dT' . \quad (3.88)$$

Other paths would also be suitable for this kind of calculation, and the extension to cases involving several phase changes is obvious since it merely involves a breaking of the integrals into enough parts to accommodate the several isothermal transitions at constant volume.

What has been said about the calculation of changes in energy by means of (3.31), (3.32), and (3.85) applies to the calculation of changes in enthalpy by means of (3.37), (3.38), and (3.89), where C_P has been substituted for $(\partial H/\partial T)_P$.

$$H = H(P, T) \quad (3.37)$$

$$dH = \left(\frac{\partial H}{\partial T}\right)_P dT + \left(\frac{\partial H}{\partial P}\right)_T dP \quad (3.38)$$

$$= C_P \, dT + \left(\frac{\partial H}{\partial P}\right)_T dP . \quad (3.89)$$

It is generally most convenient to consider enthalpy as a function of the independent variables P and T and to let V be a dependent variable that can be found from P and T through the equation of state of the system. Like E, H is a function of state and a change from a state specified by P_1 and T_1 to a state specified by P_2 and T_2 is calculated as for E.

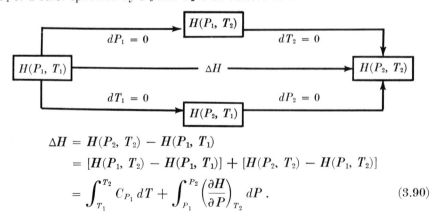

$$\Delta H = H(P_2, T_2) - H(P_1, T_1)$$

$$= [H(P_1, T_2) - H(P_1, T_1)] + [H(P_2, T_2) - H(P_1, T_2)]$$

$$= \int_{T_1}^{T_2} C_{P_1} \, dT + \int_{P_1}^{P_2} \left(\frac{\partial H}{\partial P}\right)_{T_2} dP . \quad (3.90)$$

Or, by the alternate route,

$$\Delta H = \int_{P_1}^{P_2} \left(\frac{\partial H}{\partial P}\right)_{T_1} dP + \int_{T_1}^{T_2} C_{P_2} \, dT . \qquad (3.91)$$

The differential equation (3.89) was used to evaluate the coefficient of dP in terms of the Joule-Thomson coefficient and C_P when dH was zero. In considering the liquefaction of gases, a somewhat more general situation than that described by (3.90) and (3.91) was encountered. The general situation involving a phase change, like liquefaction, vaporization, and so forth, is diagramed as it was above for energy changes. The phase change from state 1 of aggregation to state 2 involves the enthalpy change $\Delta H_{tr} = H_2(P, T) - H_1(P, T)$.

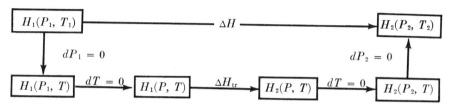

For this kind of process, whether it be reversible or not,

$$\Delta H = \int_{T_1}^{T} C_{P_1} \, dT' + \int_{P_1}^{P} \left(\frac{\partial H_1}{\partial P'}\right)_T dP' + \Delta H_{tr}$$
$$+ \int_{P}^{P_2} \left(\frac{\partial H_2}{\partial P'}\right)_T dP' + \int_{T}^{T_2} C_{P_2} \, dT' . \qquad (3.92)$$

With the aid of the second law of thermodynamics it is possible to evaluate $(\partial H/\partial P)_T$ and $(\partial E/\partial V)_T$ from the equation of state of the system. For the present, these derivatives can be taken to be zero.

Example 3.19. Calculate ΔE and ΔH when one mole water at 25°C at one atm becomes one mole steam at 130°C at two atm.

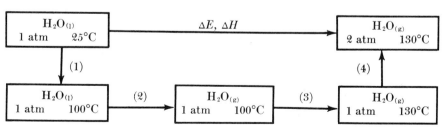

For change (1),

$$\Delta H_1 = \int_{298}^{373} C_P \, dT = 18.0 \, (373 - 298) = 1350 \text{ cal}$$
$$\Delta E_1 = \Delta H_1 - \Delta(PV)_1 = \Delta H_1 - P_1 \, \Delta V_1 \approx \Delta H_1 .$$

167

For change (2),

$$\Delta H_2 = \Delta H_{\text{vap}} = 9713 \text{ cal}$$

$$\Delta E_2 = \Delta H_2 - P \Delta V_2 = \Delta H_2 - P(V_{(g)} - V_{(l)})$$

$$\approx \Delta H_2 - RT = 9713 - 1.987 \times 373.2 = 8971 \text{ cal}.$$

For change (3),

$$\Delta H_3 = \int_{373.2}^{403.2} C_P \, dT = \int_{373.2}^{403.2} (7.1873 + 2.3733 \times 10^{-3} T + 0.2084 \times 10^{-6} T^2) \, dT$$

$$= 7.1873(403.2 - 373.2) + \frac{2.3733 \times 10^{-3}}{2} (403.2^2 - 373.2^2)$$

$$+ \frac{0.2084 \times 10^{-6}}{3} (403.2^3 - 373.2^3)$$

$$= 215.62 + 27.65 + 0.94 = 244.21 \text{ cal}.$$

$$\Delta E_3 = \int_{373.2}^{403.2} C_V \, dT = \int_{373.2}^{403.2} (C_P - R) \, dT$$

$$= 244.21 - 1.987 (403.2 - 373.2) = 184.60 \text{ cal}.$$

For change (4), since it is isothermal and since perfect gas behavior has been assumed, $\Delta H_4 = \Delta E_4 = 0$.

For the over-all change of state,

$$\Delta H = \sum_{i=1}^{4} \Delta H_i = 1350 + 9713 + 244 + 0 = 11{,}307 \text{ cal}$$

$$\Delta E = \sum_{i=1}^{4} \Delta E_i = 1350 + 8971 + 185 + 0 = 10{,}506 \text{ cal}.$$

3.20 Heat of Reaction at any Temperature

Calculation of a heat of reaction at any temperature other than the standard temperature for which heats of formation are tabulated is nothing more than the extension of the principles of the previous section. A path is invented to make the calculations as convenient as possible. The temperature of the reactants is changed to the standard temperature, the chemical or physical process is effected isothermally, and the temperature of the products is then changed from the standard temperature to the initial temperature of the reactants. The value of ΔE or ΔH for the over-all change is, then, the heat of reaction at the arbitrary temperature and is calculated by summing the three values of ΔE or ΔH for the three invented processes.

Any isothermal changes of pressure or volume required to bring the reactants or products to a standard state of pressure or volume are readily calculated by the methods of the previous section. Since the method of finding ΔE is analogous to that for finding ΔH, the problem is most practically stated as the determination of the heat of reaction at constant pressure at any temperature, given ΔH^0 at some standard temperature. A diagram clarifies the issue.

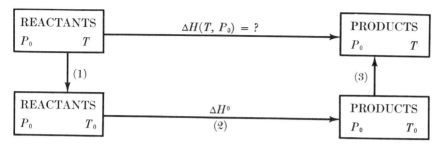

Change (1) is accomplished at the standard pressure P_0, and for this change in the temperature of all of the reactants, by (3.92),

$$\Delta H_1 = \int_T^{T_0} \sum_{\text{reactants}} C_{P_0} \, dT' .\tag{3.93}$$

Change (2) is accomplished at the standard temperature T_0 and standard pressure P_0 at which standard heats of formation of reactants and products are known and tabulated. The value of ΔH_2 is ΔH^0 and is found with the use of Table 3.3. Change (3) is accomplished at the standard pressure P_0, and for it, by (3.92),

$$\Delta H_3 = \int_{T_0}^{T} \sum_{\text{products}} C_{P_0} \, dT' .\tag{3.94}$$

For the general reaction (3.95),

$$aA + bB + \cdots \rightarrow dD + eE + \cdots\tag{3.95}$$

the increase in enthalpy at any temperature T is given by (3.96).

$$\begin{aligned}
\Delta H(T, P_0) &= \Delta H_1 + \Delta H_2 + \Delta H_3 \\
&= \int_T^{T_0} \sum_{\text{reactants}} C_{P_0} \, dT' + \Delta H(T_0, P_0) + \int_{T_0}^{T} \sum_{\text{products}} C_{P_0} \, dT' \\
&= \Delta H(T_0, P_0) + \int_{T_0}^{T} \left[\sum_{\text{products}} C_{P_0} - \sum_{\text{reactants}} C_{P_0} \right] dT' \\
&= [d \, \Delta H_f^0(D) + e \, \Delta H_f^0(E) + \cdots] \\
&\quad - [a \, \Delta H_f^0(A) + b \, \Delta H_f^0(B) + \cdots] + \int_{T_0}^{T} [dC_{P_0}(D) \\
&\quad + eC_{P_0}(E) + \cdots - aC_{P_0}(A) - bC_{P_0}(B) - \cdots] \, dT',\tag{3.96}
\end{aligned}$$

where $\Delta H_f^0(A)$ is the standard heat of formation of 1 mole A, where $C_{P_0}(A)$ is the molar heat capacity of A at pressure P_0, and so on for B, ... , D, E, ...

Equation (3.96) can be abbreviated by defining ΔC_{P_0}, ΔH^0, and ΔH by (3.97), (3.98), and (3.99).

$$\Delta C_{P_0} = \sum_{\text{products}} C_{P_0} - \sum_{\text{reactants}} C_{P_0}$$

$$= dC_{P_0}(\text{D}) + eC_{P_0}(\text{E}) + \cdots - aC_{P_0}(\text{A}) - bC_{P_0}(\text{B}) - \cdots \quad (3.97)$$

and

$$\Delta H^0 = \Delta H(T_0, P_0)$$

$$= d\,\Delta H_f^0(\text{D}) + e\,\Delta H_f^0(\text{E}) + \cdots - a\,\Delta H_f^0(\text{A}) - b\,\Delta H_f^0(\text{B}) \cdots \quad (3.98)$$

$$\Delta H = \Delta H(T, P_0) . \quad (3.99)$$

Equation (3.96) then assumes the simple appearance of (3.100).

$$\Delta H = \Delta H^0 + \int_{T_0}^{T} \Delta C_{P_0}\, dT' . \quad (3.100)$$

Equation (3.100) can be transformed from its integral form to the equivalent differential form of (3.101) as $T - T_0$ approaches dT and $\Delta H - \Delta H^0$ approaches $d(\Delta H)$ at constant pressure P_0.

$$\left(\frac{\partial\,\Delta H}{\partial T}\right)_{P_0} = \Delta C_{P_0} . \quad (3.101)$$

In view of the detailed derivation of Kirchhoff's law, (3.100) and (3.101), the following purely formal derivation of (3.101) has sufficient meaning despite its terseness to warrant mention. Let H_2 represent the enthalpy of the products and H_1 the enthalpy of the reactants at the same temperature T and pressure P_0. Then, for the complete conversion of products into reactants at T and P_0, the increase in enthalpy is

$$\Delta H = H_2 - H_1 .$$

From this, with the aid of (3.27) and (3.97),

$$\left(\frac{\partial\,\Delta H}{\partial T}\right)_{P_0} = \left(\frac{\partial H_2}{\partial T}\right)_{P_0} - \left(\frac{\partial H_1}{\partial T}\right)_{P_0}$$

$$= \Delta C_{P_0} . \quad (3.101)$$

Definite integration of (3.101) leads to (3.100); thus, at a constant pressure of P_0, if ΔH is the heat of reaction at T and ΔH^0 is the heat of reaction at T_0,

$$\int_{\Delta H^0}^{\Delta H} d(\Delta H)' = \int_{T_0}^{T} \Delta C_{P_0}\, dT'$$

$$\Delta H - \Delta H^0 = \int_{T_0}^{T} \Delta C_{P_0}\, dT' . \quad (3.100)$$

It is clear that the energy equations analogous to (3.100) and (3.101) are (3.102) and (3.103).

$$\Delta E - \Delta E^0 = \int_{T_0}^{T} \Delta C_{V_0} \, dT' \tag{3.102}$$

$$\left(\frac{\partial \Delta E}{\partial T} \right)_{V_0} = \Delta C_{V_0} . \tag{3.103}$$

In (3.102) and (3.103), ΔE and ΔE^0 are the heats of reaction at constant volume V_0 at the temperatures T and T_0.

Example 3.20. Develop an equation for ΔH as a function of temperature for the reaction

$$2 H_{2(g)} + O_{2(g)} \rightarrow 2 H_2O_{(g)} .$$

The calculation of ΔC_{P_0} and ΔH^0 of (3.100) is facilitated by good organization. Values of the following table are drawn from Tables 3.1 and 3.3.

ITEM	2 H$_{2(g)}$	+ O$_{2(g)}$	$\rightleftarrows$	2 H$_2$O$_{(g)}$	INCREMENT IN ITEM
ΔH^0_f	0	0		2(−57.7979)	−115.5958
$C^{(0)}_P$	2(6.9469)	6.0954		2(7.1873)	−5.6146
$C^{(1)}_P \times 10^3$	2(−0.1999)	3.2533		2(2.3733)	+1.8931
$C^{(2)}_P \times 10^6$	2(0.4808)	−1.0171		2(0.2084)	+0.4723

By (3.100), ΔH at any temperature T can be found if the value of ΔH^0 is known at 298.2°K, namely, −115.5958 kcal.

$$\Delta H = -115,595.8 + \int_{298.2}^{T} [-5.6146 + 1.8931 \times 10^{-3}(T') + 0.4723 \times 10^{-6}(T')^2] \, dT'$$

$$= -115,595.8 - 5.6146(T - 298.2) + \frac{1.8931 \times 10^{-3}}{2} (T^2 - 298.2^2)$$

$$+ \frac{0.4723 \times 10^{-6}}{3} (T^3 - 298.2^3)$$

$$= -115,595.8 + 1674.3 - 84.1 - 4.2 - 5.6146T + 0.9466 \times T^2 \times 10^{-3}$$
$$+ 0.1578 \times 10^{-6}T^3$$

$$\Delta H = -114,009.8 - 5.6146T + 0.9466 \times 10^{-3}T^2 + 0.1578 \times 10^{-6}T^3 .$$

For example, ΔH at 1000°K is found by substituting $T = 1000$.

$$\Delta H = -114,009.8 - 5614.6 + 946.6 + 157.8$$
$$= -118,520.0 \text{ cal} .$$

3.21 Final Temperature of an Adiabatic Reaction

It frequently happens that a reaction occurs in circumstances in which thermal contact between the reacting system and the surroundings is restricted or even absent by design. However, because ΔE or ΔH is not zero, the products of the reaction and any unconsumed reactants must change in temperature because the heat of reaction has no other place to go. The positive amount of heat liberated by an *exothermic* reaction, wherein ΔE or ΔH is less than zero, would increase the temperature of the products. Conversely, an *endothermic* reaction, wherein ΔE or ΔH is greater than zero, would be accompanied by a decrease in the temperature of the products.

For example, when $NaOH_{(s)}$ or $H_2SO_{4(1)}$ is dissolved in water, the resulting solution is at a higher temperature than the water and pure solute if they were initially at the same temperature. For isothermal solution processes of this kind, ΔE and ΔH are less than zero. Similarly, when a mixture of hydrogen and oxygen at uniform temperature is ignited, the temperature of the water produced is greater than that of the unignited mixture. As commonly performed, these processes cannot dissipate their heats of reaction swiftly enough to their surroundings to maintain the initial temperature. Performed under control with adequate stirring in good thermal contact with a large thermostat, these reactions could be performed isothermally, or nearly so.

A diagram of the changes that occur when a reaction proceeds essentially to completion under isobaric $(dP_0 = 0)$ adiabatic $(q_P = \Delta H = 0)$ conditions follows:

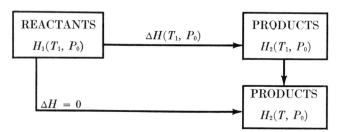

In view of Equation (3.100) and its derivation in the preceding section, the convenient path of the diagram yields (3.104) where $\Delta H(T_1, P_0)$ is the increase in enthalpy for the reaction at constant temperature T_1.

$$\Delta H = \Delta H(T_1, P_0) + \int_{T_1}^{T} \sum_{products} C_{P_0} \, dT' . \qquad (3.104)$$

But ΔH really is zero since the change is effected adiabatically and isobarically. By (3.104), since $\Delta H = 0$,

$$\Delta H(T_1, P_0) = \int_{T}^{T_1} \sum_{products} C_{P_0} \, dT' . \qquad (3.105)$$

If $\Delta H(T_1, P_0)$ is known through calculation by the methods of the preceding section, and if the heat capacities at constant pressure of the products are known, then the final temperature T achieved is readily found from (3.105).

Another possible route for the same change of state involves changing the temperature of the reactants from T_1 to T and then performing the reaction at T and P_0 as in the next diagram.

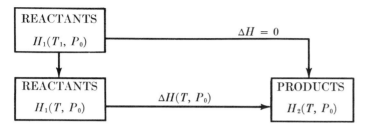

This scheme is somewhat less convenient because the temperature T is not known beforehand to facilitate the calculation of $\Delta H(T, P_0)$. To use this scheme, ΔH must be expressed as a function of T, but this inconvenience could perhaps be compensated for by the simplicity of the change of state of the reactants between T_1 and T.

Example 3.21. What is the maximum temperature achievable by a methane-air flame? For the purposes of this problem and not because the real situation warrants such approximations, assume that:

(1) The only reaction is

$$CH_{4(g)} + 2\,O_{2(g)} \rightarrow CO_{2(g)} + 2\,H_2O_{(g)}\ .$$

(2) The reaction goes to completion.

(3) Air is 20% vol O_2 and 80% vol N_2.

(4) No energy is lost by radiation or kinetic energy of flow or otherwise.

(5) All gases are perfect.

(6) The change is adiabatic and isobaric.

(7) The methane-air mixture is initially at 25°C.

The diagram of the change is this,

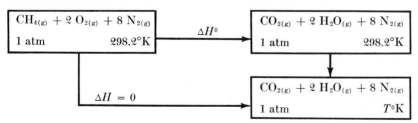

From Table 3.3,

$$\Delta H^0 = \Delta H_f^0[CO_{2(g)}] + 2\,\Delta H_f^0[H_2O_{(g)}] - \Delta H_f^0[CH_{4(g)}]$$
$$= -94.0518 + 2(-57.7979) - (-17.889) = -191.759\ \text{kcal}\ .$$

173

From Table 3.1,

$$\sum_{\text{products}} C_{P_0} = C_{P_0}[CO_{2(g)}] + 2C_{P_0}[H_2O_{(g)}] + 8C_{P_0}[N_{2(g)}]$$
$$= 72.3639 + 36.2399 \times 10^{-3}T - 3.7621 \times 10^{-6}T^2 .$$

By (3.105),

$$-191,759 = \int_T^{298.2} [72.3639 + 36.2399 \times 10^{-3}(T') - 3.7621 \times 10^{-6}(T')^2] \, dT'$$

$$191,759 = 72.3639(T - 298.2) + 18.1200 \times 10^{-3}(T^2 - 298.2^2)$$
$$-1.2540 \times 10^{-6}(T^3 - 298.2^3)$$

$$= 72.3639T + 18.1200T^2 \times 10^{-3} - 1.2540T^3 \times 10^{-6} - 21,580 - 1610 + 30$$

$$214,920 = 72.3639T + 18.1200T^2 \times 10^{-3} - 1.2540T^3 \times 10^{-6} .$$

Since the observed value is 2150°K, this cubic equation in T is best solved by trial and error near $T = 2150$. The required solution is $T = 2060°K$, but the value of this answer is doubtful not only because some of the assumptions may be in error but also because the heat capacities of Table 3.1 are expected to hold only from 300°K to 1500°K.

3.22 Adiabatic Calorimetry

Figure 3.7 is a schematic diagram of an adiabatic calorimeter. A weighed pellet P of a compound is ignited electrically through the wires I by an iron wire fuse F in an atmosphere of excess oxygen at high pressure. The com-

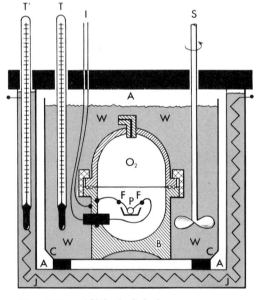

bustion vessel B is a rigid vessel made of an alloy that resists chemical attack. The heat evolved in the constant volume reactions increases the temperature of the system, which consists of the reacting chemicals, the bomb B, the stirrer S, the thermometer T, the water W and its container C. In order that the process be adiabatic, the container is supported on insulators, the top of the calorimeter is also an insulator, and an air space A of small heat capacity surrounds the container. Heat transfer to the surroundings by conduction, convection, and radiation is further reduced by electrically heating the water jacket J so that the difference in the temperatures recorded by the two thermometers T and T' is always small. The rise in temperature of the system, in which the water W is by far the most important thermally, is the measure of the heat of reaction. The

Fig. 3.7. *Adiabatic Calorimeter.*

following example illustrates the calculations that are commonly made with such a calorimeter.

Example 3.22. In order to determine the heat of combustion of naphthalene, the following experiment was performed. A pellet containing 0.9619 g benzoic acid was formed around an iron wire fuse that weighed 0.0002 g. After the bomb was sealed and filled with an excess of oxygen, it was placed in a container that held 1947.4 g water. On electrical ignition, the temperature of the water in the container rose by 2.51°C. Since air was not excluded before the bomb was closed, the high temperature of the reaction produced some nitric acid that required 4.7 ml 0.10 normal base for neutralization. The data from this part of the experiment and a repetition with naphthalene instead of benzoic acid are also tabulated. Benzoic acid was used to determine the effective heat capacity of the bomb, excess O_2, stirrer S, thermometer, and water container.

ITEM	BENZOIC ACID RUN	NAPHTHALENE RUN
Weight of Compound	0.9619 g	0.9241 g
Weight of Iron Fuse	0.0002 g	0.0002 g
Weight of Water	1947.4 g	1944.2 g
Increase in Temperature	2.51°C	3.62°C
Amount of 0.10N Base	4.7 ml	7.6 ml

Since the difference between ΔE and ΔH is ordinarily negligible except when gases are involved, the problem is most readily attacked through energy changes, even though the changes outside the bomb occurred at laboratory pressure. That is, since only condensed phases were involved outside the bomb, the values of C_V and C_P for these phases will be considered equal.

The chemical changes within the bomb are assumed to be these:

$$(1) \qquad C_6H_5COOH_{(s)} + \frac{17}{2} O_{2(g)} \rightarrow 7\ CO_{2(g)} + 3\ H_2O_{(l)}$$

$$[\text{or } C_{10}H_{8(s)} + 12\ O_{2(g)} \rightarrow 10\ CO_{2(g)} + 4\ H_2O_{(l)}]$$

$$(2) \qquad 2\ Fe_{(s)} + \frac{3}{2} O_{2(g)} \rightarrow Fe_2O_{3(s)}$$

$$(3) \qquad N_{2(g)} + \frac{5}{2} O_{2(g)} + H_2O_{(l)} \rightarrow 2\ H^+_{(aq)} + 2\ NO^-_{3\,(aq)}.$$

By the usual methods the heats of these reactions are found from heats of formation. Then $\Delta E^0 = \Delta H^0 - \Delta n_{(g)}RT_0$. For the first reaction,

$$\Delta E^0 = \Delta H^0 - \left(7 - \frac{17}{2}\right)RT_0 = -771.1 + \frac{3}{2} \times 1.987 \times 298 \times 10^{-3}$$

$$= -771.1 + 0.9 = -770.2 \text{ kcal mole}^{-1} \text{ benzoic acid.}$$

For the second reaction,

$$\Delta E^0 = \Delta H^0 - \left(-\frac{3}{2}\right)RT_0 = -196.5 + \frac{3}{2} \times 1.987 \times 298 \times 10^{-3}$$

$$= -196.5 + 0.9 = -195.6 \text{ kcal mole}^{-1} \text{ Fe}_2O_3 \text{ produced.}$$

For the third reaction,

$$\Delta E^0 = \Delta H^0 - \left(-\frac{7}{2}\right)RT_0 = -30.4 + \frac{7}{2} \times 1.987 \times 298 \times 10^{-3} = 30.4 + 2.1$$

$$= -28.3 \text{ kcal mole}^{-1} \text{ N}_2 = -14.2 \text{ kcal mole}^{-1} \text{ HNO}_3.$$

175

The diagram of the change with benzoic acid is this,

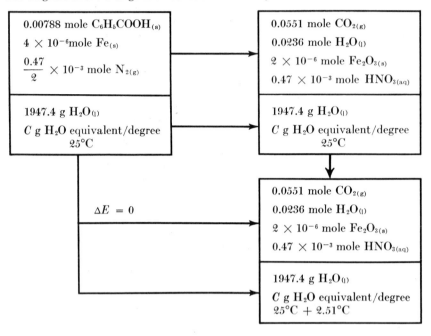

By the energy analogue of (3.104) or (3.105),

$$\Delta E = \Delta E^0 + \int_{T_1}^{T} \sum_{\text{products}} C_V \, dT'$$

$$0 = \Delta E^0 + \sum_{\text{products}} C_V(T - T_1).$$

With the substitution of numerical values for all the various ΔE^0 and C_V except the heat capacity C of the bomb, stirrers, and the like, this equation becomes

$$0 = \frac{0.9619}{122.12}(-770,200) + \frac{0.0002}{2 \times 55.85}(-195,600) + 0.47 \times 10^{-3}(-14,200) + (0.8 + 1947.4 + C)2.51$$

$$0 = -6066 - 0.35 - 6.7 + 4890 + 2.51C$$

$$C = 472 \text{ cal deg}^{-1}.$$

The isomorphous calculation for naphthalene, now that C is known, is as follows:

$$0 = \frac{0.9241}{128.16}(\Delta E^0) + \frac{0.0002}{2 \times 55.85}(-195,600) + 0.76 \times 10^{-3}(-14,200) + (1.0 + 1944.2 + 472)3.62$$

$$0 = \frac{0.9241}{128.16}(\Delta E^0) - 0.35 - 10.8 + 8750$$

$$\Delta E^0 = \frac{128.16}{0.9241}(-8739) = -1,212,000 \text{ cal}.$$

Whence,

$$\Delta H^0 = \Delta E^0 + \Delta n_{(g)} R T_0$$
$$= -1,212,000 + (10 - 12) \times 1.987 \times 298$$
$$= -1213. \text{ kcal mole}^{-1} \text{ naphthalene}.$$

The true value of ΔH^0 is -1232. kcal mole^{-1} naphthalene. It is clear from the problem that more accurate measurement of temperature would have reduced the 1.5% error and that most of this error could be accounted for by an error in temperature of about 0.03°C.

REFERENCES

Epstein, P. S., *Textbook of Thermodynamics*. New York: John Wiley & Sons, Inc., 1937.
Guggenheim, E. A., *Thermodynamics, An Advanced Treatment for Chemists and Physicists*. Amsterdam: North-Holland Publishing Co., 1957.

PROBLEMS

1. Calculate the work required to compress reversibly two moles of a perfect gas from a volume of 50.0 l to 10.0 l:
(a) At 0°C.
(b) At 100°C.
Answer: (a) 1750 cal; (b) 2390 cal.

2. With the aid of the kinetic theory, show that the energy of a perfect gas depends only upon the temperature and the amount of the gas.

3. How hot will a 2.59-g lead bullet at 50°C become if it is suddenly and adiabatically stopped from a velocity of 3.00×10^4 cm sec^{-1}?

4. Thirty g bromine at 100°C at one atm did 200 cal work and achieved a final temperature of 100°C at one atm. Find ΔE, ΔH, q, and w for the process.
Answer: $\Delta E = \Delta H = 0$; $q = 200$ cal; $w = -200$ cal.

5. One mole of a perfect gas expands isothermally at 50°C from a pressure of 3.00 atm to 2.0×10^{-3} atm. Find q, w, ΔE and ΔH.

6. Forty g propane at 25°C is heated to 100°C. If the initial and final pressures are 2.00 atm, find q, w, ΔE, and ΔH if the process is:
(a) Reversible.
(b) Irreversible and yields no work.
Answer: $\Delta E = 1196$ cal; $\Delta H = 1331$ cal; (a) $q = 1331$ cal; (a) $w = -135$ cal; (b) $q = 1196$ cal; (b) $w = 0$.

7. Two moles steam at 120°C are condensed isothermally and reversibly to water at 120°C. At this temperature, the vapor pressure of water is 1490 mm Hg and its heat of vaporization is 526 cal g^{-1}. Find w, q, ΔE and ΔH for this condensation.

8. Calculate the work done by one mole of a liquid as it vaporizes reversibly at its normal boiling point of:
(a) 200°C.
(b) 400°C.

9. Three identical gaseous samples, each of one mole of a perfect diatomic gas at 150°C at 10.0 atm, are each allowed to expand to a volume of 30.0 l. Calculate the final pressure that results and the work done by the gas when:
(a) The first sample expands adiabatically into a vacuum.
(b) The second sample expands isothermally and reversibly.
(c) The third sample expands adiabatically and reversibly.

10. Estimate the yields of liquid N_2 if a final temperature of 77°K at one atm is reached from 0°C at either 50 atm or 100 atm. The heat of vaporization of N_2 is 1350 cal mole^{-1}.

11. One mole methane explodes at 25°C in an excess of oxygen to produce $CO_{2(g)}$ and $H_2O_{(l)}$. If the heat of mixing of gases is negligible and if the reaction goes to completion, will more heat be evolved if the explosion occurs in a rigid closed vessel or in a nonrigid vessel such that initial and final pressures are both one atm? If all gases are ideal, calculate any difference.
Answer: At 25°C, 1185 cal more evolved at constant P.

12. Calculate the molar heat of solution of solid NaCl as it dissolves in a great quantity of water.

13. When one g liquid benzene at 25°C burns in an open vessel to yield gaseous CO_2 and water at 25°C at atmospheric pressure, 10.0 kcal heat are liberated. What is the molar heat of formation of benzene?
Answer: $\Delta H_f^0 = + 11.9$ kcal mole^{-1}.

14. Calculate values of ΔE^0 and ΔH^0 at 25°C:
(a) $Ag_2O_{(s)} \rightarrow 2\ Ag_{(s)} + \frac{1}{2}\ O_{2(g)}$.
(b) $H_{2(g)} + Cl_{2(g)} \rightarrow 2\ HCl_{(g)}$.
(c) $2\ SO_{2(g)} + O_{2(g)} \rightarrow 2\ SO_{3(g)}$.
(d) $C_2H_{6(g)} + H_{2(g)} \rightarrow 2\ CH_{4(g)}$.
(e) $2\ C_2H_{6(g)} + 7\ O_{2(g)} \rightarrow 4\ CO_{2(g)} + 6\ H_2O_{(l)}$.
(f) $2\ C_2H_{6(g)} + 5\ O_{2(g)} \rightarrow 4\ CO_{(g)} + 6\ H_2O_{(l)}$.
Answers: (a) $\Delta H^0 = 7306$ cal; $\Delta E^0 = 7010$ cal; (b) $\Delta H^0 = \Delta E^0 = -44,126$ cal; (c) $\Delta H^0 = -46,980$ cal; $\Delta E^0 = -46,390$ cal.

15. As one mole $NaOH_{(s)}$ is dissolved in 100 g water, the temperature rises to 52°C and then returns to the initial temperature of NaOH and H_2O, 25°C. Calculate ΔH for the solution process.

16. Calculate ΔE, ΔH, q, and w for the reversible isobaric process by which one mole liquid water at 1 atm at 25°C becomes one mole steam at 1 atm at 150°C.

17. Calculate the heat of combustion of methane at 500°C. How much heat would be evolved at constant volume at 500°C if 10.00 g methane were burned completely in a closed rigid vessel?

18. Calculate ΔE and ΔH for these changes at 25°C:
(a) $H_{2(g)}(0.1\ atm) + Cl_{2(g)}(0.1\ atm) \rightarrow 2\ HCl_{(g)}(1\ atm)$.
(b) $2\ H_{2(g)}(0.1\ atm) + O_{2(g)}(0.5\ atm) \rightarrow 2\ H_2O_{(l)}(1\ atm)$.
Answer: (a) $\Delta E = \Delta H = -44.126$ kcal.

19. What is the least work that must be done to divide one spherical drop of water of mass of 50 mg into identical spherical droplets with diameters of 1000 A?

20. Calculate the work done on a gas when it is forced isothermally, isobarically, and reversibly through one mile of horizontal pipe at ten atm if the inner diameter of the pipe is one in.
Answer: $w = 197.4$ kcal.

21. Calculate the increase in energy and the heat absorbed by one mole of an ideal monatomic crystalline solid (such as a metal) as it goes from 0°C to 200°C at constant pressure:
(a) If the solid does not expand.
(b) If the volume V of the solid at Celsius temperature τ relative to its volume V_0 at 0°C is $V = V_0(1 + \tau \times 10^{-4})$.

22. Calculate the increase in energy of one mole of a perfect monatomic gas that is heated at constant pressure from 100°C to 200°C and is also elevated one mile if its molecular weight is 30. What is ΔH for this process?
Answer: $\Delta E = 411$ cal; $\Delta H = 610$ cal.

23. Calculate the values of ΔE and ΔH for the changes of state:
(a) Two moles nitrogen ($C_V = 5R/2$) are heated from 0°C to 100°C at one atm.
(b) Three moles steam ($C_P = 8.2$ cal mole^{-1} deg^{-1}) are cooled from 150°C to 100°C at one atm.

24. One-half mole gaseous chlorine expands isothermally and reversibly at 30°C from a volume of two l to a volume of ten l. Calculate the work done by the chlorine:
(a) If it is a perfect gas.
(b) If it is a van der Waals gas.
Explain the difference in the amount of work done by the chlorine.

25. Show that the molar heat capacity at constant volume (C_V) of a perfect gas does not depend upon the volume of the gas at constant temperature.

26. Two moles of a perfect gas at 27°C at ten atm expand isothermally and reversibly until the pressure is one atm. Calculate the heat absorbed by the gas in this process.
Answer: 2750 cal.

27. One mole N_2 ($C_V = 5R/2$) expands adiabatically from a pressure of 75.0 atm at 100°C to a volume of 12.0 l. Calculate the final temperature and q, w, ΔE, and ΔH for this process if the adiabatic expansion:
(a) Is reversible.
(b) Involves 300 cal work done by the gas.
Answers: (a) 96.6°K; $q = 0$; $w = \Delta E = -1374$ cal; $\Delta H = -1922$ cal; (b) 312.8°K; $q = 0$; $w = \Delta E = -300$ cal; $\Delta H = -420$ cal.

28. Calculate the final pressure that results from reversible adiabatic compression of two moles gaseous NH_3 from 0.500 atm at 27°C until its temperature reaches 100°C. How much work is done on the ammonia?

29. One mole of a perfect diatomic gas ($C_P = 7R/2$) at 127°C expands irreversibly through a Joule-Thomson porous plug and its pressure falls from three atm to one atm. Then, at constant pressure of one atm, its temperature is changed reversibly to 27°C. Calculate w, q, ΔE, and ΔH for the over-all change.

30. Twenty l of an ideal diatomic gas at 400°C and 7.00 atm expand until the pressure of the gas is 2.00 atm. Calculate w, ΔE, and ΔH for the process if the expansion is:
(a) Isothermal and reversible.
(b) Reversible and adiabatic.
(c) Isothermal and adiabatic.
(d) Isobaric at two atm and adiabatic.
(e) Isobaric at two atm and isothermal.
Answer: Zero except: (a) $w = -4250$ cal; (b) $w = \Delta E = -2555$ cal and $\Delta H = -3580$ cal; (d) $w = \Delta E = -3110$ cal and $\Delta H = -4354$ cal; (e) $w = -2420$ cal.

31. The approximate Joule-Thomson coefficients of air at 0°C and 100°C are 0.25 and 0.15° atm^{-1}. If air at 100 atm at each of these temperatures expands adiabatically to a pressure of one atm, what yields of liquid air are expected from each process? The heat of vaporization of air may be taken as 50 cal g^{-1} and its boiling point as -185°C.

32. How much heat is evolved at 25°C when 50.0 g pure solid lead dissolve in an excess of dilute aqueous silver nitrate?

33. Calculate values of ΔH^0 and ΔE^0 for these reactions at 25°C:
(a) $H_2SO_{4\ (l)} \rightarrow 2\ H^+_{(aq)} + SO^{--}_{4(aq)}$.
(b) $H_2O_{(l)} + CO_{2(g)} \rightarrow H_2CO_{3(aq)}$.
(c) $Ag^+_{(aq)} + Br^-_{(aq)} \rightarrow AgBr_{(s)}$.
(d) $Ag_2CO_{3(s)} \rightarrow Ag_2O_{(s)} + CO_{2(g)}$.
(e) $4\ NH_{3(g)} + 5\ O_{2(g)} \rightarrow 4\ NO_{(g)} + 6\ H_2O_{(g)}$.
(f) $2\ Fe_{(s)} + 2\ NaMnO_{4(aq)} + H_2O_{(l)} \rightarrow Fe_2O_{3(s)} + 2\ MnO_{2(s)} + 2\ NaOH_{(aq)}$.

34. Calculate ΔH for each of these isothermal changes at 25°C from the data in Table 3.5:
(a) One mole $NaOH_{(s)}$ dissolves in four moles $H_2O_{(l)}$.
(b) One mole $NaOH_{(s)}$ dissolves in the solution from (a).
(c) One mole $NaOH_{(s)}$ dissolves in a huge amount of the final solution of (a).
(d) One mole $H_2O_{(l)}$ dissolves in the final solution of (a).
(e) One mole $H_2O_{(l)}$ dissolves in a huge amount of the final solution of (a).

35. What is the heat of vaporization of one mole water at 150°C? Use data of Tables 3.1 and 3.3 and assume that the molar heat capacity of the liquid is 18.0 cal deg^{-1}. The observed value is 9.10 kcal mole^{-1}.

36. Calculate ΔH at 850°C for the reaction $4\ NH_{3(g)} + 5\ O_{2(g)} \rightarrow 4\ NO_{(g)} + 6\ H_2O_{(g)}$. For NO, let $C_P = 6.665 + 1.420 \times 10^{-3}T$. *Answer:* $\Delta H = -216,310$ cal.

37. Find an expression for ΔH as a function of temperature for the reaction $N_{2(g)} + O_{2(g)} \rightarrow 2\ NO_{(g)}$.

38. Find an expression for ΔH as a function of temperature for the reaction $2\ NH_{3(g)} \rightarrow 3\ H_{2(g)} + N_{2(g)}$.

39. One mole $NaOH_{(s)}$ at 25°C is dissolved adiabatically in an open beaker in ten moles water at 25°C. What is the temperature of the solution that results if its heat capacity is 0.95 cal g^{-1}? *Answer:* 74°C.

---

40. Calculate the work done on one mole of a perfect gas at 27°C in these circumstances:
(a) Reversible compression from one atm to five atm.
(b) Reversible expansion from five atm to one atm.
(c) Irreversible expansion from the final state of (a) to the initial state of (a).

41. The potential energy possessed by a body by virtue of its position in a gravitational field is independent of the path by which it acquired the potential energy. In terms of the first law of thermodynamics, discuss what happens to this potential energy when:
(a) A body is dropped in a vacuum.
(b) A falling body suddenly is halted so that its kinetic energy becomes thermal energy.
(c) A body is dropped in a viscous fluid.

42. Calculate the work done on a spring in stretching it by three cm if its Hooke's law force constant is 1000 dyne cm^{-1}. Calculate the increase in its potential energy. If 2% of the mechanical energy is dissipated as heat, recalculate the work and change in potential mechanical energy.
Answer: $w = \Delta E = 4500$ ergs; $w = 4500$ ergs and $\Delta E = 4410$ ergs.

43. Find the temperature at which C_P of methane is a maximum. Justify the possible existence of such a maximum in terms of equipartition of energy even though the equation for C_P is not expected to be valid in this range of temperature.

44. Evaluate C_V for methane and propane at 25°C and 1000°C and justify the values in terms of equipartition of energy.

45. The heat of vaporization of water at 100°C is 539 cal g^{-1}. If steam is a perfect gas and the volume of the liquid is negligible, find w, q, ΔE, and ΔH for the vaporization of ten g H_2O at 100°C if the process is:
(a) Reversible.
(b) Irreversible to the extent that the work really done by the H_2O is 40.0 cal less than the reversible work. Explain how step (b) might occur.
Answer: $\Delta H = 5390$ cal; $\Delta E = 4978$ cal; (a) $w = -412$ cal; $q = \Delta H$; (b) $w = -372$ cal, $q = 5350$ cal.

46. Calculate the minimum work to be done in compressing two moles ammonia from 20.0 to 8.00 l at 10°C. Use the ideal gas law and van der Waals' equation and explain any difference in the results.

47. One mole of a rigid perfect diatomic gas is initially in a volume of 30.0 l at 400°K. It then experiences the following *successive* processes:
(a) From its initial state it is compressed isothermally and reversibly until its pressure is 10.0 atm.
(b) Then it is allowed to expand into an evacuated vessel until its pressure is 5.00 atm.
(c) Then it is allowed to expand adiabatically and reversibly until its volume is 10.0 l.
(d) Then it is allowed to expand irreversibly and adiabatically until it returns to its initial state.
    For each process and the whole cycle find w, q, ΔE, and ΔH, and tabulate results in calories.

48. Let a perfect gas be forced isobarically through an orifice into an evacuated rigid vessel until its pressure in that vessel rises to the isobaric value and the process stops. Show that the final temperature of the gas in the vessel before it loses heat to the walls of the vessel is γ times its initial temperature before entering the vessel.

49. Calculate the temperature that would result from adiabatic compression of one mole of a perfect gas from 2.00 atm to 200 atm if the initial temperature is 227°C. Assume that $C_V = 5R/2$. Also state and explain any other assumption required to obtain a unique answer.

50. A rubber balloon filled with O_2 at 25°C at 1.10 atm is exploded adiabatically in a large room where the atmospheric pressure is 0.98 atm. What is the temperature of the oxygen immediately after the explosion before it mixes with room air if the pop dissipates no energy?
(a) Assume that O_2 is a perfect gas with $C_V = 5R/2$.
(b) Assume that O_2 is itself a real gas.

51. Two moles hydrogen at 16.00 atm at 0.00°C are allowed to expand adiabatically as in a Joule-Thomson experiment until their pressure falls to 2.00 atm. Estimate the temperature of the final state if the Joule-Thomson coefficient of H_2 is constant at $-0.013°$ atm^{-1}.
Answer: 0.182°C.

181

52. How much heat is evolved at 25°C when 10.0 g pure solid sodium metal dissolve in an open beaker containing 4.785 moles pure water to yield hydrogen at one atm and a solution of NaOH? See Tables 3.3 and 3.5 for data.

53. Calculate ΔE and ΔH for the reaction at 25°C $Mn_{(s)} + H_2SO_{4(aq)} \rightarrow H_{2(g)} + MnSO_{4(aq)}$:
(a) At constant volume.
(b) At constant pressure.
State any assumptions made in these calculations.

54. From appropriate data available in the library, calculate ΔH for each of these isothermal changes:
(a) Two moles pure H_2SO_4 dissolve in fifty moles water.
(b) Water is added to the result of (a) to produce one molal sulfuric acid.
(c) One kilogram two molal H_2SO_4 is diluted to one molal H_2SO_4.

55. Very dilute sulphuric acid is added to one mole NaOH dissolved in four moles water until the base is just neutralized. Calculate ΔH at 25°C.
Answer: $\Delta H = -15.377$ kcal.

56. At what temperature is $\Delta H = 0$ for the isobaric reaction:
(a) $H_2O_{(l)} \rightarrow H_2O_{(g)}$?
(b) $H_{2(g)} + Br_{2(g)} \rightarrow 2\,HBr_{(g)}$?
Answer: (a) 647.6°K; (b) if $\Delta C_P = 0$, no temperature.

57. What circumstance causes the evolution of heat from a certain chemical reaction to increase as the temperature of reaction is increased if the reaction is performed:
(a) At constant pressure?
(b) At constant volume?

58. Calculate the heat of hydrogenation of acetylene to ethylene at 200°C when the reaction is carried out at:
(a) Constant volume.
(b) Constant pressure.
Assume that C_P of H_2 is $7R/2$ and that C_P of each hydrocarbon is $5R$. How hot could the reaction at constant volume become if left unattended at 200°C if the reaction goes to completion and no excess H_2 is present?
Answer: (a) $\Delta E = -41,978$ cal; (b) $\Delta H = -42,918$ cal; up to 5480°C.

FOOTNOTES

1. Guggenheim, E. A., *Thermodynamics*. Amsterdam: North-Holland Publishing Co., 1957, p. 11.

2. Woods, F. S., *Advanced Calculus*. Boston: Ginn & Co., 1934, pp. 73-4.

4 / SECOND AND THIRD LAWS

OF THERMODYNAMICS

A. THE SECOND LAW

4.1 Reversible Processes

The first law of thermodynamics does two things: it states the law of conservation of energy for heat and work; it systematizes thermochemistry. In doing these things, it points out that it is impossible to get something for nothing and that the energy of a well-defined thermodynamic state is independent of its past or future. The emphasis has been on initial and final states.

The second law of thermodynamics also emphasizes initial and final states. Whereas reversibility was of interest in the previous chapter only in regard to work, and thus indirectly in regard to heat, reversibility of a process is of paramount importance in the second law. Indeed, reversibility and irreversibility are part of the statement of this law. The words *reversible* and *irreversible* may not be mentioned, but always present is the idea of a process that can be continued, stopped, or reversed through infinitesimal changes in the variables that control or specify the states of the system and surroundings. Not only must the process occur by virtue of infinitesimal differences in the controlling variables, but it must be possible to restore the system and surroundings to their initial states merely by reversing the process through infinitesimal changes.

While performing a process through intermediate states necessarily involves a sequence of events in time, time is of no concern for equilibrium thermodynamics. A reversible process is conceived as a series of related equilibrium states. As such, it is a limit, just as an infinitesimal is a limit. A really reversible process would require eons and eons for its performance, if it ever really got started, because each step in the process could differ from equilibrium at most by an infinitesimal. A reversible process is, then, a convenient abstraction and a limiting type of process that can be approximated by a real process if its driving force is reduced sufficiently. Often the difference between a real process and a *series of equilibrium states* can be made negligible. If so, the concept has value.

If energy is exchanged between system and surroundings by virtue of an infinitesimal difference in temperature, heat is absorbed or evolved reversibly. If a liquid vaporizes because a confining ideal piston (frictionless to avoid losses of thermal energy, weightless to avoid losses in kinetic energy, and so forth) experiences an infinitesimal pressure difference, reversible expansion work is performed and the vaporization process is reversible. On the other hand, if the difference in temperature that causes the exchange of energy is not an infinitesimal, but is rather a finite difference in temperature, the heat is not reversible. Nor is the vaporization reversible if the pressure difference is finite.

It is interesting to note that the reversible vaporization could be controlled by an infinitesimal temperature difference rather than by an infinitesimal pressure difference. Suppose the ideal piston at first experiences exactly equal pressures on both sides. But if the temperature of the surroundings and thus of the system, consisting of liquid and vapor, is increased infinitesimally, the vapor pressure rises infinitesimally and drives the piston outward. The energy required to perform this expansion work and to vaporize the liquid is absorbed from the thermostated surroundings by virtue of the supposed infinitesimal increase in their temperature. Thus the process proceeds reversibly.

Any actual process that occurs spontaneously is irreversible. The terms *real*, *actual*, *spontaneous*, and *natural* each label a process as one that proceeds of its own accord if left unattended. The time rate of a process is sometimes an indication of the degree to which it approximates a reversible process. The slower the process, usually the closer it approximates reversibility. A sluggish river can be stopped by a dam (or even reversed like the Chicago River) much more easily than can a towering waterfall (like Yosemite Falls). The true criterion of the degree to which a process approaches reversibility is the magnitude of the increment in the controlling variables. A sluggish river falls less rapidly than a waterfall. The river's flow is easily reversed, for the increment in altitude per mile of sluggish river is small. Hydrogen and oxygen can exist mixed at room temperature for years, but the slow rate of reaction does not indicate the distance from equilibrium or the difficulty of preventing an exploding mixture from exploding completely. In certain circumstances, a system like a mixture of hydrogen and oxygen can be treated as though it were at equilibrium even though it is nowhere near equilibrium and even though there is no infinitesimal adjustment that could reverse the very slow changes that occur spontaneously. Such a mixture of hydrogen and oxygen has a well-defined pressure and volume at specified temperature, a definite heat capacity, and so on. But avoid finely divided platinum or a spark! If any perturbation or change can be undone or reversed so that the system is restored to its original state by infinitesimal readjustments, then a long-lived state can be assumed to be at true equilibrium. However, the illustration of hydrogen and oxygen shows that to be long-lived is not always to be at equilibrium, for what infinitesimal readjustment could undo the effect of a spark in an explosive mixture?

The thermodynamics of irreversible processes is a difficult study and is not as well developed as equilibrium thermodynamics where initial and final states are of supreme importance. When it is impossible to calculate the irreversible work involved, then this book's treatment of thermodynamics will have recourse only to the inequality of the second law; and inequalities are somewhat less than completely satisfying.

4.2 The Second Law

There are many ways of stating the second law of thermodynamics. If it is stated in words, the law states what men are convinced cannot be done. For example, the statement that perpetual motion is impossible could be taken as a crude and unwieldy statement of the conservation of energy. The most tractable statement of the second law, as for the first, is mathematical rather than verbal, for the language of mathematics is precise and its rules of logic, embodying allowed operations, are definite and simple. After an abstract and axiomatic mathematical statement shall come several statements in words, which explain the meaning of the law. Although these verbal statements shall here be proved from the mathematical statement, the reasoning processes of the proofs can be reversed. In fact, these statements of what cannot be done were originally taken as the fundamental statements by their originators, who then developed this terse mathematical statement or its equivalent.

Equations (4.1), (4.2), and (4.3) and the definitions of the symbols constitute together the second law of thermodynamics. For reversible processes,

$$dq_{\text{rev}} = T \, dS \, . \tag{4.1}$$

185

For actual or irreversible or spontaneous processes,

$$dq < T \, dS \,. \tag{4.2}$$

For any change of state,

$$\Delta S = S_2 - S_1 \,. \tag{4.3}$$

In these equations, dq is the infinitesimal heat absorbed by the system from the surroundings, T is the thermodynamic temperature of the isothermal surroundings, S_1 is the entropy of the initial state, and S_2 is the entropy of the final state. The entropy S is a function of state and thus dS is an exact differential.

With the understanding that S is a function of state and that T is the thermodynamic temperature of the surroundings, these three equations can be combined neatly into one, (4.4), wherein the equality refers to reversible processes or equilibrium states and the inequality refers to irreversible processes.

$$dq \leqslant T \, dS \,. \tag{4.4}$$

To find a definite value for the increase in entropy ΔS for a change from state 1 to state 2, it is necessary merely to invent *any* reversible path that connects states 1 and 2 or to follow the reversible path experienced by the system and to use the equality of (4.4). That is,

$$\Delta S = \int_{S_1}^{S_2} dS = S_2 - S_1 = \int_{(1)}^{(2)} \frac{dq_{\text{rev}}}{T} \,. \tag{4.5}$$

Since S is a function of state and since ΔS is independent of the path, any invented or experienced reversible path yields the same unique value of ΔS. Experience in evaluating ΔS under various circumstances often suggests one path as easiest for the calculation, even though the actual or reversible path followed by the system may have been quite another.

It shall be proved in Section 4.15 that the thermodynamic temperature of the second law is the same as the absolute temperature of the perfect gas. Actually, the second law provides the best way of defining temperature, for any real substance is suitable as thermometric substance. Hence, temperature is no longer defined in terms of ideal behavior of a special class of substance.

4.3 Adiabatic Processes

Any spontaneous or reversible adiabatic process is a process for which dq is zero during the process. For any reversible adiabatic process, $T \, dS = 0$ by (4.1). Since T is greater than zero (as can be shown),

$$dS = 0 \tag{4.6}$$

$$\Delta S = \int_{S_1}^{S_2} dS = S_2 - S_1 = 0 \,. \tag{4.7}$$

The entropy of any system is constant in a reversible adiabatic process, for $S_1 = S_2$ by (4.7) and the initial and final states are restricted only in being joined by a reversible adiabatic path.

If an adiabatic process is not reversible, then the infinitesimal increment of entropy is given by (4.2) when $dq = 0$.

$$T \, dS > dq = 0 \, .$$

Since T is greater than zero, for any irreversible adiabatic process,

$$dS > 0 \tag{4.8}$$

$$\Delta S = \int_{S_1}^{S_2} dS = S_2 - S_1 > 0 \, . \tag{4.9}$$

The entropy is not constant in an irreversible adiabatic process, for $S_2 > S_1$ by (4.9). That is, the entropy of the final state exceeds that of the intiail state if the process is irreversible and adiabatic. Thus it is said that the entropy of an isolated system, which cannot exchange matter or energy with its surroundings and cannot be worked upon by its surroundings, tends to increase. Once at equilibrium, however, the isolated system maintains a maximum entropy that is constant by virtue of (4.7).

In 1909, Caratheodory discovered a fundamental mathematical property of the first law equation $dE = dq + dw$. From the geometrical behavior of this kind of differential equation and suitable identification of mathematical and physical variables, he obtained the second law in mathematical form by the laws of mathematics.[1] In particular, in the neighborhood of any point that describes the state of a system, there are many other points that cannot be reached from that point by any adiabatic process. For example, suppose that a system reversibly evolves a positive amount of heat. Since this heat is evolved, $dq < 0$. By (4.1), $T \, dS < 0$. Since $T > 0$, $dS < 0$, and for a finite process in which a finite amount of heat is evolved by the system,

$$\Delta S = \int_{S_1}^{S_2} dS = S_2 - S_1 < 0. \tag{4.10}$$

Equation (4.10) says that S_2 is less than S_1; that is, the entropy of the final state is less than that of the initial state. If the same change of state were effected irreversibly and adiabatically, (4.9) insists that ΔS, the same ΔS since the terminal states are unchanged, be greater than zero. That is, (4.9) insists that the entropy of the final state is greater than that of the initial state. Even if the same change of state were reversible and adiabatic, (4.7) would require $S_1 = S_2$. In short, (4.10) contradicts (4.7) and (4.9). The second law says, then, that state 2 cannot be reached from state 1 by *any* kind of adiabatic process, reversible or irreversible, if the system evolves a positive amount of heat in the reversible process by which state 1 becomes

187

state 2. This limitation is imposed by the second law and not by the first law, which calls merely for conservation of energy in any form.

A definite example of this situation exists when a perfect gas is reversibly and isothermally compressed. As work is done on the gas by the surroundings, heat is evolved by the gas since the change of energy is zero at constant temperature. State 2, the final compressed state, cannot be reached from state 1 by any kind of adiabatic process, reversible or not. The second law is silent, however, on the possibility of proceeding adiabatically and isothermally from state 2, the compressed state, to state 1. This reverse process is the Joule-Thomson experiment for expansion of a perfect gas into a vacuum. The fact that the gas is here assumed to be perfect is of no importance, for the energy required to overcome van der Waal's attractions is not work. What is important and what the second law says is that there is no adiabatic process for the compression. This is a new limitation upon possible changes of state.

B. CYCLIC PROCESSES

4.4 Heat Engine

A heat engine is a device that can convert heat into work. It is commonly considered to work in cycles so that periodically the engine, commonly thought of as a working substance like a fluid, is restored to some standard state from which it can once again begin its operation. The second law of thermodynamics places certain restrictions on the performance of heat engines. The first law of thermodynamics requires merely that work produced by such a device should not exceed the heat furnished to the engine. But conservation of energy is not enough. It has been found impossible, for example, to withdraw heat at constant temperature from such huge heat reservoirs as the oceans and the atmosphere by a cyclic process and perform an equivalent amount of work. While the first law prohibits perpetual motion of the first kind, creation of energy, the second law prohibits perpetual motion of the second kind, isothermal or complete transformation of heat into work and nothing more.

The two common ways of stating the second law verbally state what cannot be done by matter, considered as an engine of some sort. The first, due to Clausius in 1854, says: It is impossible for an engine that operates in cycles to transfer heat from one reservoir to another at a higher temperature if the surroundings do not suffer a net change. From this could be deduced the mathematical statements (4.1) to (4.3). It is sufficient for this treatment to show that this verbal statement is contained in the mathematical statement.

If the surroundings do not suffer a net change in one cycle of operation, their initial and final states are the same. Because E and S are functions of state, by (3.8) and (4.3), for the surroundings

$$\left.\begin{array}{l} \Delta E_e = 0 \\ \Delta S_s = 0 \, . \end{array}\right\} \tag{4.11}$$

The subscript s indicates in (4.11) and below that the increment is for the surroundings. Since the engine works in a cycle, again by (3.8) and (4.3), for the engine in one cycle,

$$\left.\begin{array}{l} \Delta E_e = 0 \\ \Delta S_e = 0 \, . \end{array}\right\} \tag{4.12}$$

In (4.12) and below, the subscript e refers to the engine. Conservation of energy requires that the heat evolved by the low-temperature reservoir be equal to the heat absorbed by the high-temperature reservoir since the engine and reservoirs are unaffected by the surroundings, which are supposed not to change. That is, for all three, if ΔE_r is the increase in the energy of the reservoirs per cycle,

$$\Delta E = \Delta E_e + \Delta E_r + \Delta E_s = 0 \, . \tag{4.13}$$

Whence, by (4.11) and (4.12),

$$\Delta E_r = 0 \, . \tag{4.14}$$

From (4.14), since no work is done by engine, reservoirs, or surroundings,

$$\Delta E_r = q_1 + q_2 = 0 \tag{4.15}$$

where q_1 is the heat absorbed by the low-temperature reservoir at temperature T_1 and q_2 is the heat absorbed by the high-temperature reservoir at temperature T_2. From (4.15),

$$q_2 = -q_1 \, . \tag{4.16}$$

That is, the heat absorbed by the high-temperature reservoir equals the heat evolved by the low-temperature reservoir, as was concluded intuitively above.

The entropy change per cycle for the reservoirs is, by (4.5) and (4.16),

$$\Delta S_r = \frac{q_1}{T_1} + \frac{q_2}{T_2} = \frac{q_1}{T_1} - \frac{q_1}{T_2} \, . \tag{4.17}$$

But the engine, reservoirs, and surroundings comprise an isolated system for which (4.7) and (4.9) give (4.18).

$$\Delta S = \Delta S_e + \Delta S_r + \Delta S_s \geqslant 0 \, . \tag{4.18}$$

Substitution of (4.11), (4.12), and (4.17) into (4.18) gives

$$\Delta S_r = q_1 \left(\frac{1}{T_1} - \frac{1}{T_2} \right) \geqslant 0 \, . \tag{4.19}$$

If a positive amount of heat is evolved by the low-temperature reservoir, as supposed, $q_1 < 0$ and (4.19) requires that

$$\frac{1}{T_1} - \frac{1}{T_2} \leqslant 0 . \tag{4.20}$$

But (4.20) is equivalent to (4.21).

$$T_1 \geqslant T_2 . \tag{4.21}$$

That is, (4.21) says that the low-temperature reservoir with temperature T_1 really has the higher temperature if it evolves a positive amount of heat to the engine and if the mathematical statement of the second law is true. That is, the supposed operations are indeed impossible as stated verbally, because they lead inexorably to the contradiction (4.21). Moreover, this proof shows that the transfer of heat is reversible if $T_1 = T_2$ and spontaneous if $T_1 > T_2$. Briefly said, heat flows spontaneously from a high to a low temperature.

If heat does flow spontaneously from a high to a low temperature, it should be put to work. In their statement of the second law, Thomson and Planck say: A process the final result of which is merely a transformation of heat into work is impossible.

In order to deduce this verbal statement from the mathematical statement (4.1) to (4.3), let the heat engine perform a positive amount of work w on the surroundings by absorbing a positive amount of heat q from a thermal reservoir at temperature T. Since the process is adiabatic, for the surroundings,

$$\left. \begin{array}{l} \Delta E_s = w \\ \Delta S_s = 0 . \end{array} \right\} \tag{4.22}$$

Since the engine operates cyclically, for one cycle, as for (4.12),

$$\left. \begin{array}{l} \Delta E_e = 0 \\ \Delta S_e = 0 . \end{array} \right\} \tag{4.23}$$

But the engine absorbs heat q from the heat reservoir in order to do work w in one cycle; hence, by the first law,

$$\Delta E_e = q - w = 0 \tag{4.24}$$

$$\Delta E_r = -q . \tag{4.25}$$

Equation (4.25) is the result of conservation of energy for engine, reservoirs, and surroundings. Since the reservoir evolves the heat q at the temperature T, for it, by (4.5) and (4.25),

$$\Delta S_r = -\frac{q}{T} . \tag{4.26}$$

For the system, which consists of engine and reservoir, and the surroundings, (4.7) and (4.9) yield (4.27).

$$\Delta S = \Delta S_e + \Delta S_r + \Delta S_s \geqslant 0 . \tag{4.27}$$

Since (4.24) gives $q = w$, substitution of (4.24), (4.22), (4.23), and (4.26) into (4.27) gives (4.28).

$$-\frac{w}{T} \geqslant 0 . \tag{4.28}$$

For values of T greater than zero, there is no positive value of w that satisfies (4.28). That is, the second law says that there is no engine that can do work by operating in cycles if it merely absorbs heat at one temperature. Only if there were irreversible or noncyclic changes in the surroundings or system could such an engine do work. The second verbal statement of the second law is justified.

The qualification that the engine operate in a cycle is important. It is possible to transform heat isothermally completely into work, as in the isothermal reversible expansion of a perfect gas. If the pressure fell to one-half its initial value, the work done reversibly at the constant temperature T by a mole of gas would be $RT \ln 2$ by (3.46b). But the gas (heat engine) would not have returned to its initial state after doing the work and absorbing heat at the constant temperature as it worked.

A very well-known cyclic process in which a heat engine transforms into work some of the heat which is put at its disposal is the *Carnot cycle*. Although the Carnot cycle is reversible, it is convenient to develop the mathematics for an irreversible process that involves the same steps. The four parts of the cycle as experienced by the engine (the working substance, which is commonly supposed to be a compressible fluid) are: (a) *isothermal absorption* by the working substance of a positive amount of heat q_2 from the heat reservoir at the constant temperature T_2; (b) *adiabatic expansion* in which the temperature of the working substance falls from T_2 to T_1; (c) *isothermal evolution* by the working substance of a positive amount *of heat* $-q_1$ to the heat reservoir at the constant temperature T_1 such that (d) *adiabatic compression* in which the temperature of the working substance rises from T_1 to T_2 completes the cycle and returns the working substance to its initial state.

Translation of these four steps of the cycle into mathematical symbols yields (4.29) for the heats absorbed by the working substance.

$$q_2 \text{ at } T_2, \qquad dT_2 = 0 \tag{4.29a}$$

$$dq = 0, \qquad T_2 \rightarrow T_1 \tag{4.29b}$$

$$q_1 \text{ at } T_1, \qquad dT_1 = 0 \tag{4.29c}$$

$$dq = 0, \qquad T_1 \rightarrow T_2 . \tag{4.29d}$$

For the cycle, since initial and final states are alike, if w' is the positive work done by the working substance,

$$0 = \oint dE = q_1 + q_2 - w' \tag{4.30}$$

$$0 = \oint dS \geqslant \frac{q_1}{T_1} + \frac{q_2}{T_2}. \tag{4.31}$$

The efficiency ϵ_{eng} of the engine is the ratio of w', the work done by the system (engine or working substance), to the heat q_2 absorbed by the system at the higher temperature T_2. Elimination of q_1 from (4.30) and (4.31) yields (4.34) by the following manipulations. By (4.31),

$$0 \geqslant \frac{q_1}{T_1} + \frac{q_2}{T_2}, \qquad 0 \geqslant \frac{1}{T_2} + \frac{q_1}{q_2 T_1}$$

$$\frac{q_1}{q_2} \leqslant -\frac{T_1}{T_2} \left. \begin{cases} T_1 > 0 \\ q_2 > 0. \end{cases} \right\} \tag{4.32}$$

By (4.30),

$$w' = q_1 + q_2$$

$$\frac{w'}{q_2} = 1 + \frac{q_1}{q_2}. \tag{4.33}$$

Addition of (4.32) and (4.33) gives the desired result, where ϵ_{eng} is equal to the ratio of w' to q_2 by definition.

$$\epsilon_{eng} = \frac{w'}{q_2} \leqslant 1 - \frac{T_1}{T_2}$$

$$\epsilon_{eng} = \frac{w'}{q_2} \leqslant \frac{T_2 - T_1}{T_2}. \tag{4.34}$$

The efficiency ϵ of this kind of reversible cycle, the Carnot cycle, is equal to the right-hand member of (4.34). It is independent of everything except the temperatures of the two heat reservoirs. The efficiency of an irreversible cycle is less than that of a reversible one, for then the inequality obtains.

Many kinds of reversible cycles are possible. If there are, however, a maximum temperature T_2 and a minimum temperature T_1 between which any reversible cycle is confined, it can be shown that Equation (4.34) gives the maximum efficiency for any such reversible cycle. Even a reversible cycle may have an efficiency less than the greatest difference in temperatures divided by the highest temperature if some of the heat is transferred at intermediate temperatures.

Example 4.1. Calculate the maximum efficiency with which heat from these reservoirs can be converted into work. Assume that the thermodynamic temperature scale is the same as the perfect gas temperature scale. (a) Steam at 100°C and water at 25°C; (b) steam at 150°C and water at 25°C; (c) mercury vapor at 357°C and liquid mercury at 100°C; (d) helium at 2000°C (from atomic reactor) and helium at 500°C; (e) helium at 5×10^6°C (from nuclear fission) and helium at 1000°C.

With the use of Equation (4.34), $\epsilon_{\text{eng}} = (T_2 - T_1)/T_2$, and

$$\text{(a)} \qquad \epsilon_{\text{eng}} = \frac{373 - 298}{373} = 0.20$$

$$\text{(b)} \qquad \epsilon_{\text{eng}} = \frac{423 - 298}{423} = 0.30$$

$$\text{(c)} \qquad \epsilon_{\text{eng}} = \frac{630 - 373}{630} = 0.41$$

$$\text{(d)} \qquad \epsilon_{\text{eng}} = \frac{2273 - 773}{2273} = 0.66$$

$$\text{(e)} \qquad \epsilon_{\text{eng}} = \frac{5 \times 10^6 - 0.001 \times 10^6}{5 \times 10^6} = 1.0 \, .$$

4.5 Refrigerator

A refrigerator causes heat to flow from a low temperature to a high temperature. Since this process is nonspontaneous or unnatural because heat spontaneously flows from a high to a low temperature, work must be done on the system. Let w be this work done on the system, let q_1 be the heat absorbed by the working substance of the refrigerator at the low temperature T_1, and let $-q_2$ be the positive heat evolved by the working substance of the refrigerator at the high temperature T_2. These energies are related to zero by (4.35).

$$\left. \begin{array}{l} w > 0 \\ q_1 > 0 \\ q_2 < 0 \, . \end{array} \right\} \qquad (4.35)$$

The efficiency of a refrigerator is the ratio of the heat withdrawn from the surroundings, the things to be cooled, at T_1 to the work done on the system, the working substance. By definition, then, the efficiency of a refrigerator is given by (4.36).

$$\epsilon_{\text{ref}} = \frac{q_1}{w} . \qquad (4.36)$$

One cycle of operation carries the working substance of the refrigerator through an isothermal absorption of heat q_1 at T_1, an adiabatic compression in which the temperature rises from T_1 to T_2, an isothermal rejection of heat $-q_2$ at T_2, and an adiabatic expansion in which the temperature falls from

193

T_2 to T_1 and in which the cycle is completed. For one cycle, the energy and the entropy of the system do not increase; as in the previous section,

$$0 = \oint dE = q_1 + q_2 + w \tag{4.37}$$

$$0 = \oint dS \geqslant \frac{q_1}{T_1} + \frac{q_2}{T_2}. \tag{4.38}$$

Since $T_2 > 0$, (4.37) and (4.38) become

$$w = -q_1 - q_2 \tag{4.39}$$

and

$$0 \geqslant q_1 \left(\frac{T_2}{T_1}\right) + q_2. \tag{4.40}$$

Addition of (4.39) and (4.40) yields

$$w \geqslant q_1 \left(\frac{T_2}{T_1} - 1\right). \tag{4.41}$$

Since $T_2 > T_1 > 0$ by hypothesis, with the aid of (4.36), (4.41) becomes (4.42),

$$\epsilon_{ref} = \frac{q_1}{w} \leqslant \frac{T_1}{T_2 - T_1}. \tag{4.42}$$

Example 4.2. For a refrigerator that operates between $20°C$ and $-10°C$, (a) what is the maximum efficiency ϵ_{ref} predicted? (b) What is the minimum work that must be done to withdraw 1000 cal of heat from the surroundings at $-10°C$ and reject them to the room at $20°C$?

Equation (4.42) provides the solutions.

(a) $$\epsilon_{ref} = \frac{263}{293 - 263} = \frac{263}{30} = 8.8 \ (!!)$$

(b) $$w \geqslant \left(\frac{T_2 - T_1}{T_1}\right)q_1 = \frac{30}{263} \times 1000 = 114 \text{ cal}.$$

4.6 Heat Pump

A heat pump is a refrigerator the purpose of which is to heat the surroundings at the high temperature T_2 by cooling the surroundings at the low temperature T_1. It "pumps" heat to a higher temperature in the hope of doing so with an efficiency greater than unlty. The efficiency of a heat pump is defined as the ratio of the heat $-q_2$ evolved by the system at the high temperature T_2 to the work w done on the system. That is, by definition

$$\epsilon_{pump} = \frac{-q_2}{w}. \tag{4.43}$$

Although the definitions of efficiency differ for the refrigerator and heat pump because of a difference in purpose, Equations (4.35), (4.37), and (4.38) again obtain for the same kind of process, refrigeration. Since q_1 rather than q_2 is to be eliminated from the equations, (4.38) must be manipulated in a slightly different way. If $T_1 > 0$, (4.38) becomes

$$0 \geqslant q_1 + q_2 \left(\frac{T_1}{T_2} \right).$$
(4.44)

As above,

$$w = -q_1 - q_2 .$$
(4.39)

Whence, by addition and (4.43), if $T_2 > T_1 > 0$,

$$w \geqslant -q_2 \left(1 - \frac{T_1}{T_2} \right)$$

$$\epsilon_{\text{pump}} = \frac{-q_2}{w} \leqslant \frac{T_2}{T_2 - T_1} .$$
(4.45)

Although (4.45) holds the promise of cheap heat for dwellings, especially in mild climates where the difference in inside temperature T_2 and outside heat source T_1 is small, there are engineering difficulties associated with heat transfer.

C. ENTROPY CHANGES

4.7 The Fundamental Relation of Thermodynamics

In Section 3.13 the statement was made that there existed independent variables more natural than volume and temperature for the energy of closed systems. Since a closed system by definition cannot gain or lose matter, the first law (3.13) involves only heat and work.

$$dE = dq + dw .$$
(3.13)

Equation (4.4), an abbreviated form of the second law, provides a way of combining the first and second laws,

$$dq \leqslant T \, dS .$$
(4.4)

Addition of (3.13) and (4.4) yields the fundamental relation of thermodynamics for closed systems:

$$dE \leqslant T \, dS + dw .$$
(4.46)

The inequality (4.46) describes in a limited way the thermodynamic behavior of a closed system when the changes are natural or spontaneous. Of greater importance to this treatment, however, is the equality (4.46), which applies to reversible changes and equilibrium. When all work is expansion work, $dw = -P\,dV$ by (3.3), and (4.46) assumes a very important form, (4.47).

$$dE = T\,dS - P\,dV \,. \tag{4.47}$$

From (4.47) flow very readily several other useful equations. Most of what follows in this chapter is built upon either (4.46) or (4.47).

The independent variables in (4.47) appear to be S, the entropy, and V, the volume of the system. These are the natural thermodynamic variables for the energy of a closed system when only expansion work is involved. That is,

$$E = E(S, V) \,. \tag{4.48}$$

4.8 Reversible Work in a Cyclic Process

Since energy is a function of state, any cyclic process involves no energy change of the system per cycle. If the cycle is performed reversibly by a closed system, (4.46) yields (4.49).

$$0 = \oint dE = \oint T\,dS + \oint dw$$
$$-w = \oint T\,dS \,. \tag{4.49}$$

Since dw is not an exact differential, the value of (4.49) may not be zero. In particular, the Carnot cycle involves four steps that are readily described by the right-hand member of (4.49). The first and third parts of the Carnot cycle are isothermal so that T is constant for each. The second and fourth steps of the Carnot cycle are adiabatic and reversible; by (4.1), for these adiabatic reversible changes,

$$0 = dq = T\,dS \,.$$

Since $T > 0$, $dS = 0$, and the entropy is constant in the adiabatic parts of the Carnot cycle. In a two-dimensional space where T and S are the variables, the Carnot cycle then looks like Figure 4.1, where the labels on the four parts of the cycle correspond with the labels of Section 4.4 and expressions (4.29).

The integrals of (4.49) are line integrals around a closed path. The right-hand member of (4.49) is taken in the negative sense (see Appendix A), so that the value of this right-hand member is the area included by the rectangle of Figure 4.1. Thus, (4.49) says that the reversible work $-w$ done by the working substance in a Carnot cycle is the area of the rectangle of Figure 4.1.

The work done by the working substances in a Carnot cycle can be described in terms of other variables somewhat more vivid in their physical signifi-

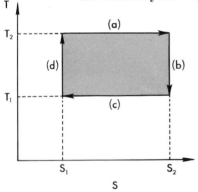

Fig. 4.1. *The Carnot Cycle in T-S Space.*

cance. If the working substance of the Carnot engine is a compressible fluid like a perfect gas, two variables suitable for work and for the specification of the state of the fluid are pressure and volume. In a two-dimensional space where P and V are the variables, the Carnot cycle then looks like Figure 4.2, where once again the labels on the four parts of the cycle correspond with the labels of Section 4.4 and expressions (4.29). The first and third parts of the cycle are isothermal so that the lines in P-V space are hyperbolas in accord with Boyle's law, PV = constant. The second and fourth parts of the cycle are adiabatics, and assume the general form shown in accord with (3.53). The line integral around the closed path of Figure 4.2 is the area of the bounded figure, as it was in Figure 4.1. Thus (4.49) says that the reversible work $-w$ done by the working substance is the bounded area of Figure 4.2. That this is true is confirmed by (3.44).

$$-w = \int_{V_1}^{V_2} P \, dV .\qquad (3.44)$$

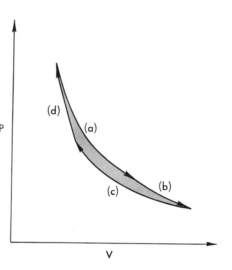

Along the first and second parts of the cycle, the integral of (3.44) is the area bounded by the V-axis and the upper curves. Along the third and fourth parts of the cycle, this integral is the area bounded by the V-axis and the lower curves, but its sign is negative since V decreases along the lower curves as the process occurs. The sum of these two areas with account of their signs is just the bounded area of Figure 4.2.

Fig. 4.2. *The Carnot Cycle in P-V Space.*

Example 4.3. One mole of a perfect gas with a molar heat capacity at constant pressure of $7R/2$ is the working substance in a Carnot cycle. The high temperature is 1000°K, the low temperature is 400°K, and in the isothermal expansion at 1000°K the work done by the gas is 1000 cal. Calculate (a) the net work done by the gas in one cycle of operation; (b) the work done on the gas, the heat absorbed by the gas, and the increments in energy, enthalpy, and entropy for each of the four parts of the cycle.

(a) For the isothermal expansion at 1000°K, $\Delta E = 0$ since the energy of a perfect gas depends only on its temperature by (3.34). It is given that $w_2 = -1000$ cal for this part of the cycle. Whence,

$$\Delta E_2 = q_2 + w_2 = q_2 - 1000 = 0$$
$$q_2 = 1000 \text{ cal} .$$

By (4.34), wherein w' is the net work done by the gas in one cycle,

$$w' = q_2 \left(\frac{T_2 - T_1}{T_2} \right)$$
$$= 1000 \left(\frac{1000 - 400}{1000} \right) = 600 \text{ cal} .$$

197

(b) For the complete cycle, $\Delta E = 0$ so that

$$\Delta E = q_2 + q_1 - w' = 0$$
$$q_1 = w' - q_2 = 600 - 1000 = -400 \text{ cal}.$$

Because the third part of the cycle is isothermal like the first part.

$$\Delta E_1 = q_1 + w_1 = 0$$
$$w_1 = -q_1 = 400 \text{ cal}.$$

For the isothermal parts, $\Delta H = 0$ by (3.35), since the enthalpy of a perfect gas is a function only of its temperature. Again, for the reversible adiabatic parts of the cycle, the entropy is constant. It is profitable at this point to summarize what is known.

PART	REVERSIBLE PROCESS	w	q	ΔE	ΔH	ΔS
a	Isothermal expansion (T_2)	-1000	1000	0	0	$\dfrac{q_2}{T_2} = \dfrac{1000}{1000}$
b	Adiabatic expansion		0			0
c	Isothermal compression (T_1)	400	-400	0	0	$\dfrac{q_1}{T_1} = \dfrac{-400}{400}$
d	Adiabatic compression		0			0
(All)	Net value for cycle	-600	600	0	0	0

The values of ΔE and ΔH for the second part of the cycle are readily calculated by the methods of Chapter 3 thus:

$$\boxed{\begin{array}{c} 1 \text{ mole} \\ T_2 = 1000°\text{K} \end{array}} \longrightarrow \boxed{\begin{array}{c} 1 \text{ mole} \\ T_1 = 400°\text{K} \end{array}}$$

By (3.40), $$C_V = C_P - R = \tfrac{7}{2}R - R = \tfrac{5}{2}R .$$

By (3.30), (3.36), (3.86), and (3.90),

$$\Delta E = \int_{T_2}^{T_1} C_V \, dT = \tfrac{5}{2} R(400 - 1000) = -1500R \text{ cal}$$

$$\Delta H = \int_{T_2}^{T_1} C_P \, dT = \tfrac{7}{2} R(400 - 1000) = -2100R \text{ cal}.$$

The values of ΔE and ΔH for the fourth part of the cycle are equal in magnitude but opposite in sign because initial and final temperatures are interchanged.

The value of w for the second and fourth parts of the cycle can be found by the first law. For example, for the second part, by (3.12),

$$w = \Delta E - q = -1500R - 0 = -1500R \text{ cal}.$$

And so the table of values is complete.

PART	REVERSIBLE PROCESS	w	q	ΔE	ΔH	ΔS
a	Isothermal expansion (T_2)	−1000	1000	0	0	1.00
b	Adiabatic expansion	−1500R	0	−1500R	−2100R	0
c	Isothermal compression (T_1)	400	−400	0	0	−1.00
d	Adiabatic compression	1500R	0	1500R	2100R	0
(All)	Net value for cycle	−600	600	0	0	0

The values for w have been found indirectly without integration. As a check, the value of w for the adiabatic compression can be found by (3.55).

$$w = \frac{nR(T_2 - T_1)}{\gamma - 1} = \frac{R(1000 - 400)}{\frac{7}{5} - 1} = 1500R .$$

4.9 Entropy Changes in an Isothermal Process

By the definition (3.21) of H and the rules of calculus,

$$dH = d(E + PV)$$
$$= dE + P \, dV + V \, dP . \qquad (4.50)$$

For any isobaric reversible process that involves only expansion work, $dP = 0$ and (4.47) is true. Hence, substitution of (4.47) into (4.50) yields (4.51).

$$dH = T \, dS - P \, dV + P \, dV + V \, dP$$
$$dH = T \, dS . \qquad (4.51)$$

Integration of (4.51) between states 1 and 2 is easy if T is constant; thus:

$$\int_{H_1}^{H_2} dH = \int_{S_1}^{S_2} T \, dS$$
$$\Delta H = T \, \Delta S . \qquad (4.52)$$

Equation (4.52) is applicable to isothermal isobaric reversible changes like phase transitions: fusion, vaporization, sublimation, and so forth.

Example 4.4. From the rounded data in this table (Rossini, F. D., *et al.*, *Selected Values of Chemical Thermodynamic Properties*. Washington, D. C.: Circular of the National Bureau of Standards 500, 1952), find the molar entropies of vaporization of the substances listed.

The molar entropies of vaporization ΔS_v as calculated by (4.52) are listed in the fourth column of the table. Of 500 substances boiling at 1 atm without dissociation or polymerization, half had ΔS_v from 21 to 23 cal mole^{-1} deg^{-1} (Trouton's rule). In general, ΔS_v increases as complexity and polarity increase.

SUBSTANCE	ΔH_v (cal mole^{-1})	T_b (°K)	$\Delta S_v = \dfrac{\Delta H_v}{T_b}$ (cal mole^{-1} deg^{-1})
CH$_4$	1,960	112	17.5
Ar	1,560	87.3	17.9
Cl$_2$	4,880	239	20.4
AgBr	37,000	1806	20.5
C$_2$H$_3$Cl	5,500	259	21.2
Zn	27,400	1180	23.2
Ag	60,700	2466	24.6
H$_2$O	9,720	373	26.0
ZnCl$_2$	30,900	1029	30.0

4.10 Entropy as a Function of Temperature

Equation (4.51) provides the means of calculating the change in entropy attendant upon a change in temperature. One of the restrictions on (4.51) is that the process for which it is written be isobaric. Division by dT and explicit statement of this restriction by a subscript leads to (4.53) if recourse is had to the definition of C_P in (3.27).

$$\left(\frac{\partial H}{\partial T}\right)_P = T\left(\frac{\partial S}{\partial T}\right)_P = C_P . \tag{4.53}$$

By the very meaning of the derivative, the increment in entropy for any reversible isobaric process that involves only expansion work on a closed system is

$$\Delta S = \int_{(1)}^{(2)} \left(\frac{\partial S}{\partial T}\right)_P dT$$

$$= \int_{T_1}^{T_2} \frac{C_P}{T} dT . \tag{4.54}$$

Even if the actual process is not reversible, (4.54) is the proper way to calculate the value of ΔS for the process that transforms the well-defined state (1) with the temperature T_1 into the well-defined state (2) with the temperature T_2. Since Table 3.1 contains C_P as a power series in T, the integration is easily performed.

In a similar way, (4.47) provides the means of calculating ΔS for a reversible process that involves no work of any kind. If the volume is constant, $dw = -P\,dV = 0$ since $dV = 0$. Then, by (4.47), the analogue of (4.51) is

$$dE = T\,dS . \tag{4.55}$$

Division by dT and explicit statement that the volume is constant leads to (4.56), where the definition of C_V is given by (3.26).

$$\left(\frac{\partial E}{\partial T}\right)_V = T\left(\frac{\partial S}{\partial T}\right)_V = C_V . \tag{4.56}$$

The unique increment in entropy for any process by which state (1) with temperature T_1 and volume V becomes state (2) with temperature T_2 and the same volume V is given by (4.57) if the system is closed.

$$\Delta S = \int_{(1)}^{(2)} \left(\frac{\partial S}{\partial T}\right)_V dT$$

$$= \int_{T_1}^{T_2} \frac{C_V}{T} dT . \tag{4.57}$$

Both (4.54) and (4.57) are readily integrated if the heat capacity C_P or C_V is independent of temperature. Then,

$$\Delta S = \int_{T_1}^{T_2} \frac{C}{T} \, dT$$

$$= C \int_{T_1}^{T_2} \frac{dT}{T}$$

$$C = \ln\left(\frac{T_2}{T_1}\right). \tag{4.58}$$

The increase in entropy ΔS is an extensive property and if n moles constitute the system with molar heat capacity C, (4.58) becomes (4.59) and similar adjustments can be made for the other equations of this section.

$$\Delta S = \int_{T_1}^{T_2} \frac{nC}{T} \, dT$$

$$= nC \ln\left(\frac{T_2}{T_1}\right). \tag{4.59}$$

Example 4.5. Calculate the increment in entropy suffered by two moles gaseous oxygen when its temperature is changed from 300.00°K to 400.00°K (a) at constant pressure; and (b) at constant volume.

From Table 3.1, for oxygen,

$$C_P = 6.0954 + 3.2533 \times 10^{-3}T - 1.0171 \times 10^{-6}T^2.$$

And from (3.40), $C_V = C_P - R$.

(a) At constant pressure, by (4.53) or (4.54),

$$\Delta S = 2 \int_{300.00}^{400.00} (6.0954 + 3.2533 \times 10^{-3}T - 1.0171 \times 10^{-6}T^2) \frac{dT}{T}$$

$$= 2 \left[6.0954 \ln\left(\frac{400.00}{300.00}\right) + 3.2533 \times 10^{-3}(400.00 - 300.00) \right.$$

$$\left. - \frac{1.0171 \times 10^{-6}}{2}(400.00^2 - 300.00^2) \right]$$

$$= 2(1.7536 + 0.3253 - 0.0356) = 4.0866 \text{ cal deg}^{-1}.$$

(b) At constant volume, by (4.57),

$$\Delta S = 2 \int_{T_1}^{T_2} \frac{C_V}{T} \, dT = 2 \int_{T_1}^{T_2} \left(\frac{C_P - R}{T}\right) dT$$

$$= 4.0866 - 2R \ln\left(\frac{T_2}{T_1}\right)$$

$$= 4.0866 - 2 \times 1.98719 \ln\left(\tfrac{4}{3}\right) = 4.0866 - 1.1434$$

$$= 2.9432 \text{ cal deg}^{-1}.$$

D. THE THIRD LAW

4.11 The Third Law Stated

Just as there are several ways of stating the second law of thermodynamics, so are there also several ways of stating the third law. For the sake of directness, the mathematically most tractable way is chosen.

The third law of thermodynamics says: At any pressure, the entropy of every crystalline solid in thermodynamic equilibrium at absolute zero is zero. The value zero is chosen as this common reference value not only because of its mathematical simplicity but also because it makes good sense when thermodynamic properties are calculated from the mechanical properties of atoms and molecules by the methods of statistical mechanics (see Chapter 9).

When there is an increase in randomness and disorder on the microscopic scale of atoms, molecules, and other invisible bits of matter, then there is also a corresponding increase in entropy of that matter. Examples 4.4 and 4.5 illustrate this idea. In the liquid the molecules of methane or water are packed tightly together, but in the gaseous state there are huge voids separating the molecules. Compared to the liquid, where rotation and diffusion are limited by favorable van der Waals contacts and hydrogen bonds and by dense packing, the gas is in frenzied activity. All entropies of vaporization of Example 4.4 were positive; as disorder increased, entropy increased. Similarly, since heats of fusion are greater than zero, destruction of order and symmetry of a crystal lattice in favor of disorder and homogeneity of a liquid is accompanied by an increase in entropy as fusion occurs. Again, the increments of entropy of Example 4.5 were positive, for increases in temperature, attended as they are by increased violence of chaotic molecular activity, mean more disorder and an increase in entropy. Moreover, the increase in entropy was less for the constant volume process of Example 4.5 than it was for the constant pressure process. The volume of oxygen at 400°K after the constant pressure process was greater than after the constant volume process, and any such increase in volume means a withdrawal from the region of condensed phases toward disorder and a greater entropy.

Not every condensed phase has the degree of order and regularity characteristic of its equilibrium state even though it be condensed slowly and carefully. The fact that an inordinately great viscosity can so retard movements that diffusion cannot supply the proper units properly oriented for the growth of crystals is only one aspect of the difficulty of attaining true equilibrium in a reasonable time at low temperatures. The ends of molecules of carbon monoxide are so similar that solid carbon monoxide contains molecules at each lattice site almost without regard for which end of the molecule is which. Once such a lattice is built, the high energy barrier, which restricts reorientation very effectively, prevents the approach to equilibrium and a more orderly structure. Similarly, the hydrogen bonds in ice can be formed in many ways; and once formed, an unlikely cooperative movement of protons is required to achieve the most orderly and stable crystal.

A crystalline species may be quite perfect in its structure yet not be at equilibrium. It is conceivable, in other words, to quench by rapid cooling and preserve a crystal that is thermodynamically metastable. The classic example is monoclinic sulfur, which is unstable but readily kept below 95°C. Such metastable but perfect crystals are not at equilibrium and would not have zero entropy at absolute zero. The excess entropy of such a metastable or glassy state, which would remain at absolute zero, is called the *zero-point entropy* and can be evaluated by statistical methods and sometimes by experiment.

It is generally believed that there is really only one most stable equilibrium state for crystals at absolute zero. Even the many energy states that differ by the very weak interaction of nuclear magnetic spin moments would probably interact among themselves and with their lattice to form one most stable state. Even if this does not occur, however, the third law is true provided the number of such states in 1 mole is much less than Avogadro's number (see Section 9.8). It is sometimes said, for example, that alloys generally exhibit residual zero-point entropy at absolute zero. However, at true equilibrium such an alloy would form either several phases or a super-lattice that would behave properly.

The third law has its origins deep in quantum mechanics. It is not surprising, then, that liquid helium, which owes its peculiar behavior to quantum effects, should behave like a crystal with regard to its entropy at absolute zero. Calculations show that a perfect gas and the electron gas of metals also behave in the ideal way.

If the entropies of all crystalline species in thermodynamic equilibrium are indeed zero at absolute zero, any change that could in principle be performed reversibly at absolute zero would have associated with it no entropy change, for all such entropies are zero by hypothesis. In his original statement of the third law, Nernst said, "As the absolute temperature approaches zero, the increment in entropy for reversible isothermal processes in crystalline solids approaches zero as a limit."

A third statement of this law says: It is impossible to reduce the temperature of any system to absolute zero by any process. Although it is possible to derive from this statement the fact that the entropies of any two substances at equilibrium at absolute zero are equal, it is sufficient for this treatment to follow the style of treatment of the second law and prove this verbal statement of an impossibility from the mathematical statement.[2]

Suppose that a reversible process by which state (1) becomes state (2) is to be used to achieve absolute zero. Such a process might be adiabatic demagnetization, in which state (1) is a paramagnetic salt like gadolinium

203

sulfate that is cooled in liquid helium in a strong magnetic field and state (2) is achieved by removing the magnetic field slowly when the salt is isolated from its surroundings. Since the atomic spins become disordered as the field is removed, the energy required for the disordering process comes from the crystal lattice and the salt is cooled. Whether this or some other process be used, the entropies of the initial and final states are given, as in (4.54), by

$$S_1(T_1) - S_1(0) = \int_0^{T_1} \frac{C_P^{(1)}}{T} \, dT \tag{4.60}$$

$$S_2(T_2) - S_2(0) = \int_0^{T_2} \frac{C_P^{(2)}}{T} \, dT . \tag{4.61}$$

And by the third law,

$$S_2(0) = S_1(0) . \tag{4.62}$$

Only an adiabatic process is acceptable, for there is no heat reservoir at a lower temperature to accept heat from the system. But for any adiabatic reversible process, by (4.7),

$$\Delta S = S_2(T_2) - S_1(T_1) = 0 . \tag{4.63}$$

Substitution of (4.60), (4.61), and (4.62) into (4.63) yields (4.64).

$$\int_0^{T_1} \frac{C_P^{(1)}}{T} \, dT = \int_0^{T_2} \frac{C_P^{(2)}}{T} \, dT . \tag{4.64}$$

If T_2 is to be zero, then the right side of (4.64) is zero because the limits of the definite integral are equal, and

$$\int_0^{T_1} \frac{C_P^{(1)}}{T} \, dT = 0 . \tag{4.65}$$

But if the process starts at a real positive temperature T_1, it is impossible to satisfy (4.65) because $C_P^{(1)}$ is greater than zero at all temperatures. Since a similar argument holds when T_1 is to be forced to zero, even the reverse process is of no use. In other words, it is impossible to achieve absolute zero by a reversible process performed a finite number of times.

Again, the process by which absolute zero is to be reached might be irreversible, such as pumping off helium gas from liquid helium in the hope that the reduction in pressure and the heat of vaporization will cause the liquid to cool toward absolute zero. By (4.9),

$$\Delta S = S_2(T_2) - S_1(T_1) > 0 . \tag{4.66}$$

In a similar way it is found as for (4.64) that

$$\int_0^{T_2} \frac{C_P^{(2)}}{T} \, dT > \int_0^{T_1} \frac{C_P^{(1)}}{T} \, dT . \tag{4.67}$$

If $T_2 = 0$, it is impossible to satisfy (4.67).

Once again, if the initial state be metastable, like a glass or solid solution, in accord with the discussion of zero point entropy,

$$S_1(0) > S_2(0) . \tag{4.68}$$

Substitution of (4.60), (4.61), and (4.68) into (4.66) yields (4.67), which cannot be satisfied if $T_2 = 0$. It is therefore impossible to reach absolute zero by a process that is reversible or irreversible, even if repeated again and again, for each repetition suffers from the same limitation. Very low temperatures, of the order of $0.001°K$, have indeed been reached by adiabatic demagnetization, but absolute zero itself is unattainable.

4.12 Standard Entropies

In fixing a common reference point for entropies of all crystalline solids at equilibrium, the third law permits the calculation of absolute values of entropy. In brief, it supplies a universal integration constant for (4.53) and (4.56). With the use of the third law for an imagined reversible process in which a crystalline solid with molar heat capacity C_P at the pressure P is warmed from absolute zero to temperature T, (4.53) yields (4.69) on integration.

$$\Delta S = S(T, P) - S(0, P) = \int_0^T \left(\frac{\partial S}{\partial T'}\right)_P dT' = \int_0^T \frac{C_P}{T'} dT' .$$

Or, since $S(0, P) = 0$ by the third law,

$$S(T, P) = \int_0^T \frac{C_P}{T'} dT' . \tag{4.69}$$

For a similar reversible process at constant volume, (4.56) yields (4.70).

$$S(T, V) = \int_0^T \frac{C_V}{T'} dT' . \tag{4.70}$$

The values of C_P for many solids have been measured at low temperatures and have been calculated theoretically by the methods of statistical mechanics. Near absolute zero, where measurements are difficult or impossible, it is common practice to extrapolate observed values to zero with theoretical expressions as guides. For many crystals, lattice vibrations are dominant in determining the heat capacity; for these, C_P is proportional to the cube of the absolute temperature. In addition to a term proportional to T^3, metals exhibit a term proportional to the temperature itself and due to the conduction electrons. Solids that exhibit quantum effects may have additive contributions to their heat capacities that vary as another power of T, like $T^{3/2}$ for spin waves. The heat capacity at low temperatures may depend measurably upon the state of division or the surface area. The

205

most common dependence, however, is that of (4.71), where $\gamma = 0$ for nonconductors.

$$C_P \approx C_V = \gamma T + BT^3 . \tag{4.71}$$

The value of γ ranges from about 1 to 40×10^{-4} cal mole^{-1} deg^{-2} and B is given by (4.72).

$$B = \frac{12\pi^4 R}{5\theta^3} . \tag{4.72}$$

In (4.72), θ is the Debye characteristic temperature, which generally varies from 50 to 500°K. Figure 4.3 illustrates the behavior of heat capacities of conductors and nonconductors near absolute zero.

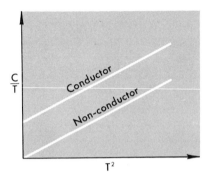

Fig. 4.3. *Typical Behavior of Heat Capacity* C *Below About 10°K.*

The absolute entropy of a substance at any temperature can be calculated if its heat capacity and its various heats of transition are known. Suppose that the absolute entropy of a gas at the temperature T is to be calculated. Below the temperature T_{tr}, the solid exists at equilibrium as the α modification with the heat capacity $C_P^{(\alpha)}$. At T_{tr}, the α form is transformed reversibly at the pressure P into the β form, the heat of transition being $\Delta H_{\alpha,\beta}$. Between T_{tr} and T_f, the heat capacity of the stable β form is $C_P^{(\beta)}$. At T_f, the β form melts reversibly with a heat of fusion ΔH_f. The liquid has the heat capacity $C_P^{(l)}$ and the heat of vaporization is ΔH_v at the pressure P at the boiling point T_b, and the heat capacity of the gas is $C_P^{(g)}$. The reversible isobaric process by which the absolute entropy is evaluated is diagrammed:

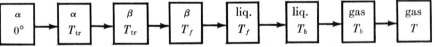

The second, fourth, and sixth steps are isothermal and the increase in entropy for each can be found by (4.52). The odd-numbered processes are not isothermal and the increase in entropy for each can be found by (4.54). For the diagrammed changes, then, since S is a function of state,

$$\Delta S = S(T, P) - S(0, P) \tag{4.73}$$

where $S(T, P)$ is the absolute entropy of the gas at the temperature T and pressure P and where $S(0, P)$, the absolute entropy of the stable crystalline solid at equilibrium at 0°K, is zero by the third law. Thus,

$$S(T, P) = \int_0^{T_{tr}} \frac{C_P^{(\alpha)}}{T} \, dT + \frac{\Delta H_{\alpha,\beta}}{T_{tr}} + \int_{T_{tr}}^{T_f} \frac{C_P^{(\beta)}}{T} \, dT + \frac{\Delta H_f}{T_f}$$

$$+ \int_{T_f}^{T_b} \frac{C_P^{(l)}}{T} \, dT + \frac{\Delta H_v}{T_b} + \int_{T_b}^{T} \frac{C_P^{(g)}}{T'} \, dT' . \tag{4.74}$$

If the substance exists as a condensed phase at T, some of the last terms of (4.74) are to be omitted.

The integrals of (4.74) are ordinarily performed graphically because of the difficulty of expressing the heat capacities by an explicit function of T that fully reflects the experimental accuracy. For example, the first integral can be expressed in two convenient ways, namely, (4.75) and (4.76).

$$S(T) = \int_0^T \left(\frac{C_P}{T'}\right) dT' \tag{4.75}$$

$$S(T) = \int_0^T C_P \, d(\ln T') . \tag{4.76}$$

If the former method were used, (C_P/T') would be plotted as a function of T'; and the area bounded by the curve, the T' axis, and the line $T' = T$ would be $S(T)$. If the latter method were used, C_P would be plotted as a function of $\ln T'$ and the area bounded by $\ln T' = \ln T$, the curve, the abscissa axis, and $\ln T'$ for some small value of T' would be calculated. The value of this integral in the immediate neighborhood of absolute zero is readily found through (4.77) or a similar equation. For a nonconductor, at these lowest temperatures where experimental values of C_P are lacking,

Table 4.1. *Standard Entropies S^o of Elements, Compounds, and Ions at $25°C$ (calories per degree per gram formula weight)**

SUBSTANCE	S^o	SUBSTANCE	S^o	SUBSTANCE	S^o
$O_{2(g)}$	49.003	$C_{(s)(graphite)}$	1.3609	$AgBr_{(s)}$	25.60
$O_{3(g)}$	56.8	$C_{(s)(diamond)}$	0.5829	$Ag_2CO_{3(s)}$	40.0
$H_{2(g)}$	31.211	$CO_{(g)}$	47.301	$Fe_{(s)}$	6.49
$OH^-_{(aq)}$	−2.519	$CO_{2(g)}$	51.061	$Fe_2O_{3(s)}$	21.5
$H_2O_{(g)}$	45.106	$CO_{2(aq)}$	29.0	$Mn_{(s)(\alpha)}$	7.59
$H_2O_{(l)}$	16.716	$CO_3^{--}{}_{(aq)}$	−12.7	$Mn_{(s)(\gamma)}$	7.72
$F^-_{(aq)}$	−2.3	$CH_{4(g)}$	44.50	$Mn^{++}{}_{(aq)}$	−20.
$F_{2(g)}$	48.6	$HCO_3^-{}_{(aq)}$	22.7	$MnO_{2(s)}$	12.7
$HF_{(g)}$	41.47	$C_2H_{2(g)}$	47.997	$MnO_4^-{}_{(aq)}$	45.4
$Cl^-_{(aq)}$	13.17	$C_2H_{4(g)}$	52.45	$Al_{(s)}$	6.769
$Cl_{2(g)}$	53.286	$C_2H_{6(g)}$	54.85	$Al_2O_{3(s)(\alpha)}$	12.186
$HCl_{(g)}$	44.617	$Pb_{(s)}$	15.51	$Ba_{(s)}$	16.
$Br^-_{(aq)}$	19.29	$Pb^{++}{}_{(aq)}$	5.1	$Ba^{++}{}_{(aq)}$	3.
$Br_{2(g)}$	58.639	$PbSO_{4(s)}$	35.2	$BaCl_{2(s)}$	30.
$Br_{2(l)}$	36.4	$ZnSO_{4(s)}$	29.8	$BaCl_2.H_2O_{(s)}$	40.
$HBr_{(g)}$	47.437	$ZnSO_4.H_2O_{(s)}$	34.9	$BaCl_2.2 H_2O_{(s)}$	48.5
$SO_{2(g)}$	59.40	$ZnSO_4.6 H_2O_{(s)}$	86.8	$BaSO_{4(s)}$	31.6
$SO_{3(g)}$	61.24	$ZnSO_4.7 H_2O_{(s)}$	92.4	$Na_{(s)}$	12.2
$SO_4^{--}{}_{(aq)}$	4.1	$Ag_{(s)}$	10.206	$Na^+_{(aq)}$	14.4
$N_{2(g)}$	45.767	$Ag^+_{(aq)}$	17.67	$NaCl_{(s)}$	17.30
$NO_{(g)}$	50.339	$Ag_2O_{(s)}$	29.09	$Na_2SO_{4(s)}$	35.73
$NO_{2(g)}$	57.47	$AgCl_{(s)}$	22.97	$Na_2SO_4.10 H_2O_{(s)}$	141.7

* Rossini, F. D., D. D. Wagman, W. H. Evans, S. Levine, and I. Jaffe, *Selected Values of Chemical Thermodynamic Properties.* Washington, D. C. 1952. Circular of the National Bureau of Standards 500.

$$S(T, P) = \int_0^T \frac{B(T')^3}{T'} \, dT' = B \int_0^T (T')^2 \, dT' = \frac{B}{3} T^3 = \frac{C_P}{3} \quad (4.77)$$

where C_P is the value at the lowest observed temperature T.

Table 4.1 lists the absolute entropies of various substances at the standard temperature of $298.16°K$. The standard entropy of $H_{(aq)}^+$ is zero by convention. The method of calculating them is illustrated in Example 4.6, which follows.

Example 4.6. From the data presented below, the third law and the assumption that $Cl_{2(g)}$ is a perfect gas with $C_P = 8.18$ cal mole^{-1} deg^{-1}, calculate the absolute standard entropy of $Cl_{2(g)}$ at $298.16°K$ at 1 atm. The data are taken from Giauque, W. F. and T. M. Powell, *J. Am. Chem. Soc.* **61**, 1970 (1939).
Fusion: $\Delta H_f = 1.531$ kcal mole^{-1} at $T = 172.12°K$.
Vaporization: $\Delta H_v = 4.878$ kcal mole^{-1} at $T = 239.05°K$.

$T(°K)$	C_P (cal mole^{-1} deg^{-1})	$T(°K)$	C_P (cal mole^{-1} deg^{-1})	$T(°K)$	C_P (cal mole^{-1} deg^{-1})
15	0.89	80	9.23	172.12	13.27
20	1.85	90	9.71	172.12	16.03
25	2.89	100	10.10	180	16.02
30	3.99	110	10.47	190	15.99
35	4.97	120	10.87	200	15.95
40	5.73	130	11.29	210	15.89
45	6.39	140	11.73	220	15.84
50	6.99	150	12.20	230	15.77
60	8.00	160	12.68	240	15.70
70	8.68	170	13.17		

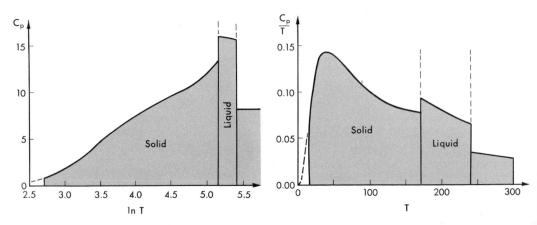

Fig. 4.4. *Graphical Integration to Obtain Absolute Entropy of Chlorine.*

With the aid of Figure 4.4 and equations from above, the absolute entropy of $Cl_{2(g)}$ is readily found by the steps indicated in the table.

ITEM	VALUE	SOURCE
Entropy of $Cl_{2(s)}$ at 15°K	0.30	(4.77)
Increase in entropy of $Cl_{2(s)}$ (15° — 172.12°K)	16.77	Figure 4.4
Entropy of fusion	8.90	(4.52)
Increase in entropy of $Cl_{2(s)}$ (172.12° — 239.05°K)	5.32	Figure 4.4
Entropy of vaporization	20.40	(4.52)
Increase in entropy of $Cl_{2(g)}$ (239.05° — 298.16°K)	1.81	(4.58)
Total = standard entropy of $Cl_{2(g)}$ (298.16°K; 1 atm)	53.50	(4.74)

The difference between this value, 53.50 cal mole^{-1} deg^{-1}, and the value from Table 4.1, 53.286 cal mole^{-1} deg^{-1}, can be ascribed to the assumptions that the gas is perfect and has a constant heat capacity of 8.18 cal mole^{-1} deg^{-1}.

E. ENTROPY OF GASES

4.13 Some Fundamental Relations

A chemist or physicist seldom finds it convenient in his experiments to control or specify some of the independent thermodynamic variables that quite naturally accompany the usual statements of the laws of thermodynamics. An example of this kind of awkward situation arose in thermochemistry. When, as often happens, only expansion work is involved in a process, the first law says directly that the heat of reaction is a function of state only if the volume is constant (or rather, if no work is done on the system by the surroundings). Since no vessel is perfectly rigid, theoretically it would be difficult to correlate theory and experiment even if it were common to perform experiments in almost rigid containers. However, by the mathematical trick presented in Section 3.7, namely, by inventing the function H, thermochemistry was simplified. In essence, the enthalpy H is more directly measured for it is easier to hold the pressure constant by operating in vessels open to the atmosphere than it is to try to experiment at constant volume. The invention of H transformed the first law into Hess's law, (3.22).

$$q_P = \Delta H. \tag{3.22}$$

A similar mathematical transformation of variables allows the fundamental equation (4.46) to be expressed in terms of independent variables more readily specified in the laboratory. As was done in Section 3.7, add $d(PV)$ to both sides of (4.46) specialized for only expansion work.

$$dE \leqslant T\,dS - P\,dV$$
$$dE + d(PV) \leqslant T\,dS - P\,dV + d(PV)$$
$$d(E + PV) \leqslant T\,dS - P\,dV + P\,dV + V\,dP$$
$$dH \leqslant T\,dS + V\,dP\,. \tag{4.78}$$

By this, pressure P has been maneuvered into the position previously held by the volume V, the awkward variable. By adding $d(-TS)$, the temperature T replaces entropy S as the second independent variable. By (4.46),

$$dE + d(-TS) \leqslant T\,dS - P\,dV + d(-TS)$$
$$d(E - TS) \leqslant -S\,dT - P\,dV\,.$$

By definition, the Helmholtz free energy function A is given by (4.79).

$$A = E - TS\,. \tag{4.79}$$

Since E, T, and S are each functions of state, the Helmholtz free energy A is also a function of state. Substitution of (4.79) into the preceding expression yields (4.80).

$$dA \leqslant -S\,dT - P\,dV\,. \tag{4.80}$$

Similarly, by (4.78),

$$dH + d(-TS) \leqslant T\,dS + V\,dP + d(-TS)$$
$$d(H - TS) \leqslant -S\,dT + V\,dP\,.$$

By definition, the Gibbs free energy function G is given by (4.81),

$$G = H - TS\,. \tag{4.81}$$

Most Americans use F instead of G for the Gibbs free energy function. However, since most Europeans use F for the Helmholtz free energy function, the symbol F is not used for either free energy in this book. Since H, T, and S are each functions of state, the Gibbs free energy G is also a function of state. Substitution of (4.81) into the preceding expression yields (4.82).

$$dG \leqslant -S\,dT + V\,dP\,. \tag{4.82}$$

In order to emphasize the importance of the functions and expressions just set forth, they are presented together in Table 4.2.

Table 4.2. *Some Fundamental Relations*

NAME OF FUNCTION	DEFINITION	RELATION
Energy	E	$dE \leqslant T\,dS - P\,dV$
Enthalpy	$H = E + PV$	$dH \leqslant T\,dS + V\,dP$
Helmholtz free energy	$A = E - TS$	$dA \leqslant -S\,dT - P\,dV$
Gibbs free energy	$G = H - TS$	$dG \leqslant -S\,dT + V\,dP$

These four definitions are always true. The four relations apply to closed systems that have only expansion work done on them. If the process undergone by the system is reversible, the relations are equalities; if irreversible, inequalities.

These four relations are the differential equations that express the four common thermodynamic functions as functions of the independent variables S, V, P, and T. It was shown in (4.48) that energy is a function of S and V by its nature. In a similar way, the other thermodynamic functions depend on two of these four variables in the manner of (4.83), (4.84), and (4.85).

$$E = E(S, V) \qquad (4.48)$$

$$H = H(S, P) \qquad (4.83)$$

$$A = A(T, V) \qquad (4.84)$$

$$G = G(T, P) . \qquad (4.85)$$

Although these variables are natural for E, H, A, and G, and thus are generally the most convenient, it is still quite correct to treat E as a function of T and V or of some other suitable set of variables.

Because its volume is immense compared to the volume changes in laboratory experiments, the atmosphere constitutes an ideal barostat for processes that can be performed in open vessels in a time so short that the diurnal variation in barometric pressure or variations due to unsettled weather are negligible. It is also relatively easy to perform experiments in thermostats in which a fluid like water or a molten salt is maintained at a constant temperature by heating or cooling devices and in which the reaction vessel is immersed. For the chemist, then, the most appropriate thermodynamic function is the Gibbs free energy $G(T, P)$. Equations (4.82) and (4.85) indicate that G is constant in any closed system that undergoes any reversible isothermal isobaric process in which all work is expansion work. There is also no change in G in any process in which the system returns to its initial state, for G is a function of state.

4.14   Some Useful Equalities

The equations of Table 4.2 not only are useful in their own right for the calculation of increments in A and G but also provide convenient definitions of T and P for statistical mechanics and convenient ways of evaluating, from equations of state, isothermal changes in E, H, and S when the volume or pressure is changed.

By the rules of calculus and the definitions of the symbols involved, (4.48) yields (4.86) for closed systems undergoing expansion work.

$$dE = \left(\frac{\partial E}{\partial S}\right)_V dS + \left(\frac{\partial E}{\partial V}\right)_S dV . \qquad (4.86)$$

211

However, substitution of the equality (4.46) into (4.86) yields (4.87).

$$T \, dS - P \, dV = \left(\frac{\partial E}{\partial S}\right)_V dS + \left(\frac{\partial E}{\partial V}\right)_S dV \,. \qquad (4.87)$$

For arbitrary variations in S and V, it is necessary that (4.88) and (4.89) be true by virtue of (4.87).

$$T = \left(\frac{\partial E}{\partial S}\right)_V \qquad (4.88)$$

$$-P = \left(\frac{\partial E}{\partial V}\right)_S \,. \qquad (4.89)$$

Although (4.89) is seldom of use, (4.88) provides a convenient definition of temperature for statistical mechanics (see Section 6.8 and Chapter 9).

Equation (4.88) is the best definition of temperature and it now replaces all others. With any substance as thermometer, the absolute temperature T is merely the limit at constant volume of the ratio of a small energy change to a small entropy change for any reversible process involving no work.

In a similar way, (4.83) and the equality (4.78) yield (4.90).

$$T \, dS + V \, dP = \left(\frac{\partial H}{\partial S}\right)_P dS + \left(\frac{\partial H}{\partial P}\right)_S dP \,. \qquad (4.90)$$

In turn, for arbitrary variations in S and P, (4.90) yields the relations (4.91) and (4.92).

$$T = \left(\frac{\partial H}{\partial S}\right)_P \qquad (4.91)$$

$$V = \left(\frac{\partial H}{\partial P}\right)_S \,. \qquad (4.92)$$

Although (4.92) is seldom used, (4.91) is in reality the important Equation (4.51).

Again, (4.84) and the equality (4.80) yield (4.93), which in turn yields (4.94) and (4.95).

$$-S \, dT - P \, dV = \left(\frac{\partial A}{\partial T}\right)_V dT + \left(\frac{\partial A}{\partial V}\right)_T dV \qquad (4.93)$$

$$-S = \left(\frac{\partial A}{\partial T}\right)_V \qquad (4.94)$$

$$-P = \left(\frac{\partial A}{\partial V}\right)_T \,. \qquad (4.95)$$

Equation (4.95) provides a convenient definition of pressure for statistical mechanics and (4.94) is useful for processes that occur at constant volume.

Lastly, for the Gibbs free energy, (4.85) and the equality (4.82) yield (4.96), which then yields (4.97) and (4.98) for arbitrary variations in T and P.

$$-S\, dT + V\, dP = \left(\frac{\partial G}{\partial T}\right)_P dT + \left(\frac{\partial G}{\partial P}\right)_T dP \tag{4.96}$$

$$-S = \left(\frac{\partial G}{\partial T}\right)_P \tag{4.97}$$

$$V = \left(\frac{\partial G}{\partial P}\right)_T . \tag{4.98}$$

Equation (4.97), the Gibbs-Helmholtz equation, finds many uses, chiefly in electrochemistry and in the dependence of G on temperature, and (4.98) is most important in regard to equilibrium constants and osmotic pressure.

Equations (4.48), (4.83), (4.84), and (4.85) state that E, H, A and G are functions of state and that increments in them are calculable along any reversible path that joins the initial and final states. The equations derived in this section thus assume that the increments are independent of the path. However, these four innocent-looking equations contain much more information. For physical systems, functions like E, H, A, and G seldom display pathological peculiarities that are the delight of the discriminating mathematician. For physically meaningful quantities like these, the two second mixed partial derivatives are equal. That is,

$$\frac{\partial^2 E}{\partial S\, \partial V} = \frac{\partial^2 E}{\partial V\, \partial S}$$

and so on for H, A, and G. If the order of such differentiation is indeed unimportant, then the eight relations just derived can be differentiated properly to give four more equalities, which are known as the *Maxwell relations*. The second mixed partial derivatives of E with respect to S and V yield, with the aid of (4.88) and (4.89),

$$\left(\frac{\partial T}{\partial V}\right)_S = -\left(\frac{\partial P}{\partial S}\right)_V . \tag{4.99}$$

In a similar way, with (4.91) and (4.92), the second mixed partial derivatives of H with respect to S and P yield

$$\left(\frac{\partial T}{\partial P}\right)_S = \left(\frac{\partial V}{\partial S}\right)_P . \tag{4.100}$$

Equations (4.99) and (4.100) are seldom used because entropy is awkward experimentally. For the calculation of changes in entropy at constant temperature from equation of state data, the following two Maxwell relations

213

are, however, very valuable. The second mixed partial derivatives of A with respect to T and V yield, from (4.94) and (4.95),

$$\left(\frac{\partial S}{\partial V}\right)_T = \left(\frac{\partial P}{\partial T}\right)_V. \tag{4.101}$$

If the pressure of a substance is given by its equation of state as a function of V and T, it is a simple matter to evaluate the right-hand member of (4.101) and thus find how entropy varies with volume at constant temperature. Finally, the second mixed partial derivatives of G with respect to T and P together with (4.97) and (4.98) yield the isothermal pressure dependence of entropy in terms that can be found from the equation of state, $V = V(T, P)$.

$$\left(\frac{\partial S}{\partial P}\right)_T = -\left(\frac{\partial V}{\partial T}\right)_P. \tag{4.102}$$

4.15 Identity of Temperature Scales

If derivatives of the kind in the right-hand members of the two preceding equations are to be found, there must be some justification that the thermodynamic temperature of the derivative is indeed the perfect gas temperature of the equation of state. Proof that the thermodynamic temperature T, defined by the second law, is the perfect gas temperature T' follows.

The usual combined form of the first and second laws is (4.47).

$$dE = T\,dS - P\,dV. \tag{4.47}$$

Division by dV at constant temperature yields

$$\left(\frac{\partial E}{\partial V}\right)_T = T\left(\frac{\partial S}{\partial V}\right)_T - P$$

and subsequent use of (4.101) leads to (4.103), an equation that relates the energy of any system directly to the variables of the equation of state.

$$\left(\frac{\partial E}{\partial V}\right)_T = T\left(\frac{\partial P}{\partial T}\right)_V - P. \tag{4.103}$$

Equation (4.103) applies to all substances and has been called the *thermodynamic equation of state*.

For a perfect gas, the energy of which is independent of its volume for isothermal changes, by (3.30),

$$0 = T\left(\frac{\partial P}{\partial T}\right)_V - P.$$

That is, at constant volume,

$$\frac{dP}{P} = \frac{dT}{T}$$

which, on definite integration from the state with pressure P_1 and temperature T_1 to the state with pressure P_2 and temperature T_2, yields (4.104).

$$\int_{P_1}^{P_2} \frac{dP}{P} = \int_{T_1}^{T_2} \frac{dT}{T}$$

$$\ln \left(\frac{P_2}{P_1}\right) = \ln \left(\frac{T_2}{T_1}\right)$$

$$\frac{P_2}{P_1} = \frac{T_2}{T_1}, \qquad (dV = 0) . \tag{4.104}$$

However, the measurement of a pressure at constant volume in a hydrogen thermometer constitutes the standard of the perfect gas temperature scale through (4.105),

$$\frac{P_2}{P_1} = \frac{T_2'}{T_1'} \tag{4.105}$$

where T_2' is the absolute gas temperature of the gas at pressure P_2 while T_1' is its gas temperature at P_1. By (4.104) and (4.105), which is really Charles law,

$$\frac{T_2'}{T_1'} = \frac{T_2}{T_1}. \tag{4.106}$$

However, (4.106) says nothing more or less than that the second law's thermodynamic temperature scale T agrees with and is identical to the perfect gas temperature scale T'.

Example 4.7. Verify that the thermodynamic equation of state (4.103) correctly describes the dependence of the energy of a perfect gas on its volume at constant temperature.

The perfect gas equation of state for 1 mole is

$$P = \frac{RT}{V}.$$

Whence,

$$\left(\frac{\partial P}{\partial T}\right)_V = \frac{R}{V} \left(\frac{\partial T}{\partial T}\right)_V = \frac{R}{V}.$$

By (4.103),

$$\left(\frac{\partial E}{\partial V}\right)_T = T \left(\frac{\partial P}{\partial T}\right)_V - P = T \left(\frac{R}{V}\right) - P = 0$$

which agrees with (3.30).

4.16 Energy of a Real Gas

The van der Waals equation,

$$\left(P + \frac{an^2}{V^2}\right)(V - nb) = nRT \tag{1.23}$$

is an equation of state which attempts in a simple way to describe the behavior of a real gas. Explicit solution for the pressure leads to

$$P = \frac{nRT}{V - nb} - \frac{an^2}{V^2}.$$

Then, toward fitting (4.103),

$$\left(\frac{\partial P}{\partial T}\right)_V = \frac{nR}{V - nb}$$

so that (4.103) becomes (4.107) in the following way.

$$\left(\frac{\partial E}{\partial V}\right)_T = T\left(\frac{nR}{V - nb}\right) - \left(\frac{nRT}{V - nb} - \frac{an^2}{V^2}\right)$$

$$\left(\frac{\partial E}{\partial V}\right)_T = \frac{an^2}{V^2}. \tag{4.107}$$

Example 4.8. Predict the final temperature of oxygen that escapes adiabatically into an evacuated chamber of such size that its final volume is ten times its initial volume at standard conditions. For O_2, C_P is constant at 4.90 cal mole^{-1} deg^{-1} and the van der Waals a is 1.36 l^2 atm mole^{-2}.

Since the change is adiabatic ($q = 0$) and involves no work ($w = 0$), ΔE is zero for the over-all change of state. A convenient diagram of the change follows.

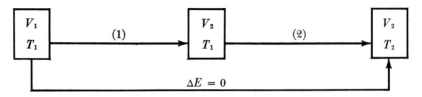

For the isothermal process (1), in which the initial molar volume V_1 becomes n times as great and finally takes the value V_2, by (3.32) and (4.107),

$$\Delta E_1 = \int_{V_1}^{V_2} \left(\frac{\partial E}{\partial V}\right)_T dV = \int_{V_1}^{V_2} \left(\frac{a}{V^2}\right) dV = -a\left(\frac{1}{V_2} - \frac{1}{V_1}\right) = \frac{a(n-1)}{nV_1}.$$

For process (2), which occurs at constant volume V_2, from (3.32) it follows that

$$\Delta E_2 = \int_{T_1}^{T_2} C_V \, dT = C_V (T_2 - T_1).$$

But since E is a function of state,

$$\Delta E = \Delta E_1 + \Delta E_2$$

$$0 = \frac{a(n-1)}{nV_1} + C_V (T_2 - T_1) \left(\frac{0.08205}{1.987}\right)$$

$$T_2 = T_1 - \frac{1.987a(n-1)}{0.08205nC_VV_1} .$$

In particular, for O_2 that begins at standard conditions,

$$T_2 = 273.16 - \frac{1.987 \times 1.36 \times 9}{0.08205 \times 10 \times 4.90 \times 22.4}$$

$$= 273.16 - 0.27 = 272.89°K .$$

4.17 Enthalpy of a Real Gas

The second law, through (4.102), permits the calculation of the Joule-Thomson coefficient from the equation of state.   In Sections 3.14 and 3.19 this coefficient was presented as an empirically observed ratio of change of temperature to change of pressure.   Now, however, the values of Table 3.2 can be calculated.

Varying the pressure isothermally for a system the enthalpy of which is described by (4.78) leads, by the equivalent formal operation of dividing by dP at constant temperature, to (4.108).

$$dH = T \, dS + V \, dP \tag{4.78}$$

$$\left(\frac{\partial H}{\partial P}\right)_T = T \left(\frac{\partial S}{\partial P}\right)_T + V . \tag{4.108}$$

By (4.102), it follows from (4.108) that

$$\left(\frac{\partial H}{\partial P}\right)_T = V - T \left(\frac{\partial V}{\partial T}\right)_P . \tag{4.109}$$

Equation (4.109) permits the calculation of the dependence of enthalpy upon pressure in isothermal processes.   As in Example 4.7, it is easy to verify that the enthalpy of a perfect gas is independent of its pressure.   The enthalpy of a real gas, however, does depend upon its pressure, and the expression of this dependence in (4.109) permits the calculation of μ, the Joule-Thomson coefficient.   By (3.57),

$$\mu = -\frac{1}{C_P} \left(\frac{\partial H}{\partial P}\right)_T$$

$$= \frac{1}{C_P} \left[T \left(\frac{\partial V}{\partial T}\right)_P - V \right] . \tag{4.110}$$

217

When the van der Waals equation is transformed into the convenient approximate form

$$PV = nRT + n\left(b - \frac{a}{RT}\right)P, \qquad (1.29)$$

Equation (4.110) permits the ready calculation not only of μ but also of the inversion temperature of a van der Waals gas. By (1.29),

$$P\left(\frac{\partial V}{\partial T}\right)_P = nR + \frac{naP}{RT^2}$$

so that, by (4.110),

$$\mu = \frac{1}{C_P}\left[\frac{nRT}{P} + \frac{na}{RT} - \frac{nRT}{P} - n\left(b - \frac{a}{RT}\right)\right]$$

$$= \frac{1}{C_P}\left(\frac{2na}{RT} - nb\right). \qquad (4.111)$$

At the inversion temperature T_i, μ is zero, so that by (4.111),

$$T_i = \frac{2a}{bR}. \qquad (4.112)$$

Example 4.9. Estimate the inversion temperature of oxygen if its van der Waals constants are $a = 1.360$ l^2 atm mole^{-2} and $b = 0.0317$ l mole^{-1}.
By (4.112),

$$T_i = \frac{2 \times 1.360}{0.0317 \times 0.08205} = 1040°K.$$

Example 4.10. Estimate the Joule-Thomson coefficient of oxygen at standard conditions from the approximate van der Waals equation of state. Values of a and b are given in Example 4.9.
By (4.111), if $C_P = 6.90$ cal mole^{-1} deg^{-1},

$$\mu = \frac{1}{6.90 \times \left(\dfrac{0.08205}{1.987}\right)}\left[\frac{2 \times 1.360}{0.08205 \times 273.2} - 0.0317\right] = 0.315° \text{ atm}^{-1}.$$

The value in Table 3.2 for O_2 is 0.366° atm^{-1}.

4.18 Entropy Changes of a Gas

Increments in entropy for reversible isothermal processes and for processes that involve only a change in temperature and could in principle be executed reversibly were calculated above in order to evaluate absolute entropies at 25°C and at the standard pressure of one atm. In order to find the increase

218

in entropy for a process that begins or ends with an arbitrary state, it is most convenient to analyze the process into two parts, one of which is isothermal and the other not isothermal. That is, if one considers the entropy of a closed system as a function of volume V and temperature T, such that

$$S = S(V, T) \tag{4.113}$$

then infinitesimal changes dV and dT in the independent variables cause a change dS in the entropy. By the rules of calculus,

$$dS = \left(\frac{\partial S}{\partial T}\right)_V dT + \left(\frac{\partial S}{\partial V}\right)_T dV . \tag{4.114}$$

The differential coefficients have already been evaluated in (4.56) and (4.101) so that

$$dS = \frac{C_V}{T} dT + \left(\frac{\partial P}{\partial T}\right)_V dV . \tag{4.115}$$

The increase in entropy for a change in volume from V_1 to V_2 and a change in temperature from T_1 to T_2 is calculated as a line integral from $S(V_1, T_1)$ to $S(V_2, T_2)$. Any path that could in principle be performed reversibly is just as good as any other because S is a function of state and dS is an exact differential. For convenience the integral is performed along two paths as diagrammed, the first being executed at constant volume and the second isothermally.

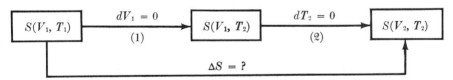

For the first process, (4.115) becomes just (4.57),

$$\Delta S_1 = \int_{T_1}^{T_2} \frac{C_V}{T} dT .$$

For the second process, (4.115) becomes

$$\Delta S_2 = \int_{V_1}^{V_2} \left(\frac{\partial P}{\partial T}\right)_V dV$$

so that, for the over-all change of state,

$$\Delta S = \Delta S_1 + \Delta S_2$$
$$= \int_{T_1}^{T_2} \frac{C_V}{T} dT + \int_{V_1}^{V_2} \left(\frac{\partial P}{\partial T}\right)_V dV . \tag{4.116}$$

If P is known as a function of V and T through the equation of state, (4.116) is readily evaluated. For example, if the system is n moles of a perfect gas with constant molar heat capacity C_V, then (4.116) becomes

$$\Delta S = nC_V \int_{T_1}^{T_2} \frac{dT}{T} + \int_{V_1}^{V_2} \left[\frac{\partial}{\partial T} \left(\frac{nRT}{V} \right) \right]_V dV$$

$$= nC_V \ln \left(\frac{T_2}{T_1} \right) + nR \int_{V_1}^{V_2} \frac{dV}{V}$$

$$= nC_V \ln \left(\frac{T_2}{T_1} \right) + nR \ln \left(\frac{V_2}{V_1} \right). \tag{4.117}$$

Each of the terms in (4.117) is greater than zero if $T_2 > T_1$ and $V_2 > V_1$. The greater the temperature or volume of a system, the less it is organized and ordered. In accord with previous discussions, an increase in randomness and disorder should be accompanied by an increase in entropy.

When the independent variables are pressure P and temperature T, as above,

$$S = S(P, T) . \tag{4.118}$$

Again by the rules of calculus,

$$dS = \left(\frac{\partial S}{\partial T} \right)_P dT + \left(\frac{\partial S}{\partial P} \right)_T dP . \tag{4.119}$$

But from (4.53) and (4.102),

$$dS = \frac{C_P}{T} dT - \left(\frac{\partial V}{\partial T} \right)_P dP . \tag{4.120}$$

For the change of state from pressure P_1 to P_2 and from temperature T_1 to T_2, it is convenient to choose the following reversible path:

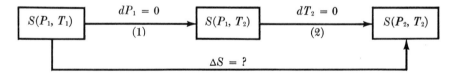

For the isobaric process, (4.120) becomes (4.54).

$$\Delta S_1 = \int_{T_1}^{T_2} \frac{C_P}{T} dT$$

For the isothermal process, (4.120) yields

$$\Delta S_2 = - \int_{P_1}^{P_2} \left(\frac{\partial V}{\partial T} \right)_P dP$$

Then, for the over-all change of state,

$$\Delta S = \Delta S_1 + \Delta S_2$$

$$= \int_{T_1}^{T_2} \frac{C_P}{T} dT - \int_{P_1}^{P_2} \left(\frac{\partial V}{\partial T}\right)_P dP. \tag{4.121}$$

Once again, if the equation of state of the system is $V = V(P, T)$, the integrals of (4.121) are readily evaluated. For n moles of a perfect gas with constant molar heat capacity C_P,

$$\Delta S = nC_P \int_{T_1}^{T_2} \frac{dT}{T} - \int_{P_1}^{P_2} \left[\frac{\partial}{\partial T}\left(\frac{nRT}{P}\right)\right]_P dP$$

$$= nC_P \ln\left(\frac{T_2}{T_1}\right) - nR \int_{P_1}^{P_2} \frac{dP}{P}$$

$$= nC_P \ln\left(\frac{T_2}{T_1}\right) + nR \ln\left(\frac{P_1}{P_2}\right). \tag{4.122}$$

If the pressure decreases, $P_1 > P_2$, and the second term of (4.122) is positive, in accord with the concept that a decrease in pressure involves a regression from the order of condensed states towards the disorder and increased entropy of a more random state.

Example 4.11. Derive (4.120) from (4.78).

By (4.78), $dH = T\, dS + V\, dP$ and (3.89) is

$$dH = C_P\, dT + \left(\frac{\partial H}{\partial P}\right)_T dP.$$

Or

$$T\, dS + V\, dP = C_P\, dT + \left(\frac{\partial H}{\partial P}\right)_T dP$$

$$dS = \frac{C_P}{T} dT + \left[\left(\frac{\partial H}{\partial P}\right)_T - V\right]\frac{dP}{T}.$$

But

$$\left(\frac{\partial H}{\partial P}\right)_T = V - T\left(\frac{\partial V}{\partial T}\right)_P. \tag{4.109}$$

Therefore

$$dS = \frac{C_P}{T} dT - \left(\frac{\partial V}{\partial T}\right)_P dP. \tag{4.120}$$

Example 4.12. Calculate the increase in entropy of two moles of a perfect gas that is suddenly released into an evacuated vessel of such size that its pressure falls from 4/3 atm to one atm.

This sudden change is irreversible and adiabatic. Since no work is done, $\Delta E = 0$ for the gas and its temperature is constant because it is perfect. The value of ΔS can be calculated from the initial and final states by (4.122).

$$\Delta S = 2 \times 1.9872 \times \ln\left(\tfrac{4}{3}\right) = 1.1434 \text{ cal deg}^{-1}.$$

This is the difference in entropy of the final states of the oxygen in Example 4.5:

$$\Delta S = 4.0866 - 2.9432 = 1.1434 \text{ cal deg}^{-1}.$$

Example 4.13. One mole H_2 at 127°C and 10 atm was cooled to 27°C at constant pressure, and then was allowed to expand irreversibly into an evacuated chamber so that its final pressure was 0.5 atm. Then it was compressed reversibly and adiabatically until its temperature was 127°C. Finally, its pressure was adjusted isothermally at 127°C until it was 10 atm. If hydrogen is a perfect gas with $C_P = 6.82$ cal mole^{-1} deg^{-1}, calculate the total change in entropy of the hydrogen.

Since the initial and final states are alike, $\Delta S = 0$. (The enterprising student may wish to verify this by actual step-by-step calculation.)

Example 4.14. Calculate the increase in entropy of a mole of a perfect diatomic gas ($C_P = 7R/2$) the initial state of which is 25°C at 1.00 atm and the final state of which is 100°C at (a) 1.00 atm; (b) 10.0 atm.

In terms of randomness and disorder, explain the difference in these two entropy changes for these two different changes of state.

(a) If the perfect diatomic gas is heated reversibly at constant pressure of 1.00 atm, (4.59) yields

$$\Delta S = \tfrac{7}{2} R \ln \left(\frac{373}{298}\right) = 1.56 \text{ cal deg}^{-1}.$$

(b) If the perfect diatomic gas is heated reversibly at 1.00 atm to 100°C and then is compressed isothermally to 10.0 atm, (4.122) yields

$$\Delta S = \tfrac{7}{2} R \ln \left(\frac{373}{298}\right) + R \ln \left(\frac{1}{10}\right) = 1.56 - 4.58 = -3.02 \text{ cal deg}^{-1}.$$

The isobaric change of state involves only an increase in temperature, which is easily interpreted as increased agitation, increased disorder, or increased entropy. The second change of state, however, involves two influences. The increase in temperature again leads to a modest increase in entropy, but the subsequent compression increases the packing and order of the molecules to such an extent that there is a net decrease in entropy.

Example 4.15. If N_2 has $C_P = 7R/2$ and is a perfect gas, calculate the absolute entropy of $N_{2(g)}$ at 100°C at 1.00 atm.

The absolute entropy of $N_{2(g)}$ at 25°C at 1.00 atm is, by Table 3.1, 45.77 cal mole^{-1} deg^{-1}. As in Example 4.14(a), at 100°C at 1.00 atm,

$$S^o = 45.77 + 1.56 = 47.33 \text{ cal deg}^{-1}.$$

F. FREE ENERGY

4.19 Conditions for Equilibrium and Spontaneity

A state of equilibrium or a reversible process is considered to be a limiting situation. A state of equilibrium is said to exist if there is no small change that could occur spontaneously. On the other hand, a reversible process is said to be performed if a small change would cause the occurrence of a spontaneous process that differs as little as desired from the limiting reversible process. A process that tends away from equilibrium is unnatural, or nonspontaneous, because it does not occur in nature.

A simple trial-and-error method of determining whether a specified system in a specified state were at equilibrium or not would be to calculate some appropriately chosen thermodynamic property at several points in the immediate neighborhood of the specified state. If the supposed changes satisfied or failed to satisfy a suitably chosen criterion of equilibrium or spontaneity, then a definite statement concerning the state of the system or kind of process could be made. Melted snow quite naturally seeks the lowest level in a valley. Once in a valley, the water flows to the lowest point. If all points in the immediate neighborhood of this lowest point are higher, a body of water collects. The size and conformation of the neighborhood determines whether the body of water is a puddle, a lake, or an ocean. If all possible changes are upward, water is in its most stable position: in the ocean. Even its position in a puddle would be stable relative to immediately adjacent regions. Similarly, the manner of choice or the number of choices for calculation may give assurance that a certain thermodynamic property always decreases or increases in the neighborhood of a state whose stability is to be determined. If so, a maximum or minimum relative to adjacent states has been found.

In Section 4.3 it was concluded that the entropy of an isolated system tends naturally and spontaneously to a maximum. In view of the discussion just ended, a suitable criterion of equilibrium in an isolated system would be that any virtual change in entropy δS leads away from the maximum and thus is less than zero. The abbreviated statement of the second law in (4.4) suggests a similar criterion for any closed system in contact with isothermal surroundings at the temperature T. For a process that is not spontaneous, and thus does not involve the inequality of (4.4), any virtual change of state that would be accompanied by a change in entropy δS and an absorption of heat δq would satisfy the relation

$$T\,\delta S \leqslant \delta q. \tag{4.123}$$

That is, if (4.123) is satisfied for any arbitrary variation in the neighborhood of the state of a closed system in contact with isothermal surroundings, then the state is an equilibrium state. What (4.123) really says is that there is no variation possible in the state of the system (as restricted) such that

$$T\,\delta S > \delta q.$$

There are other equally fundamental but much more easily used criteria of equilibrium. Such criteria are the relations of Table 4.2, each of which embodies the first and second laws for closed systems that undergo changes in which work, if any, is only expansion work. For arbitrarily chosen virtual variations, these relations can be stated as criteria of equilibrium thus:

$$\delta E + P\,\delta V - T\,\delta S \geqslant 0 \tag{4.124}$$

$$\delta H - V\,\delta P - T\,\delta S \geqslant 0 \tag{4.125}$$

$$\delta A + P\,\delta V + S\,\delta T \geqslant 0 \tag{4.126}$$

$$\delta G - V\,\delta P + S\,\delta T \geqslant 0 \tag{4.127}$$

In particular, for virtual variations made with the volume V and entropy S held constant so that δV and δS are zero, (4.124) says that any variation of energy δE involves no change in or an increase in energy. Symbolically for this situation, (4.124) becomes (4.128).

$$(\delta E)_{S,V} \geqslant 0 \,. \tag{4.128}$$

From the mode of derivation, it is clear that an unnatural change at constant entropy and volume would involve an increase in energy.

The other three analogous criteria of equilibria in closed systems all of whose work is expansion work are:

$$(\delta H)_{S,P} \geqslant 0 \tag{4.129}$$

$$(\delta A)_{V,T} \geqslant 0 \tag{4.130}$$

$$(\delta G)_{P,T} \geqslant 0 \,. \tag{4.131}$$

The last two relations are by far the most useful, for entropy is awkward to control experimentally while pressure, volume, and temperature are easily controlled. The last relation, (4.131), is most suitable for chemists. If any supposed isothermal isobaric change in a system leads to an increase in the Gibbs free energy, that system is at equilibrium Again, if the supposed isothermal isobaric change does not change the Gibbs free energy, the system is at equilibrium.

The inequality (4.4) and the relations of Table 4.2 establish in a similar way these criteria of spontaneity for closed systems doing expansion work:

$$(\delta S)_{E,V} > 0 \tag{4.132}$$

$$(\delta E)_{S,V} < 0 \tag{4.133}$$

$$(\delta H)_{S,P} < 0 \tag{4.134}$$

$$(\delta A)_{V,T} < 0 \tag{4.135}$$

$$(\delta G)_{P,T} < 0 \,. \tag{4.136}$$

Inequality (4.136), which is commonly used by chemists, says that natural or spontaneous changes that occur isothermally and isobarically involve a decrease in Gibbs free energy. In other words, the Gibbs free energy tends to a minimum in such changes in closed systems, just as water flows to the lowest elevation in the neighborhood.

The operation of a bubble counter illustrates the tendency for the entropy of a system to increase in spontaneous processes. In a bubble counter, a superheated liquid like hydrogen or ether is caused to boil at the incidence of ionizing radiation like a cosmic ray. Since this irreversible boiling along the particle's track is quite sudden, the process may be considered adiabatic. For the purposes of this illustration, the process shall be assumed to be isobaric so that for this adiabatic isobaric process involving only expansion work, by (3.22),

$$0 = q_P = \Delta H .$$

A diagram of the change of state in which 1 mole of superheated liquid at a temperature T_1 becomes a mixture of X moles of gas and $(1 - X)$ moles of liquid at the boiling point T_2 is drawn with a reversible path in order to calculate the increase in entropy.

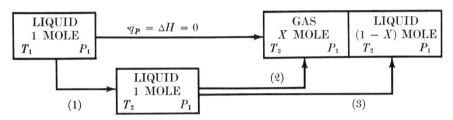

Let τ be the number of degrees by which the liquid is superheated; hence, $T_1 = T_2 + \tau$. For process (1),

$$\Delta H_1 = \int_{T_1}^{T_2} C_P \, dT = C_P(T_2 - T_1) = -C_P\tau .$$

The second process involves the vaporization of X moles with a molar heat of vaporization ΔH_v. For process (2),

$$\Delta H_2 = X \, \Delta H_v .$$

The third process involves no change of state of the $(1 - X)$ moles of liquid so that $\Delta H_3 = 0$. The over-all increase in enthalpy is zero; hence,

$$\Delta H = \Delta H_1 + \Delta H_2 + \Delta H_3$$

or

$$0 = -C_P\tau + X \, \Delta H_v .$$

Whence X, the fraction that vaporizes, is

$$X = \frac{C_P\tau}{\Delta H_v} .$$

The three increases in entropy along the reversible path are calculated in a similar way. By (4.58) and then (4.52)

$$\Delta S_1 = \int_{T_1}^{T_2} \frac{C_P}{T} \, dT = C_P \ln \left(\frac{T_2}{T_1} \right)$$

$$\Delta S_2 = \frac{X \, \Delta H_v}{T_2}$$

$$\Delta S_3 = 0$$

225

For the irreversible change, then

$$\Delta S = \Delta S_1 + \Delta S_2 + \Delta S_3 = C_P \ln \left(\frac{T_2}{T_1} \right) + \frac{X \, \Delta H_v}{T_2}$$

$$= -C_P \ln \left(\frac{T_2 + \tau}{T_2} \right) + \frac{X \, \Delta H_v}{T_2} = -C_P \ln \left(1 + \frac{\tau}{T_2} \right) + \frac{C_P \tau}{T_2} .$$

If τ is much less than T_2, the logarithm can be approximated by

$$\ln (1 + x) = x - \frac{x^2}{2} + \cdots .$$

Accordingly,

$$\Delta S = -C_P \left[\frac{\tau}{T_2} - \frac{1}{2} \left(\frac{\tau}{T_2} \right)^2 + \cdots \right] + C_P \left(\frac{\tau}{T_2} \right) \approx \frac{C_P}{2} \left(\frac{\tau}{T_2} \right)^2 .$$

This expression for ΔS is greater than zero, in agreement with the expectations of the variation form of (4.78) for spontaneous processes:

$$T \, \delta S + V \, \delta P - \delta H > 0 .$$

For at constant H and P,

$$(\delta S)_{H,P} > 0 .$$

Example 4.16. What is the change in entropy of one mole H_2O when a tiny crystal of ice is dropped into an open Dewar flask of negligible heat capacity if the flask initially contains one mole super-cooled water at $-5.00°C$? Assume that the final state achieved spontaneously is an equilibrium state. The molar C_P for water is 18.0 cal deg^{-1}; the molar C_P for ice is 9.0 cal deg^{-1}; and the molar heat of fusion ΔH_f of H_2O is 1440 cal.

This irreversible change is isobaric and adiabatic since it occurs in an open Dewar flask. Since all work is expansion work, $q_P = \Delta H = 0$ by (3.22). A diagram of the process as it achieves the final temperature T_2 is amplified by a convenient reversible path.

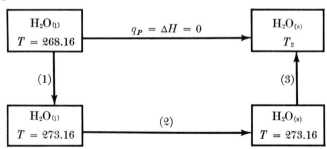

In order to verify that T_2 is 273.16°K, or that some water remains in equilibrium with the ice that crystallizes in the seeding process, the increase in enthalpy by processes (1), (2), and (3) is calculated.

$$\Delta H_1 = \int_{268.16}^{273.16} C_P \, dT = 18.0 \,(273.16 - 268.16) = 18.0 \times 5.00 \text{ cal}$$

$$\Delta H_2 = -1440 \text{ cal}$$

$$\Delta H_3 = \int_{273.16}^{T_2} C_P \, dT = 9.0 \,(T_2 - 273.16)$$

$$\Delta H = \Delta H_1 + \Delta H_2 + \Delta H_3$$

$$0 = 18.0 \times 5.00 - 1440 + 9.0 \,(T_2 - 273.16)$$

$$T_2 = 423 \,.$$

But ice cannot exist at $423°K$ at equilibrium at 1 atm. Hence, not all water solidifies and the diagram should have been this, where X is the fraction of a mole water that becomes ice.

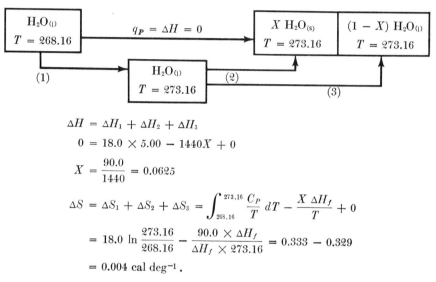

$$\Delta H = \Delta H_1 + \Delta H_2 + \Delta H_3$$

$$0 = 18.0 \times 5.00 - 1440X + 0$$

$$X = \frac{90.0}{1440} = 0.0625$$

$$\Delta S = \Delta S_1 + \Delta S_2 + \Delta S_3 = \int_{268.16}^{273.16} \frac{C_P}{T} \, dT - \frac{X \, \Delta H_f}{T} + 0$$

$$= 18.0 \ln \frac{273.16}{268.16} - \frac{90.0 \times \Delta H_f}{\Delta H_f \times 273.16} = 0.333 - 0.329$$

$$= 0.004 \text{ cal deg}^{-1} \,.$$

Once again for a spontaneous process, $(\delta S)_{H,P} > 0.$

4.20   Reversible Work

In Section 3.11 on reversible isothermal work there appeared an argument based on plausibility in support of the fact that reversible isothermal work is a function of state. The forms of the equations for the reversible expansion work performed by perfect gases and performed during isobaric phase transitions suggested that such work depends only on the initial and final states of the system. Moreover, the idea that a reversible process proceeds by virtue of a pressure difference that in the limit becomes zero suggested that such reversible work is an extremum, and as such should be a unique function of state. Now that the concept of entropy has been developed, a rigorous mathematical proof of these facts is possible. The proof begins with the fundamental equation of thermodynamics (4.46).

$$dE \leqslant T\,dS + dw .\tag{4.46}$$

By the methods of Section 4.13,

$$d(E - TS) \leqslant T\,dS + dw - d(TS)$$
$$dA \leqslant -S\,dT + dw .$$

For an isothermal process $dT = 0$, so that

$$dA \leqslant dw, \qquad (dT = 0) .\tag{4.137}$$

Or
$$\Delta A \leqslant w , \qquad (dT = 0) .\tag{4.138}$$

These two equations say that the reversible isothermal work w done on a system by the surroundings is a function of state and is equal to the increase ΔA in Helmholtz free energy of the system. Because of this, A has been called the *work function;* but since A is a function of state while work often is not, such a name is avoided here because it may be misleading.

For a reversible isothermal process in which the work done on the system is w_{rev}, (4.138) is simply

$$w_{\mathrm{rev}} = \Delta A .\tag{4.139}$$

For the same change of state accomplished by an irreversible isothermal process, (4.138) is

$$\Delta A < w .\tag{4.140}$$

Addition of (4.139) and (4.140) yields (4.141),

$$w_{\mathrm{rev}} < w ,\tag{4.141}$$

which states that reversible work done isothermally on a system is always less than irreversible work done isothermally on a system when the same change in state is effected. In terms of work done by the system, $-w_{\mathrm{rev}}$ and $-w$, multiplication of (4.141) by -1 reverses the sense of the inequality so that

$$-w_{\mathrm{rev}} > -w .\tag{4.142}$$

That is, the isothermal reversible work done by a system is greater than the irreversible isothermal work done by the system when the same change of state of the system occurs. Such isothermal reversible work is in fact a maximum. The discussions and examples of work in the first part of Chapter 3, particularly Sections 3.2 and 3.11, provide several examples of these ideas and of the fact that w depends upon the path.

Physicists and engineers are often able to use or perform work with some sort of expansion device and thus are quite content with the function A. Chemists, however, seldom are interested in expansion work but are often preoccupied with electric work or other kinds of nonexpansion work. If such nonexpansion work done on the system by the surroundings is given the symbol $w_{\text{non}PV}$ as in (3.24), then, when w_{PV} is the expansion work, the first law becomes (4.143) in infinitesimal form:

$$dE = dq + dw_{PV} + dw_{\text{non}PV} . \tag{4.143}$$

With the use of the second law, this becomes

$$dE \leqslant T\,dS + dw_{PV} + dw_{\text{non}PV} .$$

By (3.3) and the usual methods of Section 4.13,

$$d(E + PV - TS) \leqslant T\,dS - P\,dV + dw_{\text{non}PV} + d(PV - TS) .$$

That is,

$$dG \leqslant -S\,dT + V\,dP + dw_{\text{non}PV} . \tag{4.144}$$

For any isothermal $(dT = 0)$ and isobaric $(dP = 0)$ process,

$$dG \leqslant dw_{\text{non}PV} , \qquad (dT = dP = 0) . \tag{4.145}$$

Or

$$\Delta G \leqslant w_{\text{non}PV} , \qquad (dT = dP = 0) . \tag{4.146}$$

As for reversible isothermal work, these last two equations say that reversible isothermal isobaric nonexpansion work done on a system is a function of state, since G is a function of state. Moreover, such work is equal to the increase ΔG in Gibbs free energy of the system. And, as shown above, such reversible work is less than the irreversible work that must be done on the system to effect the specified change in state of the system.

If a system is subdivided so as to increase its surface area despite the action of surface tension, which tends to minimize the exposed surface area of the system, the work of subdivision leads by (4.146) to an increase in the Gibbs free energy of the system. Similarly, if electric work is done on a system, as in electrolysis to produce chemically active species like sodium or chlorine, such electric work serves to increase the Gibbs free energy of the system. If the electrolysis is performed reversibly, a minimum of electric work is done. But if the electrolysis is performed rapidly and irreversibly, the extra electric work does not appear in the activity of the chemicals, but is rather dissipated within the system and its presence is noted by a rise in the temperature of the system.

Example 4.17. Calculate the minimum work to be done on a mole of a substance at constant volume and temperature in order to raise it to a height Z in a uniform gravitational field.

If the volume and temperature are constant, the equation of state of the system, $P = P(V, T)$, assures that the pressure is also constant in this reversible process. By (3.1), (4.139), and (4.146), if the mass of 1 mole is M,

$$w = \Delta A = \Delta G = \int_0^Z Mg\,dz' = MgZ .$$

If any work in excess of MgZ were done on the system in elevating it, such extra work due to irreversibility would appear as kinetic energy of the system or the surroundings.

4.21   Free Energy Changes in Isothermal Processes

The preceding section on reversible work is a discussion of isothermal processes for which the work is calculable as work.   That section could well have been included in this section.   Since free energy is a function of state, any change of state has associated with it a definite change in free energy regardless of whether work is done or not in that change.   Quite generally, a change from state 1 to state 2 has associated with it an increase in Helmholtz free energy ΔA, where by the definition of A in (4.79),

$$\Delta A = A_2 - A_1$$
$$= (E_2 - T_2 S_2) - (E_1 - T_1 S_1)$$
$$= \Delta E - \Delta(TS) . \tag{4.147}$$

If $T_1 = T_2$, as in an isothermal process,

$$\Delta A = \Delta E - T \, \Delta S \tag{4.148}$$

where ΔA, ΔE, and ΔS are the increases in A, E, and S when the initial and final states are at the same temperature T.   In a similar way, for the Gibbs free energy, by the definition of G in (4.81),

$$\Delta G = G_2 - G_1$$
$$= (H_2 - T_2 S_2) - (H_1 - T_1 S_1)$$
$$= \Delta H - \Delta(TS) . \tag{4.149}$$

If $T_1 = T_2$, as in an isothermal process,

$$\Delta G = \Delta H - T \, \Delta S . \tag{4.150}$$

A special case of the application of (4.150) concerns an isothermal phase transition like fusion or evaporation.   If ΔH is the heat of transition, (4.52) yields for ΔS for such a change,

$$\Delta S = \frac{\Delta H}{T} . \tag{4.52}$$

Substitution in (4.150) yields

$$\Delta G = \Delta H - T \left(\frac{\Delta H}{T} \right) = 0 . \tag{4.151}$$

That is, for any isobaric isothermal reversible change in a closed system that, if it does work, does only expansion work, there is no change in the Gibbs free energy. The Gibbs free energies G_1 and G_2 of phases in equilibrium through such a process are equal, for $\Delta G = 0$ and $G_2 - G_1 = 0$ so that

$$G_2(T, P) = G_1(T, P) . \tag{4.152}$$

Equations (4.151) and (4.152) are merely another way of expressing the equality (4.131), one of the criteria of equilibrium, now a criterion of equilibrium between coexisting phases like ice and water: $(\delta G)_{P,T} = 0$.

As discussed with regard to heats of formation and Hess's law, a chemical transformation may involve well-specified initial and final states. If so, there is for such a transformation a definite increase in free energy ΔG. Equation (4.150) provides the means of calculating numerical values of ΔG^o for reactions which involve reactants and products in their standard (or specified) states if the various chemical species are listed in Table 3.3 (Heats of Formation) and Table 4.1 (Standard Absolute Entropies).

Example 4.18. Calculate ΔG^o at 25°C for the change of state

$$H_2O_{(l)} \text{ (1 atm)} \rightarrow H_2O_{(g)} \text{ (1 atm)} .$$

From Table 3.3,

$$\Delta H^o = -57.7979 - (-68.3174) = 10,519.5 \text{ cal.}$$

From Table 4.1,

$$\Delta S^o = 45.106 - 16.716 = 28.390 \text{ cal deg}^{-1} .$$

By (4.150),

$$\Delta G^o = 10,519.5 - 298.16 \times 28.390 = 2054.7 \text{ cal.}$$

The fact that $\Delta G^o > 0$ for the reaction as written is a sign that it is unnatural for water to have a vapor pressure of 1 atm at 25°C. Everyone knows that this reaction is not spontaneous, for water vapor at 25°C at 1 atm would condense to form water.

Example 4.19. Calculate ΔG^o at 25°C for the reaction

$$2 H_{2(g)} + O_{2(g)} \rightarrow 2 H_2O_{(l)}$$

where reactants and products are in their standard states at 1 atm.
From Table 3.3,

$$\Delta H^o = 2(-68,317.4) = -136,634.8 \text{ cal} .$$

From Table 4.1,

$$\Delta S^o = 2(16.716) - [49.003 + 2(31.211)] = -77.993 \text{ cal deg}^{-1} .$$

By (4.150),

$$\Delta G^o = -136,634.8 - 298.16(-77.993) = -113,380.4 \text{ cal} .$$

Application of a spark to a mixture of hydrogen and oxygen would suggest to most people, in agreement with (4.136) and the fact that $\Delta G^o < 0$, that the reaction is spontaneous, even though the initial and final states of the fire or explosion might not be quite those specified in the chemical equation.

Example 4.20. The production of energy by controlled fusion of deuterium nuclei may be accompanied by the production of cheap hydrogen if the deuterium is separated from ocean water by electrolysis. Perhaps then iron will be prepared thus:

$$3 \text{ H}_{2(g)} + \text{Fe}_2\text{O}_{3(s)} \rightarrow 2 \text{ Fe}_{(s)} + 3 \text{ H}_2\text{O}_{(g)} .$$

Is this reaction spontaneous at $25°C$ at 1 atm?

From Table 3.3,

$$\Delta H° = 3(-57.7979) - (-196.5) = +23.1 \text{ kcal} .$$

From Table 4.1,

$$\Delta S° = 3(45.106) + 2(6.49) - 21.5 - 3(31.211) = 33.2 \text{ cal deg}^{-1} .$$

By (4.150),

$$\Delta G° = 23{,}100 - 298.16 \times 33.2 = 13{,}200 \text{ cal} .$$

The reaction is not spontaneous. The idea is not promising unless some change in pressure or temperature leads to a much lower value of $\Delta G°$ (see Example 6.15).

The entropy of a system is sometimes defined or described as the energy per degree of absolute temperature that cannot be made available as work. Terms of the form $T \Delta S$ are then called the *unavailable energy* of the system at the temperature T. In support of this idea, the following argument is set forth. At constant temperature,

$$\Delta E = w + q$$
$$\Delta E = \Delta A + T \Delta S$$
$$\Delta A = w . \qquad (4.138)$$

The $T \Delta S$ term, as suggested by the second law Equation (4.1), is obviously a reversible heat term that seems not to be available as work at the temperature T. Indeed, it was proved in Section 4.4 that, as Thomson and Planck aver, a process the final result of which is merely a transformation of heat into work is impossible. Or again, there is no engine that can do work by operating in cycles if it merely absorbs heat at one temperature. But the *qualifications merely and cyclic* are the crux of the matter. Without these qualifications the concept "unavailable energy" is devoid of meaning (unavailable under what circumstances? unavailable for what?) and even incorrect and misleading.

Consider these two simple reversible processes by which an energy term $T \Delta S$ can be converted isothermally into work:

(a) One mole of a perfect gas expands isothermally and reversibly at the temperature T from a volume V_1 to a volume V_2. By (3.3), the work done by the gas is $-w$, where

$$-w = \int_{V_1}^{V_2} P \, dV = RT \int_{V_1}^{V_2} \frac{dV}{V} = RT \ln \left(\frac{V_2}{V_1}\right) .$$

Since the energy of a perfect gas depends only on its temperature, $\Delta E = 0$ so that by the first law,

$$q = -w = RT \ln \left(\frac{V_2}{V_1}\right).$$

That is, all the heat q absorbed by the gas is used by the gas as it performs positive work. For this same change in state, by (4.117),

$$\Delta S = R \ln \left(\frac{V_2}{V_1}\right).$$

Accordingly, the value of $T\,\Delta S$ is that of q; hence, the "isothermally unavailable energy" $T\,\Delta S$ has in fact been converted entirely into work. *But the system and surroundings have not been restored to their original states.*

(b) One mole of liquid water is isothermally and reversibly vaporized at its normal boiling point. By (3.3), the isobaric work done by the system is $-w$, where

$$-w = \int_{V_1}^{V_2} P \, dV = P \int_{V_1}^{V_2} dV = P\,\Delta V \approx RT \approx 1.987 \times 373.2 \approx 742 \text{ cal.}$$

Since the process is isobaric and involves only expansion work, if ΔH_v is the molar heat of vaporization, (3.22) yields

$$q_P = \Delta H_v .$$

But, for the same change in state, by (4.52),

$$\Delta S = \frac{\Delta H_v}{T}.$$

That is, the value of $T\,\Delta S$ is ΔH_v, the isobaric reversible heat absorbed by the system. Of this "isothermally unavailable energy," about 742 cal have been recovered as work. *Again, the system and surroundings have not been restored to their original states.* It seems preferable to avoid discussion of a concept that requires so many qualifications that it becomes cumbersome and yet can be greatly abused. It is perhaps suitable for those whose engines and surroundings run reversibly and only in completed cycles.

4.22 Free Energy as a Function of Temperature

It was possible to derive Kirchhoff's law, (3.100) or (3.101), in two ways.

$$\Delta H = \Delta H^\circ + \int_{T_0}^{T} \Delta C_{P_0} \, dT' \qquad (3.100)$$

$$\left(\frac{\partial \Delta H}{\partial T}\right)_{P_0} = \Delta C_{P_0} . \qquad (3.101)$$

One involved a vivid but long and detailed consideration of two routes by which a process could be performed. The other, a purely formal mathematical operation, involved interchanging the order of subtraction and differentiation. For the sake of brevity, the Gibbs-Helmholtz equation (4.97) is transformed by this latter process into a more meaningful form.

Let the Gibbs free energy of the final state of a closed system be G_2 and let its entropy be S_2. Similarly, let G_1 and S_1 refer to the Gibbs free energy and entropy of the initial state of the same closed system. It is clear that each of these symbols may consist of a sum of many terms. Then (4.97) reads for each

$$\left(\frac{\partial G_2}{\partial T}\right)_P = -S_2, \quad \text{and} \quad \left(\frac{\partial G_1}{\partial T}\right)_P = -S_1.$$

Subtraction of the latter from the former and interchanging the order of subtraction and differentiation yields (4.153), the Gibbs-Helmholtz equation in a common form.

$$\left(\frac{\partial \Delta G}{\partial T}\right)_P = -\Delta S \tag{4.153}$$

where
$$\Delta G = G_2 - G_1$$
$$\Delta S = S_2 - S_1.$$

At any temperature, however,

$$\Delta G = \Delta H - T\,\Delta S. \tag{4.150}$$

Hence, elimination of ΔS from (4.153) and (4.150) yields the usual form of the Gibbs-Helmholtz equation, (4.154).

$$\left(\frac{\partial \Delta G}{\Delta T}\right)_P = \frac{\Delta G - \Delta H}{T}. \tag{4.154}$$

This equation gives the variation of the change in Gibbs free energy with respect to variations in temperature at constant pressure for any process that can in principle be performed reversibly in a closed system.

A simple mathematical manipulation transforms (4.154) into a readily integrable form. Just for fun, take the derivative

$$\left[\frac{\partial}{\partial T}\left(-\frac{\Delta G}{T}\right)\right]_P = -\frac{1}{T}\left(\frac{\partial \Delta G}{\partial T}\right)_P + \frac{\Delta G}{T^2}.$$

By (4.154),

$$\left[\frac{\partial}{\partial T}\left(-\frac{\Delta G}{T}\right)\right]_P = -\frac{1}{T}\left(\frac{\Delta G - \Delta H}{T}\right) + \frac{\Delta G}{T^2}.$$

Hence,
$$-\left[\frac{\partial}{\partial T}\left(\frac{\Delta G}{T}\right)\right]_P = \frac{\Delta H}{T^2}. \tag{4.155}$$

If ΔH is known as a function of temperature through (3.100), Equation (4.155) is readily integrated at constant pressure. If ΔG_2 is the increase in Gibbs free energy at temperature T_2, while ΔG_1 is the increase in Gibbs free energy at temperature T_1 at the same pressure P for two changes in state that differ only in T_1 and T_2, then with the aid of (3.100), (4.155) becomes (4.156).

$$-d\left(\frac{\Delta G}{T}\right) = \frac{\Delta H}{T^2}\, dT, \qquad (dP = 0)$$

$$-\int_{(\Delta G_1/T_1)}^{(\Delta G_2/T_2)} d\left(\frac{\Delta G}{T}\right) = \int_{T_1}^{T_2} \frac{\Delta H}{T^2}\, dT$$

$$-\frac{\Delta G_2}{T_2} + \frac{\Delta G_1}{T_1} = \int_{T_1}^{T_2} \frac{\Delta H}{T^2}\, dT, \qquad (dP = 0). \qquad (4.156)$$

If the value of the integral and any three of the four quantities ΔG_1, ΔG_2, T_1 and T_2 are known, the fourth quantity can be found. In general, this fourth quantity is ΔG_2, when ΔG_1, T_1 and T_2 are known or specified. It is common, for example, to know ΔG_1 at 25°C and to know ΔH as a function of temperature from 25°C to the temperature T_2 at which ΔG_2 is sought.

If in (3.101), $\Delta C_{P_o} = 0$, then ΔH is ΔH^o and is independent of temperature; hence, (4.156) can be solved for ΔG at the temperature T in this way:

$$-\frac{\Delta G}{T} + \frac{\Delta G^o}{T_o} = \Delta H^o \int_{T_o}^{T} \frac{dT'}{(T')^2} = \Delta H^o\left(-\frac{1}{T} + \frac{1}{T_o}\right) = \frac{\Delta H^o(T - T_o)}{TT_o}$$

$$\Delta G = T\left[\frac{\Delta G^o}{T_o} - \frac{\Delta H^o(T - T_o)}{TT_o}\right], \qquad (dP = 0). \qquad (4.157)$$

It is much more likely, however, that ΔC_P in (3.101) is not zero but is rather, as in Table 3.1,

$$\Delta C_P = \Delta C_P^{(0)} + \Delta C_P^{(1)} T + \Delta C_P^{(2)} T^2 + \cdots.$$

Then, by (3.100),

$$\Delta H = \Delta H^o + \Delta C_P^{(0)}(T - T_o) + \frac{\Delta C_P^{(1)}}{2}(T^2 - T_o^2) + \frac{\Delta C_P^{(2)}}{3}(T^3 - T_o^3) + \cdots$$

$$= \Delta H_o^o + \Delta C_P^{(0)} T + \frac{\Delta C_P^{(1)}}{2} T^2 + \frac{\Delta C_P^{(2)}}{3} T^3 + \cdots, \qquad (dP = 0) \qquad (4.158)$$

where ΔH_o^o is a hypothetical heat of reaction at absolute zero at one atm. Actually ΔH_o^o is nothing more than a symbol or an integration constant.

$$\Delta H_o^o = \Delta H^o - \Delta C_P^{(0)} T_o - \frac{\Delta C_P^{(1)}}{2} T_o^2 - \frac{\Delta C_P^{(2)}}{3} T_o^3 - \cdots, \qquad (dP = 0) \qquad (4.159)$$

235

where ΔH^o is the really observed value of ΔH at the standard temperature T_o (e.g., 25°C as in Table 3.3) at 1 atm. Once ΔH is known as a function of temperature at constant pressure as in (4.158), explicit evaluation of (4.156) is possible. By (4.156) and (4.158),

$$-\frac{\Delta G}{T} + \frac{\Delta G^o}{T_o} = \int_{T_o}^{T} \frac{\Delta H}{(T')^2} \, dT'$$

$$= \int_{T_o}^{T} \frac{\left[\Delta H_o^o + \Delta C_P^{(0)} T' + \frac{\Delta C_P^{(1)}}{2} (T')^2 + \frac{\Delta C_P^{(2)}}{3} (T')^3 + \cdots \right]}{(T')^2} \, dT'$$

$$= \frac{\Delta H_o^o (T - T_o)}{T T_o} + \Delta C_P^{(0)} \ln \left(\frac{T}{T_o} \right) + \frac{\Delta C_P^{(1)}}{2} (T - T_o)$$

$$+ \frac{\Delta C_P^{(2)}}{6} (T^2 - T_o^2) + \cdots .$$

That is, when ΔH_o^o is given by (4.159), and when ΔH^o and ΔG^o are the standard increments in enthalpy and Gibbs free energy at the temperature T_o, then at any temperature T, the value of ΔG is given by (4.160).

$$\Delta G = \frac{T \Delta G^o}{T_o} - \frac{\Delta H_o^o (T - T_o)}{T_o} - \Delta C_P^{(0)} T \ln \left(\frac{T}{T_o} \right) - \frac{\Delta C_P^{(1)}}{2} T(T - T_o)$$

$$- \frac{\Delta C_P^{(2)}}{6} T(T^2 - T_o^2) - \cdots , \qquad (dP = 0) . \qquad (4.160)$$

In (3.100) and Equations (4.156) to (4.160), the qualifying remark $(dP = 0)$ indicates that the various values of ΔG and ΔH are for the change of state in which reactants (initial state) and products (final state) are at the same pressure. This pressure is one atm if values of ΔH_f^o and S^o are taken from Tables 3.3 and 4.1. In other words, the complete symbol for ΔG in (4.157) and (4.160) is $\Delta G(T, P_o)$, where T indicates that the temperature is any temperature and where P_o indicates that the pressure is the standard pressure of 1 atm. The complete symbol for ΔG^o in (4.157) and (4.160) is similarly $\Delta G(T_o, P_o)$, where T_o now indicates the standard temperature, say, 25°C. A pressure of 1 atm is part of the specification of the standard state and is then part of the superscript on ΔG^o. Appropriate care must be exercised with regard to $\Delta G(T, P_o)$ especially since it will be rather ambiguously abbreviated to ΔG^o in later chapters.

All the equations of this section apply to physical or chemical changes, just as a change like vaporization, which is commonly considered to be physical, can be described by the quasi-chemical equation,

$$H_2O_{(l)} \rightarrow H_2O_{(g)} .$$

This presentation of the dependence of free energy upon temperature is meant to show that it does indeed depend upon temperature and that its calculation at any temperature is possible. Adequate treatment of the increments in free energy at any temperature for chemical reactions would extend this presentation unduly. Accordingly, here only changes generally classified as physical will be studied. Chemical changes must wait for discussion in succeeding chapters.

Example 4.21. Calculate the increase in free energy when liquid water at 100.00°C at one atm is converted to water vapor at 100.00°C at one atm. Assume that the molar heat capacity of water varies with temperature thus:

$$C_P^{(l)} = 17.430 + 1.813 \times 10^{-3} T.$$

The molar heat capacity of water vapor from Table 3.1 is

$$C_P^{(g)} = 7.187 + 2.373 \times 10^{-3} T + 0.208 \times 10^{-6} T^2.$$

Tables 3.3 and 4.1 list standard heats of formation and entropies of $H_2O_{(l)}$ and $H_2O_{(g)}$.

For the change of state

$$H_2O_{(l)} \rightarrow H_2O_{(g)}$$

at 25°C, the data of Tables 3.3 and 4.1 yield

$$\Delta H^{\circ} = \Delta H^{\circ}_{f(g)} - \Delta H^{\circ}_{f(l)} = -57,797.9 - (-68,317.4) = 10,519.5 \text{ cal}$$

$$\Delta S^{\circ} = S^{\circ}_{(g)} - S^{\circ}_{(l)} = 45.106 - 16.716 = 28.390 \text{ cal deg}^{-1}.$$

Whence,

$$\Delta G^{\circ} = \Delta H^{\circ} - T \Delta S^{\circ} \tag{4.150}$$

$$= 10,519.5 - 298.16 \times 28.390 = 2054.7 \text{ cal}.$$

For the same change of state,

$$\Delta C_P = C_P^{(g)} - C_P^{(l)}$$

$$= (7.187 + 2.373 \times 10^{-3} T + 0.208 \times 10^{-6} T^2)$$

$$- (17.430 + 1.813 \times 10^{-3} T)$$

$$= -10.243 + 0.560 \times 10^{-3} T + 0.208 \times 10^{-6} T^2.$$

Hence, at standard pressure and at any temperature T at which the heat capacities are those assumed, by (3.100)

$$\Delta H = \Delta H^{\circ} + \int_{T_0}^{T} \Delta C_P \, dT'$$

$$= 10,519.5 + \int_{298.16}^{T} [-10.243 + 0.560 \times 10^{-3}(T')$$

$$+ 0.208 \times 10^{-6}(T')^2] \, dT'$$

$$= 13,546.9 - 10.243T + 0.280 \times 10^{-3} T^2 + 0.0693 \times 10^{-6} T^3.$$

Now that ΔH is known as a function of temperature for the temperature range of interest, it is possible to integrate (4.155) at the constant pressure of 1 atm.

$$-\left[\frac{\partial}{\partial T}\left(\frac{\Delta G}{T}\right)\right]_P = \frac{\Delta H}{T^2} \tag{4.155}$$

$$\int_{T_0}^{T} \frac{\Delta H}{T'^2}\, dT' = \int_{T_0}^{T} \frac{[13{,}546.9 - 10.243\,T' + 0.280 \times 10^{-3}T'^2 + 0.0693 \times 10^{-6}T'^3]}{T'^2}\, dT'$$

$$-\frac{\Delta G}{T} + \frac{2054.7}{298.16} = 13{,}546.9\left(-\frac{1}{T} + \frac{1}{298.16}\right) - 10.243\, \ln\left(\frac{T}{298.16}\right)$$

$$+ 0.280 \times 10^{-3}(T - 298.16) + \frac{0.0693 \times 10^{-6}}{2}\,(T^2 - 298.16^2)$$

$$\Delta G = 13{,}546.9 + 10.243\,T \ln T - 96.815\,T - 0.280 \times 10^{-3}T^2 - 0.0347 \times 10^{-6}T^3\,.$$

If $T = 373.16$, $\Delta G = 15$ cal. The discrepancy between this result and Equations (4.151) and (4.152), which say that ΔG should be zero for two phases at equilibrium, is probably attributable to inadequate heat capacity data.

4.23   Free Energy as a Function of Pressure

Infinitesimal changes in Gibbs free energy of closed systems depend upon infinitesimal changes in pressure and temperature through the basic relation (4.82).

$$dG \leqslant -S\, dT + V\, dP\,. \tag{4.82}$$

If any work is done by or on such a system, it can be only expansion work if (4.82) is to hold. At equilibrium at constant temperature, (4.82) becomes

$$dG = V\, dP, \qquad (dT = 0)\,. \tag{4.161}$$

In the elegant notation of the calculus, (4.161) is nothing but one of the previously derived relations,

$$\left(\frac{\partial G}{\partial P}\right)_T = V \tag{4.98}$$

which describes the isothermal rate of change of Gibbs free energy with respect to changes of pressure.

This equation is readily solved for finite increments in G if the volume V is known as a function of the pressure P at the temperature T. That is, if

$$V = V(P, T)\,,$$

then, by (4.98) or its equivalent in (4.161),

$$\Delta G = \int_{P_1}^{P_2} V(P, T)\, dP, \qquad (dT = 0)\,. \tag{4.162}$$

The terms of the form PV by which E and H differ have long been recognized as small in size when P is of the order of a few atmospheres and when V is the volume of a condensed phase. It is true here also that the magnitude of (4.162) for condensed phases is generally negligible when gases are also involved or when chemical changes occur to produce appreciable changes in G. When account must be taken of (4.162) for changes in condensed phases, it is often quite adequate to assume that the condensed phases are incompressible. Since their volumes are then independent of pressure, V is a constant for each phase, and, by (4.162), the increase in Gibbs free energy for each phase that suffers a change in pressure from P_1 to P_2 is

$$\Delta G = V \int_{P_1}^{P_2} dP = V \, \Delta P \,. \tag{4.163}$$

If $V = 50$ ml mole^{-1} and if $\Delta P \approx 10$ atm, the value of ΔG is only about 12 cal per mole of condensed phase.

The magnitude of ΔG is generally not negligible when gases are involved. For n moles of a perfect gas compressed reversibly and isothermally from a pressure P_1 to a pressure P_2, by (4.162),

$$\Delta G = \int_{P_1}^{P_2} \frac{nRT}{P} \, dP$$

$$= nRT \ln \left(\frac{P_2}{P_1} \right) . \tag{4.164}$$

For gas at 273°K, an increase in pressure from 1 to 11 atm requires

$$\Delta G = 1.987 \times 273 \times \ln \left(\tfrac{11}{1} \right) = 1300 \text{ cal mole}^{-1} \,.$$

These 1300 cal constitute about a hundredfold increase over the 12 cal for a mole of a typical incompressible condensed phase as its pressure is increased by 10 atm. For the sake of performing the calculation, a reversible path was followed. However, for the same isothermal pressure change, ΔG would be given by (4.164) whether or not the change really occurred reversibly because G is a function of state.

It happens that for a perfect gas at constant temperature,

$$d(PV) = d(RT), \qquad P \, dV + V \, dP = 0, \qquad V \, dP = -P \, dV \,.$$

That is, the increase $V \, dP$ in Gibbs free energy of a perfect gas is equal to the reversible work $-P \, dV$ done on it at constant temperature. In order to compress reversibly 1 mole of a perfect gas at 273°K from a pressure of 1 to 11 atm, the work done on the gas is

$$w = - \int_{V_1}^{V_2} P \, dV = -RT \ln \left(\frac{V_2}{V_1} \right) .$$

But by Boyle's law, $P_1V_1 = P_2V_2$; hence,

$$w = RT \ln \left(\frac{P_2}{P_1}\right)$$

which is (4.164) because of the special form of the equation of state of a perfect gas.

Example 4.22. As one mole $CO_{2(g)}$ at 27°C expands, its pressure falls from 3.00 atm to 1.00 atm. Calculate for this change values of ΔG, ΔA, and w if (a) CO_2 is assumed to be a perfect gas; and (b) CO_2 is assumed to behave as a van der Waals gas with $a = 3.61$ l² atm mole⁻² and $b = 0.0428$ l mole⁻¹.

Since the process is not sufficiently well defined, it is impossible to calculate w, the work involved. However, with the invention of a suitable reversible path, namely, an isothermal reversible expansion, it is possible to find ΔG and ΔA.

(a) If CO_2 is a perfect gas, by (4.162) or (4.164)

$$\Delta G = \int_{3.00}^{1.00} \left(\frac{RT}{P}\right) dP = 1.987 \times 300 \times \ln \left(\frac{1.00}{3.00}\right) = -655 \text{ cal}.$$

Similarly, by (4.80), if $dT = 0$,

$$\Delta A = -\int_{V_1}^{V_2} P\, dV = -\int_{3.00}^{1.00} P\left(-\frac{RT}{P^2}\right) dP = RT \ln \left(\frac{1.00}{3.00}\right) = -655 \text{ cal}.$$

(b) If CO_2 is a van der Waals gas, by (4.162) and (1.29),

$$\Delta G = \int_{P_1}^{P_2} \left[\frac{RT}{P} + \left(b - \frac{a}{RT}\right)\right] dP = RT \ln \left(\frac{P_2}{P_1}\right) + \left(b - \frac{a}{RT}\right)(P_2 - P_1)$$

$$= -655 + \left(0.0428 - \frac{3.61}{0.08205 \times 300}\right)(1.00 - 3.00)\left(\frac{1.987}{0.08205}\right)$$

$$= -655 + 5 = -650 \text{ cal}.$$

By (4.80), if $dT = 0$,

$$\Delta A = -\int_{V_1}^{V_2} P\, dV = -\int_{V_1}^{V_2} \left[\frac{RT}{V + \dfrac{a}{RT} - b}\right] dV$$

$$= RT \ln \left[\frac{V_1 + \dfrac{a}{RT} - b}{V_2 + \dfrac{a}{RT} - b}\right] = 1.987 \times 300 \times \ln \left(\frac{P_2}{P_1}\right) = -655 \text{ cal}.$$

It is an accident of the method of calculation that the values of ΔA are alike for the two equations of state. It is clear, however, that deviations from ideal behavior influence ΔG.

Example 4.23. Calculate the net work that must be done reversibly and isothermally on a mole of a perfect gas to transport it from its equilibrium state at the surface of the earth to its equilibrium state at a height z.

As the gas rises, its pressure decreases continuously from P_o at the surface to P at the altitude z. An infinitesimal vertical movement requires, by (3.1), that gravitational work $Mg\,dz$ be done on the gas, where M is the mass of 1 mole of gas and dz is the infinitesimal vertical movement. But for an infinitesimal movement, $dG = 0$ since the gas is at equilibrium with its immediate surroundings with respect to temperature and pressure. Hence, by (4.144), the pressure varies with altitude thus:

$$dG = V\,dP + Mg\,dz = 0\,.$$

Definite integration yields the equation for the dependence of pressure on altitude in a uniform gravitational field if the temperature of the closed system of 1 mole is constant.

$$-\int_{P_o}^{P} V\,dP = \int_{0}^{z} Mg\,dz', \qquad RT\ln\left(\frac{P_o}{P}\right) = Mgz, \qquad P = P_o e^{-Mgz/RT}\,.$$

The diagram for the isothermal change of state is this:

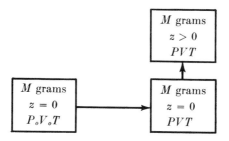

The state of the system is specified not only by three of the four variables of the perfect gas equation but also by the altitude z. With account of Boyle's law, $P_o V_o = PV$, the isothermal reversible work done on the gas at the surface of the earth where $z = 0$ is

$$w = -\int_{V_o}^{V} P\,dV = -RT\int_{V_o}^{V}\frac{dV'}{V'} = -RT\ln\left(\frac{V}{V_o}\right) = RT\ln\left(\frac{P}{P_o}\right)\cdot$$

The isothermal reversible work done on the gas as it is elevated at constant volume V is, as in Example 4.17,

$$w = \int_{0}^{z} Mg\,dz' = Mgz\,.$$

The net isothermal work ΔA is, by (4.138), the sum of the expansion and gravitational work, namely,

$$\Delta A = RT\ln\left(\frac{P}{P_o}\right) + Mgz\,.$$

But from the previous results concerning the dependence of pressure on altitude, $P = P_o \exp(-Mgz/RT)$, it follows that $\Delta A = 0$. Whatever work the gas could do by expansion is used to raise it against the force of gravity. This last statement of the law of conservation of energy could, of course, have been used to obtain the dependence of pressure on altitude without recourse to the Gibbs free energy.

4.24 Fugacity

Fugacity is a mathematical device invented by G. N. Lewis in 1901 to preserve the simple appearances of Equation (4.164) even for real gases. All gases tend to behave like perfect gases at low pressures and at high temperature. The modest size of the second virial coefficient B in the virial expansion $V = nRT/P + nB$ assures that a small enough value of P or a large enough value of T will yield the perfect gas equation within the accuracy of the measurements of P, V, and T.

Associated with any specified change of state of a gas there is a definite increment in Gibbs free energy ΔG. If there is ascribed to the initial state a fugacity f_1 and to the final state a fugacity f_2, then preservation of the form of (4.164) for an isothermal process yields (4.165).

$$\Delta G = nRT \ln \left(\frac{P_2}{P_1} \right) \tag{4.164}$$

$$\Delta G = nRT \ln \left(\frac{f_2}{f_1} \right). \tag{4.165}$$

The fugacity of a gas is defined by (4.165) and the condition that, at low pressures, the values of the fugacity and observed pressure become alike. That is, fugacity f is defined by (4.165) and (4.166).

$$\lim_{P \to 0} \left(\frac{f}{P} \right) = 1. \tag{4.166}$$

Since free energy is a well-defined property of a system and since an arbitrary zero of energy or free energy can be set, suppose that the molar Gibbs free energy of a system in some standard state is $G^o(f_o, T)$. Then, for an isothermal change of state involving n moles from this standard state to some other state with molar free energy $G(f, T)$, let

$$\Delta G = nG(f, T) - nG^o(f_o, T) = nRT \ln \left(\frac{f}{f_o} \right).$$

If the units of f are such that the numerical value of f_o is unity, the value of $G^o(f_o, T)$ is independent of f_o.[3] Then,

$$G(f, T) = RT \ln f + G^o(T). \tag{4.167}$$

For an isothermal change between states that are not standard, by (4.167)

$$\Delta G = nG(f_2, T) - nG(f_1, T) = nRT \ln \left(\frac{f_2}{f_1} \right)$$

which is (4.165) with its desired simplicity. In this way, the arbitrary but quite definite reference free energy $G^o(T)$ will always be suppressed for any observed change of state. Here $G^o(T)$ is the free energy of the gas in its standard state, which until now was taken to be a pressure of one atm. Now, however, it is clear that this standard state is the hypothetical reference state with a fugacity of one atm at the standard temperature.

A convenient way of evaluating G as a function of pressure is the following, in which the major dependence of G on the pressure is explicitly acknowledged in order that attention may be focused on the correction term. For 1 mole, by (4.98)

$$\left(\frac{\partial G}{\partial P}\right)_T = V(P, T) .$$

Whence,

$$\left[\frac{\partial}{\partial P}(G - RT \ln P)\right]_T = V(P, T) - \frac{RT}{P} . \tag{4.168}$$

But by (4.167),

$$G - RT \ln P = RT \ln \left(\frac{f}{P}\right) + G^o(T) .$$

Hence, by (4.166),

$$\lim_{P \to 0} [G - RT \ln P] = G^o(T) .$$

Despite the embarrassing infinity that seems to come from the logarithm of zero, this limit exists because all the other terms of Equation (4.169) below exist. Integration of (4.168) from a very low pressure to a finite pressure yields (4.169).

$$\int_{G^o}^{G - RT\ln P} d(G - RT \ln P)' = \int_0^P \left(V - \frac{RT}{P'}\right) dP'$$

$$G(P, T) - RT \ln P - G^o(T) = \int_0^P \left(V - \frac{RT}{P'}\right) dP' . \tag{4.169}$$

When the virial expansion (1.28) is adequate as the equation of state,

$$G(P, T) = G^o(T) + RT \ln P + \int_0^P \left(\frac{RT}{P'} + B - \frac{RT}{P'}\right) dP'$$

$$= G^o(T) + RT \ln P + BP . \tag{4.170}$$

If (4.170) is to assume the same form as the desired (4.167) for the same state, then

$$\ln f = \ln P + \frac{BP}{RT}$$

or

$$f = Pe^{BP/RT} . \tag{4.171}$$

The fugacity f has the units of pressure P and is numerically equal to P for perfect gases since for them $B = 0$. Often f is almost equal to P since B is small. If T becomes great or P becomes small, the value of the fugacity approaches that of the pressure. Evaluation of the fugacity is in no way easier because of its invention. Rather, its main justification is in (4.171), which suggests that pressure, although strictly incorrect, is often a satisfactory approximation to the true thermodynamic variable fugacity.

Example 4.24. What are the fugacities of N_2 and CO_2 at 25°C at pressures of one and fifty atm?

With the van der Waals approximation to the second virial coefficient $B = b - a/RT$,

$$B(N_2) = 0.0386 - \frac{1.348}{0.08205 \times 298.2} = -0.0165 \text{ l mole}^{-1}$$

$$B(CO_2) = 0.0428 - \frac{3.61}{0.08205 \times 298.2} = -0.1047 \text{ l mole}^{-1}.$$

By (4.171), at a pressure of one atm,

$$f(N_2) = 1.000 \exp\left(\frac{-0.0165 \times 1.000}{0.08205 \times 298.2}\right) = 0.999 \text{ atm}$$

$$f(CO_2) = 1.000 \exp\left(\frac{-0.1047 \times 1.000}{0.08205 \times 298.2}\right) = 0.996 \text{ atm}.$$

Again, at fifty atm,

$$f(N_2) = 50.00 \exp\left(\frac{-0.0165 \times 50.00}{0.08205 \times 298.2}\right) = 48.34 \text{ atm}$$

$$f(CO_2) = 50.00 \exp\left(\frac{-0.1047 \times 50.00}{0.08205 \times 298.2}\right) = 40.37 \text{ atm}.$$

G. EQUILIBRIUM IN ONE-COMPONENT SYSTEMS

4.25 Vapor Pressure as a Function of Pressure

Almost every general chemistry textbook contains a table with the vapor pressure of water as a function of temperature. After providing numerical values as an example of dynamic equilibrium between liquid and gaseous phases, the data of this table are commonly used to correct the observed pressure of a gas collected over water to the pressure that the gas would exert if dry. This kind of tabulation and use implies that the vapor pressure of water and probably the vapor pressures of all liquids are independent of the total pressure exerted on the liquids. This implication is not quite true.

The discussion of Section 4.21 led eventually to the valuable conclusion that for any isobaric isothermal reversible change in a closed system there is no change in the Gibbs free energy if any work that may be done on the system is merely expansion work. As applied to the isobaric isothermal reversible vaporization of water, where $G_2(P, T)$ is the Gibbs free energy of the vapor and $G_1(P, T)$ is that of the liquid, this conclusion reads

$$G_2(P, T) = G_1(P, T) . \tag{4.152}$$

If P is not the vapor pressure of water but is rather the total pressure of water vapor and of other species (ordinarily gases) exerted on the liquid, (4.152) is still true. For some change dP in the total pressure exerted by a gaseous mixture on the liquid there will be a change dp in the partial pressure p of water vapor. At constant temperature, the changes in free energy are equal, as required by (4.152). Hence, for the water,

$$dG_2 = dG_1$$

$$\left(\frac{\partial G_2}{\partial p}\right)_T dp = \left(\frac{\partial G_1}{\partial P}\right)_T dP .$$

By (4.161) or (4.98), if V is the molar volume of vapor and v is the much smaller molar volume of the liquid,

$$V\, dp = v\, dP, \qquad (dT = 0) .$$

That is,

$$\left(\frac{\partial p}{\partial P}\right)_T = \frac{v}{V}. \tag{4.172}$$

This derivative, which gives the isothermal rate of change of vapor pressure with respect to changes in the total pressure on the condensed phase, is very small since the molar volume v of a condensed phase is much less than the molar volume V of a gas. For water, the ratio is about 0.001.

Equation (4.172) is readily integrated at constant temperature if the condensed phase is incompressible and if the vapor behaves as a perfect gas so that $V = RT/p$. Then,

$$RT \int_{p_1}^{p_2} \frac{dp}{p} = v \int_{P_1}^{P_2} dP$$

$$RT \ln\left(\frac{p_2}{p_1}\right) = v(P_2 - P_1) . \tag{4.173}$$

In (4.173), p_2 is the vapor pressure at the total pressure P_2 while p_1 is the vapor pressure at the total pressure P_1. In the commonly used tables, $p_1 = P_1$.

Example 4.25. Calculate the vapor pressure of water at 25°C when the total pressure exerted on the water is one, ten, and one hundred atm. At 25°C under the pressure of its own vapor, water has a vapor pressure of 23.756 mm Hg. (Lange's *Handbook of Chemistry*, New York: McGraw-Hill Book Co., Inc., 1956, p. 1459.)

In (4.173), $p_1 = P_1 = 23.756/760.00 = 0.0313$ atm; hence,

$$\log p_2 = \log p_1 + \frac{v(P_2 - P_1)}{2.303RT}$$

$$= \log 23.756 + \frac{18.07 \ (P_2 - 0.0313)}{2.303 \times 82.05 \times 298.2}$$

$$= 1.37577 + 0.0003207 \ (P_2 - 0.0313) \ .$$

If $P_2 = 1.0000$ atm,

$$\log p_2 = 1.37577 + 0.0003207 \times 0.9687 = 1.37608$$

$$p_2 = 23.773 \text{ mm Hg at 1 atm} \ .$$

If $P_2 = 10.0000$ atm,

$$\log p_2 = 1.37577 + 0.0003207 \times 9.9687 = 1.37897$$

$$p_2 = 23.932 \text{ mm Hg at 10 atm} \ .$$

If $P_2 = 100.0000$ atm,

$$\log p_2 = 1.37577 + 0.0003207 \times 99.9687 = 1.40783$$

$$p_2 = 25.576 \text{ mm Hg at 100 atm} \ .$$

At 1, 10, and 100 atm, the vapor pressure is increased from its value at its vapor pressure by 0.07%, 0.74%, and 7.7%.

4.26 Equilibrium of One Component in Two Phases

When two phases remain at equilibrium despite changes in pressure or temperature common to both phases, the method of the last section again provides a differential equation that describes the system. If dG_2 is the infinitesimal change in Gibbs free energy of state 2, then by (4.82), when any work done on the closed system is expansion work,

$$dG_2 = -S_2 \, dT_2 + V_2 \, dP_2 \ .$$

Similarly, for the other state, the initial state,

$$dG_1 = -S_1 \, dT_1 + V_1 \, dP_1 \ .$$

It will be proved below in Section 5.3 that the pressure and temperature everywhere assume common values P and T in a system of the sort considered here. Hence, $dP_2 = dP_1 = dP$, the common infinitesimal change in pressure; and $dT_2 = dT_1 = dT$, the common infinitesimal change in temperature that maintains equilibrium as the pressure changes. But $dG_2 = dG_1$ as above, so that

$$-S_2 \, dT + V_2 \, dP = -S_1 \, dT + V_1 \, dP$$

$$(V_2 - V_1) \, dP = (S_2 - S_1) \, dT$$

$$\frac{dP}{dT} = \frac{\Delta S}{\Delta V} \ . \tag{4.174}$$

In (4.174), which is called the *Clapeyron equation*, ΔS is the increase in entropy attendant upon the change from state 1 to state 2, and ΔV is the increase in volume for the same change of state for the same amount of matter. The change of state is any reversible change that can be performed isobarically, equilibrium being maintained with respect to pressure, and isothermally, equilibrium being maintained with respect to temperature. The change may involve only work that is expansion work. Briefly, the Clapeyron equation (4.174) applies to reversible phase changes and describes the way pressure and temperature must vary simultaneously if both phases are to continue to coexist so that $dG_1 = dG_2$.

The Clapeyron equation is seldom used as stated. At any temperature T,

$$\Delta H = T \, \Delta S \, . \tag{4.52}$$

On substitution of (4.52) into (4.174), it becomes

$$\frac{dP}{dT} = \frac{\Delta H}{T \, \Delta V} \tag{4.175}$$

where ΔH is the heat of transition from state 1 to state 2. If ΔH and ΔV could be expressed explicitly as functions of T and P, (4.175) could be integrated. When both states are condensed phases, it is often sufficient to approximate the derivative by a ratio of finite differences. Then,

$$\frac{\Delta P}{\Delta T} = \frac{P_2 - P_1}{T_2 - T_1} = \frac{\Delta H}{T \, \Delta V} \tag{4.176}$$

where $P_2 - P_1$ is the change in pressure that accompanies the change in temperature from T_1 to T_2. It should be noted that ΔP and ΔT apply to this simultaneous adjustment of P and T, while ΔH and ΔV apply to the change of state of the phases in equilibrium.

Example 4.26. What pressure is required to decrease the freezing point of ice by $2.00°C$?

The heat of fusion of ice is 1436.3 cal mole^{-1} at $0.00°C$. The density of water at $0.00°C$ is 0.9999 g ml^{-1}; that of ice is 0.9168 g ml^{-1}. For one g,

$$\Delta V = \frac{1.0000}{0.9999} - \frac{1.0000}{0.9168} = -0.0907 \text{ ml}$$

$$\Delta H = \frac{1436.3}{18.02} \times \frac{82.05}{1.987} = 3290 \text{ ml atm} \, .$$

If $\Delta T = T_2 - T_1 = -2.00°C$, by (4.176),

$$\Delta P = \frac{3290 \times (-2.00)}{273 \times (-0.0907)}$$

$$P_2 - P_1 = 266 \text{ atm} \, .$$

That is, an absolute pressure of 267 atm would be required to maintain equilibrium between ice and water at $-2.00°C$.

4.27 Equilibrium of One Component in Gaseous and Condensed Phases

When one of the phases at equilibrium is a gas, the Clapeyron equation (4.175) assumes a rather simple approximate form. Let phase or state 2 be the gas, while phase or state 1 is a condensed phase. If the condensed phase is, for example, a liquid, the differential equation to be derived will give the dependence of vapor pressure on temperature. Then,

$$\Delta V = V_2 - V_1 = \frac{RT}{P} - V_1 \approx \frac{RT}{P}$$

where the approximation is reasonable since the molar volume V_2 of the vapor phase is about 1000 times V_1, that of the condensed phase. When this value of ΔV is substituted into the Clapeyron equation, the resulting equation is called the *Clausius-Clapeyron equation* (4.177).

$$\frac{dP}{dT} = \frac{P \, \Delta H}{RT^2}. \tag{4.177}$$

The Clausius-Clapeyron equation is readily integrated if ΔH is known as a function of temperature.

In particular, if ΔH is independent of temperature, or if a suitable average value of ΔH for the temperature range of interest can be found, then by (4.177)

$$\int \frac{dP}{P} = \frac{\Delta H}{R} \int \frac{dT}{T^2}$$

$$\ln P = -\frac{\Delta H}{RT} + C_o \tag{4.178}$$

$$\log P = -\frac{\Delta H}{2.303RT} + \frac{C_o}{2.303}. \tag{4.179}$$

The constant of integration in (4.178) or (4.179) can be evaluated if ΔH is known and if the vapor pressure P is known at one temperature T. These equations then fix the vapor pressure at other temperatures for which the assumptions in its derivation are valid. Definite integration of (4.177) when ΔH is independent of temperature and pressure yields (4.180) and (4.181).

$$\int_{P_1}^{P_2} \frac{dP}{P} = \frac{\Delta H}{R} \int_{T_1}^{T_2} \frac{dT}{T^2} = \frac{\Delta H}{R} \left(-\frac{1}{T_2} + \frac{1}{T_1} \right)$$

$$\ln \left(\frac{P_2}{P_1} \right) = \frac{\Delta H (T_2 - T_1)}{RT_2 T_1} \tag{4.180}$$

$$\log \left(\frac{P_2}{P_1} \right) = \frac{\Delta H (T_2 - T_1)}{2.303RT_2 T_1}. \tag{4.181}$$

These equations relate the five variables: ΔH, the vapor pressure P_1 at temperature T_1, and the vapor pressure P_2 at temperature T_2. If any four are known, the fifth is readily found by (4.180) or (4.181).

Example 4.27. If the heat of vaporization of water is 540 cal gram^{-1}, what is its vapor pressure at 95°C?

$$\Delta H = 18.0 \times 540 = 9720 \text{ cal mole}^{-1} .$$

At $T_2 = 373.16°$K, $P_2 = 760$ mm Hg. By (4.181),

$$\log \left(\frac{760}{P_1} \right) = \frac{9720(373.16 - 368.16)}{2.303 \times 1.987 \times 373.2 \times 368.2}$$

$$= 0.0773 = \log (1.195)$$

$$P_1 = \frac{760}{1.195} = 636 \text{ mm Hg} .$$

The observed value is 633.90 mm Hg.

Example 4.28. From (4.177), estimate the vapor pressure of water at 95°C if $\Delta H_v = 9720$ cal mole^{-1}.

$$\frac{dP}{dT} = \frac{P \, \Delta H}{RT^2} \tag{4.177}$$

$$= \frac{9720 \times 1.000}{1.987 \times 373^2} = 0.0352 \text{ atm deg}^{-1} .$$

If $\Delta T = -5.00°$,

$$\Delta P = 0.0352 \times (-5.00) = -0.176 \text{ atm} .$$

At 95°C,

$$P = 1.000 - 0.176 = 0.824 \text{ atm} = 626 \text{ mm Hg} .$$

The heat of vaporization ΔH may be known as a function of temperature of the form (4.158), where

$$\Delta H = \Delta H_o^\circ + \Delta C_P^{(0)} T + \frac{\Delta C_P^{(1)}}{2} T^2 + \frac{\Delta C_P^{(2)}}{3} T^3 + \cdots . \tag{4.158}$$

If so, (4.177) is integrated thus.

$$\frac{dP}{dT} = \frac{P \, \Delta H}{RT^2} \tag{4.177}$$

$$R \int_{P_1}^{P_2} \frac{dP}{P} = \int_{T_1}^{T_2} \frac{\Delta H}{T^2} \, dT$$

$$R \ln \left(\frac{P_2}{P_1} \right) = \int_{T_1}^{T_2} \frac{\left[\Delta H_o^\circ + \Delta C_P^{(0)} T + \frac{\Delta C_P^{(1)}}{2} T^2 + \frac{\Delta C_P^{(2)}}{3} T^3 + \cdots \right]}{T^2} \, dT$$

$$R \ln \left(\frac{P_2}{P_1} \right) = \frac{\Delta H_o^\circ (T_2 - T_1)}{T_2 T_1} + \Delta C_P^{(0)} \ln \left(\frac{T_2}{T_1} \right) + \frac{\Delta C_P^{(1)}}{2} (T_2 - T_1)$$

$$+ \frac{\Delta C_P^{(2)}}{6} (T_2^2 - T_1^2) + \cdots . \tag{4.182}$$

249

Multiplication of (4.182) by T and substitution of ΔG for the resulting left-hand member because of (4.164) yields an equation analogous to (4.160), which was the kind of result obtained so tediously in Example 4.21 for the reaction $H_2O_{(l)} \rightarrow H_2O_{(g)}$.

Example 4.29. With the aid of the equation of Example 4.21 for the increase in free energy for the reaction

$$H_2O_{(l)} \text{ (1 atm)} \rightarrow H_2O_{(g)} \text{ (1 atm)}$$

and with the assumption that gaseous H_2O behaves as a perfect gas, calculate the vapor pressure of water at 95.00°C.

For the reaction above at 95.00°C, $T = 368.16$ and $\Delta G = 13{,}546.9 + 10.243T$ $\ln T - 96.815T - 0.280 \times 10^{-3}T^2 - 0.0347 \times 10^{-6}T^3 = 145$ cal. For the reaction at 95.00°C at the unknown vapor pressure P,

$$H_2O_{(l)} \text{ (P atm)} \rightarrow H_2O_{(g)} \text{ (P atm)}$$

the value of ΔG is zero because equilibrium exists at the pressure P. When these facts are combined into a diagram, the solution is easily found thus:

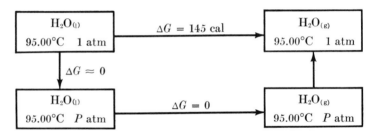

The value of ΔG for the change in which the pressure on the water is reduced to less than 1 atm is less than 1 cal since the molar volume of water is small. For the isothermal compression of water vapor, (4.164) yields

$$\Delta G = RT \ln \left(\frac{1.000}{P} \right).$$

Since ΔG is independent of the path,

$$\log P = -\frac{\Delta G}{2.303RT} = -\frac{145}{2.303 \times 1.987 \times 368.2} = -0.0861$$

$$P = 0.820 \text{ atm} = 624 \text{ mm Hg}.$$

If account is taken of the observation in Example 4.21 that, in the neighborhood of 100°C, the equation for ΔG is in error by 15 cal, then ΔG should be only 130 cal, and $P = 636$ mm Hg, in good agreement with the observed value of 633.90 mm Hg (Lange's *Handbook of Chemistry*. New York: McGraw-Hill Book Co., Inc., 1956, p. 1461).

Example 4.30. The normal boiling point of CCl_4 is 76.8°C, and its vapor pressure at 25.0°C is 115 mm Hg. (Lange's *Handbook of Chemistry*. New York: McGraw-Hill Book Co., Inc., 1956, p. 1426.) What is the molar heat of vaporization of CCl_4?

By (4.181), with $P_2 = 760$ mm Hg at $T_2 = 350.0$ and $P_1 = 115$ mm Hg at $T_1 = 298.2$,

$$
\begin{aligned}
\Delta H &= \frac{2.303 R T_1 T_2}{T_2 - T_1} \log \left(\frac{P_2}{P_1}\right) \\
&= \frac{2.303 \times 1.987 \times 298.2 \times 350.0}{51.8} \log \left(\frac{760}{115}\right) \\
&= 7560 \text{ cal mole}^{-1}.
\end{aligned}
$$

This is an effective mean value of ΔH_v over the temperature range 25.0°C to 76.8°C.

REFERENCES

For further discussions of entropy, see:
  (a) Wright, R. H., *Journal of Chemical Education*, **18** (1941), 263;
  (b) Wood, S. E., *Journal of Chemical Education*, **20** (1943), 80;
  (c) Luder, W. F., *Journal of Chemical Education*, **21** (1944), 265, 600;
  (d) Martell, A. E., *Journal of Chemical Education*, **23** (1946), 166.
Epstein, P. S., *Textbook of Thermodynamics*. New York: John Wiley & Sons, Inc., 1937.
Guggenheim, E. A., *Thermodynamics, An Advanced Treatment for Chemists and Physicists*. Amsterdam: North-Holland Publishing Co., 1957.

PROBLEMS

Vapor pressure and solution data from Lange's *Handbook of Chemistry*, New York: McGraw-Hill Book Co., Inc., 1956 unless noted otherwise.

1.   A certain engine that operates in a Carnot cycle absorbs 800 cal at 400°C in one cycle.   If it rejects heat at 100°C, how much work is done by the engine per cycle and how much heat is evolved at 100°C in each cycle?

2.   Develop the Carnot cycle for a perfect gas.

3.   What happens to a household refrigerator on a very hot day?

4.   The heat of fusion of water is 80 cal g^{-1} at 0°C.   For one gram-mole H_2O at constant temperature of 0°C, calculate ΔS when:
(a)   The water freezes.
(b)   The ice melts reversibly.
(c)   The ice melts irreversibly because the temperature is not always 0°C during melting, but is at start and finish.
Answer: (a) $\Delta S = -5.28$ cal deg^{-1}; (b) and (c) $\Delta S = 5.28$ cal deg^{-1}.

5.   Calculate the increase in entropy of one gram-mole of a monatomic crystalline solid like Cu or Mo as it changes from 300°K to 600°K at constant volume.
Answer: $\Delta S = 4.13$ cal deg^{-1}.

6.   Calculate the increase in entropy of one kg steam as it changes isobarically from 100°C to 200°C.

7.   Calculate the absolute entropy of one mole methane at 400°C at 10 atm.

8.   Calculate the absolute molar entropy of metallic silver at 100°C.

9. Show that $(\partial S/\partial P)_T = -R/P$ for a perfect gas at pressure P and interpret the negative sign in terms of randomness and disorder.

10. Calculate the inversion temperatures of H_2, N_2, Cl_2, and SO_2. *Answer:* H_2: $225°K$; N_2: $851°K$.

11. What is the change in entropy of H_2O when a tiny crystal of ice is dropped into an open Dewar flask of negligible heat capacity if the flask initially contains one mole supercooled liquid water at $-10.00°C$? What fraction of the mole of H_2O crystallizes?

12. Calculate the fugacity and molar free energy of gaseous hydrogen at $25°C$ at ten atm.

13. At what pressure does oxygen have a fugacity of one atm at $25°C$? *Answer:* 1.000978 atm.

14. Trouton's rule says that the molar entropy of vaporization of liquids is about 21 cal mole^{-1} deg^{-1} at the normal boiling point T_b. From this show that boiling points at pressure P can be corrected to 760 mm Hg by the relation $\Delta T_b = 0.00012 T_b(760 - P)$.

15. The vapor pressure of water is 92.5 mm Hg at $50.0°C$. Calculate the vapor pressure of water at $60.0°C$ and the mean molar heat of vaporization of water between $50°C$ and $100°C$.

16. From data in Example 4.4, find the vapor pressure of zinc at $500°C$. Of C_2H_3Cl at $0°C$. *Answer:* Zn: 1.62 mm Hg.

17. The vapor pressure of diethyl ether at $0°C$ is 185 mm Hg and its normal boiling point is $35°C$. What vapor pressure of ether is expected at $-75°C$, the temperature of a dry ice trap? *Answer:* 1.68 mm Hg.

---

18. Consider, as terminal states, 1 mole liquid water at 1 atm at either $20.0°C$ or $20.1°C$. In accord with the second law of thermodynamics as it applies to adiabatic changes, show that the transformation of one of these states into the other is possible in an adiabatic process, but that the reverse process is impossible adiabatically.

19. What is the greatest and least amount of heat that must be rejected per hour to the ocean at $4°C$ if a nuclear reactor provides 1000 kw (as heat) at $200°C$ for use in a Carnot-like cycle? *Answer:* 8.61 to 5.03×10^8 cal hr^{-1}.

20. What must be the upper temperature of a Carnot engine that evolves 700 cal heat per cycle at the lower temperature of $100°C$ if the engine does 400 cal work per cycle?

21. How much work must be done to freeze one kg H_2O at $0°C$ if the refrigerator rejects its heat at $25°C$?

22. Explain graphically why the efficiency or work of an engine that operates irreversibly in a Carnot-like cycle is less than that for an engine that operates reversibly under similar conditions.

23. Trouton's rule says that the molar entropy of vaporization of normal liquids at their boiling points are about 21 cal deg^{-1}. In terms of randomness and disorder, explain the following exceptions to this rule:
(a) Associated or hydrogen-bonded liquids generally have entropies of vaporization in excess of 25 cal mole^{-1}.

(b) Liquids like S, P, and HF, which vaporize to form associated or polymerized gases, have entropies of vaporization much less than 21 cal mole^{-1}.

24. Calculate the increase in entropy of three moles H_2 as it changes from 300°K to 1000°K at 1 atm.
Answer: 25.328 cal deg^{-1}.

25. Calculate the absolute standard molar entropy of gaseous SO_2 from these data [Giauque, W. F. and C. C. Stephenson, *J. Am. Chem. Soc.* **60**, 1389 (1938)]:

$$T_f = 197.64°K \qquad 1.769 \text{ kcal mole}^{-1} = \Delta H_f$$
$$T_b = 263.08°K \qquad 5.960 \text{ kcal mole}^{-1} = \Delta H_v.$$

$T(°K)$	C_p(cal mole^{-1} deg^{-1})	$T(°K)$	C_p(cal mole^{-1} deg^{-1})
15	0.83	130	12.83
20	1.66	140	13.31
25	2.74	150	13.82
30	3.79	160	14.33
35	4.85	170	14.85
40	5.78	180	15.42
45	6.61	190	16.02
50	7.36	197.64	M.P.
55	8.02	200	20.97
60	8.62	210	20.91
70	9.57	220	20.86
80	10.32	230	20.81
90	10.93	240	20.76
100	11.49	250	20.71
110	11.97	260	20.66
120	12.40	263.08	B.P.

Assume $C_p = 9.7$ cal mole^{-1} deg^{-1} for gaseous SO_2.

26. At 25°C find $\Delta S°$ at 1 atm for these changes:
(a) $Pb_{(aq)}^{++} + SO_{4(aq)}^{--} \rightarrow PbSO_{4(s)}$.
(b) $3 O_{2(g)} \rightarrow 2 O_{3(g)}$.
(c) $Ag_2O_{(s)} \rightarrow 2 Ag_{(s)} + \frac{1}{2} O_{2(g)}$.
(d) $C_{(s)} + 2 H_{2(g)} \rightarrow CH_{4(g)}$.
(e) $H_2O_{(l)} \rightarrow H_2O_{(g)}$.
Justify the sign of ΔS for each reaction in terms of randomness and disorder.

27. Calculate the absolute molar entropy of Cl_2 at 300°C at one atm and then at three atm.

28. Predict the final temperature of CO_2 that escapes adiabatically into an evacuated chamber of such size that its final volume is twenty times its initial volume at 25°C and 1.00 atm.
Answer: 24.53°C.

29. Calculate the Joule-Thomson coefficients of H_2 and SO_2 at 25°C. For SO_2, $C_P = 9.7$ cal mole^{-1} deg^{-1}.

30. Calculate the absolute entropy of one mole gaseous hydrogen at -20°C at 0.200 atm.

31. Under what circumstances is it true that $w = \Delta E = \Delta G$?

253

32. Calculate ΔG^o and ΔA^o at 25°C for these changes:
(a) $H_{2(g)} + F_{2(g)} \rightarrow 2\ HF_{(g)}$.
(b) $HF_{(g)} \rightarrow H^+_{(aq)} + F^-_{(aq)}$.
(c) $H_{2(g)} + F_{2(g)} \rightarrow 2\ H^+_{(aq)} + 2\ F^-_{(aq)}$.
(d) $2\ Ag_{(s)} + Cl_{2(g)} \rightarrow 2\ AgCl_{(s)}$.
(e) $ZnSO_4 \cdot 7\ H_2O_{(s)} \rightarrow ZnSO_4 \cdot 6\ H_2O_{(s)} + H_2O_{(g)}$.
Answers: (a) $\Delta G^o = \Delta A^o = -129.4$ kcal; (b) $\Delta G^o = -1.4$ kcal; $\Delta A^o = -0.8$ kcal;
(c) $\Delta G^o = -132.16$ kcal, $\Delta A^o = -130.98$ kcal.

33. Which is more volatile at 25°C, diamond or graphite, if the species in the equilibrium vapor of each are the same? Does this result say anything *directly* about their sublimation temperatures at 1 atm?

34. From whatever is useful in the following data find the standard molar heat of formation of gaseous iodine atoms if the standard state of I_2 is solid at 25°C at 1 atm.
(a) By spectroscopic means it is known that at absolute zero at any pressure $\Delta H = +35.6$ kcal for the reaction $I_{2(g)} \rightarrow 2\ I_{(g)}$.
(b) At 25°C the molar heat of sublimation of I_2 is 14.9 kcal.
(c) At 25°C the vapor pressure of solid I_2 is 0.31 mm Hg.
Answer: $\Delta H^o_f = 25{,}700$ cal.

35. Two moles argon, a perfect monatomic gas, at 2.000 atm are compressed reversibly at 25°C until their pressure is 10.00 atm. Then the argon expands freely and irreversibly into an evacuated vessel of such size that the final pressure is 2.000 atm. Calculate and tabulate ΔE, ΔH, ΔA, ΔG, ΔS, q, and w for the compression, for the expansion, and for the whole process.

36. Calculate ΔG and ΔA for two moles of a perfect gas that changes isothermally and irreversibly from a pressure of 10.0 atm to 0.200 atm at 0°C. Recalculate ΔG and ΔA for the same process when the gas is a real van der Waals gas, namely, methane.

37. What is the fugacity of steam at 150°C at a pressure of 4.000 atm?

38. Is there any pure substance the vapor pressure of which decreases as the total pressure increases? Explain.

39. What is the increase in the vapor pressure of ice at -10°C due to the presence of air at atmospheric pressure? The density of ice is 0.92 g cm^{-3} and its vapor pressure at -10°C is 1.95 mm Hg.
Answer: $\Delta p = 1.8 \times 10^{-3}$ mm Hg.

40. The melting point of benzene increases by about 0.03°C per atmosphere. If the specific gravities of solid and liquid benzene are 1.02 and 0.89 at the melting point of 5.5°C at 1 atm, what is the heat of fusion of benzene?

41. Explain the origin of the constant B in this empirical vapor pressure equation:

$$\ln P = -\frac{A}{T} + B \ln T + C.$$

42. Estimate the vapor pressure of ice at -20°C if the heat of fusion of ice is 80 cal g^{-1}, if the heat of vaporization of water is 600 cal g^{-1}, and if the vapor pressure of ice at 0°C is 4.59 mm Hg.
Answer: 0.773 mm Hg.

---

43. Calculate the increase in entropy of a system consisting of one mole water at 30°C and one mole water at 20°C when they are mixed and achieve equilibrium adiabatically and isobarically.
Answer: $\Delta S = 0.0051$ cal deg^{-1}.

44. Is there any adiabatic process at 25°C at 1 atm by which water can be formed from hydrogen and oxygen? Explain. Is there any temperature at which water could be produced adiabatically and isobarically from hydrogen and oxygen? Explain.

45. Calculate the amount of heat absorbed from the surroundings at 50°F by a heat pump in one cycle of operation if it must yield one Btu per cycle at 75°F. What is the work done on the pump per cycle? What is its greatest efficiency?

46. An engine that is to operate in a Carnot cycle is to do 1000 cal work per cycle. If the upper and lower temperatures are 100°C and 4°C, what must be the minimum difference in entropies of the working substance for these two temperatures? Could water be a suitable working substance? Explain.
Answer: $S_2 - S_1 = 10.42$ cal deg^{-1}; yes, if engine is big enough.

47. Two bodies of equal heat capacity but different temperature are placed in thermal contact with each other but out of thermal contact with their surroundings. In terms of their initial temperatures, find the final common temperature of both at equilibrium when:
(a) No work is done by them.
(b) They produce work reversibly by means of a heat engine that operates cyclically.

48. Compare the isobaric increases in entropy from 25°C to 100°C for one mole each methane and propane and explain any difference in terms of randomness and disorder. Compare three moles methane to one of propane.

49. Just as electric polarization decreases as temperature rises at constant electric field, the magnetic moment M of a paramagnetic substance likewise decreases with increasing temperature T at constant magnetic field strength $\mathcal{H}$. If the magnetic work done on a paramagnetic substance is $\mathcal{H} \, dM$, find an expression for the exact differential $d(A - \mathcal{H}M)$. Then, if entropy is a function of T and $\mathcal{H}$, show that reversible adiabatic ($dS = 0$, or isentropic) demagnetization of a paramagnetic substance causes its temperature to decrease. (Neglect expansion work throughout the problem.)

50. By definition, the isobaric coefficient of thermal expansion α is

$$\alpha = \frac{1}{V} \left(\frac{\partial V}{\partial T} \right)_P$$

and, by definition, the isothermal coefficient of compressibility β is

$$\beta = -\frac{1}{V} \left(\frac{\partial V}{\partial P} \right)_T.$$

With the aid of the second law, show that for a real gas

$$C_P - C_V = \frac{V T \alpha^2}{\beta}.$$

51. Calculate the increase in enthalpy when one mole gaseous oxygen at 25°C changes from a pressure of one atm to a fugacity of one atm.
Answer: $\Delta H = -0.0079$ joules.

52. The vapor pressure of ammonia at 25°C is 9.90 atm. Calculate the absolute entropy of liquid ammonia at ten atm pressure at 25°C. The normal boiling point of ammonia is -33°C and $S^\circ = 46.01$ cal mole^{-1} deg^{-1} at 25°C (Rossini, F. D., et al., Circular 500 N.B.S., 1952).

53. The normal boiling point of SO_2 is $-10°C$, and its vapor pressure at $25°C$ is 3.80 atm. Calculate the absolute molar entropies of liquid and saturated gaseous SO_2 at $0°C$ from $S°$ in Table 4.1. For gaseous SO_2, $C_P = 9.7$ cal mole^{-1} deg^{-1}. *Answer:* 33.14 cal deg^{-1}, 57.62 cal deg^{-1}.

54. One mole N_2, a perfect gas with $C_P = 7R/2$, is caused to change its state from 3.00 atm at $200°C$ to 1.00 atm at $0°C$ by three different processes. Find and tabulate q, w, ΔE, ΔH, and ΔS for this change of state for these processes:
(a) The gas expands reversibly and adiabatically until its temperature is $0°C$; then it is brought isothermally to the final state.
(b) By expanding irreversibly through a Joule-Thomson porous plug, the pressure of the gas falls to 1 atm; then it is brought isobarically to the final state.
(c) The gas expands freely into an evacuated vessel; then it is cooled suddenly without expansion work until the final state is reached.

55. It is observed that a tiny bit of light can cause the reaction $H_{2(g)} + Cl_{2(g)} \rightarrow 2HCl_{(g)}$ to occur suddenly and to an extent quite out of proportion to the cause. In terms of the entropy change for such an adiabatic process, explain the spontaneity of this reaction at $25°C$.

56. Find ΔE, ΔH, ΔS, and w for one mole of an ideal gas with $C_V = 5R/2$ as it changes from an initial state at 4.00 atm at $250°C$:
(a) To 1.00 atm by reversible adiabatic expansion.
(b) To 1.00 atm at $200°C$ by irreversible adiabatic expansion (if this is possible).
(c) To 1.00 atm at $50°C$ by irreversible adiabatic expansion (if this is possible).
What is the maximum work that could be done by the gas between these same three pairs of terminal states in any kind of process done once? Find ΔE, ΔH, and ΔS for these processes that produce more work.

57. The vapor pressure of bromine at $25°C$ is 0.298 atm, and it boils at one atm at $59°C$. Find $\Delta E°$, $\Delta H°$, $\Delta S°$, $\Delta A°$, and $\Delta G°$ at $25°C$ for the vaporization of one mole of bromine.
Answer: $\Delta E° = 6430$ cal; $\Delta H° = 7020$ cal; $\Delta S° = 21.1$ cal deg^{-1}; $\Delta A° = 124$ cal; $\Delta G° = 716$ cal.

58. What value of the isothermal coefficient of compressibility (see Problem 50) of a condensed phase will cause the approximate expression $\Delta G = V \Delta P$ to be in error by one joule if $V = 50$ ml and $\Delta P = 100$ atm?
Answer: 39×10^{-6} atm^{-1}.

59. Calculate the rate with which vapor pressure changes with respect to total pressure near the critical point.

60. Suppose three phases of a pure substance are in equilibrium at a certain pressure and temperature. If none of the phases disappears, find (if possible) the rate of change of pressure with respect to temperature.

61. Discuss the Clapeyron equation near and at the critical point.

62. The density of ice II is 1.21 g ml^{-1}; that of ice III is 1.10 g ml^{-1}. Calculate ΔH for the transformation of one mole of ice II into ice III if these two phases are in equilibrium at 3260 atm at $-25.0°C$ and at 2450 atm at $-31.0°C$ (*Int. Crit. Tables IV*, p. 11).
Answer: $\Delta H = 1200$ cal mole^{-1}.

63. What is the minimum value of the molar heat of vaporization of bromine at $25°C$ if the stable state is liquid at $25°C$ and if the standard entropies of liquid and gas are those of Table 4.1?

64. Two crystalline species of an element are in equilibrium at 1500°C at one atm. At 25°C, their standard entropies differ by 0.100 cal mole^{-1} deg^{-1}. If their molar heat capacities are equal above 25°C, what is the molar heat of formation of the form which is metastable at 25°C?

FOOTNOTES

1. For details see: Margenau, H., and G. M. Murphy, *The Mathematics of Physics and Chemistry*. Princeton, New Jersey: D. Van Nostrand Company, Inc. Landsberg, P. T., "Foundations of Thermodynamics," *Reviews of Modern Physics*, **28** (1956), 363.

2. Guggenheim, E. A., *Thermodynamics*. Amsterdam: North-Holland Publishing Co., 1957, pp. 192-4.

3. For a discussion of dimensioned arguments of logarithms, see Copley, G. N., *Journal of Chemical Education*, **35** (1958), 366; and Boggs, J. E., *ibid*, p. 30.

5 / THE PHASE RULE

AND SOLUTIONS

A. THE PHASE RULE

5.1 Definitions and Concentration

The first and second laws of thermodynamics establish the concept of a thermodynamic function of state, state the law of conservation of energy for changes that involve heat and work, and propose several criteria of equilibrium and spontaneity of processes that involve or can involve heat. These laws and the third, which fixes a constant of integration at absolute zero, have been applied in detail to processes that are generally called physical. Before these laws can be applied in their fullness to chemical phenomena, it is fitting that they be applied to systems that are not pure substances and do not obey the law of definite proportions: solutions.

A *solution* is a physically homogeneous mixture that changes continuously in composition on the formation of a new phase. A portion of matter that is physically homogeneous acts as a continuum in the experiment at hand. Many experiments, but not all, with monochromatic X rays would evidence a lack in homogeneity because the wavelengths of X rays and sizes of atoms are of comparable magnitude and thus sometimes interact to show diffraction phenomena. The circumstances in which visible light exhibits its wave nature and the discreteness and inhomogeneity of matter are generally confined to colloid chemistry and spectroscopy. Accordingly, when the experiment at hand is a commonplace vaporization or fusion, the visible portions of matter in the experiment appear alike in every part in each phase and each phase is then termed *physically homogeneous*. In other words, physically homogeneous in general means having dimensions of the order of or greater than the wavelength of light. A *mixture* is a portion of matter that does not obey the law of multiple or definite proportions. Air, gasoline, and a crystalline defect structure like that of FeS_{1+x} are examples of mixtures, for accurate chemical or elemental analysis of each would show varying results from sample to sample. Indeed, it is tempting to say that air, gasoline, and iron sulfide are mixtures because by a physical process like fractional distillation each can be changed continuously in composition as a gas phase of nitrogen, pentane, or sulfur forms. But such a statement begs the definition. Salt and water form one liquid phase at equilibrium if somewhat less than 40 g salt are mixed with 100 g water at room temperature. The amount of salt could be 20 g, 2 g, or 2 micrograms. When such a liquid mixture is frozen, pure solid water crystallizes and the concentration of salt in the liquor increases continuously to a certain maximum value, the solubility of salt ($NaCl \cdot 2 H_2O$) in water. That is, salt water is a solution.

There are certain aggregations of matter that are properly solutions and yet behave like pure substances in a physical separation process like distillation. Constant-boiling hydrochloric acid, used as a standard in analytical chemistry, boils at a definite temperature and pressure without change in composition. But a change in pressure or crystallizing ice from such a solution does indeed cause the composition to vary continuously. Similarly, eutectic mixtures and racemic mixtures behave like pure substances on melting, but some other physical process would betray their nonstoichiometry. These vagaries are part of the matter of this chapter.

The proportions in which pure components are mixed to form solutions are specified in many ways. Industrial workers often specify percentages by weight or volume for convenience in formulation, but proportions so specified seldom if ever have chemical significance. Analytical chemists find it convenient to measure volumes and thus specify a chemically meaningful amount per unit volume. The molarity C_i of a solution is the number of gram-moles of solute i per liter of solution; the formality F_i of a solution is the number of gram-formula weights of solute i per liter of solution; the normality $N_{\pm i}$ of a solution is the number of gram-equivalent weights of solute i per liter of solution. In mathematical terms, if V is the actual volume

259

in milliliters of solution that results when W_i grams of species i are dissolved, then

$$C_i = \frac{W_i}{M_i} \times \frac{1000}{V} \tag{5.1}$$

$$F_i = \frac{W_i}{M_i} \times \frac{1000}{V} \tag{5.2}$$

$$N_{\pm i} = \frac{nW_i}{M_i} \times \frac{1000}{V}. \tag{5.3}$$

In these equations, M_i is the molecular or formula weight of the pure solute i in grams and n is the number of protons, electrons, or their equivalent (divided, of course, by Avogadro's number) that are lost or gained by M_i grams of solute in the particular reaction of interest. The normality is always an integral multiple of the formality or molarity.

If a solution expands with an increase in temperature, the number by which its normality, formality, or molarity is expressed decreases as the temperature rises for the amount of solute is unchanged by supposition. In order to avoid this dependence on temperature, which is as unpredictable as changes in density, physical chemists commonly express concentrations in terms of molality. The molality m_i of a solution is the number of gram-molecular weights per kilogram of solvent, which is here called species 1. Mathematically,

$$m_i = \frac{W_i}{M_i} \times \frac{1000}{W_1} \tag{5.4}$$

where W_i grams of solute with gram molecular weight M_i are dissolved in W_1 grams of solvent. If no new phases are generated or if no matter is transferred to phases already in contact with the solution, m_i is independent of temperature, barring decomposition by chemical reaction of solute or solvent. That is,

$$\frac{dm_i}{dT} = 0 . \tag{5.5}$$

The numerical value of m_i often fails to exhibit fully the chemical nature of a solution; hence, mole fraction was invented. If W_i grams of species i with gram molecular weight M_i are mixed with $(C - 1)$ other components, then the mole fraction N_i of species i is given by (5.6).

$$N_i = \frac{\dfrac{W_i}{M_i}}{\displaystyle\sum_{j=1}^{C} \frac{W_j}{M_j}}. \tag{5.6}$$

By (5.6),

$$\sum_{i=1}^{C} N_i = \frac{\displaystyle\sum_{i=1}^{C} \frac{W_i}{M_i}}{\displaystyle\sum_{j=1}^{C} \frac{W_j}{M_j}} .$$

But the summations merely count, perhaps in a different order, the numbers of gram-moles of the C components so that

$$\sum_{i=1}^{C} N_i = 1 . \tag{5.7}$$

As for m_i, if the phase under consideration loses no matter to other phases and does not undergo chemical changes such as reaction or dissociation of molecules,

$$\frac{dN_i}{dT} = 0 . \tag{5.8}$$

As defined for gaseous solutions, M_i has a definite measurable value. As applied to liquid or solid solutions, the molecular weight of the solvent may sometimes have any arbitrary value, but in this treatment simplicity and indeed common use ordinarily require that M_i for solute and solvent be the molecular weight of the vapor.

Example 5.1. At 20°C, the density of an aqueous solution containing 15.00% by weight H_2SO_4 is 1.102 g ml^{-1}. Calculate its formality, normality, and molality.

The number of grams of pure H_2SO_4 in 1 l of this solution are $1.102 \times 1000 \times 0.1500$, or 165.3 g. Since the formula weight of H_2SO_4 is 98.08, this is 1.685 gram formula weights per liter. That is, the formality is 1.685. And if both protons are lost in an acid-base reaction, the normality is $2 \times 1.685 = 3.370$.

The molality of the solution is readily found by (5.4), for $W_1 = 1102 - 165 = 937$ g water.

$$m_2 = \frac{165.3}{98.08} \times \frac{1000}{937} = 1.799 .$$

5.2 Chemical Potential

When discontinuities in physical properties like density or index of refraction exist in a system, more than one phase is present. It is generally most convenient to write the usual thermodynamic equations for each phase just as though it were an independent system, a kind of subsystem. This was done in Section 4.26 in deriving the Clapeyron equation for one component in two phases. If the phases that coexist are solutions, allowance must be made for continuous changes in composition of each through the transfer of matter across phase boundaries from one phase to another. No longer are equations for closed systems adequate.

Let $\mathbf{C}$ be the minimum number of independently variable components or chemical substances out of which the several coexisting phases of a system can be made. In addition to the usual independent thermodynamic variables like pressure and temperature there will then be up to $\mathbf{C}$ more independent variables that must be specified in order to define the size and state of the system. These $\mathbf{C}$ variables are usually taken to be the numbers of gram-moles of the $\mathbf{C}$ components out of which the system can be prepared. Just as (4.48) established entropy and volume as the natural independent variables for the energy of a closed system that, if it works, does only expansion work, so also for open systems experiencing only expansion work the energy is a natural function of entropy and volume as well as of the number n_i of gram-moles of the various components. That is,

$$E = E(S, V, n_1, n_2, \cdots n_i, \cdots n_{\mathbf{C}}) . \tag{5.9}$$

Infinitesimal changes in these $\mathbf{C} + 2$ variables will lead to an infinitesimal change dE in the energy of the system. By the usual rule of calculus,

$$dE = \left(\frac{\partial E}{\partial S}\right)_{V,n} dS + \left(\frac{\partial E}{\partial V}\right)_{S,n} dV + \sum_{i=1}^{\mathbf{C}} \left(\frac{\partial E}{\partial n_i}\right)_{S,V,n_j} dn_i \tag{5.10}$$

where the subscript n means that the number of moles of each component is held fixed and where the subscript n_j indicates that the number of moles of each component except for the ith component is held constant. If all dn_i were zero, (5.10) would apply to a closed system as does Equation (4.46).

$$dE = T\, dS - P\, dV . \tag{4.46}$$

Comparison of (5.10) with (4.46) for a closed system then yields (5.11),

$$dE = T\, dS - P\, dV + \sum_{i=1}^{\mathbf{C}} \mu_i\, dn_i \tag{5.11}$$

where the chemical potential μ_i of species i is defined by (5.12).

$$\mu_i = \left(\frac{\partial E}{\partial n_i}\right)_{S,V,n_j} . \tag{5.12}$$

By the usual methods of Section 4.13 it is possible to obtain from (5.11) analogous expressions for dH, dA, and dG in the following way.

$$dE + d(PV) = d(PV) + T\, dS - P\, dV + \sum_{i=1}^{\mathbf{C}} \mu_i\, dn_i$$

$$dH = T\, dS + V\, dP + \sum_{i=1}^{\mathbf{C}} \mu_i\, dn_i \tag{5.13}$$

$$dE - d(TS) = -d(TS) + T\, dS - P\, dV + \sum_{i=1}^{\mathbf{C}} \mu_i\, dn_i$$

$$dA = -S\, dT - P\, dV + \sum_{i=1}^{\mathbf{C}} \mu_i\, dn_i \tag{5.14}$$

$$dE + d(PV - TS) = d(PV - TS) + T\,dS - P\,dV + \sum_{i=1}^{\mathbf{C}} \mu_i\,dn_i$$

$$dG = -S\,dT + V\,dP + \sum_{i=1}^{\mathbf{C}} \mu_i\,dn_i\,. \tag{5.15}$$

From the method of derivation and from the definition of the chemical potential in (5.12), it is clear that

$$\mu_i = \left(\frac{\partial E}{\partial n_i}\right)_{S,V,n_j} = \left(\frac{\partial H}{\partial n_i}\right)_{S,P,n_j} = \left(\frac{\partial A}{\partial n_i}\right)_{T,V,n_j} = \left(\frac{\partial G}{\partial n_i}\right)_{T,P,n_j}. \tag{5.16}$$

Moreover, as in (5.9),

$$G = G(T, P, n_1, n_2, \cdots n_i, \cdots n_{\mathbf{C}}) \tag{5.17}$$

and so on for H and A. The really important feature of (5.16) and (5.17) is that the chemical potential μ_i is a partial molar quantity as in (3.79) when the Gibbs free energy G is the extensive property. Hence, by the natural extension of (3.80) from two to $\mathbf{C}$ components,

$$G(T, P, n_i) = \sum_{i=1}^{\mathbf{C}} n_i \mu_i(T, P)\,. \tag{5.18}$$

The various thermodynamic equations of Chapters 3 and 4 were developed for closed systems. Since conservation of matter was assumed for each system, it was often unnecessary to call explicit attention to the fact that each equation was written for a fixed number n of moles and that extensive properties like V and G were proportional to n. Sometimes, as in (3.11), (3.46), (4.122), (4.164), and others, there is an n as a reminder that extensive properties are mentioned. All these equations can be transformed into an intensive form by taking the appropriate derivative. For example, (4.98) becomes (5.19) when the order of partial differentiation is unimportant.

$$V = \left(\frac{\partial G}{\partial P}\right)_{T,n} \tag{4.98}$$

$$\frac{\partial V}{\partial n_i} = \left[\frac{\partial}{\partial P}\left(\frac{\partial G}{\partial n_i}\right)\right]_{T,n}$$

$$\overline{V}_i = \left(\frac{\partial \mu_i}{\partial P}\right)_{T,n}. \tag{5.19}$$

In a similar way, by partial differentiation, (4.167) becomes (5.20), a much more common form.

$$G(f, T) = nRT \ln f + nG^o(T) \tag{4.167}$$

$$\left(\frac{\partial G}{\partial n}\right)_{T,P} = RT \ln f + G^o(T)\,.$$

If the chemical species is one of several, it is labeled i and

$$\mu_i = RT \ln f_i + \mu_i^o(T) . \tag{5.20}$$

Equation (5.20) thus expresses the chemical potential as a function of the fugacity f_i of the gas relative to a reference value $\mu_i^o(T)$, which depends only on the temperature T and the definition of the standard state of fugacity. When the species i is not a gas, an analogous equation (5.21) can be written.

$$\mu_i = RT \ln a_i + \mu_i^o(T) . \tag{5.21}$$

In (5.21), a_i is the activity of species i at the temperature T relative to some arbitrary standard state with chemical potential $\mu_i^o(T)$. The value of $\mu_i^o(T)$ is the molar Gibbs free energy in the standard reference state of unit activity $(a_i = 1)$, and is numerically equal to the standard molar Gibbs free energy of formation at the standard temperature. When these concepts are developed for chemically reacting systems in Chapter 6, the reason for the name *chemical potential* will be apparent.

5.3 The Phase Rule Proved

It is reasonable enough to expect, as in (5.17), that the Gibbs free energy of a one-phase system should be a function of just $C + 2$ independent variables — namely, the pressure P, the temperature T, and the amounts in moles of the various components in that one phase. However, it is not intuitively clear how many variables are really independent when several phases, each perhaps a solution, coexist at equilibrium. The phase rule is a convenient simple device for determining the number of components, the number of phases, or the number of independent intensive variables that must be specified at equilibrium in order to fix the state of any system. Its proof involves a bit of tedious mathematical reasoning, but from this reasoning comes a clear restatement of the conditions of equilibrium in a most useful form.

The criterion of equilibrium of (4.128) as stated for a closed system is a convenient starting point for the development of the phase rule of Gibbs. With explicit statement of the fact that the system is closed by the use of the subscript n, (4.128) becomes (5.22).

$$(\delta E)_{S,V,n} \geqslant 0 . \tag{5.22}$$

If surface effects can be neglected, each of the extensive properties of a system of **P** homogeneous phases is the sum of the values of the extensive property in each phase. In other words, the energy or volume of a system is the sum of the energies or volumes of its parts, the **P** phases. And the same applies to entropy and the moles of each of the **C** components out of which the system is made. Mathematically, if a superscript indicates the phase,

$$E = \sum_{j=1}^{P} E^{(j)} \tag{5.23}$$

$$V = \sum_{j=1}^{P} V^{(j)}$$

$$S = \sum_{j=1}^{P} S^{(j)} \tag{5.24}$$

$$n_i = \sum_{j=1}^{P} n_i^{(j)}, \qquad (i = 1, 2, \cdots, C).$$

Equation (5.23) says that the energy of the system is the sum of the energies of its phases, and (5.24) says the same for volumes, entropies, and moles of each of the C components. The values of V, S, and n_i in (5.24) are to be held constant in order to apply the criterion (5.22) of equilibrium. For some small variation $\delta V^{(j)}$ in the volume of phase j, for some small variation $\delta S^{(j)}$ in the entropy of phase j, and for some small variation $\delta n_i^{(j)}$ in the number of moles of component i in phase j, there will be by (5.10) a small change $\delta E^{(j)}$ in the energy of phase j such that

$$\delta E^{(j)} = T^{(j)} \, \delta S^{(j)} - P^{(j)} \, \delta V^{(j)} + \sum_{i=1}^{C} \mu_i^{(j)} \, \delta n_i^{(j)} . \tag{5.25}$$

Equation (5.25) assumes that there are no force fields (e.g., gravitational, electric, magnetic) affecting the system and that there is only a uniform normal external pressure $P^{(j)}$ on each phase. The temperature of phase j is $T^{(j)}$ and in it the chemical potential of component i is $\mu_i^{(j)}$. In other words, (5.25) treats phase j as a system in itself.

In order to preserve equilibrium in the system of P phases there must be simultaneous coordinated changes in entropy, volume, and numbers of moles of the various components if the total values of (5.24) for the system of phases are to remain constant. That is, if the volume of phase j increases by $\delta V^{(j)}$, there must be a decrease in volume of one or more of the other phases if the volume V of the whole system is constant. The same applies to a loss of moles $\delta n_i^{(j)}$ from phase j; these moles of i must appear elsewhere in the system. The same applies to $\delta S^{(j)}$ and S. By (5.23) and (5.25), the energy change that results (in the absence of other extraordinary restraints such as osmotic membranes that prevent the transfer of some component from one phase to another) is

$$\delta E = \sum_{j=1}^{P} \delta E^{(j)} = \sum_{j=1}^{P} T^{(j)} \, \delta S^{(j)} + \sum_{j=1}^{P} [-P^{(j)}] \, \delta V^{(j)} + \sum_{j=1}^{P} \sum_{i=1}^{C} \mu_i^{(j)} \, \delta n_i^{(j)} .$$

If equilibrium is to be maintained in the system, this variation in energy

δE must be greater than or equal to zero by (5.22). In other words,

$$\sum_{j=1}^{P} T^{(j)} \, \delta S^{(j)} + \sum_{j=1}^{P} [-P^{(j)}] \, \delta V^{(j)} + \sum_{j=1}^{P} \sum_{i=1}^{C} \mu_i^{(j)} \, \delta n_i^{(j)} \geqslant 0$$

provided

$$\delta V = \sum_{j=1}^{P} \delta V^{(j)} = 0$$

$$\delta S = \sum_{j=1}^{P} \delta S^{(j)} = 0 \qquad\qquad (5.26)$$

$$\delta n_i = \sum_{j=1}^{P} \delta n_i^{(j)} = 0, \qquad (i = 1, 2, \cdots, C) .$$

In order to show that at equilibrium the temperatures of any two phases labeled 1 and 2 are equal, let there be no changes in volume of any phase [$\delta V^{(j)} = 0$ for all j] and no transfer of matter across phase boundaries [$\delta n_i^{(j)} = 0$ for all i and j], and let the only entropy change occur in phases 1 and 2 [$\delta S^{(j)} = 0$ for $1 \neq j \neq 2$]. By (5.26),

$$T^{(1)} \, \delta S^{(1)} + T^{(2)} \, \delta S^{(2)} \geqslant 0$$

$$\delta S^{(1)} + \delta S^{(2)} = 0 .$$

Elimination of $\delta S^{(2)}$ from these two relations yields

$$[T^{(1)} - T^{(2)}] \, \delta S^{(1)} \geqslant 0 .$$

If $\delta S^{(1)}$ is greater than zero, $T^{(1)} \geqslant T^{(2)}$; if $\delta S^{(1)}$ is less than zero, $T^{(1)} \leqslant T^{(2)}$. Since $\delta S^{(1)}$ is not zero, these two relations are satisfied only if $T^{(1)} = T^{(2)}$.

A spontaneous increase in the entropy of phase 1 such that $\delta S^{(1)}$ is greater than zero, perhaps by absorption of a positive amount of heat from phase 2, requires that $[T^{(1)} - T^{(2)}] \, \delta S^{(1)} < 0$ or that $T^{(1)} < T^{(2)}$. This is nothing more than a statement that heat flows spontaneously from a high to a low temperature.

In order to show that at equilibrium in the absence of such things as fields and membranes the pressures of any two phases labeled 1 and 2 are equal, let there be no changes in entropy in any phase [$\delta S^{(j)} = 0$ for all j] and no transfer of matter from phase to phase [$\delta n_i^{(j)} = 0$ for all i and j], and let the only volume change occur between phases 1 and 2 [$\delta V^{(j)} = 0$ for $1 \neq j \neq 2$]. By (5.26),

$$-P^{(1)} \, \delta V^{(1)} - P^{(2)} \, \delta V^{(2)} \geqslant 0$$

$$\delta V^{(1)} + \delta V^{(2)} = 0 .$$

Elimination of $\delta V^{(2)}$ yields

$$[P^{(2)} - P^{(1)}] \, \delta V^{(1)} \geqslant 0 .$$

If the volume of phase 1 increases, $\delta V^{(1)} > 0$ and $P^{(2)} \geqslant P^{(1)}$. If the volume of phase 1 decreases, $\delta V^{(1)} < 0$ and $P^{(2)} \leqslant P^{(1)}$. But since the volume of phase 1 must change, these two relations are satisfied only if $P^{(1)} = P^{(2)}$ so that the pressure is uniform throughout the system.

A spontaneous increase in the volume of phase 1 requires $[P^{(2)} - P^{(1)}] \delta V^{(1)} < 0$ and since $\delta V^{(1)}$ is supposed to be greater than zero, $P^{(2)} < P^{(1)}$. That is, the volume of a phase with a high pressure increases spontaneously and at the expense of a phase with a low pressure.

In order to show that the chemical potential of any species i is the same anywhere in the system, let there be no changes in volume or entropy of any phase $[\delta V^{(j)} = \delta S^{(j)} = 0$ for all $j]$ and let the only transfer of any component be a transfer of δn_i moles of component i between the arbitrarily chosen phases 1 and 2, each of which contains component i. Then, as before, by (5.26),

$$\delta V = \sum_{j=1}^{P} \delta V^{(j)} = 0$$

$$\delta S = \sum_{j=1}^{P} \delta S^{(j)} = 0$$

$$\delta n_i = \sum_{j=1}^{P} \delta n_i^{(j)} = \delta n_i^{(1)} + \delta n_i^{(2)} = 0$$

and

$$\mu_i^{(1)} \, \delta n_i^{(1)} + \mu_i^{(2)} \, \delta n_i^{(2)} \geqslant 0 \, .$$

Elimination of $\delta n_i^{(2)}$ from these relations yields

$$[\mu_i^{(1)} - \mu_i^{(2)}] \, \delta n_i^{(1)} \geqslant 0 \, .$$

If the amount of component i in phase 1 increases, $\delta n_i^{(1)}$ is greater than zero and $\mu_i^{(1)} \geqslant \mu_i^{(2)}$; if the amount of i in phase 1 decreases, $\mu_i^{(1)} \leqslant \mu_i^{(2)}$. Hence, at equilibrium, $\mu_i^{(1)} = \mu_i^{(2)}$, which is like (4.152) but more general. In other words, the Clapeyron equation, founded as it is on equality of chemical potentials, is true for one component of two solutions as well as for one component of two pure phases.

If it happens that phase 1 does not initially contain component i, it could gain some i from phase 2 so that $\mu_i^{(1)} \geqslant \mu_i^{(2)}$ at equilibrium. But phase 1 could not lose component i if it initially had none, so that the chemical potential of i in a phase in which it is not actually present may be greater than it is in other phases that actually contain component i.

For a spontaneous flow of component i from any phase labeled 2, which initially contains i, to another phase labeled 1, the relation is, in contrast to that above, $[\mu_i^{(1)} - \mu_i^{(2)}] \delta n_i^{(1)} < 0$. If $\delta n_i^{(1)}$ is greater than zero as supposed, $\mu_i^{(1)} < \mu_i^{(2)}$. That is, spontaneous transfer of matter to phase 1 is from a region of high chemical potential $\mu_i^{(2)}$ to a region of low chemical potential

$\mu_i^{(1)}$. Chemical potential is to the transfer of matter as pressure is to a change of volume or as temperature is to heat.

These necessary conditions of equilibrium, namely, equality of temperature, pressure, and chemical potential of each component, are also sufficient conditions for equilibrium, for with them (5.26) is satisfied thus:

$$T \sum_{j=1}^{P} \delta S^{(j)} - P \sum_{j=1}^{P} \delta V^{(j)} + \sum_{i=1}^{C} \mu_i \sum_{j=1}^{P} \delta n_i^{(j)} \geqslant 0$$

$$T(0) - P(0) + \sum_{i=1}^{C} \mu_i(0) = 0 .$$

The necessary and sufficient conditions for equilibrium in a system of P phases and C components, subject to the conditions specified above, are (5.27).

$$\left.\begin{array}{l} T^{(1)} = T^{(2)} = \cdots = T^{(j)} = \cdots = T^{(P)} \\[4pt] P^{(1)} = P^{(2)} = \cdots = P^{(j)} = \cdots = P^{(P)} \\[4pt] \mu_1^{(1)} = \mu_1^{(2)} = \cdots = \mu_1^{(j)} = \cdots = \mu_1^{(P)} \\[4pt] \mu_2^{(1)} = \mu_2^{(2)} = \cdots = \mu_2^{(j)} = \cdots = \mu_2^{(P)} \\[4pt] \cdots \qquad\qquad\qquad \cdots \\[4pt] \mu_i^{(1)} = \mu_i^{(2)} = \cdots = \mu_i^{(j)} = \cdots = \mu_i^{(P)} \\[4pt] \cdots \qquad\qquad\qquad \cdots \\[4pt] \mu_C^{(1)} = \mu_C^{(2)} = \cdots = \mu_C^{(j)} = \cdots = \mu_C^{(P)} . \end{array}\right\} \quad (5.27)$$

The number of equations of condition in (5.27) is $(C + 2)\,(P - 1)$. The number of intensive variables is $(C + 1)P$, for in each phase there is a temperature $T^{(j)}$, pressure $P^{(j)}$, and $(C - 1)$ mole fractions that are independently variable, the last mole fraction in each phase being specified by (5.7):

$$\sum_{i=1}^{C} N_i^{(j)} = 1, \qquad (j = 1, 2, \cdots, P) . \tag{5.7}$$

The number of degrees of freedom F, or the number of intensive thermodynamic variables that can be adjusted independently at equilibrium without change in the number of phases P or number of components C, is the difference in these two quantities. That is,

$$F = (C + 1)P - (C + 2)\,(P - 1)$$
$$= CP + P - CP - 2P + C + 2$$
$$F = C - P + 2 . \tag{5.28}$$

Equation (5.28) is the powerful and celebrated phase rule of Gibbs. Since it deals only with the intensive variables temperature, pressure, and chemical potential, it is not concerned with the amount of matter in a system. At least one of the variables in (5.9) or (5.17) is not independent and intensive and is not counted by $\mathbf{F}$; one of these variables specifies the size of a system containing even only one phase. If several phases coexist at equilibrium, the number of independent variables in (5.9) and (5.17) is further reduced by virtue of (5.27).

When temperature or pressure is fixed, the rule reads

$$\mathbf{F} = \mathbf{C} - \mathbf{P} + 1, \qquad dT \text{ or } dP = 0 \tag{5.29}$$

as a recounting of variables will verify. When temperature and pressure are constant, it reads

$$\mathbf{F} = \mathbf{C} - \mathbf{P}, \qquad (dT = dP = 0) . \tag{5.30}$$

Quite naturally, relaxation of some of the conditions about fields and membranees will lead to increased values of $\mathbf{F}$. By their very meaning, $\mathbf{F}$, $\mathbf{C}$, and $\mathbf{P}$ are zero or real positive integers.

B. SIMPLE SYSTEMS

5.4 Phase Diagrams of One-Component Systems

If a system can be prepared at equilibrium from one pure chemical substance, it is a one-component system. At any temperature and pressure the system may actually contain several identifiable chemical or molecular species in different phases, but if the state of the system at equilibrium can in principle be reproduced from one pure substance, the system is said to contain just one component.

Really pure water is as unobtainable as it is familiar in textbooks. Perhaps deionization with ion exchange resins and storage in a completely insoluble container would yield just H_2O (and a few hydronium and hydroxide ions, of course). However, this dihydrogen oxide would not really be at equilibrium until it had been transformed in part into various molecular species, among which would be H_2 and O_2. The attainment of true equilibrium in this system requires a very long time, which is of no concern in the study of equilibrium thermodynamics. Nor is the feasibility of analyzing for the infinitesimal amounts of H_2 and O_2 of any concern here. In fact, even at about 2000°C only 1% is dissociated. What is of importance is that, at equilibrium, at least in principle, really pure water contains dissolved in it traces of decomposition products that, if they were only hydrogen and oxygen, would be $2 H_2$ for every O_2. In other words, several chemicals may be present in a one-component system.

Heating pure N_2O_4 until it decomposes by the reaction

$$N_2O_4 \rightarrow 2 NO_2$$

or even until it comes to equilibrium with N_2, O_2, and the other oxides of nitrogen, does not change it from being a one-component system. Heating pure $CaCO_3$ until

$$CaCO_3 \rightarrow CaO + CO_2$$

does not change it either, nor does causing pure solid $Na_2SO_4 \cdot 10 \ H_2O$ to form an aqueous solution render it a system of two components. Only loss of some of these equilibrium species or initially impure substances leads to multi-component systems.

When $C = 1$, as it does in one-component systems, the phase rule says that the degrees of freedom F depend upon the number of phases P that coexist. By (5.28), when temperature and pressure are variable,

$$F = C - P + 2 \qquad\qquad (5.28)$$
$$= 1 - P + 2 = 3 - P .$$

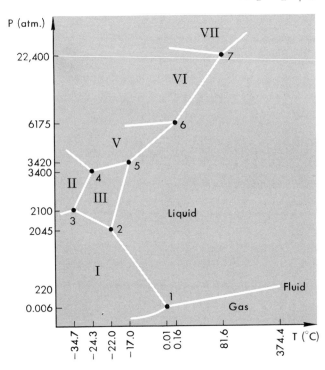

In order that the system be something more than a vacuum, P must be greater than zero. Since the maximum value of F is then 2, these two degrees of freedom are readily expressed graphically as the two independent variables of a plane area. One degree of freedom is a curve, and no degree of freedom is a fixed point.

Figure 5.1 is the phase diagram of water with nonlinear scales of pressure and temperature because of the great range of variables to be shown. A diagram such as this cannot be predicted by the phase rule. Such a diagram is a summary of experimental data systematized and coordinated by use of the phase rule. The phase rule does not predict the existence of certain states of matter at certain temperatures and pressures, but it does tell what is possible and impossible at equilibrium. For example, it is impossible to have four phases coexisting at equilibrium, for if $P = 4$ then $F = 3 - 4 = -1$, which is ridiculous because it

Fig. 5.1. *A Caricature of the Phase Diagram of H_2O. A cubic form of ice can be formed by condensation of water vapor at very low temperatures (below about $-75°C$); this form differs from ice I in the arrangement of oxygen atoms as in diamond. The O-O distances are 2.76 A in cubic form, 2.75 A in hexagonal form; H atoms are probably randomly arranged as in ice I. See F. V. Shallcross and G. B. Carpenter,* J. Chem. Phys. **26,** *782 (1957).*

implies that the system by its nature fixes more independent variables than exist to be fixed.

In a one-component system it is possible to have three phases coexisting. Then $\mathbf{P} = 3$ and $\mathbf{F} = 0$ so that there are no intensive variables that can be set at will. The thermodynamic state of a one-component system containing three coexisting phases at equilibrium is completely specified by the nature of that one component. In Figure 5.1, there are seven numbered points, called *triple points* because at each there coexist three phases at equilibrium. Each triple point is a manifestation of the nature of water. Table 5.1 lists the three phases that can coexist at these fixed conditions. There is only one gaseous and one liquid phase, but there are six or seven different solid phases. At each of these points of no degree of freedom there meet three curves and three areas.

Table 5.1. *Triple Points in* H_2O *System*

POINT (FIG. 5.1)	FIXED INTENSIVE PROPERTIES*		THE THREE PHASES COEXISTENT AT EQUILIBRIUM		
	PRESSURE (ATM)	TEMPERATURE (°C)			
1	0.00602	0.0099[†]	Steam	Water	Ice I
2	2,045	−22.0	Water	Ice I	Ice III
3	2,100	−34.7	Ice I	Ice II	Ice III
4	3,400	−24.3	Ice II	Ice III	IceV
5	3,420	−17.0	Water	Ice III	Ice V
6	6,175	0.16	Water	Ice V	Ice VI
7	22,400	81.6	Water	Ice VI	Ice VII

When two phases $(\mathbf{P} = 2)$ exist together at equilibrium in a one-component $(\mathbf{C} = 1)$ system, the phase rule requires one degree of freedom, either temperature or pressure. That is,

$$\mathbf{F} = \mathbf{C} - \mathbf{P} + 2 \qquad (5.28)$$
$$= 1 - 2 + 2 = 1 .$$

When either temperature or pressure is specified, the state of the system is fixed. There is, then, a functional dependence of one of these variables on the other, and the curves of a figure like Figure 5.1 define this functional dependence and exhibit in their property of linear extension the one degree of freedom. Along each such curve two phases coexist at equilibrium. The curve that begins at 1 and proceeds to 219.5 atm and 374.4°C separates regions labeled *liquid* and *gas*. It is the vapor pressure curve of pure H_2O, and along it gas and liquid are in equilibrium. The curve that proceeds upward to the left from point 1 describes the variation in the freezing point of water with pressure. The solid curve that proceeds downward to the left

* Bridgman, P. W., *Journal of Chemical Physics*, **3,**597 (1935), and *Journal of Chemical Physics*, **5,** 964 (1937).
† See Example 5.14.

from 1 describes the sublimation of ice, and the dashed curve from 1 describes the vaporization of supercooled water. Supercooled water is not in an equilibrium state, and the line is dashed. Relative to immediately adjacent states it is stable, but ice I is the most stable form of H_2O at these pressures and temperature.

If the scales of pressure and temperature in Figure 5.1 were true, the slopes of the curves would yield values of the derivative of P with respect to T. By the Clapeyron equation (4.175), this derivative is related to the discontinuities in enthalpy ΔH and volume ΔV on crossing the curve (i.e., on changing phases).

$$\frac{dP}{dT} = \frac{\Delta H}{T \, \Delta V}.$$ (4.175)

If the slope of a curve that describes the equilibrium of one component in two phases is known or can be found from a phase diagram, either ΔH or ΔV can be calculated from the Clapeyron equation.

Example 5.2. The volume decrease when ice I becomes ice II at $-40.0°C$ is 217.4 $cm^3 \, kg^{-1}$ of ice. At this temperature, the rate of change of pressure with respect to temperature is 8.8 atm deg^{-1} (*International Critical Tables IV*, p. 11). What is the increase in enthalpy at $-40.0°C$ of the reaction below?

$$H_2O_{(s)}(I) \rightarrow H_2O_{(s)}(II) .$$

By (4.175),

$$\Delta H = T \times \Delta V \times \frac{dP}{dT}$$

$$= 233 \times \left(-217.4 \times \frac{18}{1000}\right) \times 8.8 \times \left(\frac{1.987}{82.05}\right)$$

$$= -195 \text{ cal mole}^{-1} .$$

When only one phase $(\mathbf{P} = 1)$ is present in a one-component system $(\mathbf{C} = 1)$, there are two degrees of freedom, for

$$\mathbf{F} = \mathbf{C} - \mathbf{P} + 2$$ (5.28)

$$= 1 - 1 + 2 = 2 .$$

The temperature and pressure may be varied independently, and at equilibrium any of the points in an area can be achieved continuously from any other point in the same area. At the boundaries of such areas — that is, along the curves of one degree of freedom — two phases exist. At the boundaries there is a discontinuous change in volume, enthalpy, and some other properties.

Isothermal changes in phase diagrams like Figure 5.1 are described by vertical paths. Suppose that 1 mole gaseous H_2O at a very low pressure is compressed isothermally and reversibly at $-10.0°C$. At 1.95 mm Hg the pressure remains constant as gaseous H_2O is condensed by compression to form ice I, for the pressure is dependent upon the specification of temperature at $-10.0°C$ along a curve $(F = 1)$ that separates two areas. Once all the H_2O is solidified as ice I, the pressure may rise once again during the compression, for in the area labeled I there are two degrees of freedom. At 1090 atm, isothermal reversible compression causes the ice to melt; the line joining 1 and 2 is crossed and the pressure and temperature remain constant as the reversible compression converts ice I into liquid water. When the system is all liquid, the pressure once again rises continuously as the water is compressed until a pressure of 4360 atm is reached. Once again a boundary of the area labeled *liquid* is crossed and the pressure remains fixed as the water becomes ice V at $-10.0°C$. Continued isothermal compression of ice V would lead eventually to ice VI at 6169 atm and perhaps eventually to ice VII. [Data from *International Critical Tables IV*, p. 11.]

Isobaric changes are described by horizontal lines in Figure 5.1. If ice I is heated at one atm pressure, it begins to melt at $0.0024°C$. If the melting is performed reversibly the temperature is constant until all the ice I has disappeared, for along the curve 1-2 there is one degree of freedom that is fixed by fixing the pressure. Both temperature and pressure may be varied independently within the area labeled liquid; hence, at one atm the temperature rises until bubbles form and the water boils at $100.0°C$. Further reversible heating merely boils away the liquid at $100.0°C$. When the last trace of liquid has vaporized, further isobaric heating increases the temperature of the gas continuously.

It is possible reversibly to transform liquid water at $25°C$ into water vapor at $25°C$ without ever having two phases present. This is accomplished by circling around the critical point at 219.5 atm at $374.4°C$ instead of proceeding directly along a vertical isotherm. The critical point terminates the vapor pressure curve of water, for at the critical state the two fluid phases become so much alike that their densities, enthalpies, and other properties are indistinguishable. Another way of considering the route by which liquid water at $25°C$ can be transformed reversibly and continuously (without a phase change) into water vapor at $25°C$ is to circle around the dome-shaped region of interest with regard to van der Waals' equation when pressure and volume are ordinate and abscissa as in Figure 1.6.

In real processes that approach equilibrium spontaneously, the free energy or chemical potential of a system tends to a minimum just as entropy tends to a maximum. By methods already developed it is possible to calculate the chemical potential of a phase at any temperature and pressure. The equations to be used are analogous to (4.97) and (4.98).

$$\left(\frac{\partial \mu_i}{\partial T}\right)_P = -\overline{S}_i \qquad (5.31)$$

$$\left(\frac{\partial \mu_i}{\partial P}\right)_T = \overline{V}_i. \qquad (5.19)$$

273

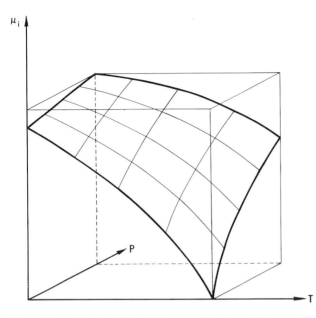

Fig. 5.2. *Chemical Potential μ_i as a Function of Pressure P and Temperature T.*

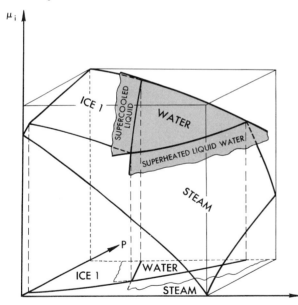

Fig. 5.3. *Chemical Potential Surfaces of H_2O Near the Low-Pressure Triple Point. (Figures like this near this triple point and near the critical point are given by S. H. Bauer, J. Chem. Ed. 35, 289 [1958].)*

Since it is evident from Table 4.1 and the third law that ordinarily the entropy $\bar{S}_i$ of any species or phase is greater than zero, by (5.31)

$$\left(\frac{\partial \mu_i}{\partial T}\right)_P < 0 .$$

That is, the chemical potential of a component of a phase decreases as the temperature rises isobarically. If the phase is a pure component, $\bar{S}_i$ is always greater than zero. Similarly, since the partial molar volume of a phase is almost always greater than zero, by (5.19)

$$\left(\frac{\partial \mu_i}{\partial P}\right)_T > 0 .$$

That is, an isothermal increase in the pressure of a system leads to an increase in its chemical potential. For each component of each phase, then, there is a surface $\mu_i = \mu_i(T, P)$ of the sort shown in Figure 5.2. When two phases coexist at some pressure and temperature, as along a curve in Figure 5.1, the chemical potentials of their components are equal by (5.27). If the three surfaces that describe the chemical potentials of solid, liquid, and gas are given simultaneously as functions of P and T, Figure 5.3 is generated. The intersection of two surfaces yields a curve along which two phases have equal chemical potentials. When such curves are projected on the P-T plane the curves of Figure 5.1 are generated. The chemical potential manifested at equilibrium is the lowest of the three surfaces at any value of P and T, and only the lowest surface has been shown in Figure 5.3. At the triple point, all three surfaces meet because all three chemical potentials are equal at the triple point.

The chemical potential of a metastable phase is greater than that of another phase at the same temperature and pressure. It is appropriate, then, that the surface describing the chemical potential of supercooled and superheated liquid in Figure 5.3 be above those of the solid and gas. Since the solid or gas is absent in these metastable situations, equilibrium is not established and the metastable liquid phase may exist as a metastable phase until crystal nucleation or bubble formation occurs. Superheating of solids that can melt or supercooling of gases that can crystallize has not been observed.

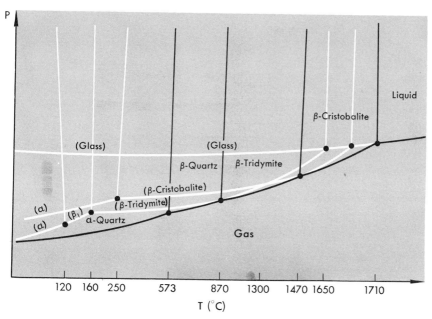

Fig. 5.4. *Caricature of Phase Diagram of SiO₂. Black curves depict equilibrium states; white curves depict metastable states. In addition to the common crystalline species of SiO₂ shown in this figure, there are two new crystalline forms: one is dense (3.01 g cm⁻³) and is formed at 750°C at 35,000 atm (L. Coes, Jr., Science 118, 131 [1953]); the other is made by oxidizing SiO at about 1300°C (A. Weiss and A. Weiss, Naturwissenschaften 41, 12 [1954]).*

The phase diagram of SiO_2, a one-component system, is given in Figure 5.4. This diagram summarizes the well-known experimental facts on page 276.

There are four equilibrium triple points shown at 573°, 870°, 1470°, and 1710° in Figure 5.4. Each is at a junction of three continuous curves and involves the coexistence of vapor and two condensed phases. There are five other triple points at the junction of three white curves. If only one form

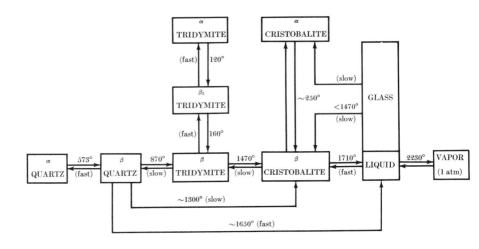

of crystal existed, there would be only one triple point just as there is only one in the H_2O system at low pressures. The crossing of the curves of metastable β-quartz and metastable β-cristobalite at 1300° is in no way a fixed point, but heating β-quartz to a temperature slightly above 1300° causes it to become β-cristobalite, which in its turn may become β-tridymite, the only crystalline phase really at equilibrium at low pressures at 1300°C.

Although the glassy, liquid, and crystalline species all contain four oxygen atoms arranged tetrahedrally about a silicon atom at a distance of about 1.6 A, there are several regular ways and many random ways in which these tetrahedra can be linked by sharing an oxygen atom at their common corner. Transformations between α and β forms of crystals of the same name are much faster than transformations between species of different name, because the latter transformations involve breaking of Si-O bonds while the former generally involve minor movements of atoms or tetrahedra. With the exception that devitrification of glassy SiO_2 seems to proceed slowly only to cristobalite, any transformation from a metastable form to a more stable form may be expected to proceed at a very slow rate and often only in the presence of a flux like sodium tungstate or lithium salts. Quartz is a much more common mineral than tridymite or cristobalite. Metastable forms, like the glass, are somewhat more soluble and somewhat more chemically active than the stable form at any temperature.

5.5 Gaseous Solutions

Gaseous mixtures have never been observed to form more than one phase. A gravitational or electric field may cause a preferential distribution of the various components (e.g., in a gravitational field, the heaviest species prefer the bottom), but in the gaseous phase there are never at equilibrium any discontinuities in density, index of refraction, and so forth. With $\mathbf{P} = 1$ for one-phase systems,

$$\mathbf{F} = \mathbf{C} - \mathbf{P} + 2 \tag{5.28}$$
$$= \mathbf{C} + 1.$$

One-component gaseous systems ($\mathbf{C} = 1$) were described at length in Chapter 1. The two degrees of freedom ($\mathbf{F} = 2$) — namely, any two of the three: P, V, and T — together with the equation of state of the one component that constitutes the phase and system are sufficient to fix the values of the pressure P, volume V, and temperature T. By two intensive variables (P, T), and one extensive variable (V) which is not counted by the phase rule, the state of the system is thus specified at equilibrium in the absence of fields and special constraints like a barrier that confines the gas to an unexpectedly small volume.

In order to specify the state of a gaseous system of more than one component, all but one of the concentrations of the several components must be specified in addition to the values of T and P. For example, dry air is a mixture mainly of nitrogen, oxygen, and argon. With three components ($\mathbf{C} = 3$), the state of air is not completely specified until four independent intensive variables are specified ($\mathbf{F} = 3 + 1$). The four most convenient ones would probably be pressure, temperature, and volume percentage of oxygen and argon. But density or index of refraction could have been specified instead of any of those chosen.

Dalton's law of partial pressures is a statement of the fact that there are huge voids available for interpenetration of molecules in the gaseous state. It says: the total pressure of a gaseous mixture is the sum of the pressures that each of the components of the mixture would exert if each were alone at the same temperature T in the same vessel of volume V. Let $p_i(V, T)$ be the partial pressure that component i would exert if alone. Then, by this law, the total pressure $P(V, T)$ is given by (5.32).

$$P(V, T) = \sum_{i=1}^{\mathbf{C}} p_i(V, T) . \tag{5.32}$$

This law assumes that chemical or physical interactions among the several components can be neglected and that all gases are ideal in behavior. Deviations from ideal behavior are realized through combinations of second virial coefficients into one second virial coefficient in the equation of state of the mixture.

The mole fraction of a species i in a gaseous solution is very simply related to the partial pressure if Dalton's law obtains. By (1.19) for each species i,

$$p_i = \frac{n_i R T}{V}. \tag{5.33}$$

For the mixture, by (5.32) and (5.33),

$$P = \sum_{i=1}^{C} p_i$$

$$= \frac{RT}{V} \sum_{i=1}^{C} n_i . \tag{5.34}$$

By the definition of mole fraction N_i in (5.6) it follows from (5.33) and (5.34) that

$$N_i = \frac{W_i/M_i}{\sum_{j=1}^{C} (W_j/M_j)} \tag{5.6}$$

$$= \frac{n_i}{\sum_{j=1}^{C} n_j} .$$

Or,

$$N_i = \frac{p_i}{P} . \tag{5.35}$$

That is, the mole fraction of any species is equal to its partial pressure divided by the total pressure of the solution.

Another law called *Amagat's law of partial volumes* is similar to and can be derived from Dalton's law if the gases are ideal. Amagat's law says: the total volume V of a gaseous mixture is the sum of the volumes v_i that each of the components would occupy if each were alone at the same temperature T in a volume v_i such that the pressure of each was the same as the total pressure P of the mixture. Mathematically,

$$V(P, T) = \sum_{i=1}^{C} v_i(P, T) . \tag{5.36}$$

Amagat's law is derived from Dalton's law thus. By hypothesis and the perfect gas law for species i,

$$v_i = \frac{n_i RT}{P} \tag{5.37}$$

$$P \sum_{i=1}^{C} v_i = RT \sum_{i=1}^{C} n_i . \tag{5.38}$$

But by (5.34),

$$PV = RT \sum_{i=1}^{C} n_i .$$

Hence,

$$V = \sum_{i=1}^{C} v_i . \tag{5.36}$$

As for partial and total pressures, the relation among mole fraction and volumes is simple. By (5.37) and (5.38),

$$\frac{v_i}{\sum\limits_{j=1}^{C} v_j} = \frac{n_i}{\sum\limits_{j=1}^{C} n_j} .$$

That is, by (5.36) and (5.6),

$$\frac{v_i}{V} = N_i . \tag{5.39}$$

All these relations are based on the common-sense idea that pressure and volume depend directly upon the number of particles in the gaseous mixture. Dalton's law says that the kind of particle is unimportant; what is important is that it has the kinetic energy characteristic of an independent and free particle at the temperature T and that it is free to move throughout the common volume V. Amagat's law says the same concerning volumes when pressures and temperatures of the species are constant. The expressions for the mole fractions are nothing more than a counting operation in which pressure or volume is the measure of the number of particles, all other variables being constant.

Example 5.3. If dry air is an ideal solution of 78.0% by volume N_2, 21.0% by volume O_2, and 1.0% by volume Ar, calculate the density of air at 27°C at 1.0000 atm pressure if its relative humidity is 80.0%. The vapor pressure of water at 27°C is 26.7 mm Hg.

The partial pressure of H_2O in the humid air is $0.800 \times 26.7/760 = 0.0281$ atm. If the air were dried at constant temperature and volume, its pressure dry would be less than one atm by just 0.0281 atm. Hence, since volume fractions are the same as mole fractions or pressure fractions by (5.35) and (5.39),

$$p_{N_2} = 0.9719 \times 0.780 = 0.758_1 \text{ atm}$$
$$p_{O_2} = 0.9719 \times 0.210 = 0.204_1 \text{ atm}$$
$$p_{Ar} = 0.9719 \times 0.010 = 0.009_7 \text{ atm} .$$

By the perfect gas law as expressed in (5.33),

$$\frac{W_i}{V} = \frac{M_i p_i}{RT} .$$

Accordingly, since the density ρ of the mixture is the sum of the masses of the several species divided by their common volume V,

$$\rho = \frac{\sum\limits_i W_i}{V} = \sum\limits_i \frac{W_i}{V} = \frac{1}{RT} \sum\limits_i M_i p_i .$$

Hence,

$$\rho = \frac{(28.01 \times 0.758_1 + 32.00 \times 0.204_1 + 39.94 \times 0.009_7 + 18.02 \times 0.0281)}{0.08206 \times 300.2}$$

$$= \frac{28.66}{0.08206 \times 300.2} = 1.164 \text{ g l}^{-1} .$$

5.6 Entropy of Mixing

Why are gaseous solutions homogeneous? Or why is it unlikely that all the molecules of a gas should at some time gather in one small part of their container? On the molecular level, the explanation is that the number of different ways of arranging the myriads of particles is much greater in the homogeneous situation. On the basis of probabilities alone, it is clear that the random and disordered state is more likely to occur out of all possible states than is an orderly spatial arrangement in a small region just because there are more places to put the molecules if their arrangement is random. The thermodynamic explanation, as expected, is based upon the relative entropies of unmixed and mixed states. Both questions and others related to them are answered in essence by a study of a two-component system. The second question is a special case of the first if one component is an uncomponent.

Equations (5.20) and (5.31) provide a convenient expression for the partial molar entropy $\bar{S}_i$ of component i.

$$\mu_i = RT \ln f_i + \mu_i^o(T) \tag{5.20}$$

$$\bar{S}_i = - \left(\frac{\partial \mu_i}{\partial T} \right)_P \tag{5.31}$$

$$= -R \ln f_i - \frac{d\mu_i^o}{dT}$$

That is, for an ideal gas i,

$$\bar{S}_i = -R \ln p_i + \bar{S}_i^o \tag{5.40}$$

where the partial pressure p_i replaces the fugacity f_i and where

$$\bar{S}_i^o = -\frac{d\mu_i^o}{dT}.$$

The total entropy S of a system containing just components A and B is, by (5.40) and (3.80),

$$S = n_A \bar{S}_A + n_B \bar{S}_B$$

$$= -n_A R \ln p_A - n_B R \ln p_B + n_A \bar{S}_A^o + n_B \bar{S}_B^o \tag{5.41}$$

where p_A and p_B are the partial pressures of the two components A and B.

Toward the preparation of gaseous solution of A and B, into one of the two chambers of a thermostated vessel are put n_A moles of gas A, and into the other chamber are put n_B moles of gas B. The chambers are separated by a very thin planar barrier that can be slipped out without disturbing either gas. The pressures on the two gases are equalized and the initial state of the system is shown in Figure 5.5. Since $p_A^o = p_B^o$, the entropy S_1 of the unmixed gases is, by (5.41),

$$S_1 = -n_A R \ln p_A^o - n_B R \ln p_A^o + n_A \overline{S_A^o} + n_B \overline{S_B^o} . \qquad (5.42)$$

Slipping the very thin barrier vertically out of the way does not stir the gases. Since their pressures are equal and there is no nonideal interaction,

no change in pressure or volume is noted externally when equilibrium has been reached. Nor has removing the barrier involved heat, since ideal gases mix without heat effects. There would, of course, be heat associated with mixing if a chemical reaction or physical interaction with nonzero potential energy occurred, a nonideal physical interaction being considered a very weak chemical reaction. In other

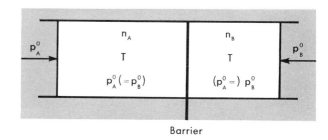

Fig. 5.5. *Unmixed Gases.*

words, if the barrier were replaced after complete mixing, an observer outside the system would not be aware of a change in the system if he did not analyze the gases in the chambers. To such an ignorant observer, $\Delta S = 0$ because he is not aware of a change on removing and replacing the barrier, and (5.42) gives the value of S_2, the entropy of the system after mixing.

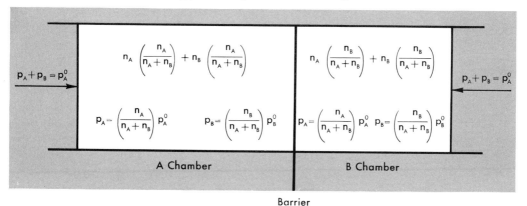

Fig. 5.6. *Mixed Gases.*

To an observer who can distinguish gas A from B, however, by some physical or chemical test, the final state of the system is shown in Figure 5.6, where (5.35) has been used to calculate the partial pressures. The partial pressures of A and B are the same in each compartment and the

281

left-hand compartment has the fraction $n_A/(n_A + n_B)$ of the molecules in both chambers. The entropy S_2 of the final state of the system is the sum of the entropies of the two parts and is the same as if no barrier were present; hence, by (5.41) and $p_A^o = p_B^o$,

$$S_2 = -n_A R \ln N_A p_A^o - n_B R \ln N_B p_A^o + n_A \overline{S_A^o} + n_B \overline{S_B^o} . \tag{5.43}$$

The increase in entropy is, then, by (5.42) and (5.43),

$$\Delta S = S_2 - S_1$$

$$= -n_A R \ln N_A - n_B R \ln N_B . \tag{5.44}$$

The increase in entropy per mole of A and B is

$$\overline{\Delta S} = \frac{\Delta S}{n_A + n_B} = -N_A R \ln N_A - N_B R \ln N_B . \tag{5.45}$$

If C pure components had been present in C chambers, $\overline{\Delta S}$ would have been given by (5.46).

$$\overline{\Delta S} = -R \sum_{i=1}^{C} N_i \ln N_i . \tag{5.46}$$

Since $\ln N_i$ is less than zero because N_i ranges from almost zero to unity, the value of $\overline{\Delta S}$ in (5.45) or (5.46) is greater than zero. This fits the concept that in a spontaneous adiabatic process like this there should be an increase in entropy because of the increase in disorder. The value of $\overline{\Delta S}$ is zero when A and B are *indistinguishable to the experimenter*. If A were O_2 and B were N_2 and if the analyses were performed by noting the pressure or color in the chambers beforehand and afterward, $\overline{\Delta S}$ would be zero. If A were O_2 and B were N_2 and if the analyses were performed by noting the chemical properties of O_2 and N_2 before and after the mixing, then $\overline{\Delta S}$ would be greater than zero. If A were $O^{16}O^{16}$ and B were $O^{18}O^{18}$ and if the analyses were performed by noting the chemical properties of O_2 before and after mixing, $\overline{\Delta S}$ would be zero. If A were $O^{16}O^{16}$ and B were $O^{18}O^{18}$ and if the analyses were performed by a mass spectrometer, $\overline{\Delta S}$ would be greater than zero. Similarly, as long as a chemist performs reactions with the natural mixture of isotopes, he is unconcerned by this entropy of mixing if his reaction does not lead to a partial separation of isotopes, even though an entropy of mixing would exist at absolute zero and could require a new reference level of entropy in using the third law. But as long as Cl^{35} behaves like Cl^{37}, a crystal of $Cl_{2(s)}$ that happens to have the usual mixture of Cl_2^{35}, $Cl^{35}Cl^{37}$, and Cl_2^{37} at absolute zero provides just as suitable a reference of absolute entropy as crystals containing only Cl_2^{35} or Cl_2^{37}. Further discussion of this entropy of mixing of isotopes is presented in Chapter 9 in the study of statistical mechanics.

C. TWO- AND THREE-COMPONENT SYSTEMS

5.7 Vapor Pressure of a Solution

The vapor pressure of a solution is the total pressure of the gases in equilibrium with the liquid or solid solution. When the gases are ideal, the vapor pressure is the sum of the vapor pressures of the several volatile components as they exist in their diluted states in the solution. The interactions of mixed species in a condensed phase are so diverse, and subtle interactions often have so marked an influence upon vapor pressures, that vapor pressures of solutions can seldom be predicted. Mere tabulation of the observed values often enough is tacit admission that little more can be done with regard to most solutions.

There are, however, certain solutions the behavior of which can be described rather well by simple mathematical expressions. Although any really observed solution may behave as predicted only over a limited range of composition, and even then only as a limiting case never quite achieved, the mathematical expression may be simple enough to warrant a little relaxation from rigor especially when little else is available as a description. One of the simplest of such mathematical abstractions is Raoult's law: at constant temperature, the partial pressure p_i of species i in the gas phase in equilibrium with an ideal solution of mole fraction N_i in the condensed phase is

$$p_i = N_i p_i^o \qquad (5.47)$$

where p_i^o is the vapor pressure of the pure species i at the constant temperature. Species i may be either solute or solvent. Indeed, when the pure components exist in the same state of aggregation as the solution, the distinction between solvent and solute is more a matter of convenience than sense. Whether toluene or benzene is solvent in a solution of the two depends upon the viewpoint of the experimenter. The prejudice that the solvent be present in excess is, however, quite general.

If the gas phase behaves ideally, the total pressure P is given by Dalton's law (5.32).

$$P = \sum_{i=1}^{C} p_i \,. \qquad (5.32)$$

Since the mole fraction $N_i^{(g)}$ of species i in the gas phase is given by (5.35),

$$N_i^{(g)} = \frac{p_i}{P} \qquad (5.35)$$

the compositions of both phases are quite simply related when both behave ideally. Ideal behavior for gaseous solutions means behavior in accord with

283

Dalton's law (5.32); ideal behavior for nongaseous solutions means behavior in accord with Raoult's law (5.47). The phase rule is, of course, applicable whether behavior is ideal or not.

5.8   Solutions of Two Volatile Components

Since a solution is by definition physically homogeneous, it is one phase ($\mathbf{P} = 1$). If it is made by mixing arbitrary amounts of two pure substances, it is a two-component or binary system ($\mathbf{C} = 2$). The number of degrees of freedom $\mathbf{F}$ that must be specified to fix the state of such a system or solution is three, for $\mathbf{F} = \mathbf{C} - \mathbf{P} + 2 = 3$. These three independent intensive variables are ordinarily chosen to be temperature, pressure, and mole fraction of one of the components in the solution. These three independent variables could be graphed in a three-dimensional figure, but the simplification attendant upon transforming to two independent variables by holding either temperature or pressure constant is usually worth the sacrifice in generality. Maintaining isothermal or isobaric conditions is equivalent to taking a planar section of the three-dimensional figure. For such a section, for a two-component solution,

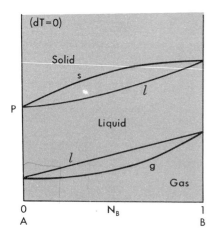

$$\mathbf{F} = \mathbf{C} - \mathbf{P} + 1 \qquad (5.29)$$
$$= 2 - 1 + 1 = 2 .$$

One composition variable and either pressure or temperature are the two degrees of freedom commonly chosen.

If the system should consist of two phases ($\mathbf{P} = 2$), say, a gaseous solution and a liquid solution, then at equilibrium, by (5.29), there is only one degree of freedom. At constant temperature, either composition or pressure is independent; at constant pressure, either composition or temperature. And if three phases ($\mathbf{P} = 3$) should be present, by (5.29) there should be no degree of freedom in a two-component system. The mere presence of three phases would specify the state of the system through the natures of its two components. But if the temperature or pressure be not held constant, the state of a two-component system is completely fixed ($\mathbf{F} = 0$) only if four phases coexist at equilibrium, for $\mathbf{F} = \mathbf{C} - \mathbf{P} + 2$; $0 = 2 - \mathbf{P} + 2$; $\mathbf{P} = 4$.

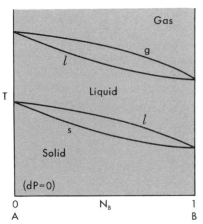

Fig. 5.7. *Isothermal and Isobaric Phase Diagrams of Ideal System.*

Figure 5.7 contains the two phase diagrams that are plane sections at constant temperature or pressure of the three-dimensional figure relating composition, temperature, and pressure variables for a two-component system in which gaseous, liquid, and solid solutions are homogeneous. The abscissas are the mole fraction of component B in one of the phases. When N_B is zero as it is at the left, none of B is present; when N_B is unity, only B is present. The upper diagram shows how pressure and composition are related at constant temperature, while the lower diagram shows how temperature and composition are related at constant pressure. The qualitative symmetry of *mirror images* between the diagrams is worthy of note. Two phases coexist at equilibrium when the independent variables have the values within the closed regions bounded by two curves. One of the curves gives the values of the independent variables in one phase, and the other in the second phase.

The forms of the lower pair of curves in the upper diagram of Figure 5.7 can be derived from Dalton's and Raoult's laws. For the gas, by Dalton's law (5.32),

$$P = p_A + p_B . \tag{5.48}$$

By Raoult's law (5.47), however,

$$p_A = p_A^o N_A^{(l)} , \quad \text{and} \quad p_B = p_B^o N_B^{(l)} \tag{5.49}$$

where $N_i^{(l)}$ is the mole fraction of species i in the liquid. Substitution of (5.49) into (5.48) with account of (5.7) yields (5.50), a straight line with slope $(p_B^o - p_A^o)$.

$$
\begin{aligned}
P &= p_A^o N_A^{(l)} + p_B^o N_B^{(l)} \\
&= p_A^o (1 - N_B^{(l)}) + p_B^o N_B^{(l)} \\
&= (p_B^o - p_A^o) N_B^{(l)} + p_A^o .
\end{aligned}
\tag{5.50}
$$

Since the vapor is richer and the liquid is poorer in the more volatile component B at equilibrium, the vapor curve falls below the straight line (5.50). The proof follows. By (5.35) and (5.32), the mole fraction of B in the gas is

$$N_B^{(g)} = \frac{p_B}{p_A + p_B} .$$

On continuation with Raoult's law (5.47),

$$
\begin{aligned}
N_B^{(g)} &= \frac{N_B^{(l)} p_B^o}{N_A^{(l)} p_A^o + N_B^{(l)} p_B^o} \\
&= \frac{N_B^{(l)}}{N_B^{(l)} + N_A^{(l)} \epsilon}
\end{aligned}
\tag{5.51}
$$

where

$$\epsilon = \frac{p_A^o}{p_B^o} < 1 .$$

The denominator of (5.51) is less than unity since it would be unity by (5.7) if ϵ were unity. Hence,

$$N_B^{(g)} > N_B^{(l)} . \qquad (5.52)$$

The forms of the other pairs of curves in Figure 5.7 can be calculated tediously. It is perhaps simplest to regard these curves as summaries of experimental data. It is quite possible, for example, that the imposition of pressure would never lead to solidification at constant temperature as implied by the upper diagram of Figure 5.7. Only if the liquid contracts on solidification would increased pressure convert liquid to solid at constant temperature. Or if the pressure were low enough, the solid might sublime and the liquid region in the lower diagram might be absent. The reason for combining diagrams in this way is to show the analogous behavior of gas-liquid and liquid-solid equilibriums.[1]

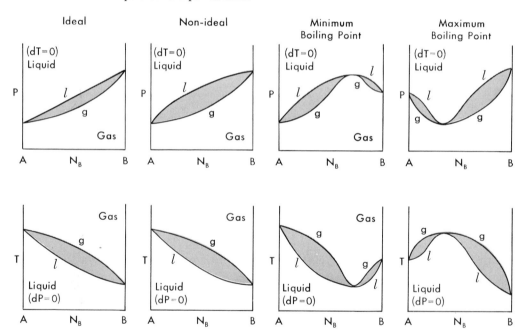

Fig. 5.8. *Related Phase Diagrams.*

It is much more common to find only two-phase equilibriums presented in one diagram of these kinds. Figure 5.8 has been prepared for gas-liquid solutions, but isomorphous diagrams exist for liquid-solid and gas-solid solutions. For these diagrams $C = 2$, and by (5.29) $F = 2 - P + 1 = 3 - P$.

In regions outside those bounded and closed by two curves, one solution phase ($P = 1$) is present and the two independent variables ($F = 2$) are composition and either temperature or pressure. Within the gray regions bounded by two curves, two solution phases ($P = 2$) are present and the independent variable ($F = 1$) is composition or one of the other variables, P or T. When N_B is zero or unity, the system contains only one component and the values of P and T are independent of each other except when two phases coexist at equilibrium.

Although the compositions that correspond to the maxima and minima of the four right-hand diagrams of Figure 5.8 do not correspond to pure substances or stoichiometric formulas, the compositions of liquid and vapor are alike. That is, upon vaporization or condensation at these maxima or minima, the solutions behave like pure substances at the specified temperatures and pressures in that such physical changes cause no change in composition of either solution. The behavior of solutions during distillation is discussed in the next section.

Table 5.2. *Behavior of Some Volatile Two-Component Systems*

A COMPONENT	B COMPONENT		
	NONIDEAL	MINIMUM BOILING POINT	MAXIMUM BOILING POINT
Water	Ammonia	Ethanol	Hydrogen fluoride
	Hydrogen peroxide	Isobutyl alcohol	Hydrogen chloride
	Ethylene glycol	Secondary butyl alcohol	Perchloric acid
	Glycerol	Tertiary butyl alcohol	Nitric acid
Carbon tetrachloride	Cyclohexane	Ethanol	Rare
	Benzene	Methyl ethyl ketone	
Methanol	Water	Carbon tetrachloride	Rare
	Ethanol	Acetone	
	Dioxane	n-Heptane	
Acetic acid	Water	Ethanol	Pyridine
	Ethylene chloride	Toluene	
	Acetone	Chlorobenzene	
Toluene	Benzene	Ethanol	Rare
	Carbon tetrachloride	Stannic chloride	

Table 5.2 lists some pairs of volatile liquids that form systems of three of the four types of Figure 5.8. Components that form ideal solutions are similar in physical and chemical properties. Chemical species containing isotopic substitutions probably approach ideal behavior most closely, although there are a few pairs like CCl_4-$SnCl_4$, chlorobenzene-bromobenzene,

n-hexane-n-heptane, or ethylene dibromide-propylene dibromide that behave almost ideally. Nonideal solutions contain species not quite different enough to have minimum or maximum boiling points. A minimum boiling point or maximum vapor pressure originates in repulsive forces between species quite unlike each other. Maximum boiling points and minimum vapor pressures occur in mixtures in which the components interact strongly by the formation of hydrogen bonds or by ionization or neutralization. Hydrogen chloride and diethyl ether interact strongly as acid and base to form a loose complex with an unusually low vapor pressure. Acetone and chloroform also attract each other strongly in their liquid mixtures and exhibit a maximum boiling point.

The transition from a nonideal system to one having a maximum or minimum boiling point can be thought of as a continuous variation in intermolecular forces. A binary system with vapor pressures larger than expected but intermediate between those of two pure components is described in Figure .5.9a. As intermolecular repulsions increase, a maximum in vapor pressure appears as in Figure 5.9b. The upper curves in Figure 5.9 are the liquid curves of Figure 5.8 and describe the composition of liquid in equilibrium with vapor at the various pressures. Their ordinates are, by Dalton's law or something akin to it, the sum of the ordinates of the other solid curves, which describe the pressure of each component as a function of liquid composition. The calculation of one of these curves from that for the other component by means of the Duhem-Margules equation is beyond the scope of this book. Addition of vapor composition curves to these uppermost curves would generate the nonideal and minimum boiling point curves of Figure 5.8.

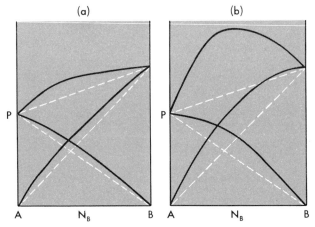

Fig. 5.9. *Continuity of Forms of Phase Diagrams.*

The dotted lines in Figure 5.9 are predicted by Raoult's law for ideal solutions. Although the observed solid curves obviously deviate from linearity, in the region of pure components solid lines of this kind are often almost straight. This linearity when one species is present in great excess is expressed mathematically by Henry's law (5.53).

$$p_i = N_i K(T) . \qquad (5.53)$$

Henry's law says that the mole fraction N_i of species i that dissolves in a solvent at a temperature T is proportional to the partial pressure exerted by i. The empirical proportionality factor $K(T)$ depends only on temperature. When the gaseous species that dissolves forms un-ionized and ionized species in solution, as Cl_2 or SO_2 does in water, Henry's law is sometimes modified to (5.54), in which $(1 - x)$ is the fraction dissolved in molecular form and thus in direct equilibrium with the gas phase.

$$p_i = (1 - x)N_i K(T) . \tag{5.54}$$

Example 5.4. Predict the composition and total pressure of the gas in equilibrium with a solution of n-hexane and n-heptane in which the mole fraction of n-hexane is 0.400 at 50.0°C. At 50.0°C the vapor pressures of pure n-hexane and n-heptane are 408 mm Hg and 141 mm Hg. (Lange's *Handbook of Chemistry.* New York: McGraw-Hill Book Co., Inc., 1956, p. 1430.)

By Raoult's law (5.47),

$$p(\text{hexane}) = 0.400 \times 408 = 163 \text{ mm Hg}$$

$$p(\text{heptane}) = 0.600 \times 141 = 85 \text{ mm Hg} .$$

By (5.35), the mole fraction of hexane in the gas phase is

$$N = \frac{163}{163 + 85} = 0.657 .$$

The vapor is far richer in the more volatile component than is the liquid, in accord with (5.52). The total pressure is 248 mm Hg.

Example 5.5. At 0°C, 23.5 ml deoxygenated air and 48.9 ml O_2 (at standard conditions) dissolve in one l water when the partial pressure of such air or O_2 is 1.000 atm. (Lange's *Handbook of Chemistry.* New York: McGraw-Hill Book Co., Inc., 1956, p. 1093.) Calculate the molality of air dissolved in water at 0°C and the Henry's law constants $K(T)$ for O_2 and the other gases at 0°C.

By definitions (5.4) and (5.6) for molality m_i and mole fraction N_i, if $i = 2$ in a dilute two-component solution,

$$m_2 = \frac{W_2}{M_2} \times \frac{1000}{W_1}$$

and

$$N_2 = \frac{W_2/M_2}{(W_1/M_1) + (W_2/M_2)} \approx \frac{W_2}{M_2} \times \frac{M_1}{W_1} .$$

Since $M_1 = 18.02$ for water, for dilute aqueous solutions,

$$\frac{m_2}{N_2} = \frac{1000}{M_1} = \frac{1000}{18.02} = 55.5 .$$

Since 1 mole O_2 would occupy about 22.4 l, m_2 is

$$\frac{48.9}{22.4 \times 10^3} = 2.18 \times 10^{-3} .$$

However, by (5.53), $p_2 = N_2 K(T) = (m_2/55.5)K(T)$. If p_2 is expressed in millimeters of Hg, for O_2

$$K(T) = \frac{p_2 \times 55.5}{m_2} = \frac{760 \times 55.5}{2.18 \times 10^{-3}} = 1.93 \times 10^7 \text{ mm Hg} .$$

Similarly, for the other gases of air,

$$K(T) = \frac{760 \times 55.5 \times 22.4 \times 10^3}{23.5} = 4.02 \times 10^7 \text{ mm Hg .}$$

Since air is 21.0% vol O_2 and 79.0% vol others, for all gases

$$m_2 = 55.5 \left(\frac{0.210 \times 760}{1.93 \times 10^7}\right) + 55.5 \left(\frac{0.790 \times 760}{4.02 \times 10^7}\right) = 1.29 \times 10^{-3} .$$

Example 5.6. Listed below are the partial pressures p_{SO_2} of $SO_{2(g)}$ in equilibrium with aqueous solutions of SO_2 of total molality m at $25°C$ [H. F. Johnstone and P. W. Leppla, *Journal of the American Chemical Society*, 56, 2233 (1934)]. In the third column are the molalities of H^+. Calculate the average Henry's law constant at $25°C$.

pSO_2 (atm $\times 10^3$)	$m \times 10^3$	$m_{H^+} \times 10^3$
0.27	2.484	2.156
1.20	6.203	4.718
2.29	9.546	6.663
2.67	10.84	7.35
6.71	20.59	11.87
9.11	25.61	13.86
13.50	33.28	16.65

Since only the first ionization of H_2SO_3 is important, the molality of hydrogen ions equals the molality of bisulfite ions. Hence, the fraction $(1 - x)$ of SO_2 not ionized is

$$(1 - x) = \frac{m - m_{H^+}}{m} .$$

In these dilute solutions, where the number of moles of water far exceeds the number of moles of SO_2,

$$N_{SO_2} = \frac{m}{55.5 + m} \approx \frac{m}{55.5} .$$

By (5.54), the Henry's law constant is therefore

$$K(T) = \frac{55.5 p_{SO}}{(m - m_{H^+})} .$$

The values of $K(T)$ found by calculation yield a mean value of 43.9 atm.

5.9 Fractional Distillation

The two-component system acetone-water exhibits nonideal behavior at pressures less than 2.5 atm and a minimum boiling point at pressures greater than 2.5 atm. Figures 5.10 and 5.11 for this system have been drawn from the values of Table 5.3, which contains equilibrium data for this system at 1.00 and 13.5 atm total pressure.

The normal boiling points of water and acetone are $100.0°C$ and $56.5°C$. The lower curve of Figure 5.10 describes the temperatures at which liquid solutions of water and acetone first begin to boil at 1 atm. The upper curve describes the temperatures at which gaseous solutions of water and acetone first begin to condense at 1 atm. These two curves naturally meet at $100.0°C$ and $56.5°C$. The temperatures at which a mixture of acetone and water first begins to vaporize or first begins to condense are not the same. A

Table 5.3. *Equilibrium Data for Acetone-Water System**

MOLE PERCENTAGE ACETONE IN LIQUID	1.00 ATMOSPHERE		13.5 ATMOSPHERES	
	TEMPERATURE (°C)	MOLE PERCENTAGE ACETONE IN VAPOR	TEMPERATURE (°C)	MOLE PERCENTAGE ACETONE IN VAPOR
0.0	100.0	0.0	194.3	0.0
1.0	92.0	27.9	184.9	19.5
2.5	84.2	47.0	176.4	33.4
5.0	75.6	63.0	168.8	44.4
10.0	66.9	75.4	163.1	52.8
20.0	62.4	81.3	159.8	58.7
30.0	61.1	83.2	158.2	61.8
40.0	60.3	84.2	157.2	64.4
50.0	59.8	85.1	156.6	66.9
60.0	59.2	86.3	156.2	69.7
70.0	58.8	87.5	156.0	73.4
80.0	58.2	89.7	156.0	79.6
90.0	57.4	93.5	157.6	88.5
95.0	56.9	96.2	158.2	93.4
97.5	56.7	97.9	158.5	96.4
100.0	56.5	100.0	158.7	100.0

mixture of 0.500 moles acetone and 0.500 moles water would show first signs of boiling at 59.8°C at 1 atm. If none of the vapor were withdrawn from the system, the last drop to vaporize would disappear at 82.7°C. The composition of this last drop that vaporizes would be that of the liquid in equilibrium with a gaseous solution with a mole fraction of acetone of 0.500. This last drop would have a mole fraction of acetone of 0.028, and this would also be the composition of the first drop to condense from a gaseous solution with mole fraction of 0.500. Just as the last drop to vaporize is poor in acetone, the first drop to vaporize is rich in acetone, the more volatile component. The first vapor to come from a liquid with mole fraction of 0.500 has a mole fraction of acetone of 0.851 and would be vaporized at 59.8°C.

At temperatures between 59.8°C and 82.7°C, two phases are

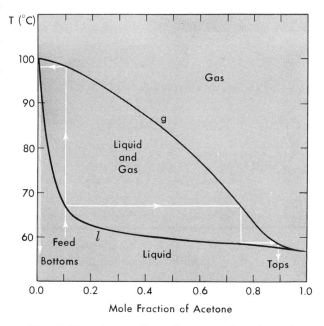

Fig. 5.10. *Acetone-Water System at One Atmosphere.*

* Othmer, D. F. and F. R. Morley, *Industrial and Engineering Chemistry*, **38**, 751 (1946).

present in a system with an over-all mole fraction of 0.500. The two curves labeled l and g of Figure 5.10 give the compositions of the liquid and gaseous solutions at the intermediate temperatures. For example, at 80.0°C, the mole fraction of acetone in the gas is 0.550, and in the liquid it is 0.035. The process of fractional distillation takes advantage of this disparity in concentration in order to separate a solution into its components. For example, if a liquid solution containing 1 mole acetone for every 9 moles water were heated until a little vapor were formed, the first vapor would be formed at 66.9°C and would have a mole fraction of acetone of 0.754. Total condensation of this little bit of vapor would yield a liquid solution with a mole fraction of acetone of 0.754. The first vapors from this newly condensed solution would be generated at 58.3°C and would have a mole fraction of acetone of 0.890. This vapor could be condensed totally to yield a little liquid with mole fraction of acetone equal to 0.890. Repeated partial vaporization and total condensation enriches the distillate in the more volatile component and leaves behind a solution richer and richer in the less volatile component. Thus, a partial separation is effected by the stepwise process as shown in Figure 5.10. Continuation of this stepwise process in the two-phase region of the phase diagram would lead eventually to a little acetone that was almost pure.

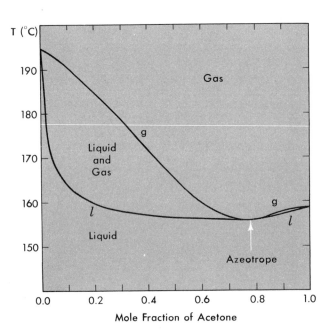

Fig. 5.11. *Acetone-Water System at 13.5 Atmospheres.*

Similarly, a little pure water could be separated from the original solution containing 9 moles water and 1 mole acetone by vaporizing all but a little of it at 98°C. The little liquid left unvaporized would contain only about 0.2 mole per cent acetone. Repetition of the stepwise process would yield eventually a little water that was almost pure.

The composition data of Table 5.3 for the acetone-water binary system are plotted in another way in Figure 5.12. The ordinate Y_B is the mole fraction of acetone in the gaseous solution; the abscissa X_B is the mole fraction of acetone in the liquid solution in equilibrium with the gaseous solution of composition Y_B. Gas and liquid would be equal in concentration along the diagonal. The stepwise process of Figure 5.10 is shown also in Figure 5.12. The number of completed steps in Figure 5.10 or 5.12 is the number of complete vaporization-condensation operations. In the jargon of distillers, each step is called a *plate*. A plate represents one two-phase equilibrium of the sort that occurs in a simple distillation. The *feed* is the solution to be separated; the *tops* is the distillate; the *bottoms* is the highest boiling fraction obtained.

A fractional distillation is never performed by placing the condensed distillate from a one-plate distillation into another one-plate still. Rather, continuously bringing two phases into intimate contact so as to establish equilibriums at several temperatures is done in a fractionating column. Figure 5.13 is a schematic diagram of a three-plate column of the kind that might separate acetone-water mixtures in the way of the example. Pre-heated feed enters at one of the plates of the column. Hot vapors from below bubble under the bubble caps of a plate and come to equilibrium with the liquid of that plate. Condensation yields the heat of vaporization to maintain the temperature of each plate and to cause vaporization of vapors richer in the more volatile component. As liquid collects at a plate it overflows to the plate below. Thus, the less volatile species tend to flow downward as liquids and the more volatile species tend to flow upward as vapors. Vapors from the top plate are continuously condensed and most are returned as reflux to the top plate, or perhaps to the plate next to the top. A small part of the distillate is taken off as tops. The liquid that collects at the bottom plate is richest in the less volatile component. A bit of it is taken off as bottoms from time to time.

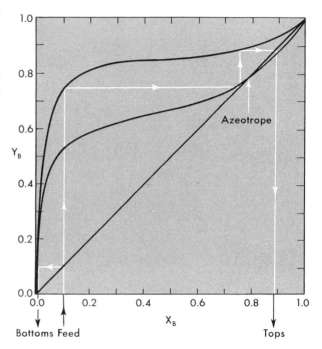

Fig. 5.12. *Acetone Composition of Vapor and Liquid.*

The column diagramed in Figure 5.13 appears as a continuously connected series of distinct one-plate distillations. Actual fractional distillation columns are designed merely to facilitate the attainment of liquid-gas equilibrium. Some columns are packed with glass balls or helices that provide a large surface area within the column. Some columns are empty except for a rapidly spinning band along their axes. Some contain bubble-caps or their equivalent. The performance of a fractional distilling column is given in terms of *theoretical plates*. The number of steps of the sort shown in

293

Figure 5.12 that account for the performance of the column as it separates a known mixture is the number of theoretical plates, even though the precise location of these plates in the column cannot be identified as simply as for bubble-caps.

The operation of a fractionating column is formulated mathematically through three kinds of balance: material, component, and enthalpy. At a steady state, the amount of vapor that leaves a plate must equal the amount of distillate that reaches it; this is the material balance. The component balance takes account of the fact that chemical changes do not occur. And the heat or enthalpy balance at each plate takes account of the fact that the process is adiabatic and almost isobaric, and that each plate receives heat from below and passes it on to the plate above. In other words, matter is conserved, no chemical reactions occur, and heat from the heater eventually leaves by the condenser. The ratio of reflux to distillate is called the *reflux ratio;* it provides a convenient parameter in terms of which the operation of a column is described. When no tops are taken off, the reflux ratio is infinity for there is no distillate and the idealized example for the three-plate separation of acetone and water is as stated. When some distillate (almost pure acetone) is withdrawn, then the steps in Figure 5.12 are to be constructed between the curve and a line of slope less than unity in the upper left-hand half of the figure. This construction, then, shows the need of more plates for a given separation as the amount of distillate taken off increases.

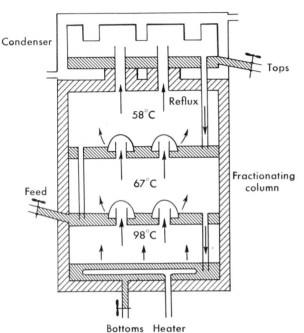

Fig. 5.13. *Schematic Diagram of Fractionating Column.*

It is impossible to obtain almost-pure acetone by fractionating a mixture of acetone and water with mole fraction of acetone less than 0.780 at 13.5 atm. The stepwise construction and the process it describes lead inexorably to the azeotropic mixture that boils at 156°C at 13.5 atm. This mixture, with its maximum vapor pressure and minimum boiling point, behaves under these conditions like a pure substance in that liquid and vapor have the same composition ($X_B = Y_B$ in Figure 5.12). Azeotropes can be broken by varying the pressure, as here, or by adding a third substance, which modifies the phase relations. Similarly, at 13.5 atm it would be impossible to obtain pure or almost pure water by fractional distillation of solutions containing more than 78 mole per cent acetone, but pure acetone could be separated as bottoms from such acetone-rich mixtures. Each of the two loops of Figure 5.11, then, behaves like the single loop of Figure 5.10, even though the azeotrope is not a pure substance. At the stated pressure of 13.5 atm, Figure 5.11 behaves as two simple figures like Figure 5.10 in juxtaposition.

What has been said of fractionation of gas-liquid systems applies detail by detail to gas-solid and liquid-solid systems. Two examples of liquid-solid systems that form only one liquid and one solid phase are those of Ni-Cu and Ni-Pd, shown in Figures 5.14 and 5.15 (*Metals Handbook*, American Society for Metals, Cleveland, O., 1948). For example, cooling a homogeneous melt containing Cu with a mole fraction of 0.40 leads to crystals with mole fraction of 0.27 at 1350°C. Crystals with gradually increasing mole fraction continue to form until at 1290°C at equilibrium all the melt has crystallized. Since diffusion is a slow process in the solid state, it is unlikely that crystals formed in a real cooling would be homogeneous. Nor would the last bit have crystallized at 1290°C, for the last of the melt would be richer than 0.40 in Cu because some crystals would be rich in Ni.

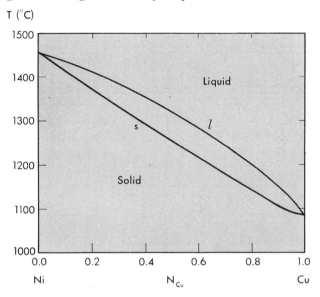

Fig. 5.14. *Nickel-Copper System.*

5.10 Immiscible Liquids and Solids

Complete miscibility generally occurs only in the gaseous phase. No one has ever observed two gas phases at equilibrium, but to have more than one liquid or solid phase coexistent is quite common. When two liquids like bromoben-

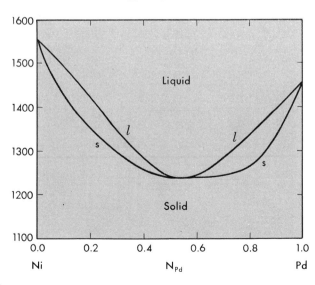

Fig. 5.15. *Nickel-Palladium System.*

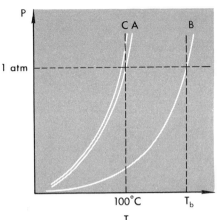

Fig. 5.16. *Total Vapor Pressure Above Immiscible Liquids.*

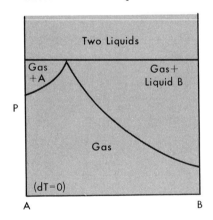

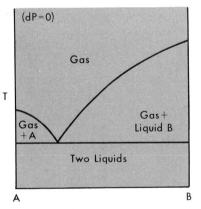

Fig. 5.17. *Immiscible Liquids.*

zene and water coexist and yet do not dissolve in each other to a significant extent, each behaves as though the other were not present. Provided both condensed phases are present, the total vapor pressure of the system at any temperature is merely the sum, by Dalton's law, of the vapor pressures of each. Figure 5.16 shows how the vapor pressures of two immiscible liquids add at various temperatures. Curve A is for water, curve B is for bromobenzene, nitrobenzene, or other volatile substance, and curve C is their sum. Note that the sum becomes one atm somewhat below 100°C.

In the absence of its pure condensed phase a component may assume any gaseous pressure less than its vapor pressure at a given temperature. That is, its concentration in the vapor may range from a certain maximum value to zero at a fixed temperature. The regions labeled gas in Figure 5.17 have pressures or concentrations less than the maximum for either component. As the temperature of the gas decreases or as its pressure rises, one or both liquids may appear. One pure liquid coexists at equilibrium with gaseous solution in the regions labeled gas and liquid; in them, there is one degree of freedom since there are two phases ($\mathbf{P} = 2$) and two components ($\mathbf{C} = 2$). This one degree of freedom is vapor composition, or either pressure or temperature. The pressure at which both liquids coexist with vapor at a given temperature was shown by Figure 5.16 to be fixed. In the upper diagram of Figure 5.17, where the horizontal isobar and the two curves that describe the maximum pressure attained by the gas phase meet, there are three phases ($\mathbf{P} = 3$), namely, two pure immiscible liquids and one gaseous solution. By (5.29) for this two-component ($\mathbf{C} = 2$) system, $\mathbf{F} = \mathbf{C} - \mathbf{P} + 1 = 2 - 3 + 1 = 0$. The lower phase diagram of Figure 5.17 is drawn for the constant pressure of the fixed point ($\mathbf{F} = 0$) of the upper diagram. Once again the mirror-image symmetry is evident.[1]

Steam distillation is the artifice by which a low-pressure distillation is performed without vacuum apparatus. Perhaps a substance decomposes at its normal boiling point. If it is volatile, immiscible with water as a liquid, and stable in steam, it can be steam-distilled at a temperature less than 100°C at 1 atm. The composition of the gas phase is readily calculated from (5.35) and the condition that the sum of the vapor pressures must equal the atmospheric pressure P of the laboratory.

$$N_i = \frac{p_i}{P} \qquad (5.35)$$

$$P = p_A + p_B . \qquad (5.55)$$

Example 5.7. The vapor pressures of bromobenzene (ϕBr) and water at 80°C are 66.2 and 355.1 mm Hg. (Lange's *Handbook of Chemistry*. New York: McGraw-Hill Book Co., Inc., 1956, pp. 1425, 1461.) The normal boiling point of ϕBr is 156°C. Calculate: (a) the temperature at which ϕBr steam-distills in a laboratory where the barometric pressure is 760 mm Hg; (b) the weight percentage of ϕBr in the vapors in such a steam distillation.

(a) The pair of vapor pressures at the pair of temperatures for each component fix a straight line of the form of (4.179) when log p is graphed as a function of $1/T$. From these two straight lines, trial and error establishes that the sum of the vapor pressures is 760 mm Hg at 95.4°C where the vapor pressures are 643 and 117 mm Hg.

(b) By (5.35) and the definition of mole fraction,

$$N_{H_2O} = \frac{p_{H_2O}}{P} = \frac{n_{H_2O}}{\sum_i n_i}$$

$$N_{\phi Br} = \frac{p_{\phi Br}}{P} = \frac{n_{\phi Br}}{\sum_i n_i} .$$

Division of one equation by the other yields

$$\frac{n_{H_2O}}{n_{\phi Br}} = \frac{p_{H_2O}}{p_{\phi Br}} = \frac{(W_{H_2O}/M_{H_2O})}{(W_{\phi Br}/M_{\phi Br})} .$$

Since the molecular weights are 18.0 and 157,

$$\frac{W_{H_2O}}{W_{\phi Br}} = \frac{p_{H_2O} \, M_{H_2O}}{p_{\phi Br} \, M_{\phi Br}} = \frac{643 \times 18.0}{117 \times 157} = 0.630 .$$

The weight percentage of bromobenzene is, then,

$$100 \times \left(\frac{1.000}{1.000 + 0.630} \right) = 61.4\% .$$

Phase diagrams like the lower one of Figure 5.17 are common for liquid-solid equilibria in two-component systems. Some of the binary systems in which solubility of pure solid in pure solid is negligible and in which there is only one liquid phase are Al-Sn, Bi-Cd, Bi-Cu, Cu-Li, KCl-AgCl, C_6H_6-CH_3Cl, and C_6H_6-CH_3COOH. Figure 5.18 is drawn for the Bi-Cd system at constant pressure. Pure Cd melts at 321°C, and pure Bi melts at 271°C. There is only one liquid phase ($\mathbf{P} = 1$) at all compositions in this two-component ($\mathbf{C} = 2$) system; hence, by (5.29), when only liquid is present, $\mathbf{F} = \mathbf{C} - \mathbf{P} + 1 = 2 - 1 + 1 = 2$. Composition and temperature are independently variable in the area labeled liquid. As a Bi-rich liquid is cooled, it eventually reaches a temperature at which pure solid Bi comes out of solution. While solid Bi and liquid coexist at equilibrium, there are two phases ($P = 2$) and two components ($C = 2$) so that, by (5.29), $F = C - P + 1 = 1$ and either temperature or composition is independent. The slanted curve that begins at 271°C in Figure 5.18 describes the temperature-dependence of the compo-

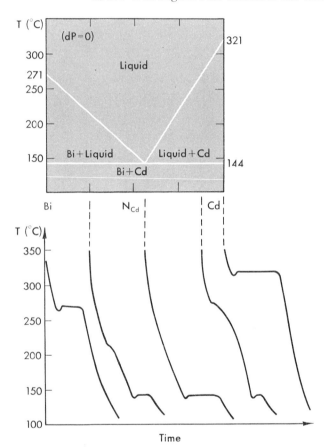

sition of liquid solutions in equilibrium with solid Bi. Any system with values of temperature and over-all composition such that it is in the triangular area at the left consists of solid Bi in equilibrium with liquid solution. The composition of the liquid is given by the slanted line and the composition of the solid is given by $N_{Cd} = 0$, the vertical side of the area. Similarly, systems whose temperatures and over-all composition locate them in the right-hand triangular area consist of pure Cd crystals and liquid solution. These slanted curves may be considered as the limit of the solubility of Bi or Cd in the liquid or they may be thought of as the observed freezing points of Bi or Cd in the presence of a solute that lowers the freezing point of the pure substances. The slanted curves, then, give the temperature and composition of liquid solutions that contain crystals of either pure component.

At 144°C, a liquid solution of Bi and Cd deposits both pure crystalline components at the same time. The mixture of crystals that results is called an *eutectic mixture* and contains two different phases. The eutectic mixture forms from a solution saturated with respect to both pure components; or, the eutectic mixture forms when the freezing point of the liquid has been lowered as far as possible by adjustments in composition. At the eutectic temperature, in the presence of two solids and one liquid phase ($P = 3$), there is no degree of freedom, for, by (5.29), $F = C - P + 1 = 0$. The temperature and compositions of all phases are fixed, just as they were in Figure 5.17.

When things like viscosity and rates of crystallization do not obstruct

Fig. 5.18. *Bismuth-Cadmium System at Constant Pressure.*

the attainment of equilibrium, it is common practice to determine a phase diagram by cooling homogeneous melts of various composition at a constant rate. As crystalline phases separate, the rate of decrease in temperature changes, and can become zero if $F = 0$, because the formation of a crystalline lattice furnishes thermal energy equal to the heat of fusion. Cooling curves for several mixtures of Bi and Cd are drawn below the phase diagram of Figure 5.18. When $F = 0$, as it does at 144°C for the eutectic mixture or when a pure component freezes, the temperature remains constant. However, when $F = 1$, as it does when the liquid changes continuously in composition as the pure crystals of either component form, the temperature falls, but at a different rate.

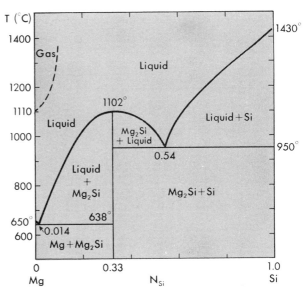

Fig. 5.19. *Magnesium-Silicon System at Constant Pressure.* (Metals Handbook, *American Society for Metals, Cleveland, O. [1948], p. 1226.*)

Figure 5.19 is the phase diagram of the Mg-Si system. Magnesium forms a compound Mg_2Si with silicon. This compound is a pure substance and is just as eligible to be considered a component as is Mg or Si. If Mg and Mg_2Si were chosen as components, their phase diagram would be the left third of Figure 5.19. This left third is exactly analogous to the phase diagram of the Bi-Cd system in Figure 5.18, just as the right two-thirds is. Here Mg_2Si, if pure, is a one-component system. At 1102°C it melts to form a liquid that will again solidify as Mg_2Si if cooled. At 1102°C for this system there is no degree of freedom when crystalline Mg_2Si is in equilibrium with its melt.

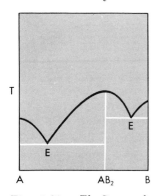 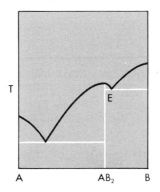 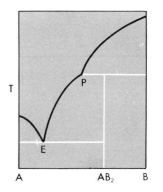

Fig. 5.20. *The Source of a Peritectic Point* P.

When the melting points of two elements differ greatly, as in the Cu-Li system, the eutectic mixture generally contains very little of the high-melting component. However, when there exists a great disparity in melting points of a compound and an element, it is possible for their eutectic mixture to occur at a composition that does not lie at an intermediate value. The eutectic is then called a *peritectic*. The continuous transformation from eutectic E to peritectic P, conceived as a continuous increase in the melting point of B, is shown in Figure 5.20. The system Bi-Au, which exhibits a peritectic like that in Figure 5.20, is shown in Figure 5.21. As the temperature of pure $BiAu_2$ is increased, it decomposes to pure solid Au and liquid with $N_{Au} = 0.36$ at 373°C, and at 675°C the Au dissolves in the liquid phase with $N_{Au} = 0.67$. Cooling a liquid with $N_{Au} = 0.50$ leads to the precipitation of pure Au at 510°C, to transformation of the Au into $BiAu_2$ at 373°C with some excess liquid, to continued formation of $BiAu_2$ from the liquid, and finally at 240°C to precipitation of $BiAu_2$ and Bi from the liquid, which has become so concentrated in Bi through the formation of $BiAu_2$ that Bi also precipitates.

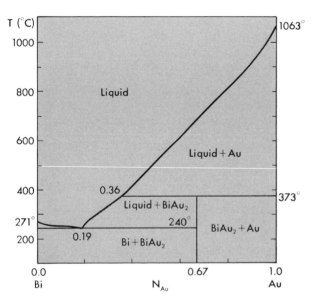

Fig. 5.21. *Bismuth-Gold System at Constant Pressure.* (Metals Handbook, *American Society for Metals, Cleveland, O. [1948], p. 1170.*)

The constant temperature diagrams that could be constructed for alloy systems are seldom used. For hydrates, however, it is common to plot pressure-composition phase diagrams at constant temperature. When two crystalline hydrates (or one hydrate and a liquid solution) coexist with the vapor phase of H_2O ($P = 3$), there is no degree of freedom, for, by (5.29), $F = C - P + 1 = 2 - 3 + 1 = 0$. That is, at the specified constant temperature, two different hydrates of a two-component system have a fixed vapor pressure. Figure 5.22 summarizes the observed values for the $CuSO_4$-H_2O system at 25°C. Two phases ($P = 2$, $F = 1$) coexist in all areas except that labeled solution. Three immiscible phases ($P = 3$, $F = 0$) coexist at over-all compositions given by the heavy black horizontal lines. The composition of each of the three coexistent immiscible phases is fixed, as is the pressure of the gaseous H_2O; the relative amounts of the three phases are not fixed until the over-all composition of all three is specified by fixing the abscissa of a figure like Figure 5.22.

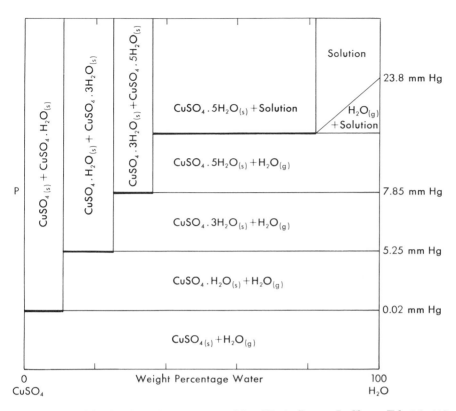

Fig. 5.22. *The CuSO₄-H₂O System at 25°C.* (*T. S. Logan,* **J.** Chem. Ed. **35,** *148* [1958]; pressures are not drawn to scale.)

5.11 Partial Miscibility

The two-component systems considered above have been remarkable in one of two ways: either the liquid and solid phases were homogeneous for all compositions or the components were altogether insoluble in each other in liquid or solid phases. There is, of course, no such thing as absolute insolubility, but often it is reasonable to neglect such things as the 0.05% or less of Bi that dissolves in solid Cd. When two components dissolve in each other to a limited extent the phase diagram is often similar to Figure 5.23 for the Zn-Pb system. The two values of composition given by the dome-shaped curve at any temperature from 417.8°C to about 750°C are the compositions of the two liquid phases that coexist for over-all compositions and temperatures in the region labeled "two liquid phases." Above about 750°C, the consolute or critical solution temperature, there is only one homogeneous liquid phase for any composition; that is, the two solutions have achieved a

301

common composition and have thus become one phase at about 750°C. This dome-shaped curve thus describes the limited solubility of liquid Zn in liquid Pb or of liquid Pb in liquid Zn at the constant pressure for which the phase diagram is drawn.

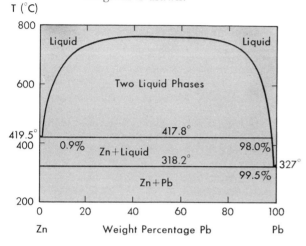

Fig. 5.23. *Partial Miscibility in the Zinc-Lead System at Constant Pressure.* (Metals Handbook, *American Society for Metals, Cleveland, O. [1948], p. 1239.*)

The Parkes process for the recovery of silver dissolved in lead smelted from common lead ores takes advantage of the fact that the eutectic point is displaced to 99.5% Pb because of the great extent of the region containing two liquid phases. From 1% to 2% zinc is stirred into the impure molten lead and the solid zinc-rich phase that separates below about 418°C carries with it most of the silver that was dissolved in the lead. (The presence of silver and other impurities really makes the system one of several components.) This solid zinc-silver layer is skimmed from the molten lead and its silver is recovered by distilling off the zinc.

Table 5.4. *Compositions and Maximum Consolute Temperatures of Some Two-Component Systems*

COMPONENT A	COMPONENT B	TYPE OF PHASES	WEIGHT PERCENTAGE A*	CONSOLUTE TEMPERATURE (°C)
n-hexane	aniline[†]	liquid	67	69.0
n-octane	aniline[†]	liquid	~63	71.8
n-decane	aniline[†]	liquid	~60	77.5
n-dodecane	aniline[†]	liquid	~58	83.7
water	phenol[‡]	liquid	34.2	65.85
water	n-butanol[‡]	liquid	32.5	125.15
copper	lead[§]	liquid	~35	~1000
gold	nickel[§]	solid	~55	840
gold	platinum[§]	solid	~60	~1180

* It is possible that a range of compositions exists at the consolute temperature. See Kohler, F., and O. K. Rice, *Journal of Chemical Physics*, **26**, 1614 (1957) and references therein.

† Shepard, A. F., A. L. Henne, and T. Midgley, Jr., *Journal of the American Chemical Society*, **53**, 1948 (1931).

‡ Hill, A. E., and W. M. Malisoff, *Journal of the American Chemical Society*, **48**, 918 (1926).

§ *Metals Handbook*, American Society for Metals, Cleveland, O., 1948, pp. 1200, 1172, 1174.

The extent of the region exhibiting two liquid phases is readily determined in either of two ways. The composition of the liquid layers that coexist at some temperature can be determined directly, or indirectly since the over-all composition of the two-phase system and the amount and composition of each phase are interrelated. Also, the temperature at which a second liquid phase just appears or just disappears in a mixture of known composition may be observed. Sometimes such measurements must be made at elevated pressures to prevent the vaporization of one of the components near the consolute temperature. Like liquids, two solid solutions can achieve a common composition at a consolute temperature. Some examples of two-component systems with maximum consolute temperatures are listed in Table 5.4. The compositions at the consolute temperature are difficult to fix exactly because of the small slope in this region. Temperatures closely related to the consolute temperatures of hydrocarbons with aniline have been useful for characterizing the hydrocarbons; the so-called *aniline point* is the temperature at which a mixture of equal volumes of aniline and hydrocarbon becomes one phase on heating.

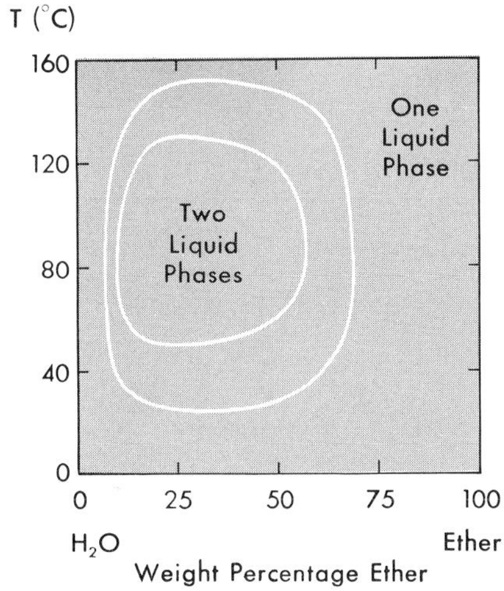

Some binary systems exhibit both a maximum and a minimum consolute temperature; among these systems are nicotine-water, methyl ethyl ketone-water, secondary butyl alcohol-water, β-picoline-water, three of the methyl piperidines and water, and some glycol ethers and water. Figure 5.24 is drawn for the monobutyl ethers of ethylene glycol in water.

Fig. 5.24. *Solubilities of Monobutyl Ethers of Ethylene Glycol in Water.* (*H. L. Cox and L. H. Cretcher, J. Am. Chem. Soc.* **48**, *451* [*1926*].) *The inner curve is for the n-butyl ether; the outer, for isobutyl ether.*

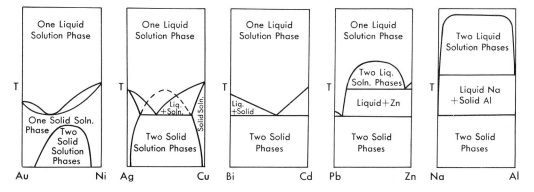

Fig. 5.25. *Development of Regions of Immiscibility. The temperature scales of the diagrams differ; data from* Metals Handbook, *American Society for Metals, Cleveland, O. (1948).*

Figure 5.25 illustrates typical ways in which regions of immiscibility develop from homogeneous solid and liquid solutions as properties of the components change. Since absolute insolubility does not occur, the Bi-Cd system is an extreme form of the Ag-Cu system in which solid solutions contain of the order of 10% solute rather than 0.1%. Similarly, the Na-Al system is an extreme version of the Pb-Zn system.

5.12 Quantitative Interpretation of Two-Component Phase Diagrams

The phase diagrams discussed in Sections 5.9, 5.10, and 5.11 not only provide quantitative data about temperatures and pressures and qualitative data about the kind and number of phases present, but also provide quantitative information about the amounts of two coexistent phases when the over-all

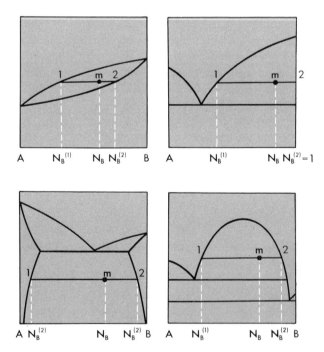

Fig. 5.26. *Quantitative Interpretation of Phase Diagrams.*

composition of the system is known. Several typical circumstances of interest are shown in Figure 5.26 and are labeled equivalently so that each is correctly described by the following mathematical development of the so-called *lever law.*

Let N_B be the mole fraction of B in the two-phase binary system; let $N_B^{(1)}$ be the mole fraction of B in phase 1 and let $N_B^{(2)}$ be its mole fraction in phase 2, which coexists with phase 1; let n be the total number of moles of A and B in both phases; and let $n_i^{(j)}$ be the number of moles of component i in phase j. Then,

$$n = n_A^{(1)} + n_A^{(2)} + n_B^{(1)} + n_B^{(2)} . \tag{5.56}$$

By (5.6),

$$N_B = \frac{n_B^{(1)} + n_B^{(2)}}{n} \tag{5.57}$$

$$N_B^{(1)} = \frac{n_B^{(1)}}{n_A^{(1)} + n_B^{(1)}} \tag{5.58}$$

$$N_B^{(2)} = \frac{n_B^{(2)}}{n_A^{(2)} + n_B^{(2)}} \tag{5.59}$$

Whence

$$nN_B = n_B^{(1)} + n_B^{(2)} = [n_A^{(1)} + n_B^{(1)}]N_B^{(1)} + [n_A^{(2)} + n_B^{(2)}]N_B^{(2)} .$$

But, by (5.56)

$$nN_B = [n_A^{(1)} + n_B^{(1)}]N_B + [n_A^{(2)} + n_B^{(2)}]N_B .$$

Equating the expressions for nN_B yields

$$[n_A^{(1)} + n_B^{(1)}]N_B + [n_A^{(2)} + n_B^{(2)}]N_B = [n_A^{(1)} + n_B^{(1)}]N_B^{(1)} + [n_A^{(2)} + n_B^{(2)}]N_B^{(2)} . \tag{5.60}$$

Since the moles of A and B in phase 1 are $[n_A^{(1)} + n_B^{(1)}]$ and in phase 2 are $[n_A^{(2)} + n_B^{(2)}]$, it follows from (5.60) that

$$\frac{\text{TOTAL MOLES IN PHASE (1)}}{\text{TOTAL MOLES IN PHASE (2)}} = \frac{n_A^{(1)} + n_B^{(1)}}{n_A^{(2)} + n_B^{(2)}} = \frac{N_B^{(2)} - N_B}{N_B - N_B^{(1)}} . \tag{5.61}$$

But $N_B^{(2)} - N_B$ is the length of the line joining points m and 2, while $N_B - N_B^{(1)}$ is the length of the line joining points 1 and m. Hence, if $n^{(1)}$ is the total number of moles in phase 1 and if $n^{(2)}$ is the total number of moles in phase 2, by (5.61),

$$(\overline{m2}) \times n^{(2)} = (\overline{1\,m}) \times n^{(1)} . \tag{5.62}$$

As the point m approaches point 2, the amount of phase 1 decreases until, at point 2, only phase 2 exists. Equation (5.62) is the lever law, so called because of its similarity to the lever law of mechanics. An analogous law is readily developed in a similar way when N_B is a weight fraction and the n's refer to weights. The ordinate may be temperature, pressure, or any noncomposition variable.

305

Example 5.8. From Figure 5.21 for the Bi-Au system, estimate the amounts of the phases present at 375°C and at 370°C when the mole fraction of Au is 0.50.

At 375°C, solid Au and liquid solution are at equilibrium. Since the mole fraction of Au in the liquid is 0.36, the ratio of moles of Au and Bi in liquid to moles of Au (and Bi) in solid is

$$\frac{1.00 - 0.50}{0.50 - 0.36} = \frac{50}{14} = 3.6 \,.$$

At 370°C, solid $BiAu_2$ and liquid solution are at equilibrium. Since the mole fraction of Au in the liquid is 0.34 and since each mole of $BiAu_2$ involves three "moles" of Bi and Au, the ratio of moles of Bi and Au in liquid to moles of $BiAu_2$ in solid is

$$\frac{0.67 - 0.50}{\frac{1}{3}(0.50 - 0.34)} = 3\left(\frac{17}{16}\right) = 3.2 \,.$$

5.13 Phase Diagrams of Three-Component Systems

In a system of three components ($C = 3$), there may be up to four degrees of freedom, for, by (5.28), when only one phase is present ($P = 1$),

$$F = C - P + 2 \qquad (5.28)$$
$$= 3 - 1 + 2 = 4 \,.$$

If either temperature or pressure is held constant, three or fewer degrees of freedom may occur. Three and four degrees of freedom are awkward for graphing; hence, it is customary to prepare phase diagrams of three-component systems in two dimensions by fixing both temperature and pressure. Then, by (5.30),

$$F = C - P \qquad (5.30)$$
$$= 3 - P \leqslant 2 \,.$$

The two degrees of freedom that remain under these circumstances when $P = 1$ are two composition variables. These two independent variables may conveniently be thought of as two of the three mole fractions, where the third is fixed by (5.7).

$$\sum_{i=1}^{i=C=3} N_i = 1 \,. \qquad (5.7)$$

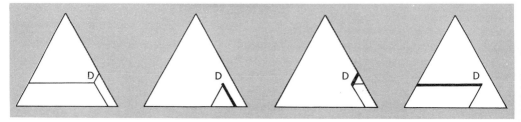

Fig. 5.27. *A Geometrical Property of an Equilateral Triangle.*

This condition (5.7) is automatically satisfied by graphing on a set of coordinates fixed by an equilateral triangle. For, in an equilateral triangle, the sum of the three distances drawn from a point within the triangle parallel to each of the three sides is equal to the side of the equilateral triangle. Let D be an arbitrary point in an equilateral triangle, as in Figure 5.27. The three distances drawn parallel to each of the sides of the triangle are shown at the left. In view of the equality of all sides in any size equilateral triangle and the equality of opposite sides of parallelograms, the sum theorem stated above is obvious from Figure 5.27. A system of coordinates that utilizes this geometrical property is described in Figure 5.28. A point such as D represents a system containing 25% A, 10% B, and 65% C. Superposition of these coordinates yields Figure 5.29, wherein the percentages may be by weight, volume, mole, ...

When a diagram like Figure 5.29 contains no curves, the system is homogeneous and contains only one phase. Three-component gaseous mixtures or mixtures of ethanol-methanol-water at room temperature and pressure are examples of systems of only one phase. When two phases coexist at equilibrium for certain compositions, a curve with one degree of freedom ($\mathbf{F} = \mathbf{C} - \mathbf{P} = 3 - 2 = 1$) cuts the diagram, as in Figure 5.30. At the temperature and pressure for which this figure is drawn, B and C are only partly miscible in each other; but as component A is added, they become more and more miscible until at point E, called a *plait point* or *isothermal critical point*, the system becomes one homogeneous phase.

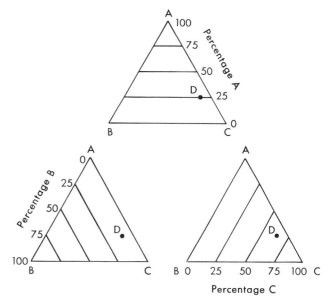

Fig. 5.28. *A System of Coordinates.*

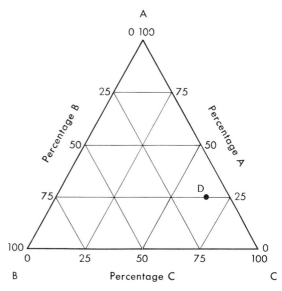

Fig. 5.29. *Triangular Coordinate System.*

307

In order to indicate the compositions of coexistent phases, *tie lines* like *FG* are added to the figure. In the region crossed by tie lines there coexist two phases with the compositions given by the ends of the tie lines. The system acetic acid-water-chloroform is like Figure 5.30.

The system aniline-water-phenol is shown without tie lines in Figure 5.31, the pressure being maintained high enough to keep all phases liquid. At 167°C, aniline and water have a consolute point when phenol is absent, but addition of phenol lowers the temperature at which mixtures of the three components separate into two liquid phases. Phenol and water have a consolute point at 67°C, and aniline and phenol are miscible in all proportions above 50°C. The isotherms of Figure 5.31 have in a way added a third dimension to the phase diagram.

When two or three pairs of partly miscible components become part of a three-component system, somewhat more complicated diagrams are possible. Figure 5.32 shows the transition in which immiscible regions are pictured as growing in area through changes in the natures of the components or in the temperature. In the regions crossed by tie lines there are two phases, and in the triangular region in the lower right-hand diagram, there coexist three phases with compositions given by the vertexes of the triangle. In this latter case, **P** = 3 and **F** = 0.

When the pure components A, B, and C are of different states of aggregation, for example when A is H_2O and B and C are salts or when A and B are liquids and C is a solid, a somewhat different phase diagram is drawn. In the three-component system of Figure 5.33, B is a salt that forms a crystalline hydrate B · n H_2O; C is anhydrous as a salt and is less soluble in H_2O than B; and C and B form a compound

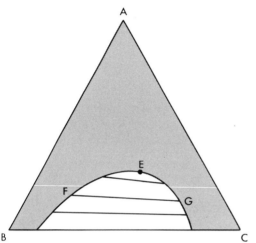

Fig. 5.30. *Three Components, One Pair Partly Miscible.*

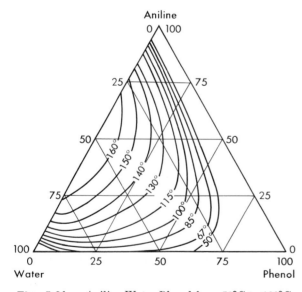

Fig. 5.31. *Aniline-Water-Phenol from 50°C to 160°C.* (Int. Crit. Tables *III*, p. 412.)

B_2C. Tie lines cover regions of one degree of freedom at fixed temperature and pressure, and in the unmarked regions three phases coexist with compositions given by the corners of the triangular area in which the over-all composition of the system falls. Points of no degree of freedom are indicated with large dots.

Figure 5.34 represents a system consisting of water W, a salt S, and an organic compound O that is miscible in all proportions with water at the fixed temperature and pressure. The salt S dissolves more in water W than in the liquid organic component O. With a diagram of this sort[1] it is possible to discuss accurately the processes of "salting out" and precipitation of a salt by addition of another solvent. A consideration of the similar

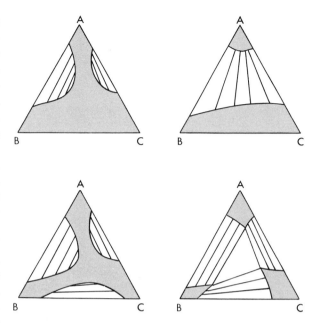

Fig. 5.32. *Encroachment of Immiscible Regions.*

triangles involved will verify that any point on a line like SM contains W and O in the same relative proportions. If pure salt S is added to a mixture of composition M, the over-all composition will vary along the line MS. When the over-all composition corresponds to points within the triangular region, three phases coexist, one of them rich in O. Thus, O has been salted out of M.

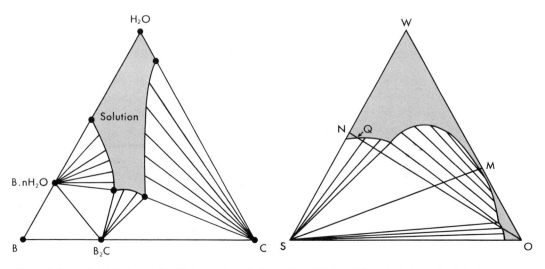

Fig. 5.33. *Solubilities of $B.nH_2O$, B_2C, and C in H_2O.*

Fig. 5.34. *Water-Salt-Organic Liquid System.*

When O is added to an aqueous solution of composition N, nothing happens until S begins to precipitate at Q. And when enough O has been added to give compositions within the triangular region, the solid salt S and two liquid layers coexist. Further addition of O would lead to the disappearance of the water-rich liquid layer and eventually to the solution of the salt in a layer very rich in O.

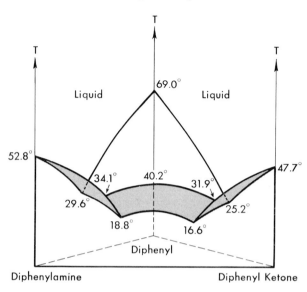

Three dimensional triangular phase diagrams, in which the third dimension is temperature plotted vertically above a planar diagram like those above, are valuable in the study of alloys and ceramics. Each of the three vertical faces then represents a temperature-composition phase diagram of a two-component system. Figure 5.31 could be developed in this way, and Figure 5.35 describes an organic system with two eutectics at 18.8°C and 16.6°C at which three solids and one liquid coexist. One of the solids is the compound $(C_6H_5)_2NH \cdot (C_6H_5)_2CO$ melting at 40.2°C.

Fig. 5.35. *Diphenyl-Diphenylamine-Diphenyl Ketone System at Constant Pressure. Fixed temperatures are noted on diagram. (H. H. Lee and J. C. Warner, J. Am. Chem. Soc. 55, 209, 4474 [1933].)*

D. COLLIGATIVE PROPERTIES OF NONELECTROLYTES

5.14 Ideal Solution of One Volatile Component

Because of the discrete nature of matter, when the vapor pressure of a substance becomes small enough, it becomes less a pressure and more a measure of the probability that a molecule will or can escape. It is often verified experimentally that the influence of the vapor of a certain compound appears to be negligible. If so, for all practical purposes, its vapor pressure is effectively zero. The vapors above many solutions are essentially only those of the liquid solvent so that, if species 1 is the solvent, Raoult's law degenerates thus:

$$p_i = N_i p_i^o \tag{5.47}$$

$$p_i^o = 0, \quad (i \neq 1)$$

$$p_1 = P$$

$$= N_1 p_1^o. \tag{5.63}$$

In other words, if only species 1 is volatile, p_1 is the total pressure P. Let N_2 be the sum of the mole fractions of the nonvolatile species. Then, by (5.7),

$$N_1 = 1 - N_2 \qquad (5.64)$$

where N_1 is the mole fraction of the volatile species 1. By (5.63) and (5.64),

$$p_1 = (1 - N_2)p_1^o \doteq p_1^o - N_2 p_1^o \,.$$

Whence,

$$N_2 = \frac{p_1^o - p_1}{p_1^o} \,. \qquad (5.65)$$

Since N_2 measures the numbers of nonvolatile molecules relative to all molecules present, Equation (5.65) says that the vapor pressure lowering $(p_1^o - p_1)$ is proportional to the fraction of nonvolatile molecules. A property that varies according to the number of particles without regard to their kind is called a *colligative property*. The pressure of a mixture of ideal gases is such a colligative property when volume and temperature are constant. So also is the lowering of vapor pressure of a solvent by solutes, as in (5.65).

Example 5.9. Exactly 100 g water contain 1.000 g urea and 2.000 g sucrose at 25°C. At 25°C, the vapor pressure of water is 23.756 mm Hg. (Lange's *Handbook of Chemistry*. New York: McGraw-Hill Book Co., Inc., 1956, p. 1459.) Predict the vapor pressure of the solution.

If N_2 is the summation of mole fractions of all nonvolatile components as in (5.64), then

$$N_2 = \frac{(1.000/60.06) + (2.000/342.3)}{(100.0/18.02) + (1.000/60.06) + (2.000/342.3)} = \frac{0.01665 + 0.00584}{5.5508 + 0.017 + 0.006}$$

$$= \frac{0.02249}{5.574} = 0.00404 \,.$$

By (5.65),

$$p_1^o - p_1 = 0.00404 \times 23.756 = 0.096 \text{ mm Hg}$$

$$p_1 = p_1^o - 0.096 = 23.660 \text{ mm Hg} \,.$$

Note that use of (5.63) to obtain this result requires great calculational accuracy.

5.15 Boiling Point of Solution of One Volatile Component

A solution of one volatile component boils when its vapor pressure, namely, that of its volatile component, equals the pressure of the surrounding atmosphere. The vapor pressure p_1 of an ideal solution of one volatile component is less than p_1^o, that of the pure volatile component, because in (5.65) p_1^o and N_2 are positive quantities. Figure 5.36 shows that the boiling point T_b of such a solution is greater than the boiling point T_o of the pure solvent species 1. Although pressure and fugacity may differ in nonideal solutions, the approximations to follow in this derivation justify assuming ideal behavior of gas and liquid solution despite the deviations expected from ideal behavior. For an ideal gas, $p_1 = f_1$ and (5.20) becomes

$$\mu_1^{(g)} = RT \ln p_1 + \mu_1^{o(g)} . \qquad (5.66)$$

For the volatile solvent 1, if the solution is ideal,

$$\mu_1^{(l)} = RT \ln N_1 + \mu_1^{o(l)} . \qquad (5.67)$$

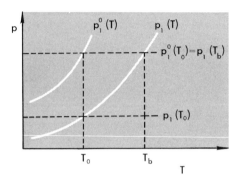

In (5.67) the reference level of chemical potential is the pure volatile solvent, for when $N_1 = 1$, $\mu_1^{(l)} = \mu_1^{o(l)}$. The term $RT \ln N_1$ is related to the entropy of mixing of the liquid solution.

When vapor and liquid solution are in equilibrium at the boiling point, the chemical potentials of the volatile solvent, which is really present in both phases, are equal. Hence, by (5.66) and (5.67),

$$RT \ln p_1 + \mu_1^{o(g)} = RT \ln N_1 + \mu_1^{o(l)} .$$

Fig. 5.36. *Boiling Point of a Solution.*

Since $p_1 = 1$ atm at the boiling point,

$$\mu_1^{o(g)} - \mu_1^{o(l)} = RT \ln N_1 . \qquad (5.68)$$

Just as Equations (5.19) and (5.31) are the counterparts of (4.98) and (4.97),

$$V = \left(\frac{\partial G}{\partial P} \right)_T \qquad (4.98)$$

$$\overline{V}_i = \left(\frac{\partial \mu_i}{\partial P} \right)_T \qquad (5.19)$$

$$-S = \left(\frac{\partial G}{\partial T} \right)_P \qquad (4.97)$$

$$-\overline{S}_i = \left(\frac{\partial \mu_i}{\partial T} \right)_P \qquad (5.31)$$

so also is there a counterpart of (4.155), namely, (5.69).

$$\frac{\overline{H}_i}{T^2} = -\left[\frac{\partial}{\partial T} \left(\frac{\mu_i}{T} \right) \right]_P \qquad (5.69)$$

$$\frac{\Delta H}{T^2} = -\left[\frac{\partial}{\partial T} \left(\frac{\Delta G}{T} \right) \right]_P . \qquad (4.155)$$

That is, (5.69) applies to 1 mole of kind i as distinguished from all other components, while (4.155) applies to any change of state in a closed system. By (5.69) and (5.68),

$$-\left\{\frac{\partial}{\partial T}\left[\frac{\mu_1^{o(g)}}{T} - \frac{\mu_1^{o(l)}}{T}\right]\right\}_P = \frac{\overline{H}_1^{o(g)}}{T^2} - \frac{\overline{H}_1^{o(l)}}{T^2}$$

$$= -\left[\frac{\partial}{\partial T}(R \ln N_1)\right]_P = -R\left(\frac{\partial \ln N_1}{\partial T}\right)_P.$$

But $\overline{H}_1^{o(g)} - \overline{H}_1^{o(l)}$ is just the molar heat of vaporization of the solvent from the solution. For ideal solutions and approximately for dilute nonideal solutions, this heat of vaporization is just ΔH_v for the pure solvent. Hence,

$$-R\left(\frac{\partial \ln N_1}{\partial T}\right)_P = \frac{\Delta H_v}{T^2}. \tag{5.70}$$

Equation (5.70) is readily integrated, for $N_1 = 1$ when the boiling point is T_o; that is,

$$-\int_0^{\ln N_1} d(\ln N_1)' = \int_{T_o}^{T_b} \frac{\Delta H_v}{R T^2} \, dT.$$

If ΔH_v is independent of temperature,

$$-\ln N_1 = \frac{\Delta H_v}{R}\left(-\frac{1}{T_b} + \frac{1}{T_o}\right)$$

$$-\ln N_1 = \frac{\Delta H_v(T_b - T_o)}{R T_b T_o}. \tag{5.71}$$

But, by (5.64), this becomes

$$-\ln (1 - N_2) = \frac{\Delta H_v(T_b - T_o)}{R T_b T_o}. \tag{5.72}$$

When $-1 < x < 1$, $-\ln (1 - x) = x + x^2/2 + \cdots$. Since $0 < N_2 \ll 1$, the first term of this series expansion is sufficient. And since T_b is approximately equal to T_o for common solvents, (5.72) becomes

$$N_2 \approx \frac{\Delta H_v(T_b - T_o)}{R T_b T_o} \approx \frac{\Delta H_v(T_b - T_o)}{R T_o^2}. \tag{5.73}$$

Since the molality m_2 of nonvolatile solutes is related to their mole fraction N_2 by the approximate relation

$$N_2 = \frac{n_2}{n_1 + n_2} \approx \frac{1}{n_1}\left(\frac{W_2}{M_2}\right) = \frac{M_1}{W_1}\left(m_2 \times \frac{W_1}{1000}\right) = \frac{M_1 m_2}{1000}$$

it follows that the boiling point elevation $\Delta T_b = T_b - T_o$ is given by (5.74).

$$\left.\begin{array}{l} \Delta T_b = K_b m_2 \\ K_b = \dfrac{RT_o^2 M_1}{1000 \, \Delta H_v} \cdot \end{array}\right\} \qquad (5.74)$$

The value of the ebullioscopic constant K_b depends only on the properties of the solvent: T_o, its normal boiling point; M_1, its molecular weight;[2] and ΔH_v, its molar heat of vaporization. Table 5.5 contains calculated values of ebullioscopic constants for several common solvents. The value for water is a matter of memory for students of general chemistry.

Table 5.5. *Calculated Values of Ebullioscopic Constants K_b*

SOLVENT	ΔH_v (PURE)* (CAL MOLE^{-1})	T_o* ($^\circ$K)	M_1	K_b
H_2O	9720	373.16	18.02	0.514
SO_2	5960	263.14	64.07	1.480
NH_3	5580	239.73	17.03	0.348
CCl_4	7170	349.9	153.84	5.22
$CHCl_3$	7020	334.4	119.39	3.78
CH_3OH	8430	337.9	32.04	0.862
C_2H_5OH	9220	351.7	46.07	1.227
C_6H_6	7350	353.3	78.11	2.642
$C_6H_5CH_3$	8000	383.8	92.13	3.370
$n\text{-}C_8H_{18}$	8360	398.8	114.22	4.318

Example 5.10. Derive Equations (5.74) from (4.180).

$$\ln\left(\frac{P_2}{P_1}\right) = \frac{\Delta H_v(T_2 - T_1)}{RT_1 T_2} \cdot \qquad (4.180)$$

Let Equation (4.180) refer to the solution. Then, as in Figure 5.36, when state 2 refers to the boiling point of the solution,

$$T_2 = T_b$$
$$P_2 = p_1(T_b) = p_1^o(T_o) = 1 \text{ atm}.$$

Let state 1 refer to the normal boiling point of pure solvent; then, by Raoult's law (5.63),

$$T_1 = T_o$$
$$P_1 = p_1(T_o) = N_1 p_1^o(T_o).$$

* Data taken from: Rossini, F. D., D. D. Wagman, W. H. Evans, S. Levine, and I. Jaffe, *Selected Values of Chemical Thermodynamic Properties.* Washington, D. C.: Circular of the National Bureau of Standards 500 (1952); Rossini, F. D., K. S. Pitzer, W. J. Taylor, J. P. Ebert, J. E. Kilpatrick, C. W. Beckett, M. G. Williams, and H. G. Werner, *Selected Values of Properties of Hydrocarbons.* Washington, D. C.: Circular of the National Bureau of Standards C461 (1947).

Substitution of these values into (4.180) yields

$$\ln\left[\frac{p_1^o(T_o)}{N_1 p_1^o(T_o)}\right] = \frac{\Delta H_v(T_b - T_o)}{RT_b T_o}$$

$$-\ln N_1 = \frac{\Delta H_v(T_b - T_o)}{RT_b T_o}. \tag{5.71}$$

The derivation from (5.71) to (5.74) proceeds as above.

Example 5.11. Calculate the boiling point of the solution of Example 5.9 at 1.000 atm.

The molality of nonvolatiles is 0.2249. By Table 5.5 and (5.74),

$$\Delta T_b = 0.514 \times 0.225 = 0.115°C.$$

The boiling point is predicted to be 100.115°C.

The elevation ΔT_b in the boiling point is a colligative property because it depends through (5.74) on the number of independent particles of solute. When a substance dissolves without association or dissociation, as urea and sucrose do in water, the value of ΔT_b is predicted correctly. However, when the molecular weight of solute used to calculate its molality does not correspond to the weight of the solute species that actually exist in the solution, (5.74) leads to a false prediction. For example, a substance that ionizes when dissolved produces more than one solute particle per formula weight; its ΔT_b is observed to be greater than predicted. Carboxylic acids generally dimerize through the formation of hydrogen bonds when dissolved in nonpolar solvents; for such solutions, ΔT_b is observed to be less than predicted.

Observation of ΔT_b for a solution permits the calculation of an average molecular weight of solute as it exists in solution. Equation (5.74) provides an estimate of m_2, and (5.4) yields M_2, the effective molecular weight of solute. In order to avoid changes in boiling temperature due to changes in atmospheric pressure or to impurities in the solvent, it is common to determine simultaneously the boiling points of solvent and solution with accurately compared thermometers.

Example 5.12. When 764 mg of a nonvolatile solute were dissolved in 120 g benzene, its boiling point was raised by 0.083°C. What is the molecular weight of the solute?

By (5.74),

$$m_2 = \frac{\Delta T_b}{K_b} = \frac{0.083}{2.64} = 0.0314.$$

By (5.4),

$$M_2 = \frac{W_2 \times 1000}{m_2 \times W_1} = \frac{0.764 \times 1000}{0.0314 \times 120} = 203.$$

5.16 Freezing Point of Solution

If two phases coexist at equilibrium in a two-component system, there are two degrees of freedom. One of these, the pressure, is commonly taken to be about 1 atm because of the way experiments are ordinarily performed. The other independent variable is either temperature or composition. Equations (5.74) for boiling point elevation assert that at equilibrium both temperature and composition cannot be independent as a solution boils. An equation of the same sort links the freezing point of a solution and its composition.

When a pure solid component is deposited from a solution because the solution begins to freeze or because the solution is saturated with respect to that component at the temperature of the solution, the chemical potential of that pure solid is its reference value at that temperature; that is,

$$\mu_1^{(s)} = \mu_1^{o(s)} . \tag{5.75}$$

The chemical potential of this component 1 as it exists in solution, either as a solvent or solute, is given by (5.67); that is,

$$\mu_1^{(l)} = RT \ln N_1 + \mu_1^{o(l)} . \tag{5.67}$$

At equilibrium, the chemical potentials of components really present in two phases are equal by (5.27); hence, by (5.75) and (5.67), $\mu_1^{(s)} = \mu_1^{(l)}$ and

$$\mu_1^{o(s)} - \mu_1^{o(l)} = RT \ln N_1 . \tag{5.76}$$

When $N_1 = 1$ in (5.67), the chemical potential of the liquid is its value in the pure state. Accordingly, the value of $\mu_1^{o(l)} - \mu_1^{o(s)}$ is just the molar free energy of fusion at the freezing point T_f of the solution. When $N_1 = 1$ in (5.76), this molar free energy increment is of course zero and the temperature is the normal freezing point T_o. By (5.69) and (5.76),

$$-\left[\frac{\partial}{\partial T}\left(\frac{\mu_1^{o(s)} - \mu_1^{o(l)}}{T}\right)\right]_P = \frac{\overline{H}_1^{o(s)} - \overline{H}_1^{o(l)}}{T^2} = -\left[\frac{\partial}{\partial T}(R \ln N_1)\right]_P .$$

But $\overline{H}_1^{o(l)} - \overline{H}_1^{o(s)}$ is the molar heat of fusion of the component that crystallizes so that

$$R\left(\frac{\partial \ln N_1}{\partial T}\right)_P = \frac{\Delta H_f}{T^2} . \tag{5.77}$$

Definite integration at constant pressure from the freezing point T_o of pure component 1 ($N_1 = 1$) to the state when $T = T_f$ at $N_1 < 1$ yields

$$\int_0^{\ln N_1} d(\ln N_1)' = \int_{T_o}^{T_f} \frac{\Delta H_f}{RT^2} \, dT .$$

If ΔH_f is independent of temperature,

$$\ln N_1 = \frac{\Delta H_f}{R}\left(-\frac{1}{T_f} + \frac{1}{T_o}\right)$$

$$-\ln N_1 = \frac{\Delta H_f(T_o - T_f)}{RT_f T_o}. \tag{5.78}$$

By the same methods used in proceeding from (5.71) to (5.74) it follows that

$$\left.\begin{aligned} \Delta T_f &= K_f m_2 \\ K_f &= \frac{RT_o^2 M_1}{1000\,\Delta H_f}. \end{aligned}\right\} \tag{5.79}$$

Here ΔT_f is the freezing point depression caused by the presence of solute. If the solution is ideal at all concentrations, (5.78) describes the solubility of component 1 in any solvent at the temperature T_f if T_o is the melting point of pure component 1.

Table 5.6. *Values of Some Cryoscopic Constants K_f*

COMPONENT THAT CRYSTALLIZES	ΔH_f (PURE)* (CAL MOLE^{-1})	T_o* (°K)	M_1	K_f
Water	1436.3	273.16	18.02	1.862
Benzene	2350	278.7	78.11	5.12
Cyclohexane	637	279.7	84.16	20.5
Acetic acid	2800	289.8	60.05	3.58

Table 5.6 lists values of the cryoscopic constant K_f as calculated by (5.79). Once again the value for water is the empirical value memorized by freshmen. These values, like the ebullioscopic constants, depend only upon the nature of component 1, and the value of molecular weight M_1 chosen is arbitrary since the ratio of M_1 to ΔH_f is the only thing of importance.[3]

Equations (5.79) can be derived from (4.180) as Equations (5.74) were in Example 5.10. The student who attempts the proof in this way will find Figure 5.37 of some value. The curves that separate liquid and solid phases may be assumed to be parallel and almost vertical.

Like the elevation in boiling point, the depression of freezing point is a colligative property in that it depends only upon the number of particles through the molality m_2. A measurement of ΔT_f with a solvent of known K_f yields an experimental value of molality m_2 through (5.79). With known masses of solute and solvent, an average molecular weight of noncrystallizing components can then be calculated through (5.4). When K_f is large, as it is for camphor and cyclopentadecanone, even a dilute solution provides a

* See Table 5.5 for references.

great ΔT_f and ultimately an accurate molecular weight M_2. However, for solvents with large cryoscopic constants K_f, it is advisable to determine the melting point of the solvent before adding solute lest the presence of impurities give a falsely large ΔT_f.

Measurements of freezing point depressions are preferred to measurements of boiling point elevations because the effect of pressure variations on condensed phases is negligible. When multijunction thermocouples are used to record directly the difference in freezing points of pure solvent and solution by using the solution as cold junction and pure solvent as hot junction, values of ΔT_f may be reported to within about $0.00002°C$. Mercury thermometers record temperatures within about $0.001°C$. In order to make such measurements meaningful, it is necessary to analyze the solution that exists in equilibrium with pure crystalline solvent. Spontaneous crystallization withdraws solvent, concentrates the solution, and leads ultimately to too low a value of solution freezing point or unknown molecular weight of solute. If a solution tends to supercool, this change in concentration can be serious, since the first seed crystal leads at once to many crystals if supercooling is appreciable. When it is not possible to analyze the solution in equilibrium with crystalline solvent, the freezing point of the solution is taken as the temperature at which crystals first appear or just dissolve.

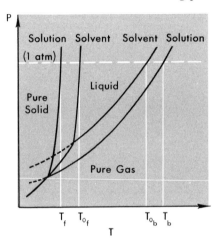

Fig. 5.37. *Vapor Pressures of Pure Solvent and Its Ideal Solution.*

Previous discussions of phase diagrams have mentioned some of the situations in which liquids and solids can coexist at equilibrium. In view of the several kinds of behavior noted in the examples given in those previous sections, it should be clear that the freezing point of a pure substance is not always greater than its solution. Nonideal behavior is most simply treated by recourse to a phase diagram, which after all is merely an orderly record of experiments.

Example 5.13. A sample of camphor used in the Rast method of determining molecular weights had a melting point of $176.5°C$. The melting point of a solution containing 0.522 g camphor and 0.0386 g of an unknown was $158.8°C$. If the unknown compound was a hydrocarbon containing 7.7% H, what was its molecular formula? The K_f of camphor is 37.7.

By (5.79) and the value of K_f of camphor,

$$m_2 = \frac{\Delta T_f}{K_f} = \frac{176.5 - 158.8}{37.7} = 0.470 .$$

By (5.4),

$$M_2 = \frac{W_2}{m_2} \times \frac{1000}{W_1} = \frac{0.0386 \times 1000}{0.470 \times 0.522} = 157 .$$

The empirical formula is found to be CH thus:

$$\frac{0.077/1.008}{0.923/12.01} = \frac{H}{C} = 0.995 \approx 1.0 \ .$$

Since $157/13$ is about 12, the molecular formula is $C_{12}H_{12}$.

Example 5.14. Calculate the triple point of pure water, pure ice I; and pure water vapor. Exactly zero degrees Celsius is defined as the temperature achieved by a mixture of pure ice and water in equilibrium with air at one atm.

Exactly zero degrees is lower than this triple point because of the effect of dissolved gases on the freezing point and because of the influence of pressure on the melting point of ice. The former effect is calculated by (5.79) and the result of Example 5.5, which found the molality of dissolved gases to be 1.29×10^{-3}; hence,

$$\Delta T_f = 1.862 \times 1.29 \times 10^{-3} = 0.0024°C \ .$$

The latter effect is calculated by the Clapeyron equation (4.176) as in Example 4.26; hence,

$$\Delta T = \left(\frac{T \, \Delta V}{\Delta H}\right) \Delta P = \frac{273.2 \times (-0.0907)}{3290} (0.0060 - 1.0000) = 0.0075°C \ .$$

Since these effects are independent and additive, the triple point in the system of pure H_2O is $0.0075°C + 0.0024°C$, or $+0.0099°C$.

Example 5.15. The atomic heats of fusion of Bi and Cd are 2630 cal and 1460 cal, respectively. The melting point of pure Bi is 271°C and that of pure Cd is 321°C. [F. D. Rossini, *et al.*, National Bureau of Standards Circular 500 (1952)] Calculate the eutectic temperature and its composition in the Bi-Cd system. (See Figure 5.18.)

At the eutectic temperature, one liquid solution is in equilibrium with pure solid Bi and pure solid Cd. Let N_{Cd} be the mole fraction of Cd in the ideal liquid solution, and let T be the eutectic temperature. Then, by (5.78),

$$-\ln N_{Cd} = \frac{1460 \times (594 - T)}{1.987 \times 594 \times T} \ .$$

Similarly, for the ideal solution considered as saturated with Bi,

$$-\ln (1 - N_{Cd}) = \frac{2630 \times (544 - T)}{1.987 \times 544 \times T} \ .$$

Solution of these simultaneous equations for N_{Cd} and T yields the result, which can be verified by substitution:

$$N_{Cd} = 0.564$$
$$T = 406°K, \quad \text{or} \quad 133°C \ .$$

5.17 Distribution of Solute Between Immiscible Solutions

The previous sections discussed the equilibrium of a component present in two coexistent phases one of which was pure. In the section on boiling points of solutions, the gaseous phase was pure volatilized solvent; in the preceding section on freezing points of solutions and solubility, the crystalline phase was pure. When none of the coexistent phases, of which there may be several, is a pure component, the necessary equality of chemical potentials of a component in coexisting phases again permits a simple description of the equilibrium state.

The chemical equation for the change by which molecule with formula A_n dissolved in solution phase 1 is transferred to solution phase 2 where it exists as A is:

$$A_n \rightarrow nA .$$

If $n > 1$, several species with the formula A are polymerized in solution 1; if $n = 1$, the molecular species is the same in both solutions. Since either A or A_n can be made from the same component A, the existence of the polymer in one solution does not increase the number of components. The chemical potential of this component in phase 1 is given by (5.80), which is similar to (5.67) and (5.76).

$$\mu_{A_n}^{(1)} = RT \ln N_{A_n} + \mu_{A_n}^{o(1)} . \tag{5.80}$$

When the value of N_{A_n} is unity, the chemical potential of A_n is equal to its standard reference value $\mu_{A_n}^{o(1)}$ at the specified temperature. Similarly, the chemical potential of the n moles of A in phase 2 is given by (5.81).

$$n\mu_A^{(2)} = nRT \ln N_A + n\mu_A^{o(2)} . \tag{5.81}$$

At equilibrium, the chemical potentials of initial and final states are equal so that

$$nRT \ln N_A + n\mu_A^{o(2)} = RT \ln N_{A_n} + \mu_{A_n}^{o(1)} .$$

Whence

$$RT \ln \left(\frac{N_A^n}{N_{A_n}} \right) = \mu_{A_n}^{o(1)} - n\mu_A^{o(2)}$$

$$\left(\frac{N_A^n}{N_{A_n}} \right) = \exp\left[-\frac{n\mu_A^{o(2)} - \mu_{A_n}^{o(1)}}{RT} \right]. \tag{5.82}$$

The right-hand member of (5.82) depends only on the temperature; hence, at a fixed temperature,

$$\frac{N_A^n}{N_{A_n}} = K(T) . \tag{5.83}$$

The constant $K(T)$ is called the *distribution coefficient*. When $K(T)$ is small, component A exists mainly as A_n in solution phase 1; when $K(T)$ is large, the distribution of component A between solutions is such that most exists as A in solution phase 2. When the compositions of the solutions are expressed in terms other than mole fraction, the distribution coefficient assumes a new value but its functional form is the same. For example, in terms of molarities C_i, when molarity can be used instead of the true thermodynamic variable activity of (5.21), a derivation like that of (5.83) yields (5.84).

$$K_c = \frac{C_A^n}{C_{A_n}} \cdot \qquad (5.84)$$

In a system of three components (two solvents and one solute A) and two phases (the two solutions), there are three degrees of freedom: pressure, temperature, and one composition variable. Equations (5.7) and (5.83) then fix all other compositions.

The concept of a distribution coefficient is of considerable importance in the purification of substances. Zone refining of solids to obtain great purity is accomplished by causing small liquid regions to pass slowly through an impure solid ingot. The impurities pass into the liquid phases and, as the liquid zones progress along the solid bar while impure solid melts ahead of and purer solid recrystallizes behind each liquid zone, these impurities are gradually swept to the end of the solid ingot. Extraction with solvents also is a means of purification that depends upon distribution of a component between phases. An organic chemist may wish to remove a substance from a reaction medium or an analytical chemist may wish to remove impurities from a precipitate. Addition of a solvent immiscible with the impure material permits by filtration, decantation, or use of separatory funnel the separation of immiscible phases one of which is the desired product or contains it in a volatile solvent. Many ingenious techniques have been developed for repeating automatically these kinds of extraction and zone refining in order to obtain a purer and purer product.

It is often necessary to minimize the amount of extracting liquor because of its cost, because of difficulty in recovering the product from it, or because it dissolves product as well as impurities. Repeated extraction with several portions of extracting liquor dissolves more product or removes more impurity than one extraction with the same amount of liquor. Let V_2 be the total amount of extracting liquor used. Each of the n extractions uses a volume V_2/n to remove y moles of soluble component from a solution that initially contained n_o moles dissolved in a volume V_1. As in (5.84), let the distribution coefficient for this extraction be given by (5.85).

$$K = \frac{C_1}{C_2} \cdot \qquad (5.85)$$

For the first of the n extractions, (5.85) reads

$$K = \frac{(n_o - y_1)/V_1}{y_1/(V_2/n)} \tag{5.86}$$

whence

$$K y_1 V_1 = \left(\frac{V_2}{n}\right)(n_o - y_1)$$

$$y_1 = \frac{V_2/n}{KV_1 + (V_2/n)} n_o.$$

The moles remaining behind are then, by (5.86),

$$n_o - y_1 = \frac{KV_1 y_1}{(V_2/n)}$$

$$= \frac{KV_1}{V_2/n}\left[\frac{V_2/n}{KV_1 + (V_2/n)}\right] n_o$$

$$= \left[\frac{KV_1}{KV_1 + (V_2/n)}\right] n_o. \tag{5.87}$$

Similarly, after a second extraction of y_2 moles from a solution containing $(n_o - y_1)$ moles in the volume V_1, by (5.87),

$$(n_o - y_1) - y_2 = \left[\frac{KV_1}{KV_1 + (V_2/n)}\right](n_o - y_1)$$

$$= \left[\frac{KV_1}{KV_1 + (V_2/n)}\right]^2 n_o.$$

After n similar extractions, the amount remaining behind in V_1 is

$$n_o - \sum_{i=1}^{n} y_i = \left[\frac{KV_1}{KV_1 + (V_2/n)}\right]^n n_o. \tag{5.88}$$

If only one extraction were performed with the total volume V_2, $n = 1$ in (5.88); hence, the amount left behind is

$$n_o - y_1 = \left(\frac{KV_1}{KV_1 + V_2}\right) n_o. \tag{5.89}$$

In order to show that repeated extractions leave less behind it is necessary to show that in (5.88) and (5.89)

$$n_o - \sum_{i=1}^{n} y_i < n_o - y_1.$$

That is,

$$\left[\frac{KV_1}{KV_1 + (V_2/n)}\right]^n < \left(\frac{KV_1}{KV_1 + V_2}\right)$$

$$\left[\frac{1}{1 + (V_2/KV_1 n)}\right]^n < \left[\frac{1}{1 + (V_2/KV_1)}\right]$$

$$1 + \frac{V_2}{KV_1} < \left(1 + \frac{V_2}{KV_1 n}\right)^n .$$

By the binomial expansion, the right side becomes

$$1 + \frac{V_2}{KV_1} < 1 + n\left(\frac{V_2}{KV_1 n}\right) + \frac{n(n-1)}{2}\left(\frac{V_2}{KV_1 n}\right)^2 + \cdots$$

$$0 < \frac{n(n-1)}{2}\left(\frac{V_2}{KV_1 n}\right)^2 + \cdots . \qquad \text{Q.E.D.}$$

Example 5.16. A solution that occupies a volume of 100 ml and contains 1.0 mole percentage of impurity is to be purified by extraction with a total volume of 1000 ml of extracting solvent that dissolves only the impurity. If the ratio of concentration of impurity in solution to its concentration in extract is 2.00, what mole percentage purity can be obtained by ten and by 100 extractions of equal size?

In the symbols of Equations (5.85) to (5.88), $K = 2.00$, $V_1 = 100$, $V_2 = 1000$, and $n = 10$ or 100. If $n = 10$, the fraction of the impurity that remains unextracted is, by (5.88),

$$\frac{n_o - \sum_{i=1}^{10} y_i}{n_o} = \left[\frac{KV_1}{KV_1 + (V_2/10)}\right]^{10} = \left[\frac{2.00 \times 100}{2.00 \times 100 + (1000/10)}\right]^{10}$$

$$= \left(\frac{200}{300}\right)^{10} = 0.0173 .$$

If $n = 100$,

$$\frac{n_o - \sum_{i=1}^{100} y_i}{n_o} = \left[\frac{2.00 \times 100}{2.00 \times 100 + (1000/100)}\right]^{100} = \left(\frac{200}{210}\right)^{100} = 0.0076 .$$

Ten extractions yield a purity of 99.983%, while 100 yield a purity of 99.992%, despite the somewhat unfavorable value of distribution coefficient K.

5.18   Osmosis

Osmosis is the process by which a solvent or some species of a solution passes through a membrane that is not permeable to other species of the solution. While the barrier to the mixing of solutions in the last section was immiscibility, for osmosis the barrier is a membrane that sorts out molecules by their physicochemical properties. At equilibrium, the chemical potentials of the components that can penetrate the membrane are equal on the two sides of

323

the membrane just as the chemical potential of a species in two coexisting phases is the same in both. There is, however, no restriction on the chemical potentials of components that cannot pass through the membrane. When the phases in contact with the membrane are at the same temperature and yet differ in concentration, equilibrium can be achieved by the imposition of pressure on one of the phases. The membrane must be mechanically strong enough to support this difference in pressure.

The extraordinary pressure that must be exerted upon a solution to increase the vapor pressure or chemical potential of that component which penetrates the membrane to the vapor pressure or chemical potential of the pure component at a fixed temperature is the *osmotic pressure* of the solution. The osmotic pressure equalizes the chemical potentials on both sides of the membrane and thus establishes equilibrium with respect to the permeating species. Without a difference in pressure, this species would pass spontaneously through the membrane from the phase of high chemical potential to the solution where its chemical potential is lower. Osmotic pressure is a property of the solution and does not depend upon the nature of a membrane that is truly semipermeable or upon the theory or mechanism of operation of that membrane.

The equation that relates vapor pressure p and total pressure P at constant temperature when equilibrium is established for one component in two phases has been developed; it is (4.172).

$$\left(\frac{\partial p}{\partial P}\right)_T = \frac{v}{V} . \tag{4.172}$$

The volume of the liquid phase is v and that of the gas phase is V, which can be suitably approximated by the perfect gas equation of state. Hence,

$$\left(\frac{\partial p}{\partial P}\right)_T = \frac{vp}{RT} . \tag{5.90}$$

If p_2 is the vapor pressure of the volatile solvent in the concentrated solution at the high pressure P_2, and if p_1 is the vapor pressure of the volatile solvent in the same solution at the low (atmospheric) pressure P_1, and if the solution is incompressible so that the (partial) molar volume v_1 of the volatile solvent is constant, (5.90) as it applies to the volatile solvent in the concentrated solution is readily integrated isothermally thus:

$$\int_{p_1}^{p_2} \frac{dp}{p} = \int_{P_1}^{P_2} \frac{v_1}{RT} dP$$

$$\ln\left(\frac{p_2}{p_1}\right) = \frac{v_1}{RT}(P_2 - P_1) . \tag{5.91}$$

If the concentrated solution were pure solvent, (5.91) would be just (4.173). At equilibrium with respect to the volatile component that penetrates the membrane, the vapor pressure p_2 of the concentrated solution at the high total pressure P_2 is equal to the vapor pressure of the dilute solution at the low pressure P_1. The pressure difference $P_2 - P_1$ is just sufficient to increase the vapor pressure of the volatile solvent in the concentrated solution from p_1 at low total pressure P_1 to the vapor pressure p_2 of the dilute solution at the same low pressure P_1. When the dilute solution is pure solvent, the pressure difference $P_2 - P_1$ is the osmotic pressure Π of the concentrated solution. With p_1^o replacing p_2 as the vapor pressure of pure solvent and p_1 still the vapor pressure of the solution at the low pressure, (5.91) then reads:

$$\ln \left(\frac{p_1^o}{p_1}\right) = \frac{v_1 \Pi}{RT}. \tag{5.92}$$

The difference in pressures P_1 and p_1^o is ordinarily not sufficient to affect the value of Π by changing p_1 and p_1^o. Yet, when the vapor is not ideal, fugacities must be used in place of vapor pressures.

There exists a convenient approximate form of (5.92) of a kind found empirically by van't Hoff. By Raoult's law (5.47) at the low pressure P_1 or p_1^o,

$$p_1 = N_1 p_1^o.$$

Hence, by the approximate methods used in Sections 5.15 and 5.16,

$$\frac{\Pi v_1}{RT} = -\ln N_1 \tag{5.93}$$

$$\approx N_2 \approx \frac{n_2}{n_1}, \qquad (n_2 \ll n_1).$$

If $n_1 v_1 = V$, the volume of solvent or approximately the volume of solution,

$$\Pi V = n_2 RT. \tag{5.94}$$

Since Π is proportional to n_2, osmotic pressure is classed as a colligative property because it depends upon the number of dissolved particles and not on their kind.

The magnitudes of the osmotic pressures produced by even dilute solutions are great. Some of the earliest experiments performed by Abbé Nollet in 1748 involved the passage of so much water through an animal membrane into a solution of ethanol and water that the membrane sometimes burst. The preparation of a strong membrane that was truly semipermeable to water was at last achieved by the botanist Pfeffer in 1877. He formed membranes of colloidal cupric ferrocyanide as Traube had already done, but he did so in porous ceramic pots by soaking them in cupric sulfate and then in potassium ferrocyanide. Such membranes supported by a ceramic are able to support a few hundred atmospheres pressure without damage and were used by the modern experimenters H. N. Morse and J. C. W. Frazer (1901–1923) and the Earl of Berkeley and E. G. J. Hartley (1906–1909).

The technique of Berkeley and Hartley was elegant. In Figure 5.38, which is a diagram of their apparatus, M is a ceramic tube that supports the

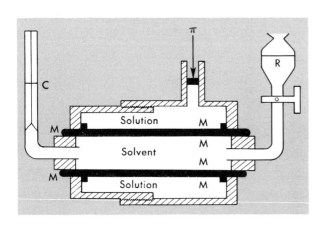

membrane of $Cu_2Fe(CN)_6$. The annular space between M and the outer tube was filled with solution, the apparatus was placed in a thermostat, and the ceramic tube M was filled with solvent from a reservoir R until its level in the capillary stood at a fixed mark C. Pressure was then exerted on the solution through a piston in order to prevent osmosis. When the solvent level remained at the mark C, indicating no loss or gain of solvent by osmosis, the pressure exerted on the solution was its osmotic pressure II. Thus the solution was not diluted by osmosis and equilibrium

Fig. 5.38. *Diagram of Osmotic Pressure Apparatus of Berkeley and Hartley.*

was achieved swiftly. Some of their measurements of osmotic pressure of solutions of sucrose and α-methylglucoside at 0°C are presented in Table 5.7 together with observed values of the vapor pressures of the solutions as calculated from data in *International Critical Tables III*, p. 293. Also tabulated are values of II predicted by (5.92) and (5.94). The exact thermodynamic equation (5.29) is well verified when v_1 is assumed to be that for pure water, 0.01802 l.

Table 5.7. *Observed and Calculated Values of Osmotic Pressure at 0°C for Aqueous Solutions of Sucrose and α-Methylglucoside. (International Critical Tables III, p. 293; IV, p. 430.)*

	SUCROSE				α-METHYLGLUCOSIDE			
	p_1	II	II	II	p_1	II	II	II
	(obs.)	(obs.)	(5.92)	(5.94)	(obs.)	(obs.)	(5.92)	(5.94)
MOLALITY	(mm Hg)	(atm)	(atm)	(atm)	(mm Hg)	(atm)	(atm)	(atm)
1.0	4.489	24.76	24.76	22.4	—	25.0	—	22.4
2.0	4.381	54.9	55.0	44.8	4.384	53.8	54.2	44.8
3.0	4.257	90.0	90.6	67.2	4.273	86.4	86.1	67.2
4.0	4.132	129.7	128.8	89.6	4.159	120.2	119.7	89.6

The cause of osmosis is the difference in vapor pressures or fugacities or chemical potentials of the component that can penetrate the semipermeable membrane. The mechanism by which this component passes through the semipermeable membrane is an unsettled theoretical matter. The solute bombardment theory proposed by van't Hoff is not satisfactory. Although the form of (5.94) suggests an analogy with an ideal gas, it is necessary to picture the solute molecules as pushing the membrane against the solvent during osmosis and thus forcing solvent to enter the solution. But the solute particles are not free like gas molecules and, if solute molecules bombard the membrane, so also must solvent molecules. The three main theories of the mechanism of osmosis consider the solvent as distilling through pores in the membrane, as dissolving in the membrane, or as proceeding through the membrane as through a sieve. This last theory, the molecular sieve theory, is particularly appealing for solutions of polymers. It is quite likely that all these theoretical aspects of the mechanism are true in part and that any particular example of osmosis is described most suitably by emphasis on one of the three.

Osmosis is of paramount importance in biology. The walls of plant and animal cells are permeable to water and to some of the solutes that occur in the fluids surrounding cells. If the surrounding fluid is more concentrated in solutes that do not penetrate the cell wall than is the fluid within the cell, the cell loses fluid by osmosis. Such a surrounding solution is termed *hypertonic*, and as it shrinks the cell undergoes *plasmolysis*. If the surrounding fluid is *hypotonic* (too dilute), the cells accumulate fluid and may burst. *Hemolysis* is the term for the loss of red hemoglobin by burst blood cells; it occurs when the osmotic pressure of blood falls to about half the normal value of 7.65 atm at 37°C. Cells will not change in an isotonic solution such as the normal saline solution containing about 0.9% NaCl. Intravenous feeding or injections must be done with solutions isotonic with blood.

Blood absorbs nutrients by osmosis through villi in the small intestine and distributes them to bodily tissues by osmosis. A foetus receives nourishment, excretes wastes, and "breathes" by osmosis through the placenta of the uterus. The normal absorption of water through the large intestine can be modified by a dose of epsom salts. Ductless glands secrete their products into the bloodstream by osmosis because their fluids are hypotonic relative to blood. The flow of water in such glands is due in part to osmosis caused by a difference in concentration between ends of the gland. The osmotic pressure of the blood tends to counter the flow of water out through blood vessels because of the hydrostatic blood pressure. The kidneys regulate the salt concentration of the blood, and the formation and concentration of urine in the kidneys is linked closely to the osmotic pressure of the blood. The kidneys remove by osmosis the nitrogenous cell wastes that the blood carries from the cells. Fresh or very salty water sensitizes exposed pain nerves because of osmotic pressure differences. Physiological saline solutions are used to bathe exposed tissues in surgery and to preserve tissues alive outside the body for a day or two. The sensation of thirst is stimulated by changes in osmotic pressure.

327

Outside the human body, osmosis is also of universal biological import. Leaves of plants take water and food from the veins by osmosis and plant roots take water from the soil by osmosis. Canned foods are preserved from attack by bacteria because the syrup is hypertonic relative to bacterial fluids and the bacteria are thus inactivated through plasmolysis. The theories for the mechanism of osmosis suggest that the distinction between osmosis and diffusion, which may influence some of these examples from biology, is perhaps not definite.

Example 5.17. A solution of 0.635 g of a protein in 100 ml water has an osmotic pressure due to the protein of 2.35 cm H_2O at 27°C. What is the molecular weight of the protein?

By (5.93),

$$\Pi = \frac{n_2 R T}{V}$$

$$\frac{2.35}{13.6 \times 76.0} = \frac{0.635}{M_2} \times \frac{0.08205 \times 300}{0.100}$$

$$M_2 = 69,000 \,.$$

Example 5.18. With the aid of Raoult's law, predict the osmotic pressure of a one-molal aqueous solution at 0°C.

The mole fraction of water in a 1.00-molal solution is

$$N_1 = \frac{1000/18.02}{(1000/18.02) + 1.00} = 0.9820 \,.$$

By Raoult's law (5.47),

$$N_1 = \frac{p_1}{p_1^o} = 0.9820 \,.$$

Substitution in (5.93) yields the answer.

$$\Pi = \frac{RT}{\bar{v}_1} (-\ln N_1) = \frac{0.08205 \times 273.2}{0.0180} \times (-\ln 0.9820) = 22.6 \text{ atm} \,.$$

The observed values in Table 5.7 for sucrose and α-methyl glucoside are about 2 atm greater, the difference being due to failure of Raoult's law.

E. COLLIGATIVE PROPERTIES OF ELECTROLYTES

5.19 Membrane Equilibriums

All membrane equilibriums are alike in this: At equilibrium, the chemical potentials of those species which pass through the membrane are alike on both sides of the membrane. After osmosis, the Donnan membrane equilibrium is of biological importance. It explains most of the swelling of gelatin in water and the need for an excess of a neutral electrolyte in characterizing proteins by their sedimentation velocities. The rapid movement of charged protein molecules past other charged particles and ions proceeds as though an imaginary barrier existed where there is really only a difference in velocity.

Some organic molecules ionize to form a small ion and a huge organic ion. Alkali salts of complex organic acids are an example of a kind of compound that forms some ions so large that they cannot pass through a membrane that allows small ions like Na^+ and Cl^- to pass freely. Similarly, protein molecules and ions are much larger than H_3O^+ and Cl^- ions that might be associated with them and that would pass freely through many membranes that would refuse passage to proteins.

Suppose that a solution of a protein A and its hydrochloride $(AH_n)^{+n}Cl_n^{-n}$ is separated from a solution of hydrochloric acid by a membrane that is permeable to H_2O, H_3O^+, and Cl^-. The movement of the ions is restricted in two ways: The solutions on each side of the membrane must be electrically neutral and the chemical potentials of the hydrochloric acid in each solution must be equal at equilibrium. Since the chemical potential of an electrolyte is the sum of the chemical potentials of its ions, the chemical potential of hydrochloric acid with ionic activities a_{H^+}, and a_{Cl^-} is given by a sum of expressions like (5.21). That is,

$$\mu_{H^+Cl^-} = RT \ln a_{H^+} + RT \ln a_{Cl^-} + \mu_{H^+}^o + \mu_{Cl^-}^o .$$

With superscripts to identify solutions, at equilibrium, it follows that

$$\mu_{H^+Cl^-}^{(1)} = \mu_{H^+Cl^-}^{(2)}$$
$$RT \ln a_{H^+}^{(1)} + RT \ln a_{Cl^-}^{(1)} = RT \ln a_{H^+}^{(2)} + RT \ln a_{Cl^-}^{(2)}$$
$$a_{H^+}^{(1)} a_{Cl^-}^{(1)} = a_{H^+}^{(2)} a_{Cl^-}^{(2)} . \tag{5.95}$$

Although the un-ionized or zwitter-ionized protein A and its cationic form $(AH_n)^{+n}$ do not appear in (5.95) because they cannot pass through the membrane, they exert their influence upon the activities of H^+ and Cl^- through the charge on $(AH_n)^{+n}$ and its activity. The concentrations that exist after the ions have adjusted to the equilibrium state are listed below with account of the condition of electroneutrality of each solution and of the n basic sites on A.

				MEMBRANE		
$\frac{1}{n}$ A	$\frac{1}{n}$ $(AH_n)^{+n}$	H^+	Cl^-	|||	H^+	Cl^-
$\left(\frac{a}{n}\right)$	$\left(\frac{b}{n}\right)$	$(a + x)$	$[(a + b) + x)]$	|||	$(c - x)$	$(c - x)$

By (5.95), if activities and concentrations are alike,

$$(c - x)^2 = (a + x)(a + b + x) . \tag{5.96}$$

The values of a and b are fixed by the experimenter and the ionization constant of the protein cation. The osmotic pressure developed after the transfer of x moles per liter of HCl depends upon the difference in concentrations. This difference is

$$\Delta = \left(\frac{a}{n}\right) + \left(\frac{b}{n}\right) + (a + x) + [(a + b) + x] - (c - x) - (c - x)$$

$$= \left[(a + b)\left(\frac{n + 1}{n}\right) + a - 2c\right] + 4x .$$

But by (5.96),

$$c^2 - 2cx + x^2 = a(a + b) + x(a + b) + ax + x^2$$

$$c^2 - a(a + b) = x(2c + 2a + b)$$

$$x = \frac{c^2 - a(a + b)}{2a + b + 2c} .$$

If c^2 is greater than $a(a + b)$, ions will move into the protein solution in order to attain equilibrium. If c is much greater than a and b, x approaches $c/2$ and Δ approaches $2a + b$ for large n; in such circumstances, it is possible to measure the molecular weight of the protein by osmotic pressure because the excess of acid makes a small relative to b. It is also possible to measure the molecular weight osmotically at the isoelectric point when a is much greater than b and c; then x approaches $-(a/2)$ and Δ becomes a/n, the concentration of protein with no net charge. As c decreases from a large value, Δ rises from the value b to a maximum and then decreases to a/n at the isoelectric point. For these reasons, osmotic pressure measurements are made either at the isoelectric point or in the presence of a great excess of acid in both solutions.

The swelling of gelatin is accounted for in most part by this difference in osmotic pressure. The gelatin itself is the membrane, and when the value of Δ is great the tendency for swelling through absorption of water is great due to the great osmotic pressure.

5.20 Colligative Properties of Solutions of Electrolytes

Although he realized fully the limitations involved, van't Hoff found it convenient to compare the colligative effect (a vapor pressure lowering, a freezing or boiling point change, or an osmotic pressure) observed for a solution of an electrolyte to that expected if there were no ionization. This empirical ratio is called *van't Hoff's i* and is defined by (5.97), where the subscript zero indicates the expected value.

$$i = \frac{\Pi}{\Pi_o} = \frac{\Delta T_f}{(\Delta T_f)_o} = \frac{\Delta T_b}{(\Delta T_b)_o} = \frac{\Delta p_1}{(\Delta p_1)_o} . \tag{5.97}$$

In (5.97), the numerators are observed values and the denominators are values calculated by (5.92) or (5.93), (5.78) or (5.79), (5.71) or (5.74), and (5.65), just as though ionization did not occur. If each ion or molecule really exerted its full influence on the colligative properties, the value of i would be the number of independent units formed by one formula weight. For sugar, i would be one; for NaCl, 2; for $MgCl_2$, 3; for $FeCl_3$, 4; for $K_4Fe(CN)_6$, 5; and so on. However, the observed values of the numerators generally are not strictly proportional to the number of ions or particles because they are not really independent or ideal in their influence. That i does approach an ideal limit for very dilute solutions is shown in Figure 5.39. Tabulations of empirically observed values of i allow the prediction of colligative

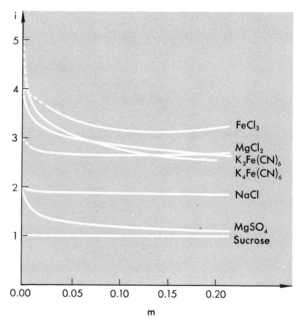

Fig. 5.39. *Typical Variation of* i *With Molality in Aqueous Solutions.* (*Freezing point data from* Int. Crit. Tables *IV, p. 254.*)

properties; and (5.97) justifies the prediction of three colligative properties from a measurement of the fourth.

Example 5.19. The freezing point of a sample of abnormal blood was found to be $-0.402°C$. What was its osmotic pressure at $37°C$?

By (5.97) and (5.79),

$$\Delta T_f = i(\Delta T_f)_o = iK_f m_2 .$$

Hence, the effective molality of solutes in this sample of blood was

$$im_2 = \frac{\Delta T_f}{K_f} = \frac{0.402}{1.86} .$$

By (5.97) and (5.94),

$$\Pi = i\Pi_o = i\left(\frac{n_2 RT}{V}\right) \approx im_2 RT$$

$$\approx \frac{0.402}{1.86} \times 0.08205 \times 310 = 5.50 \text{ atm, lower than normal.}$$

5.21 Degree of Ionization

The facts that X-ray determinations of crystal structure have established the existence of ions in the solid state, that dissolving ionic crystals frequently involves only small energy changes, that mixing such ionic solutions yields very fast reactions or negligible heat effects in the absence of reaction, and that ionic solutions conduct an electric current well are some of the evidence for complete ionization of chemicals like the salts listed in Figure 5.39. Between these and the typically nonionic, nonconducting, slowly reacting solutions there are solutions that are intermediate in these kinds of property. There is really no discontinuity in behavior that can serve to classify a solution as ionic, slightly ionic, or nonionic. Rather, when the degree of ionization of solutions containing weak or slightly ionized electrolytes like weak organic acids is low, it is customary to give a numerical measure of the apparent degree of ionization. Sometimes a measurement of a colligative property is suitable.

Let $A_a B_b$ be the formula of a compound that ionizes to form a cations each with charge z_+ and b anions with charge z_-. The process of ionization, considered as incomplete, is described by the equation

$$A_a B_b \rightleftharpoons a\,A^{z_+} + b\,B^{z_-}\,.$$

The apparent molality of solutes — dissolved $A_a\,B_b$ and ions without distinction as to kind — in a solution that is m_2 molal in $A_a\,B_b$ before ionization is then

$$m_2(1 - \alpha) + am_2\alpha + bm_2\alpha$$

where α is the apparent degree of ionization. For dilute solutions, a colligative property like freezing point lowering is then predicted to be

$$\Delta T_f = (1 - \alpha + a\alpha + b\alpha)K_f m_2\,.$$

But by (5.79), $(\Delta T_f)_0 = K_f m_2$ so that by (5.97),

$$i = \frac{\Delta T_f}{(\Delta T_f)_0} = \frac{K_f m_2(1 - \alpha + a\alpha + b\alpha)}{K_f m_2}$$

$$= 1 - \alpha + a\alpha + b\alpha\,. \qquad (5.98)$$

If the total number of ions produced, namely, $a + b$, is denoted by ν, it follows from (5.98) that the degree of ionization is given by

$$\alpha = \frac{i - 1}{\nu - 1}\,. \qquad (5.99)$$

A fractional value of α for a weak electrolyte has real meaning and can be found by measurement of i through a measurement of a colligative property. When ionization is complete, as it is at all concentrations for strong electrolytes like $NaCl$, $MgCl_2$, and many others like them, α is unity but i approaches ν in value only in very dilute solutions where solvation effects and electrostatic interactions among ions do not interfere with ideal behavior.

Example 5.20. Calculate the degree of ionization of dichloroacetic acid from the freezing point depressions ΔT_f and molalities m listed below [*International Critical Tables IV*, p. 262].

For the 0.100 molal solution, by (5.79)

$$(\Delta T_f)_o = 1.86 \times 0.100 = 0.186°C \,.$$

By (5.97),

$$i = \frac{0.300}{0.186} = 1.61 \,.$$

Since the acid forms two ions as it ionizes, $\nu = 2$ and by (5.99),

$$\alpha = \frac{1.61 - 1}{2 - 1} = 0.61 \,.$$

m	ΔT_f (°C)	α
0.0040	0.0148	0.99
0.0100	0.0356	0.91
0.0200	0.0690	0.85
0.0500	0.1615	0.74
0.100	0.300	0.61
0.200	0.560	0.50
0.500	0.126	0.36

The other values listed above were calculated in a similar way.

5.22 Very Dilute Solutions of Electrolytes

Inasmuch as there exist mutual electrostatic interactions among ions and solvent, it is not surprising that the values of i at finite concentrations of Figure 5.39 deviate markedly from the ideal value ν. Calculation of this deviation is accomplished most simply through g, the osmotic coefficient of the solvent. For ideal solutions of nonelectrolytes,

$$\Pi_o = -\frac{RT}{v_1} \ln N_1 \,. \tag{5.93}$$

For nonideal solutions of nonelectrolytes with ideal behavior in the vapor,

$$\Pi = \frac{RT}{v_1} \ln \left(\frac{p_1^o}{p_1} \right) \,. \tag{5.92}$$

For infinitely dilute solutions of electrolytes with ideal behavior in the vapor and liquid, the equation would be

$$\Pi = -\nu \frac{RT}{v_1} \ln N_1 \,. \tag{5.100}$$

However, for nonideal solutions of nonelectrolytes ($\nu = 1$) or electrolytes ($\nu > 1$),

$$\Pi = -g\nu \frac{RT}{v_1} \ln N_1 \,. \tag{5.101}$$

The osmotic coefficient g corrects for deviations from ideality in the liquid beyond those accountable in terms of the ν fragments per formula weight. When the influence of these ν fragments is recognized, (5.92) becomes (5.102).

$$\Pi = \nu \frac{RT}{v_1} \ln \left(\frac{p_1^o}{p_1} \right) \,. \tag{5.102}$$

With the understanding that fugacities and vapor pressures are used interchangeably, comparison of (5.101) and (5.102) yields the definition of g in (5.103).

$$-g \ln N_1 = \ln \left(\frac{p_1^o}{p_1} \right).$$ (5.103)

Since $\Pi = i\Pi_o$, it is clear from (5.93) and (5.101) that g corrects ν to an effective value i by the equation

$$i = g\nu .$$ (5.104)

The value of g in very dilute solutions has been calculated theoretically by Debye and Huckel in terms of a constant α that is characteristic of the solvent and a function I that depends upon the ionic concentrations. For a single electrolyte in which charges on cation and anion are the positive integers z_+ and $-z_-$,

$$1 - g = \frac{\alpha}{3} z_+ |z_-| \sqrt{I} .$$ (5.105)

The value of α depends upon Avogadro's number N, the density ρ of solvent, the electronic charge e, the dielectric constant κ of solvent, the gas constant R, and the absolute temperature T according to (5.106).

$$\alpha = N^2 \left(\frac{2\pi\rho}{1000} \right)^{1/2} \left(\frac{e^2}{\kappa R T} \right)^{3/2} .$$ (5.106)

For water at 0°C, $\alpha = 1.122$; at 25°C, $\alpha = 1.173$.

The value of I in (5.105) is called the *ionic strength* of the solution. It depends on the molality m of the electrolyte, on the numbers of cations a and anions b, and on the positive integers z_+ and $|z_-|$, which give the number of charges per ion, by the relation

$$I = \tfrac{1}{2}(az_+^2 + bz_-^2)m .$$ (5.107)

For a solution of several electrolytes in which each ionic species i of charge z_i (a small positive or negative integer) has an ionic molality m_i, the ionic strength I has the value

$$I = \tfrac{1}{2} \sum_i z_i^2 m_i .$$ (5.108)

The Debye-Huckel expression for the osmotic coefficient is somewhat more complicated for a very dilute solution of several electrolytes:

$$1 - g = \frac{2\alpha}{3 \sum_i m_i} I^{3/2} .$$ (5.109)

The Debye-Huckel theory is valuable because it establishes the value of g at infinite dilution, which is a standard reference state. The predictions of the theory are accurate for aqueous solutions when I is less than about 0.01. In solvents of lower dielectric constant, deviations occur at even smaller values of ionic strength.

Example 5.21. Predict the lowering in the freezing point of a kg water in which are dissolved 0.0020 formula weights of KNO_3 and 0.0010 formula weights of $Ba(NO_3)_2$.

If these ions acted independently, the predicted lowering of freezing point would be $\Delta T_f = K_f \sum_i m_i$. Since the molality of nitrate ions is 0.004,

$$\Delta T_f = 1.86(0.0020 + 0.0010 + 0.0040)$$
$$= 1.86 \times 0.0070 = 0.0130°C .$$

The osmotic coefficient g takes account of the fact that the ions are really not independent. For this solution,

$$I = \tfrac{1}{2} \sum_i z_i^2 m_i \qquad (5.108)$$

$$= \tfrac{1}{2}(1^2 \times 0.0020 + 1^2 \times 0.0040 + 2^2 \times 0.0010) = 0.0050$$

$$1 - g = \frac{2\alpha}{3 \sum_i m_i} I^{3/2} \qquad (5.109)$$

$$= \frac{2 \times 1.122}{3 \times 0.0070} (0.0050)^{3/2} = 0.0378 .$$

Hence,

$$g = 0.9622$$
$$\Delta T_f = 0.9622 \times 0.0130 = 0.0125°C .$$

5.23 Activity Coefficients

An activity coefficient is that number, generally of the order of unity, by which pressure or concentration must be multiplied to yield fugacity or activity. The activity coefficient of component i of a gaseous solution in which component i has a fugacity f_i and a partial pressure p_i is f_i/p_i. When p_i approaches zero because the total pressure approaches zero, the activity coefficient approaches unity as in (4.166), which is part of the definition of fugacity for a pure substance.

$$\lim_{P \to 0} \left(\frac{f}{P} \right) = 1 . \qquad (4.166)$$

When the reference state is pure liquid, an activity coefficient f_i allows for the failure of Raoult's law, as it applies to the solution, to predict the observed vapor pressure p_i of the ideal vapor thus:

$$p_i = f_i N_i p_i^o . \qquad (5.110)$$

Similarly, for a solute species i with an activity a_i and a molality m_i, the activity coefficient γ_i of a solute is

$$\gamma_i = \frac{a_i}{m_i}. \tag{5.111}$$

Like other activity coefficients, γ_i approaches unity as $\sum_i m_i$ approaches zero. Knowing f_i or γ_i one can calculate p_i or a_i, but this is of no particular advantage since the method of calculating f_i, p_i, γ_i, or a_i is equally tedious by any method. Rather, the advantage of an activity coefficient lies in the ease of thinking thermodynamically by neglecting it, working with ideal solutions, and then finally mending the ideal equations by inserting activity coefficients here and there as needed.

It is impossible to measure the activity or activity coefficient of just one ion because it is impossible to obtain a solution containing just cations or just anions. It is possible, however, to measure these things for an electrolyte 1 mole of which yields a cations of charge z_+ and b anions of charge z_-, where z_+ and $|z_-|$ are small positive integers that express the multiple of the electronic charge $\pm e$ on the ion. The chemical potential of such an electrolyte is

$$\mu_i = \mu_i^o + RT \ln a_i = a\mu_+^o + aRT \ln a_+ + b\mu_-^o + bRT \ln a_-.$$

Whence,

$$a_i = a_+^a a_-^b = a_\pm^\nu. \tag{5.112}$$

The quantity $a_\pm$ as defined by (5.112) is called the *mean activity* of the electrolyte. To this mean activity there is attributed a mean activity coefficient $\gamma_\pm$ such that

$$a_\pm = \gamma_\pm m_\pm. \tag{5.113}$$

That is, for a solution m_i molal in the electrolyte, m_+ molal in cations, and m_- molal in anions,

$$\begin{aligned}
a_\pm^\nu &= \gamma_\pm^\nu m_\pm^\nu = (\gamma_+ m_+)^a (\gamma_- m_-)^b \\
&= \gamma_+^a (am_i)^a \gamma_-^b (bm_i)^b = (a\gamma_+)^a (b\gamma_-)^b m_i^\nu \\
&= a^a b^b \gamma_\pm^\nu m_i^\nu. \tag{5.114}
\end{aligned}$$

Analogous relations hold for solutions with compositions expressed in molarities, but it must be remembered that in dilute solutions the ratio of molarity to molality is the density of the solution.

The relationship of the activity coefficient f_1 of a solvent to its osmotic coefficient g is found through (5.103), the definition of g for the solvent species 1, with fugacities replacing vapor pressures; that is,

$$-g \ln N_1 = \ln \left(\frac{f_1^o}{f_1} \right). \tag{5.115}$$

When the vapors are ideal, $f_1^o = p_1^o$ and by (5.110) $f_1 = p_1$. Then,

$$-g \ln N_1 = \ln \left(\frac{p_1^o}{f_1 N_1 p_1^o} \right) = -\ln N_1 - \ln f_1$$

$$\ln f_1 = (g - 1) \ln N_1. \tag{5.116}$$

When the standard reference state of a solute component 2 is pure component 2, an equation analogous to (5.116) applies to it because there is in such cases no way of distinguishing solute and solvent; hence,

$$\ln f_2 = (g_2 - 1) \ln N_2. \tag{5.117}$$

When the standard reference state of a solute is its hypothetical ideal state of unit molality, the Debye-Huckel expression for the mean activity coefficient $\gamma_\pm$ of one electrolyte is

$$-\ln \gamma_\pm = \alpha z_+ \mid z_- \mid \sqrt{I} \tag{5.118}$$

where α and I have the same meanings as in the preceding section. Equation (5.118) is often stated in terms of decadic logarithms. Then, for water,

$$-\log \gamma_\pm = 0.487 z_+ \mid z_- \mid \sqrt{I}, \qquad (0°C) \tag{5.119}$$

$$-\log \gamma_\pm = 0.509 z_+ \mid z_- \mid \sqrt{I}, \qquad (25°C). \tag{5.120}$$

The calculation of activity coefficients $\gamma_\pm$ from freezing point depressions is somewhat tedious.[4]

Although Debye and Huckel were the first to establish a theoretical basis for (5.118) and similar equations, relationships linking activity coefficients to the square root of a concentration had been established empirically. If ions were really distributed at random in a solution, i and $\gamma_\pm$ would not differ from ν and unity, for a truly random arrangement of ions has no special stability. In an electric field, gaseous dipolar molecules tend to become aligned in the field (Chapter 1), but incessant bombardment renders alignment far from perfect. Similarly, in the neighborhood of an ion in solution there collect ions of opposite charge. Only the incessant continual bombardment by all the particles of the solution prevents this electrostatic attraction from creating a fair degree of order. Near an ion where the electrostatic potential is Φ (Φ is positive near cations and negative near anions), the energy of an ion is $z_\pm e\Phi$ and the ratio of local concentration to average concentration throughout the solution is $\exp\left(-\frac{z_\pm e\Phi}{kT} \right)$. This Boltzmann factor is less than unity for like ions ($z_\pm$ and Φ have the same sign), but for unlike ions ($z_\pm$ and Φ differ in sign) it is greater than unity. Thus each ion tends to collect oppositely charged ions around itself in a kind of ion atmosphere despite thermal disordering processes. Solution of the electrostatic problem in which the region

337

around an ion is considered to be a homogeneous dielectric yields a potential of the form

$$\Phi = \frac{z_\pm e}{\kappa r} \exp\left(-\frac{r}{a}\right)$$

provided $z_\pm e\Phi$ is much less than kT. The constant a, called the *Debye length*, is a rough measure of the distance to which an ion exerts its influence in organizing the nearby solution. Its value is

$$a = \left(\frac{1000\kappa RT}{8\pi N^2 e^2 \rho I}\right)^{1/2}.$$

For an aqueous solution with $I = 0.01$ at $25°C$, $a = 30.4$ A. Relating the electrostatic energy of the ion cloud about an ion to the extraordinary term $RT \ln \gamma_\pm$ of the free energy yields (5.118) and similar equations. When ion size and solvation become important, more complex expressions result. Indeed, outside the very dilute range of concentrations the electrostatic problem is a most difficult one.

Example 5.22. Calculate from the data of Table 5.3 the activity coefficients of acetone and water in a 2.5 mole per cent acetone solution at 1.00 atm at 84.2°C. At 84.2°C, the vapor pressures of pure acetone and pure water are 1820 and 420 mm Hg.

From Table 5.3, the mole fraction of acetone in the vapor is 0.470; hence, if the vapor is ideal at 1.00 atm, its fugacity is 0.470. Raoult's law would predict a vapor pressure of

$$p_2 = p_2^\circ N_2 \tag{5.47}$$

$$= \frac{1820}{760} \times 0.025 = 0.0598 \text{ atm}.$$

By (5.110),

$$f_2 = \frac{0.470}{0.0598} = 7.9.$$

Similarly, for water,

$$f_1 = \frac{0.530}{(420/760) \times 0.975} = 0.98.$$

The magnitudes of the activity coefficients f_i indicate that in this mixture Raoult's law greatly underestimates the fugacity of acetone and slightly overestimates that of water.

REFERENCES

Findlay, A., and A. N. Campbell, *The Phase Rule and Its Applications*. New York: Longmans, Green & Co., Inc., 1938.

Gibbs, J. W., *The Collected Works of J. Willard Gibbs*. New Haven, Conn.: Yale University Press, 1948.

Glasstone, S., *Textbook of Physical Chemistry*. Princeton, N. J.: D. Van Nostrand Company, Inc., 1946.

Guggenheim, E. A., *Thermodynamics, An Advanced Treatment for Chemists and Physicists*. Amsterdam: North-Holland Publishing Co., 1957.

International Critical Tables. New York: McGraw-Hill Book Company, Inc., Vol. III, IV.

Landolt-Börnstein, *Zahlenwerte und Funktionen . . . II* Band 3. Teil. Berlin: Verlag Julius Springer, 1956.

PROBLEMS

[Vapor pressure and solution data from Lange's *Handbook of Chemistry*. New York: McGraw-Hill Book Co., Inc., 1956, unless noted otherwise.]

1. An aqueous solution of HCl has 2.00% by weight HCl and a density of 1.016 g ml^{-1}. Calculate its molality and molarity.

2. Is there any pure substance that can decompose to give more than two phases if the temperature is arbitrarily specified? Explain.
Answer: Yes, in a field or not at equilibrium.

3. Calculate the number of degrees of freedom at equilibrium:
(a) Liquid and vapor of a pure substance.
(b) Oxygen, steam, oxygen dissolved in water at 25°C.
(c) Ice I; dilute aqueous HCl; N$_2$, HCl, and H$_2$O in vapor.
Give particular reasonable values of the proper number of intensive variables for each situation to fix its state.
Answer: (a) 1; (b) 1; (c) 2.

4. If the densities of the various kinds of H$_2$O increase in the order gas, I, liq., III, II, V, VI, VII, then find the signs of the various ΔH's for the several possible transformations.

5. A mixture of 30% vol Ne and 70% vol Ar has a total pressure of 650 mm Hg at 70°C in a volume of 3.42 l.
(a) How many moles of Ar are present?
(b) What is the density of the mixture?

6. Explain (as in Section 5.6) why all the molecules of a gas probably will not gather in one small region of their container.

7. The mole fraction of *n*-hexane in the vapor above a solution of *n*-hexane and *n*-heptane is 0.750 at 50°C. What is the composition of the liquid solution? See Example 5.4 for data.
Answer: Mole fraction of hexane = 0.509.

8. When the total pressure above a certain ideal solution of two volatile components is 400 mm Hg, the mole fraction of one of the components in the vapor is 0.400, while in the liquid it is 0.500. What are the vapor pressures of each of the pure components?

9. Hydrogen sulfide obeys Henry's law. What does this indicate about H$_2$S dissolved in water?

10. How many grams O$_2$ dissolve in 600 ml water at 0°C when the partial pressure is 400 mm Hg? See Example 5.5 for data.

11. Describe the fractional distillation of an acetone-water solution at 1 atm if the liquid feed, with H$_2$O mole fraction 0.70, is fed preheated into the next to the bottom plate of a fractional distilling column of six plates.

12. When an organic compound immiscible with water was steam-distilled at 750 mm Hg at 98°C, the vapor contained 50% by weight water. Estimate its molecular weight.
Answer: 296.

13. If the vapor pressure of water at 90°C is 526 mm Hg, how many grams chlorobenzene will be distilled per gram of water collected in the distillate if chlorobenzene is steam-distilled at 90°C at a total pressure of 734 mm Hg?

14. Sketch the temperature-composition phase diagram of the pyridine-formamide system from these data [S. Stephanou, C. A. Vander Werf, and H. H. Sisler, *Journal of the American Chemical Society*, **70**, 264 (1948)]:
(a) Only one liquid phase exists; no solid solutions or compounds exist, except of course pyridine and formamide.
(b) There is a simple eutectic at 32.3% mole formamide at −56.7°C.
(c) Pure pyridine melts at −41.5°C; pure formamide, at 2.2°C.
(d) Crystals first form from cooling melts thus: at −50°C from 20% mole formamide; −42°C at 40% mole formamide; −22°C at 60% mole formamide; −10°C at 80% mole formamide. With this sketch, describe what happens when a melt with composition 50% mole formamide cools and what happens when pyridine is added to formamide at −45°C until the system is eventually almost all pyridine.

15. From Figure 5.24, determine the composition and amounts of the two phases in equilibrium at 80°C if 40.0 g water are mixed with 60.0 g isobutyl ether.
Answer: 17 g with 6% wt ether; 83 g with 71% ether.

16. Sketch qualitatively the phase diagram of the water-ethanol-ethyl acetate system at 0°C and 25°C if water and ethyl acetate are not miscible in all proportions but other pairs are, and if ethyl acetate and water become more soluble in each other (with or without ethanol) as the temperature rises.

17. In 700 g water were dissolved 30.0 g sucrose ($C_{12}H_{22}O_{11}$) and 30.0 g glucose ($C_6H_{12}O_6$). What is the vapor pressure of this solution at 30°C if the vapor pressure of water is 31.82 mm Hg?

18. The freezing point of a solution of 0.138 g of a nonvolatile solute in 15.2 g benzene is 0.53°C less than the freezing point of pure benzene. What are the molecular weight of the substance and normal boiling point of the solution?
Answer: 88; 80.4°C.

19. Estimate the eutectic temperature and composition in the Au-Tl system if:
(a) The melting points of pure Au and Tl are 1063°C and 304°C.
(b) Only one liquid phase exists and no compounds or solid solutions exist.
(c) The heats of fusion of Au and Tl are 3030 cal and 1030 cal gram-atom^{-1}.
The thermodynamic data are from F. D. Rossini, *et al.*, Circular of the National Bureau of Standards 500 (1952).

20. When CdI_2 is dissolved in a mixture of ether and H_2O at 30°C, its concentration in the aqueous phase is five times that in the ether-rich phase. [*International Critical Tables III*, p. 421]. If 500 ml of a 0.0324 molar solution of CdI_2 in ether is mixed with 100 ml water, how many grams of CdI_2 enter the aqueous phase at equilibrium?

21. How much dextrose ($C_6H_{12}O_6$) must be dissolved in one l water to yield a solution with an osmotic pressure of 7.65 atm at 37°C?
Answer: 54.4 g.

22. If van't Hoff's i is independent of temperature, at what temperature will 2.00 molal NaCl boil if it freezes at −6.90°C? [Data from *International Critical Tables, IV*, p. 254.]

23. The freezing point of a 0.20 molal aqueous solution of a weak electrolyte that ionizes into two ions is $-0.416°C$. Calculate the degree of ionization.

24. Calculate the freezing point of 0.00152 molal $CoCl_2$.

---

25. The specific gravity of an aqueous solution of ammonium hydroxide containing 8.00% by weight NH_3 was found to be 0.965 at 20°C. At 20°C, the density of water is 0.998 g ml^{-1}. Find the molarity and molality of NH_3.

26. Calculate the error in chemical potential made in assuming that pure Cl_2 is ideal at 50°C at 10.0 atm.
Answer: 45 cal.

27. Calculate the degrees of freedom at equilibrium, and (if the system exists) give particular examples of observable values of enough intensive variables to specify the state of the system:
(a) At constant pressure, gaseous NH_3 and H_2O, pure ice I, and NH_3 dissolved in liquid water.
(b) Air and its aqueous solution.
(c) At arbitrary constant T and P, liquid O_2 and N_2 (one phase), $O_{2(s)}$, $N_{2(s)}$.

28. Show that $\mu_i = \overline{H}_i - T\overline{S}_i$ and find a value of $\overline{H}_i$ for an ideal solution, in which $\mu_i = RT \ln N_i + \mu_i^o$.

29. Sketch the phase diagram of Fe from data in Chapter 2 and thermodynamic data [F. D. Rossini *et al.*, *Circular of the National Bureau of Standards 500* (1952)] below:

Transition	$T(°C)$	ΔH(cal gram-atom^{-1})
$\alpha \rightarrow \beta$	760	~ 0
$\beta \rightarrow \gamma$	907	217
$\gamma \rightarrow \delta$	1400	150
$\delta \rightarrow$ liq.	1535	3,600
liq. $\rightarrow$ vapor	2800	92,700

30. Air saturated with water vapor at 25°C is dried by passage through a dry-ice trap at $-75°C$, where the vapor pressure of ice is 9.0×10^{-4} mm Hg. If the process occurs at constant pressure of 760 mm Hg, what is the final pressure of H_2O in the effluent dried air after it is warmed to 25°C out of further contact with H_2O?

31. What is the minimum amount of isothermal work required to sort out a mixture of distinguishable ideal gases into pure species?

32. Calculate the entropy of unmixing of 100 g air considered as 21% vol O_2, 78% vol N_2, and 1% vol Ar.
Answer: $\Delta S = -3.94$ cal deg^{-1}.

33. Calculate the composition of the vapor at 0°C above a solution containing 3 moles $SiCl_4$ and 4 moles CCl_4. At 0°C, the vapor pressures of $SiCl_4$ and CCl_4 are 77.4 and 34.2 mm Hg.

34. The vapor pressures of *n*-hexane and *n*-heptane at 0°C are 45.5 and 11.4 mm Hg. What is the composition of a solution of these two substances if its total vapor pressure at 0°C is 37.3 mm Hg?

35. At 25°C, 500 ml H_2O dissolve 15.03 ml CH_4 (S.T.P.) under a partial pressure of methane of one atm. If Henry's law holds, what pressure is required to cause 0.00100 mole methane to dissolve in 300 ml water?
Answer: 2.48 atm.

36. An ideal solution of two components with vapor pressures of 400 mm Hg and 300 mm Hg when pure contains two moles of the more volatile component and five moles of the less volatile one. Calculate:
(a) The total vapor pressure of the solution.
(b) The composition of the vapor in equilibrium with a solution of this composition.
(c) The composition of the last drop to vaporize from such a solution when none of the vapor is withdrawn from contact with the unvaporized mixture.
(d) The composition of the last drop to vaporize when the distillate from such a solution is continuously condensed elsewhere and is thus withdrawn from contact with the unvaporized mixture.

37. Aniline ($C_6H_5NH_2$) has a vapor pressure of 18.3 mm Hg at 80°C and 45.5 mm Hg at 100°C. Predict the temperature and vapor composition during steam distillation of aniline at 755.0 mm Hg total pressure. At 98.0°C, the vapor pressure of H_2O is 707.3 mm Hg.

38. Sketch the temperature-composition phase diagram of the Au-Pb system given [*Metals Handbook*, American Society for Metals, Cleveland, O., 1948, p. 1173]:
(a) Only one liquid phase and no solid solutions exist.
(b) Compounds: Au_2Pb and $AuPb_2$.
(c) Peritectics: 418° at 45% wt Pb; 254° at 72% wt Pb.
(d) Eutectic: 215° at 85% wt Pb.
(e) Melting points: Au at 1063°C; Pb at 327°C.
Label areas of sketch with phases present and describe quantitatively the constitution of these systems:
(f) 40% wt Pb at 418°C.
(g) 70% wt Pb at 230°C.
(h) 50% wt Pb at 200°C.

39. Construct the phase diagram of the liquid system aniline-hexane given [D. B. Keyes and J. H. Hildebrand, *Journal of the American Chemical Society*, **39**, 2126 (1917)] the following temperatures of complete miscibility:

% wt Hexane	T(°C)	% wt Hexane	(T°C)
9.6	26.1°	35.9	59.2
14.8	43.9	41.6	59.4
16.3	45.9	48.0	59.6
20.0	49.9	62.9	57.9
21.0	51.4	73.1	53.9
27.2	56.0	80.6	47.2
31.0	58.2	88.1	35.6
34.6	58.2	93.8	16.5

If 150 g of a mixture containing 80.0% hexane were at 40°C, how much aniline would be in the hexane-rich layer?

40. From Figures 5.10 and 5.11, calculate the amounts of acetone and water in gaseous and liquid phases when a system consisting of 3 moles acetone and 2 moles water is held at equilibrium:
(a) At 1 atm at 70°C.
(b) At 1 atm at 65°C.
(c) At 13.5 atm at 160°C.
(d) At 13.5 atm at 158°C.

41. From Figure 5.31, sketch the temperature composition diagram of aniline-water system and find the composition of the phases at equilibrium at 155°C. *Answer:* 20% wt and 73% wt aniline.

42. When 0.0321 g of a compound containing 68% wt C, 10% wt H, and 22% wt O was dissolved in 0.722 g cyclohexane, the solution had a freezing point of 0.15°C. What is the molecular weight and true formula of the compound? *Answer:* $C_8H_{14}O_2$.

43. Estimate the eutectic temperature and composition in the Al-Ge system if:
(a) The melting points of pure Al and Ge are 660°C and 960°C.
(b) Only one liquid phase exists and no compounds or solid solutions exist.
(c) The heats of fusion of Al and Ge are 2.6 and 8.3 kcal gram-atom^{-1}.
The numerical data are from F. D. Rossini, *et al.*, Circular of the National Bureau of Standards 500 (1952).
Answer: 822°K.

44. Calculate the heats of fusion of A and B and the maximum amount of pure A that can be recovered by one crystallization of a melt containing 15% mole B. Pure A melts at 100°C, forms an eutectic with B at 70% mole B at 30°C, and pure B melts at 120°C. Only one liquid phase exists, and no solid solutions or compounds exist. *Answer:* $\Delta H_A = 3870$ cal; $\Delta H_B = 9400$ cal; 92.4% mole of A present.

45. The osmotic pressure of an aqueous solution containing exactly 1 g nonvolatile substances in 100.0 ml water is exactly 1 atm at 27°C. What is the average weight of the solute particles? Why was the qualification "average" made?

46. How tall a column of solution with density 1.010 g ml^{-1} can be supported at equilibrium by the osmotic pressure developed by 0.532 molar nonelectrolyte in water at 20°C? At 0°C?

47. What should be the vapor pressure of an aqueous solution that is to have an osmotic pressure of 7.65 atm at 37°C? The vapor pressure of H_2O at 37°C is 47.07 mm Hg.

48. What is the vapor pressure of 1.000 molal NaCl at 0°C if its freezing point is -3.37°C? [Data from *International Critical Tables IV*, p. 254.] The vapor pressure of H_2O at 0°C is 4.58 mm Hg.
Answer: 4.43 mm Hg.

49. Calculate the activity of NaCl, the mean activity of NaCl, and the vapor pressure of 0.004 molal NaCl at 25°C. The vapor pressure of pure water at 25°C is 23.756 mm Hg.

50. What is the osmotic pressure of 0.00250 molal KNO_3 at 0°C? What is van't Hoff's i and the freezing point of this solution?
Answer: 0.110 atm; -0.00914°C.

51. A solution containing several species is ideal with respect to species i if $\mu_i = RT \ln N_i + \mu_i^0$. From this by means of (5.69) show that the enthalpy of mixing species i in such a solution is zero. If $G = G(T, P, N_i)$ is an extensive property, show from general considerations that at constant T and P, $\sum_i N_i \, d\bar{G}_i = 0$. Then show that a solution ideal in all but one species is ideal also in the last.

52. State the phase rule for a system simultaneously in gravitational and electrostatic fields. Give concrete examples with $He_{(g)}$ and $HCl_{(g)}$ as system.

53. For any phase of a system, derive the Gibbs-Duhem equation: $\sum_i n_i \, d\mu_i - V \, dP + S \, dT = 0$. Another form is: $\sum_i N_i \, (d\mu_i - \overline{V}_i \, dP + \overline{S}_i \, dT) = 0$.

54. At 25°C, the vapor pressure of solid iodine is 0.31 mm Hg and the standard entropies of solid and gaseous iodine are 27.9 and 62.3 cal mole^{-1} deg^{-1} [F. D. Rossini *et al.*, Circular of the National Bureau of Standards 500 (1952)]. If C_p for the solid is 13 cal mole^{-1} deg^{-1} and if I_2 is a rigid diatomic molecule, sketch the chemical potentials of solid and gaseous I_2 as functions of temperature at 1 atm. Then find the temperature at which the solid would sublime at one atm.
Answer: 164°C.

55. What is the density at 37°C and 0.950 atm of air (21% vol O_2; 79% vol N_2) to which have been added: (1) CO_2 so that the final mixture has 3% vol CO_2; or (2) enough H_2O to saturate the gases at 37°C? The vapor pressure of H_2O at 37°C is 47.07 mm Hg.

56. Calculate the increase in entropy suffered by one l dry air at 1.0000 atm at 25°C as it becomes saturated with H_2O vapor at 25°C by addition of $H_2O_{(g)}$ at its vapor pressure of 23.76 mm Hg:
(a) If the gaseous volume remains constant.
(b) If the total pressure remains constant at 1.0000 atm.

57. The normal boiling point of cymene ($C_{10}H_{14}$) is 175.0°C. On a day when the atmospheric pressure was somewhat less than 760 mm Hg, an ideal solution of several nonvolatile substances in cymene boiled at 176.8°C. On the same day at the same total pressure, steam distillation of the same solution at 96.4°C, where the vapor pressure of water is 667.3 mm Hg, gave a distillate containing 44.7% by weight cymene and 55.3% by weight H_2O. What was the vapor pressure of cymene above the same solution at 50°C? What was the mole fraction of cymene in the same solution?
Answer: 11.2 mm Hg; 0.932.

58. At 37°C, 12.2 ml N_2 (S.T.P.) dissolve in one l water at one atm N_2. What volume of N_2, measured at 37°C at 1.000 atm, will be released by 1 l water as the partial pressure of N_2 falls from 5.00 atm to 0.80 atm? If the Henry's law constant $K(T)$ for He is half that of N_2, what volume of He will be released under similar conditions? The difference in volumes finds application in deep-sea diving.

59. Estimate by a graphical method the temperature at which an equimolar liquid solution of chlorobenzene and bromobenzene will have a total vapor pressure of 1.000 atm. At 110°C the vapor pressure of C_6H_5Cl is 418 mm Hg; at 130°C, 724 mm Hg. At 110°C, the vapor pressure of C_6H_5Br is 198 mm Hg; at 130°C, 373 mm Hg. What will be the composition of vapor?

60. The normal boiling points of H_2O and D_2O are 100.00°C and 101.42°C. Throughout this problem assume that no HDO if formed and that all solutions are ideal.
(a) Calculate the vapor pressure of D_2O at 100.00°C if its molar heat of vaporization is 9.96 kcal mole^{-1}.
(b) Construct a pressure-composition diagram for the H_2O-D_2O system at 100.00°C with liquid and vapor curves.
(c) What would be the composition of the first drop of liquid to form upon condensing a gaseous mixture with mole fraction of D_2O of 0.200 at 100.00°C?
(d) What would be the composition of the first vapor to form upon vaporization of a liquid mixture with mole fraction of D_2O of 0.200 at 100.00°C?
(e) About how many theoretical plates would be required to separate a mixture of D_2O and H_2O into solutions that contain each species 95% mole pure?
Answer: (e) About 100.

61. How much steam must be *furnished* to steam-distill one mole of a substance with a normal boiling point of 200°C and a molar heat of vaporization of 10.0 kcal mole⁻¹? The steam-distillation is done at a total pressure of 760 mm Hg and the vaporization is adiabatic, all thermal energy coming from steam at 100°C at one atm.

62. By what mechanism could two solids not in contact with each other (as solids) influence each other's melting points? [*Hint:* R. H. Petrucci, *Journal of Chemical Education*, **35**, 367 (1958); **36**, 603 (1959).]

63. Sketch the phase diagram of the HF-KF system from these facts [G. H. Cady, *Journal of the American Chemical Society*, **56**, 1431 (1934)]:
(a) The transition temperature for α-KHF₂ to β-KHF₂ occurs at 195°C.
(b) α-KHF₂, β-KHF₂, and liquid HF are in equilibrium at 195°C when the overall mole percentage of HF is 53.82.
(c) Compounds and melting points: KF, 880°C; β-KF·HF, 239.0°C; KF·2 HF, 71.7°C; 2 KF·5 HF, 64.3°C; KF·3 HF, 65.8°C; KF·4 HF, 72.0°C; HF, −83.7°C.
(d) Eutectic temperatures and mole percentages of HF: −97°C at 93.11%; 63.6°C at 77.1%; 62.4°C at 72.7%; 61.8°C at 69.69%; 68.3°C at 64.9%; 229.5°C at 48.60%. Describe what happens at 65.0°C as KF is gradually added to liquid HF until the mixture is mostly KF.

64. From the phase diagram of the Al-Zn system as compiled by The American Society for Metals, explain in detail what happens as a melt containing:
(a) Three moles Zn to 7 moles Al is cooled reversibly to 100°C.
(b) 90% by weight Zn is cooled reversibly to 100°C.
(c) Pure zinc at 500°C has Al added to it until the weight percentage of Al is 80%.

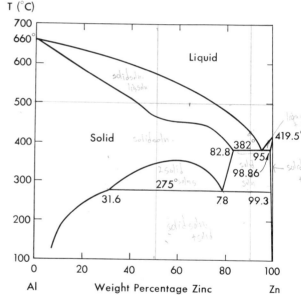

Fig. 5.40. *Aluminum-Zinc System.* (Metals Handbook, *American Society for Metals, Cleveland, O.* [*1948*], *p. 1167*.)

65. Sketch the phase diagram at constant *T* and *P* for the system H₂O, A, B, at 20°C if these hydrates dissolve in and remain in equilibrium with the aqueous solution: A·H₂O; A·3 H₂O; A·B·H₂O; 2 B·H₂O. Pure A and B cannot remain at equilibrium in the presence of the solution.

66. Urea (H₂NCONH₂) is soluble in alcohol (CH₃CH₂OH) but is not volatile from the solution. With data from Table 5.5, for a solution of 5.00 g urea in 800 g alcohol, find:
(a) The diminution in the vapor pressure of alcohol at 70.0°C due to the presence of the urea.
(b) The increase in boiling point of the solution at one atm.
Answer: (a) 2.62 mm Hg; (b) 0.128°C.

67. Find the compositions and temperatures of the three simple binary eutectics and the one simple ternary eutectic in the system LiF-NaF-KF and sketch the phase diagram at constant pressure with isotherms if:
(a) No compounds or solid solutions are formed.
(b) Only one liquid phase exists.
(c) The melting points are: LiF, 845°C; NaF, 995°C; and KF, 856°C.
(d) The heats of fusion are: LiF, 2400 cal mole^{-1}; NaF, 7800 cal mole^{-1}; KF, 6800 cal mole^{-1}.
The numerical data are from F. D. Rossini, *et al.*, Circular of the National Bureau of Standards 500, Washington, D. C. (1952). Assume the solutions are ideal.
Answer: Ternary eutectic; calc. 500°C; obs, 454°C.

68. Sometimes in zone refining (passing small liquid regions through a solid ingot) the material left behind is richer rather than poorer in an impurity. Under what circumstances will this occur? Describe the phase diagram for this case.

69. Why can solutions of equal osmotic pressures differ in tonicity?

70. The hydrochloride of a high molecular weight amine containing only one amine group per molecule is placed on one side of a membrane permeable to all dissolved species except the amine and its cation. The concentration of the amine hydrochloride is 0.001 molal; 0.001 molal HCl is placed on the opposite side of the membrane. What pressure must be exerted on what solution to prevent the transfer of matter through the membrane because of osmosis at 37°C? Assume that the concentration of neutral amine is negligible and that all osmotic coefficients are unity.

71. The freezing point of 0.01000 molal $CaCl_2$ is -0.05112°C. What freezing point is predicted by the Debye-Huckel theory? What is the osmotic pressure of 0.01000 molal $CaCl_2$ at 0°C? [Data from *International Critical Tables IV*, p. 254.]

72. What would be the osmotic pressure of 5.0% acetone in water solution at one atm at 75.6°C? See Table 5.3 for data and assume the vapor pressures of pure acetone and water are 1430 mm Hg and 290 mm Hg.

73. Calculate the chemical potentials of Na^+, Br^-, and NaBr in 0.0030 molal NaBr at 25°C if $\mu^o_{Na^+} = -62,589$ cal mole^{-1} and $\mu^o_{Br^-} = -24,574$ cal mole^{-1} [Rossini, F. D., *et al.*, Circular of the National Bureau of Standards 500 (1952)].

74. Calculate ΔH for the change at 25°C: NaBr $(0.0030m) \rightarrow$ NaBr $(0.0015m)$.

FOOTNOTES

1. Smith, N. O., *Journal of Chemical Education*, 35 (1958), 125.

2. The choice of M_1 is arbitrary in condensed phases. See: Bijvoet, J. M. and A. F. Peerdeman, *Journal of Chemical Education*, 35 (1958), 240.

3. Bijvoet, J. M. and A. F. Peerdeman, *Journal of Chemical Education*, 35 (1958), 240.

4. For details, see Lewis, G. N. and M. Randall, *Thermodynamics and the Free Energy of Chemical Substances*. New York: McGraw-Hill Book Company, Inc., 1923, p. 282.

6 / CHEMICAL

EQUILIBRIUM

A. ISOTHERMAL CHANGES

6.1 The Equilibrium Constant

The purpose of this chapter is to apply known principles in new ways, namely, in situations in which chemical rather than physical changes can occur. Although it may be somewhat difficult to distinguish between chemical and physical changes when the change involves processes like the breaking of hydrogen bonds in vaporizing water or the solvation of ions in solution processes, nevertheless the restraint forbidding so-called chemical changes is now to be removed. No longer is it customary to choose a minimum number of independent components of a system. Rather, with each really existing species recognized explicitly, one or more relations among these various species are to be found. The relations so found will impose one or more conditions on these species and will leave unspecified a number of variables just equal to the number of degrees of freedom predicted by the phase rule if dependent species had first been eliminated from the list.

These relations are equilibrium constants. For example, the partition coefficient of Section 5.17 is a relation or equilibrium constant of this kind. A system consisting of a solute distributed between immiscible solutions was considered a three-component $(C = 3)$ system of two phases $(P = 2)$. As such, the degrees of freedom at constant pressure and temperature were given by (5.30).

$$F = C - P \qquad (5.30)$$
$$= 3 - 2 = 1 .$$

The single degree of freedom is the mole fraction of one component in one of the phases. The partition coefficient relates the compositions of the immiscible solutions at equilibrium; it relates the concentrations of solute in each solution when these two concentrations are each of interest; it relates the equilibrium concentrations of A and A_n for the reaction $A_n \rightarrow nA$ just as though A_n and A were different components; it places a restriction upon the dissociation process in which n fragments A are generated from A_n by a physicochemical process. The reaction above could describe the extraction of acetic acid from benzene, where it exists mainly as dimer, by water, where it exists mainly as monomer. This same reaction could represent the vaporization of water from hydrogen-bonded liquid $(H_2O)_n$ to molecular gas H_2O.

For any change in which a formula weights of A, b of B, and so on become d formula weights of D, e of E, and so on, the general reaction is

$$a\,A + b\,B + \cdots \rightleftharpoons d\,D + e\,E + \cdots \qquad (6.1)$$

A, B, . . . D, E, . . . recognized as species that are generally not as simply related as A_n is to A. It is assumed that (6.1) is a balanced equation so that mass, kinds of atom, and charge are conserved in this closed system. At equilibrium, if the change of (6.1) involves only expansion work, $\Delta G = 0$ at constant pressure and temperature by (4.131) or (4.152). By virtue of (5.18), the Gibbs free energy G_2 of the products D, E, . . . is given by (6.2).

$$G(T, P, n_i) = \sum_{i=1}^{C} n_i \mu_i(T, P) \qquad (5.18)$$

$$G_2 = d\mu_D + e\mu_E + \cdots \qquad (6.2)$$

Similarly, the Gibbs free energy G_1 of the reactants A, B, . . . is given by (6.3).

$$G_1 = a\mu_A + b\mu_B + \cdots . \qquad (6.3)$$

By (4.152), $G_1 = G_2$ and

$$a\mu_A + b\mu_B + \cdots = d\mu_D + e\mu_E + \cdots \qquad (6.4)$$

Equation (6.4) is the desired relation that imposes a condition upon the several species of (6.1) because at equilibrium all these species are not independent and classifiable as components. From the list of the reactants and products one species may be omitted in counting the minimum number of species out of which the system can be made, for the reaction considered is the means of generating this last species, which is not a component or independent intensive variable. There is one relation like (6.4) for each chemical equation like (6.1).

Equation (6.4) is transformed into the more familiar form of an equilibrium constant thus. By (5.20),

$$aRT \ln f_A + a\mu_A^o(T) + bRT \ln f_B + b\mu_B^o(T) + \cdots$$
$$= dRT \ln f_D + d\mu_D^o(T) + eRT \ln f_E + e\mu_E^o(T) + \cdots .$$

That is,

$$- \{[d\mu_D^o(T) + e\mu_E^o(T) + \cdots] - [a\mu_A^o(T) + b\mu_B^o(T) + \cdots]\}$$
$$= RT[(\ln f_D^d + \ln f_E^e + \cdots) - (\ln f_A^a + \ln f_B^b + \cdots)] .$$

The left-hand member of this last equation is just $-\Delta G^o$, the Gibbs free energy decrease for reaction (6.1) when reactants in their standard states of unit fugacity at temperature T are transformed entirely into products in their standard states of unit fugacity at the same temperature T. On continuation,

$$-\Delta G^o = RT \ln \left(\frac{f_D^d f_E^e \cdots}{f_A^a f_B^b \cdots} \right)$$

$$\exp \left(-\frac{\Delta G^o}{RT} \right) = \frac{f_D^d f_E^e \cdots}{f_A^a f_B^b \cdots} .$$

The left-hand member of this last equation depends only upon the temperature (and, of course, the natures of the given species A, B, ... D, E, ...); hence, it may be represented by the function $K_e(T)$, which is known as the *equilibrium constant at the temperature T*. Then, by definition,

$$K_e(T) = \frac{f_D^d f_E^e \cdots}{f_A^a f_B^b \cdots} . \tag{6.5}$$

For the reverse reaction

$$d\,D + e\,E + \cdots \rightleftharpoons a\,A + b\,B + \cdots \tag{6.6}$$

it follows similarly that

$$K_e'(T) = \frac{f_A^a f_B^b \cdots}{f_D^d f_E^e \cdots} . \tag{6.7}$$

By (6.5) and (6.7), however,

$$K_e(T) = [K_e'(T)]^{-1} . \tag{6.8}$$

That is, reversal of a reaction changes the sign of ΔG^o (but not its absolute value) and changes the equilibrium constant K_e into its reciprocal. The convention that the fugacities of products be placed in the numerator is universal.

349

In an exactly analogous way, with (5.21),

$$\mu_i = RT \ln a_i + \mu_i^\circ(T) \tag{5.21}$$

Equation (6.4) leads to another equilibrium constant K_a, where

$$K_a = \frac{a_D^d a_E^e \cdots}{a_A^a a_B^b \cdots}. \tag{6.9}$$

For the reversed reaction (6.6) there is again an equilibrium constant K_a',

$$K_a' = \frac{a_A^a a_B^b \cdots}{a_D^d a_E^e \cdots} \tag{6.10}$$

where

$$K_a = (K_a')^{-1}. \tag{6.11}$$

These equilibrium constants K_e and K_a and their reciprocals impose equilibrium restrictions on the fugacities or activities of species that can in principle suffer a reversible change describable by a chemical equation. They depend only on the temperature. And although initially the values of f_i and a_i are arbitrary, at equilibrium their product as given by the expression for the equilibrium constants is independent of their initial values.

6.2 Interrelationships of Equilibrium Constants

The equilibrium constants of the previous section are indeed constants, but it is generally convenient to use near-constant expressions that are of the same functional form but that avoid the tedium of obtaining fugacities and activities from pressures and concentrations. For example, when gases are ideal and form an ideal solution, fugacities equal partial pressures and (6.5) becomes (6.12).

$$K_p = \frac{p_D^d p_E^e \cdots}{p_A^a p_B^b \cdots}. \tag{6.12}$$

The value of K_p as defined by (6.12) is almost independent of everything except temperature for systems that are nearly ideal. Because K_p is much more readily determined, it is used much more often than K_e.

When activity coefficients approach unity, as they really do in dilute solutions, it is convenient to define a quasi constant K_c by (6.13).

$$K_c = \frac{C_D^d C_E^e \cdots}{C_A^a C_B^b \cdots}. \tag{6.13}$$

Equation (6.13) is analogous to (6.9) and the value of K_c is almost independent of everything except T.

There is a simple relation between K_p and K_c for gases. Since C_i is the number of moles of kind i per liter of solution, by the perfect gas law,

$$p_i = \frac{n_i RT}{V} = C_i RT . \tag{6.14}$$

By (6.12) and (6.13), however,

$$K_p = \frac{(C_D RT)^d (C_E RT)^e \cdots}{(C_A RT)^a (C_B RT)^b \cdots} = K_c (RT)^{(d+e+\cdots)-(a+b+\cdots)}$$

As in (3.61), if $\Delta n_{(g)}$ is the increase in the number of moles of gaseous species for the reaction considered,

$$K_p = K_c (RT)^{\Delta n_{(g)}} . \tag{6.15}$$

6.3 Dissociation

The process by which one pure substance decomposes into other substances is dissociation. If none of the decomposition products escapes from the system, the system may contain several chemical species but it still consists of just one component. The phase rule (5.28) then becomes $\mathbf{F} = \mathbf{C} - \mathbf{P} + 2 = 3 - \mathbf{P}$. If only one phase exists, as in systems in which decomposition products dissolve in the pure substance, there are two degrees of freedom: temperature and pressure are independent of each other and each may be specified arbitrarily. For example, pure gaseous PCl_5 dissociates measurably into gaseous PCl_3 and gaseous Cl_2 at about 250°C; gaseous I_2 dissociates measurably into two I atoms at about 1000°C; about 1% H_2O is dissociated into H_2, O_2, and other species at about 2000°C.

When a pure substance dissociates to form a system of two phases, one degree of freedom remains: either temperature or pressure. For example, pure solid NH_4SH dissociates appreciably at 25°C into NH_3 and H_2S; once the temperature is specified, the total pressure of the gaseous solution or the partial pressure of either gaseous species is determined by the nature of NH_4SH. If the pressure and temperature were each fixed at some arbitrary value, the two phases could in general not continue to coexist at equilibrium; one would disappear. That is, if pressure and temperature are experimentally made independent, $\mathbf{F} = 2$ and $\mathbf{P} = 1$ because $\mathbf{F} = 3 - \mathbf{P}$.

It is possible for dissociation to yield a system of three phases that coexist at equilibrium. Then, with $\mathbf{C} = 1$ and $\mathbf{P} = 3$, there is no degree of freedom. If fusion and vaporization are regarded as chemical changes, then the triple points in the system H_2O exemplify this lack of freedom in the choice of pressure or temperature. Similarly, equal numbers of moles of CaO and CO_2 coexist at equilibrium with $CaCO_3$ only at a definite temperature and pressure, just as a system made of 2 H_2 plus O_2 consists of only one component, H_2O,

351

regardless of the temperature or pressure. It is common, however, not to restrict the ratio of CaO to CO_2 to unity and thus the system becomes one of two components. It is clear also that dolomite, a pure substance with the formula $CaCO_3 \cdot MgCO_3$, cannot exist in equilibrium with three other phases such as $CaO_{(s)}$, $MgO_{(s)}$, and $CO_{2(g)}$ unless the system is transformed into one of two components by withdrawal or addition of one of the decomposition products.

For the homogeneous gaseous dissociation

$$AB_b \rightleftharpoons A + b\,B \tag{6.16}$$

let ρ_o be the density of pure gaseous AB_b before decomposition and let ρ be the density at equilibrium when the fraction α of 1 mole AB_b has dissociated. The number of moles of A generated from AB_b is then α; the number of B is $b\alpha$; and the number of AB_b intact is $(1 - \alpha)$. The total number of moles of gas without regard to species at equilibrium is, then, $(1 - \alpha) + b\alpha + \alpha = 1 + b\alpha$. Since the volume of a mixture of perfect gases is directly proportional to the number of moles of gas of any kind and inversely proportional to the density at constant pressure and temperature, it follows that density is inversely proportional to moles. Hence, for 1 mole AB_b initially,

$$\frac{\rho_o}{\rho} = \frac{1/1}{1/(1 + b\alpha)} = 1 + b\alpha$$

$$\alpha = \frac{\rho_o - \rho}{b\rho}. \tag{6.17}$$

If the total pressure of the mixture is P, then by Dalton's law and (5.35), the partial pressures at equilibrium are

$$p_A = N_A P = \frac{\alpha}{1 + b\alpha} P$$

$$p_B = N_B P = \frac{b\alpha}{1 + b\alpha} P$$

$$p_{AB_b} = N_{AB_b} P = \frac{1 - \alpha}{1 + b\alpha} P.$$

Substitution of these values into the expression for K_p as given by (6.12) and (6.16) yields K_p as a function of P, b, and α.

$$K_p = \frac{p_A p_B^b}{p_{AB_b}}$$

$$= \left(\frac{\alpha P}{1 + b\alpha}\right)\left(\frac{b\alpha P}{1 + b\alpha}\right)^b \left[\frac{1 + b\alpha}{(1 - \alpha)P}\right]$$

$$= \frac{\alpha(\alpha b P)^b}{(1 - \alpha)(1 + b\alpha)^b}. \tag{6.18}$$

An important case of (6.18) occurs when $b = 1$; then,

$$K_p = \frac{\alpha^2 P}{1 - \alpha^2} \cdot \tag{6.19}$$

Example 6.1. Pure PCl_5 dissociates at 200°C until its density falls to 3.880 g l⁻¹ at one atm at equilibrium. [Calculated from D. P. Stevenson and D. M. Yost, *Journal of Chemical Physics*, **9**, 403 (1941).] Calculate K_p, K_c, and the percentage dissociated if the reaction is

$$PCl_{5(g)} \rightleftharpoons PCl_{3(g)} + Cl_{2(g)} .$$

In terms of previous notation, A is PCl_3, B is Cl_2, and b is unity. Since the molecular weight of PCl_5 is 208.3,

$$\rho_o = \frac{g}{V} = \frac{MP}{RT} = \frac{208.3 \times 1.000}{0.08205 \times 473.1} = 5.366 \text{ g l}^{-1} .$$

By (6.17),

$$\alpha = \frac{\rho_o - \rho}{b\rho} = \frac{5.366 - 3.880}{3.880} = 0.3830 .$$

That is, 38.30% is dissociated. By (6.19),

$$K_p = \frac{0.3830^2 \times 1.0000}{1 - 0.3830^2} = 0.1719 \text{ atm} .$$

Since $\Delta n_{(g)} = b + 1 - 1 = 1$, by (6.15),

$$K_c = \frac{K_p}{RT} = \frac{0.1719}{0.08205 \times 473.1} = 4.429 \times 10^{-3} \text{ moles l}^{-1} .$$

Example 6.2. Predict the percentage of PCl_5, which is dissociated at 10.0 atm total pressure at 200°C, where $K_p = 0.1719$ for the reaction $PCl_5 \rightleftharpoons PCl_3 + Cl_2$.

By (6.19),

$$K_p = \frac{\alpha^2 P}{1 - \alpha^2}$$

$$0.1719 = \frac{\alpha^2}{1 - \alpha^2} \times 10.00$$

$$\alpha = \sqrt{\frac{1}{59.16}} = 0.1300 .$$

Only 13.00% of PCl_5 is dissociated at 200°C at 10.00 atm, less than at 1.000 atm because the increased pressure favors the reduction in volume that comes with association.

When the products of dissociation A and B are indistinguishable to the experimenter who uses K_p or K_c, the forms of (6.18) and (6.19) are somewhat different. The reaction is now

$$A_{b+1} \rightleftharpoons (b + 1)A . \tag{6.20}$$

353

The derivation of (6.17) remains the same, but since the partial pressures of A and B are no longer distinguishable from each other, for (6.20)

$$p_A = \frac{(b+1)\alpha}{1+b\alpha} P$$

and

$$p_{Ab+1} = \frac{1-\alpha}{1+b\alpha} P \cdot$$

Then, by (6.12),

$$K_p = \left[\frac{(b+1)\alpha P}{(1+b\alpha)} \right]^{b+1} \left[\frac{(1+b\alpha)}{(1-\alpha)P} \right]$$

$$= \frac{[(b+1)\alpha]^{b+1} P^b}{(1+b\alpha)^b (1-\alpha)} \cdot \tag{6.21}$$

When $b = 1$, as it does for diatomic molecule A_2,

$$A_2 \rightleftharpoons 2\,A$$

and

$$K_p = \frac{4\alpha^2 P}{1-\alpha^2} \cdot \tag{6.22}$$

Example 6.3. At elevated temperatures, gaseous iodine dissociates to atoms to such an extent that observed pressures P deviate measurably from expected pressures P_o. If the total pressure difference is due to dissociation, calculate K_p for the process $I_{2(g)} \rightleftharpoons 2\,I_{(g)}$ at 800°C if $P_o = 0.3153$ atm and if $P = 0.3429$ atm [M. L. Perlman and G. K. Rollefson, *Journal of Chemical Physics*, 9, 362 (1941)].

The increase in pressure $P - P_o$ is a direct measure of the number of molecules dissociated; for, when α is the fraction dissociated, the total number of moles of all kinds is $(1 - \alpha)$ of I_2 plus 2α of I, or $(1 + \alpha)$. Since pressure is proportional to the number of free particles at constant volume and temperature,

$$\frac{P}{P_o} = \frac{1+\alpha}{1}$$

$$\alpha = \frac{P - P_o}{P_o} \cdot$$

By (5.35),

$$p_I = \left(\frac{2\alpha}{1+\alpha} \right) P = \frac{2(P - P_o)}{P_o} \times \frac{P_o}{P} \times P = 2(P - P_o)$$

and

$$p_{I_2} = \left(\frac{1-\alpha}{1+\alpha} \right) P = \frac{P_o}{P} \times P - \left(\frac{P - P_o}{P_o} \right)\left(\frac{P_o}{P} \right) P = 2P_o - P\,.$$

Hence,

$$K_p = \frac{p_I^2}{p_{I_2}} = \frac{[2(P - P_o)]^2}{2P_o - P}$$

$$= \frac{(2 \times 0.0276)^2}{0.2877} = 1.060 \times 10^{-2} \text{ atm}\,.$$

Example 6.4. At what pressure is only 1.0% I_2 not dlssociated to atoms at 800°C if $K_p = 1.060 \times 10^{-2}$ atm for the reaction

$$I_{2(g)} \rightleftharpoons 2\, I_{(g)} \qquad ?$$

If 1.0% is not dissociated, $\alpha = 0.990$; by (6.22),

$$P = K_p \left(\frac{1 - \alpha^2}{4\alpha^2}\right) = 1.060 \times 10^{-2} \left(\frac{1 - 0.9801}{4 \times 0.9801}\right) = 5.38 \times 10^{-5} \text{ atm} .$$

6.4 Free Energy and the Equilibrium Constant

When reactants and products are in well-defined thermodynamic states at the same temperature but at various nonstandard activities and fugacities, the evaluation of the increase in Gibbs free energy for the isothermal reaction can be calculated by a combination of methods already known. Let the reaction be: a moles of A at any fugacity f'_A and b of B at f'_B become d moles of D at any fugacity f'_D and e of E at f'_E. That is,

$$a\,A + b\,B \rightarrow d\,D + e\,E . \qquad (6.23)$$
$$\quad f'_A \quad\quad f'_B \quad\quad f'_D \quad\quad f'_E$$

The state diagram of this reaction as it is thought to occur through the standard states of reactants and products is the following.

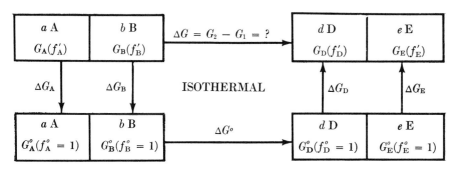

By (5.18) and (5.20), the Gibbs free energy of the final state is

$$G_2 = d\mu_D + e\mu_E$$
$$= dRT \ln f'_D + d\mu^o_D + eRT \ln f'_E + e\mu^o_E .$$

Similarly, for the initial state,

$$G_1 = a\mu_A + b\mu_B$$
$$= aRT \ln f'_A + a\mu^o_A + bRT \ln f'_B + b\mu^o_B .$$

Whence, for the over-all change of (6.23),

$$\Delta G = G_2 - G_1$$

$$= RT \ln \left(\frac{f_D'^d f_E'^e}{f_A'^a f_B'^b} \right) + \Delta G^o \tag{6.24}$$

where

$$\Delta G^o = (d\mu_D^o + e\mu_E^o) - (a\mu_A^o + b\mu_B^o) .$$

As in (6.5), let

$$Q_e(T) = \frac{f_D'^d f_E'^e}{f_A'^a f_B'^b} . \tag{6.25}$$

On substitution of (6.25) into (6.24), the latter becomes (6.26),

$$\Delta G = \Delta G^o + RT \ln Q_e . \tag{6.26}$$

The same result is obtained when each reactant is brought individually to the standard state and is allowed to react to give products in their standard state, each product then being brought individually to its real final state. By the methods of Section 4.24, for the state diagram above

$$\left. \begin{aligned}
\Delta G_A &= aG_A^o - aG_A = aRT \ln \left(\frac{1}{f_A'} \right) \\[2ex]
\Delta G_B &= bG_B^o - bG_B = bRT \ln \left(\frac{1}{f_B'} \right) \\[2ex]
\Delta G_D &= dG_D - dG_D^o = dRT \ln \left(\frac{f_D'}{1} \right) \\[2ex]
\Delta G_E &= eG_E - eG_E^o = eRT \ln \left(\frac{f_E'}{1} \right) .
\end{aligned} \right\} \tag{6.27}$$

and

But

$$\left. \begin{aligned}
\Delta G &= (dG_D + eG_E) - (aG_A + bG_B) \\
\Delta G^o &= (dG_D^o + eG_E^o) - (aG_A^o + bG_B^o) .
\end{aligned} \right\} \tag{6.28}$$

Substitution of Equations (6.28) into the summation of Equations (6.27) yields (6.24).

$$\Delta G - \Delta G^o = RT \ln \left(\frac{f_D'^d f_E'^e}{f_A'^a f_B'^b} \right) . \tag{6.24}$$

With this equation ΔG can be calculated for any isothermal change for which ΔG^o and the fugacities f_i' of reactants and products are known. When reactants and products are in their standard states, f_i' is unity for all i and $\Delta G = \Delta G^o$.

If the initial and final states are in equilibrium, ΔG in (6.26) is zero if only expansion work is involved; hence, f_i' becomes f_i, Q_e becomes K_e, and

$$0 = \Delta G^o + RT \ln K_e$$

$$\Delta G^o = -RT \ln K_e. \tag{6.29}$$

Equation (6.29), anticipated in Section 6.1, relates ΔG^o and K_e at the fixed temperature T.

Equations analogous to (6.24), (6.25), (6.26), and (6.29) can be derived in a similar way for the reaction

$$a\,A + b\,B \rightarrow d\,D + e\,E, \tag{6.30}$$

$$a_A' \qquad a_B' \qquad a_D' \qquad a_E'$$

where a_i' is the arbitrary activity of species i. By the same methods as above, with a_i' in place of f_i',

$$\Delta G = \Delta G^o + RT \ln \left(\frac{a_D'^d a_E'^e}{a_A'^a a_B'^b}\right) \tag{6.31}$$

$$Q_a(T) = \frac{a_D'^d a_E'^e}{a_A'^a a_B'^b} \tag{6.32}$$

$$\Delta G = \Delta G^o + RT \ln Q_a \tag{6.33}$$

and $$\Delta G^o = -RT \ln K_a. \tag{6.34}$$

The method of evaluating ΔG^o at the standard temperature of 25°C from the heats of formation of Table 3.3 and the standard absolute entropies of Table 4.1 was described in Section 4.21 for physical and chemical processes. Equations (6.29) and (6.34) then yield values of K_e and K_a, or the approximate equilibrium constants K_p and K_c, at 25°C for any change involving species listed in these tables. When a particular change involves both gases and pure condensed phases, the numerical value of the equilibrium constant is correct when the fugacities or pressures of gases are given in atmospheres and when activities of pure condensed phases are unity. Similarly, for reactions involving solutes with standard states referred to the hypothetical one molal reference value, molality is the correct unit of activity or concentration for use in K_a or Q_a, even when pure species and gases are involved in the same reaction.

Example 6.5. From Tables 3.3 and 4.1, calculate the vapor pressure of water at 25°C.

The reaction of interest is $H_2O_{(l)} \rightleftharpoons H_2O_{(g)}$. In Example 4.18, ΔG^o was found to be 2,054.7 cal. The equilibrium constant for this reaction is $K = f_{H_2O}/a_{H_2O} = f_{H_2O}$ for the activity of pure liquid water at 1 atm is unity. If the change in the activity of water with pressure is ignored and if water vapor is a perfect gas, $K = K_p = p_{H_2O}$. By (6.29),

$$\ln K_p = -\frac{\Delta G^\circ}{RT}$$

$$\log p_{H_2O} = -\frac{2054.7}{2.3026 \times 1.9872 \times 298.16} = -1.5061 = 8.4939 - 10$$

$$p_{H_2O} = 0.03118 \text{ atm} = 23.70 \text{ mm Hg} .$$

The observed value is 23.756 mm Hg. (Lange's *Handbook of Chemistry*. New York: McGraw-Hill Book Company, Inc., 1956, p. 1459.)

Example 6.6. Account for the factor of four by which Equations (6.19) and (6.22) differ.

$$AB \rightleftharpoons A + B, \qquad K_p = \frac{\alpha^2 P}{1 - \alpha^2} \tag{6.19}$$

$$A_2 \rightleftharpoons 2\,A, \qquad K_p = \frac{4\alpha^2 P}{1 - \alpha^2} . \tag{6.22}$$

The difference between these two situations may be real or it may arise from the attitude of the experimenter. A chemist would ordinarily recognize the difference between PCl_3 and Cl_2 as generated from PCl_5, but would ordinarily classify all iodine atoms from I_2 as indistinguishable. On the other hand, a physicist may wish to distinguish between radioactive I^{129} and stable I^{127} as they come from $I^{127}I^{129}$ and, on the other hand, care very little, when he makes measurements of the anomalous pressures exhibited by pure gaseous PCl_5 at elevated temperatures, whether PCl_3 differs chemically from Cl_2.

Although the experimental value of K_e may come from a system containing reactants and products, the value of ΔG° given by

$$\Delta G^\circ = -RT \ln K_e \tag{6.29}$$

is the increase in Gibbs free energy when pure reactants at unit fugacity are transformed entirely into pure products each at unit fugacity. For the experimenter who distinguishes B from A,

$$\Delta G^\circ_{AB} = -RT \ln \left(\frac{\alpha^2 P}{1 - \alpha^2} \right) .$$

For the one who does not distinguish B from A,

$$\Delta G^\circ_{A_2} = -RT \ln \left(\frac{\alpha^2 P}{1 - \alpha^2} \right) - RT \ln 4 .$$

When the latter experimenter decides that B is to be distinguished from A, he must sort out the mixture of A and B that he once regarded as pure A because of ignorance or an established convention.

The entropy of mixing 1 mole A and 1 mole of similar but distinguishable B is $2\,\overline{\Delta S}$, where

$$\overline{\Delta S} = -R \sum_{i=1}^{\mathbf{C}} N_i \ln N_i . \tag{5.46}$$

Since the mole fraction of each is $\frac{1}{2}$,

$$2\overline{\Delta S} = -2R[\tfrac{1}{2} \ln \tfrac{1}{2} + \tfrac{1}{2} \ln \tfrac{1}{2}] = -2R \ln \tfrac{1}{2} = R \ln 4 .$$

The entropy of purifying A and B is then $-R \ln 4$. Since the enthalpy of mixing or separating species of an ideal solution is zero (see Problem 5.51), the free energy of purification at the temperature T is just $-T \Delta S$, or $RT \ln 4$. Both experimenters reach the same value of ΔG^o_{AB} when both distinguish B from A, for

$$\Delta G^o_{AB} = \Delta G^o_{A_2} + RT \ln 4 .$$

Example 6.7. Calculate the solubility product constant of AgCl at 25°C. From the data of Tables 3.3 and 4.1, for the reaction

$$AgCl_{(s)} \rightleftharpoons Ag^+_{(aq)} + Cl^-_{(aq)}$$

$$\Delta G^o = \Delta H^o - T \Delta S^o \tag{4.150}$$

$$\Delta H^o = 25.31 + (-40.02) - (-30.36) = 15{,}650 \text{ cal}$$

$$\Delta S^o = 17.67 + 13.17 - 22.97 = 7.87 \text{ cal deg}^{-1}$$

$$\Delta G^o = 15{,}650 - 298.2 \times 7.87 = 13{,}300 \text{ cal}$$

$$\ln K_a = -\frac{\Delta G^o}{RT} \tag{6.34}$$

$$\log K_a = -\frac{13{,}300}{2.303 \times 1.987 \times 298.2} = -9.75 = 0.25 - 10$$

$$K_a = 1.8 \times 10^{-10} .$$

Example 6.8. Calculate the increase in free energy for the reaction

$$Zn_{(s)} + 2 H^+_{(aq)} \rightarrow H_{2(g)} + Zn^{++}_{(aq)} .$$

Activity:	1.00	0.100	0.200	0.100
ΔH^o_f (kcal)	0.00	0.00	0.00	-36.43
S^o (cal deg^{-1})	9.95	0.00	31.21	-25.45

The thermodynamic data are from F. D. Rossini, *et al.*, Circular of the National Bureau of Standards 500 (1952).

$$\Delta H^o = -36{,}430 \text{ cal}$$

$$\Delta S^o = -4.19 \text{ cal deg}^{-1}$$

As in (4.150),

$$\Delta G^o = \Delta H^o - T \Delta S^o$$

$$= -36{,}430 - 298.2(-4.19) = -35{,}180 \text{ cal} .$$

As in (6.25) and (6.32),

$$Q = \frac{a'_{Zn^{++}} f'_{H_2}}{a'_{Zn} a'^2_{H^+}} = \frac{0.100 \times 0.200}{1 \times 0.100^2} = 2 .$$

As in (6.26) and (6.33),

$$\Delta G = \Delta G^o + RT \ln Q$$

$$= -35{,}180 + 1.987 \times 298.2 \times 0.6932$$

$$= -35{,}180 + 411 = -34{,}770 \text{ cal} .$$

6.5 Standard Free Energy

Just as it was convenient to establish for compounds and ions a table of enthalpies of formation from elements, it is also convenient to establish a table of free energies of formation. Again the elements in their stable states at 1 atm are the standards of reference with zero free energy of formation. The value of ΔG_f^o, the free energy of formation or the standard free energy of a substance, is the free energy increase of the reaction in which the substance in its standard state at 25°C is formed from the elements in their standard states at 25°C.

Values of ΔG^o for any reaction can be found from these standard free energies in the same way that values of ΔH^o for any reaction have long been found from enthalpies of formation. The standard free energies of reactants are subtracted from the standard free energies of products. For the reaction in which A and B in their standard states at 25°C become D and E in their standard states at 25°C, namely,

$$a\,A + b\,B \rightarrow d\,D + e\,E \tag{6.35}$$

the increase in free energy ΔG^o is given by (6.36).

$$\Delta G^o = [d\,\Delta G_f^o(D) + e\,\Delta G_f^o(E)] - [a\,\Delta G_f^o(A) + b\,\Delta G_f^o(B)]. \tag{6.36}$$

Table 6.1 contains a list of standard free energies at 25°C.

Table 6.1. *Standard Free Energies ΔG_f^o at 25°C** (*kilocalories per gram formula weight*)

SUBSTANCE	ΔG^o_f	SUBSTANCE	ΔG^o_f	SUBSTANCE	ΔG^o_f
$OH^-_{(aq)}$	-37.595	$CO_{(g)}$	-32.8079	$CrO_4^{--}{}_{(aq)}$	-168.8
$H_2O_{(g)}$	-54.6357	$CO_{2(g)}$	-94.2598	$Cr_2O_7^{--}{}_{(aq)}$	-300.5
$H_2O_{(l)}$	-56.6902	$CH_3OH_{(l)}$	-39.73	$HCrO_4^-{}_{(aq)}$	-177.5
$F^-_{(aq)}$	-66.08	$C_2H_5OH_{(l)}$	-41.77	$H_2CrO_{4(aq)}$	-178.5
$HF_{(g)}$	-64.7	$Pb^{++}{}_{(aq)}$	-5.81	$Ag_2CrO_{4(s)}$	-148.57
$Cl^-_{(aq)}$	-31.350	$PbS_{(s)}$	-22.15	$Al_2O_{3(s)}(\alpha)$	-376.77
$HCl_{(g)}$	-22.769	$Zn^{++}{}_{(aq)}$	-35.184	$BaCl_{2(s)}$	-193.8
$I^-_{(aq)}$	-12.35	$ZnS_{(s)}$	-47.4	$BaCl_2.H_2O_{(s)}$	-253.1
$I_{2(g)}$	4.63	$Ag^+_{(aq)}$	18.430	$BaCl_2.2\ H_2O_{(s)}$	-309.7
$HI_{(g)}$	0.31	$Ag_2O_{(s)}$	-2.586	$Na^+_{(aq)}$	-62.589
$S^{--}{}_{(aq)}{}^*$	20.6	$AgCl_{(s)}$	-26.224	$Na_2CO_{3(s)}$	-250.4
$H_2S_{(g)}$	-7.892	$AgI_{(s)}$	-15.85	$NaHCO_{3(s)}$	-203.6
$H_2S_{(aq)}$	-6.54	$OsO_{4(g)}$	-67.9	$KF_{(s)}$	-127.42
$NO_{(g)}$	20.719	$OsO_{4(s)}(I)$	-70.5	$KCl_{(s)}$	-97.592
$NH_{3(g)}$	-3.976	$OsO_{4(s)}(II)$	-70.7	$KClO_{3(s)}$	-69.29
$NH_{3(aq)}$	-6.37	$Fe_2O_{3(s)}$	-177.1	$KBr_{(s)}$	-90.63
$NH_4^+{}_{(aq)}$	-19.00	$Fe_3O_{4(s)}$	-242.4	$KI_{(s)}$	-77.03

* All values except that of $S^{--}{}_{(aq)}$ are from Rossini, F. D., D. D. Wagman, W. H. Evans, S. Levine, and I. Jaffe, *Selected Values of Chemical Thermodynamic Properties.* Washington, D. C.: Circular of the National Bureau of Standards 500 (1952). The value for $S^{--}{}_{(aq)}$ is that given by Waggoner, W. H., *Journal of Chemical Education*, **35,** 339 (1958).

The values of Table 6.1 were determined by several experimental methods and the best value has been listed. One such method is to measure the equilibrium constant K_e or K_a and calculate ΔG^o by (6.29) or (6.34). Another method is to measure heats of reaction and absolute entropies calorimetrically, as was done in preparing Tables 3.3 and 4.1, and from such values to calculate ΔG^o as in the preceding section. If a few of the values of ΔG^o found in these ways are themselves free energies of formation, then the many other values of ΔG^o for reactions that do not involve elements can be analyzed into parts attributable to the compounds that partake in the reactions. The values of Table 6.1 are a consistent set of so-called best values chosen from among several differing values determined by various methods. With Table 6.1 it is possible to calculate the increase in Gibbs free energy or the equilibrium constant of any reaction that involves the substances listed and their elements. An important goal of equilibrium chemistry is a table containing entries of ΔH_f^o, S^o, and ΔG_f^o for every conceivable substance. Such a table would be most useful in predicting possible reactions and the extent to which they could go. Whether or not the predicted possible change will occur slowly or rapidly is, however, a matter for chemical kinetics, for equilibrium thermodynamics is not concerned with time.

Example 6.9. Calculate the free energy of formation ΔG_f^o of NO from Tables 3.3 and 4.1.

The reaction of interest is

$$N_{2(g)} + O_{2(g)} \to 2\,NO_{(g)} .$$

ΔH_f^o(kcal) 0.000	0.000	2(21.600)
S^o(cal deg^{-1}) 45.767	49.003	2(50.339)

$$\Delta H^o = 2(21,600) = 43,200 \text{ cal}$$

$$\Delta S^o = 2(50.339) - (49.003 + 45.767) = 5.908 \text{ cal deg}^{-1}$$

$$\Delta G^o = 43,200 - 298.2(5.908) = 41,438 \text{ cal} .$$

For 1 mole $NO_{(g)}$, $\Delta G_f^o = 20.719$ kcal, which is the entry in Table 6.1.

Example 6.10. Over what range of humidity is $BaCl_2 \cdot H_2O_{(s)}$ stable at 25°C?

At a constant temperature of 25°C in a two-component system $(C = 2)$ of $BaCl_2$ and H_2O,

$$F = C - P + 1 . \tag{5.29}$$

If only one solid phase is present with the gaseous phase $(P = 2)$, there is one degree of freedom $(F = 1)$, the partial pressure of water vapor. If two solid phases were present, the partial pressure of H_2O would be fixed $(F = 0)$. The extreme pressures that limit the range of stability of $BaCl_2 \cdot H_2O_{(s)}$ are those established at equilibrium by the reactions

$$BaCl_2 \cdot H_2O_{(s)} \rightleftharpoons BaCl_{2(s)} + H_2O_{(g)}$$

and

$$BaCl_2 \cdot 2\,H_2O_{(s)} \rightleftharpoons BaCl_2 \cdot H_2O_{(s)} + H_2O_{(g)} .$$

For the former reaction, by (6.36) and Table 6.1,

$$\Delta G^\circ = (-193.8 - 54.6) - (-253.1) = 4.7 \text{ kcal.}$$

The equilibrium constant is merely p_{H_2O} since the activities of the pure condensed phases are unity. By (6.29),

$$\log p_{H_2O} = -\frac{\Delta G^\circ}{2.303RT} = -\frac{4.7 \times 10^3}{2.303 \times 1.987 \times 298.2} = -3.4 = 0.6 - 4.0$$

$$p_{H_2O} = 4 \times 10^{-4} \text{ atm.}$$

Similarly, for the latter reaction,

$$\Delta G^\circ = (-253.1 - 54.6) - (-309.7) = 2.0 \text{ kcal}$$

$$\log p_{H_2O} = -\frac{2.0 \times 10^3}{2.303 \times 1.987 \times 298.2} = -1.5 = 0.5 - 2.0$$

$$p_{H_2O} = 3 \times 10^{-2} \text{ atm .}$$

Since the vapor pressure of water is 3.1×10^{-2} atm, the limits on relative humidity are almost 100% and $100 \times [(4 \times 10^{-4})/(3.1 \times 10^{-2})] = 1.3\%$.

Example 6.11. Can PbS precipitate from an aqueous solution in which the lead ion molality is 1.0×10^{-2} and the sulfide ion molality is fixed at 1.0×10^{-22} by saturating the solution with H_2S in the presence of a suitable buffer?

The reaction of interest is

$$\text{Pb}^{++}_{(aq)} + \text{S}^{--}_{(aq)} \rightarrow \text{PbS}_{(s)} .$$

By (6.36), for this reaction

$$\Delta G^\circ = -22.15 - (-5.81 + 20.6) = -37.0 \text{ kcal .}$$

By (6.31),

$$\Delta G = -37,000 + 1.987 \times 298.2 \times 2.303 \times \log\left(\frac{1}{1.0 \times 10^{-2} \times 1.0 \times 10^{-22}}\right)$$

$$= -37,000 + 32,800 = -4200 \text{ cal .}$$

Since ΔG is less than zero, the reaction is spontaneous and $\text{PbS}_{(s)}$ can precipitate.

This result can be confirmed by showing that the product of the initial ionic concentrations exceeds the solubility product constant K_{sp}, which can be calculated from ΔG° for the reaction

$$\text{PbS}_{(s)} \rightleftharpoons \text{Pb}^{++}_{(aq)} + \text{S}^{--}_{(aq)} .$$

By (6.34),
$$\log K_{sp} = -\frac{\Delta G^\circ}{2.303RT} = -\frac{+37.0 \times 10^3}{2.303 \times 1.987 \times 298.2}$$

$$= -27.1 = 0.9 - 28.0$$

$$K_{sp} = 8 \times 10^{-28} .$$

But the product of the initial concentrations is 1.0×10^{-24}, about 1000 times in excess of K_{sp}. Precipitation is possible.

B. NONISOTHERMAL CHANGES

6.6 Free Energy as a Function of Temperature

The dependence upon temperature of the increment in free energy for a change that occurs at constant pressure was developed in detail in Section 4.22, but the application of the theoretical developments of that section to chemical changes was reserved to this chapter. The superscript on ΔG^o then referred to the standard temperature T_o. Now, however, this superscript refers to the standard state at 1 atm regardless of the temperature. Because of this ambiguity of notation and the importance of the subject, the equations for ΔG^o, where $\Delta G^o = -RT \ln K$, are now to be developed in notation that befits this chapter.

At 1 atm, as in (4.155),

$$-\left[\frac{\partial}{\partial T} \left(\frac{\Delta G^o}{T} \right) \right] = \frac{\Delta H^o}{T^2}. \tag{6.37}$$

If ΔH^o, the increase in enthalpy of the system as reactants in their standard states become products in their standard states, is known as a function of temperature, (6.37) is readily integrated to give (6.38), which is like (4.156).

$$-\int_{\Delta G_1^o/T_1}^{\Delta G^o/T} d\left(\frac{\Delta G^o}{T} \right)' = \int_{T_1}^{T} \frac{\Delta H^o}{T'^2} \, dT'$$

$$-\frac{\Delta G^o}{T} + \frac{\Delta G_1^o}{T_1} = \int_{T_1}^{T} \frac{\Delta H^o}{T'^2} \, dT'. \tag{6.38}$$

At the definite reference temperature T_1, the increase in Gibbs free energy is ΔG_1^o.

Over small temperature ranges ΔT, it is often sufficient to assume that a large ΔH^o is essentially constant since chemical energies are commonly great relative to the integral of a small ΔC_P over the small temperature range ΔT. Then, as in (4.157),

$$-\frac{\Delta G^o}{T} + \frac{\Delta G_1^o}{T_1} = -\Delta H_1^o \left(\frac{1}{T} - \frac{1}{T_1} \right)$$

$$= \frac{\Delta H_1^o (T - T_1)}{T T_1} \tag{6.39}$$

where ΔH_1^o is the increase in enthalpy at T_1, T, and all intermediate temperatures.

If the experimental accuracy and the magnitudes of ΔC_P and ΔT justify expressing ΔH^o as a function of temperature, then as in (3.100), (4.158), and (4.159)

$$\Delta H^\circ = \Delta H_1^\circ + \int_{T_1}^{T} \Delta C_P \, dT'$$

$$= \Delta H_1^\circ + \int_{T_1}^{T} [\Delta C_P^{(0)} + \Delta C_P^{(1)} T' + \Delta C_P^{(2)} T'^2 + \cdots] \, dT'$$

$$= \Delta H_1^\circ + \Delta C_P^{(0)}(T - T_1) + \tfrac{1}{2} \Delta C_P^{(1)}(T^2 - T_1^2) + \tfrac{1}{3} \Delta C_P^{(2)}(T^3 - T_1^3) + \cdots$$

That is,

$$\Delta H^\circ = \Delta H_o^\circ + \Delta C_P^{(0)} T + \tfrac{1}{2} \Delta C_P^{(1)} T^2 + \tfrac{1}{3} \Delta C_P^{(2)} T^3 + \cdots \qquad (6.40)$$

where ΔH_o° is an integration constant of the form

$$\Delta H_o^\circ = \Delta H_1^\circ - \Delta C_P^{(0)} T_1 - \tfrac{1}{2} \Delta C_P^{(1)} T_1^2 - \tfrac{1}{3} \Delta C_P^{(2)} T_1^3 - \cdots \qquad (6.41)$$

Substitution of (6.40) into (6.38) yields (6.42), which is like (4.160).

$$-\frac{\Delta G^\circ}{T} + \frac{\Delta G_1^\circ}{T_1} = \int_{T_1}^{T} \frac{[\Delta H_o^\circ + \Delta C_P^{(0)} T' + \tfrac{1}{2} \Delta C_P^{(1)} T'^2 + \tfrac{1}{3} \Delta C_P^{(2)} T'^3 + \cdots]}{T'^2} \, dT'$$

$$= \Delta H_o^\circ \left(\frac{T - T_1}{TT_1}\right) + \Delta C_P^{(0)} \ln \left(\frac{T}{T_1}\right) + \frac{\Delta C_P^{(1)}}{2}(T - T_1)$$

$$+ \frac{\Delta C_P^{(2)}}{6}(T^2 - T_1^2) + \cdots$$

$$\Delta G^\circ = \frac{T \Delta G_1^\circ}{T_1} - \frac{\Delta H_o^\circ(T - T_1)}{T_1}$$

$$- \Delta C_P^{(0)} T \ln \left(\frac{T}{T_1}\right) - \frac{\Delta C_P^{(1)}}{2} T(T - T_1)$$

$$- \frac{\Delta C_P^{(2)}}{6} T(T^2 - T_1^2) - \cdots \qquad (6.42)$$

Like ΔG°, the equilibrium constant K is a function of temperature. At any temperature T,

$$\Delta G^\circ = -RT \ln K . \qquad (6.43)$$

At the reference temperature T_1,

$$\Delta G_1^\circ = -RT_1 \ln K_1 . \qquad (6.44)$$

Equations (6.43) and (6.44) may be substituted into (6.39) or (6.42) in order to obtain K at any temperature from K_1 known at T_1. When ΔH° is assumed to be constant throughout the temperature interval T_1 to T_2, the dependence of K on T is obtained directly thus. For perfect gases, (6.29) says

$$-\frac{\Delta G^\circ}{T} = R \ln K_p .$$

Then, by (6.37)

$$\left[\frac{\partial}{\partial T}\left(-\frac{\Delta G^o}{T}\right)\right]_P = \frac{\Delta H^o}{T^2}$$

$$\left[\frac{\partial}{\partial T}\left(R \ln K_p\right)\right]_P = \frac{\Delta H^o}{T^2}$$

$$\left[\frac{\partial}{\partial T}\left(\ln K_p\right)\right]_P = \frac{\Delta H^o}{RT^2} \tag{6.45}$$

$$\int_{\ln K_{p_1}}^{\ln K_{p_2}} d(\ln K_p) = \int_{T_1}^{T_2} \frac{\Delta H^o}{RT^2} \, dT$$

$$\ln\left(\frac{K_{p_2}}{K_{p_1}}\right) = \frac{\Delta H^o(T_2 - T_1)}{RT_2 T_1}. \tag{6.46}$$

Equation (6.46) permits the calculation of K_p at T_2 when K_p is known at T_1 and when ΔH^o is constant between T_1 and T_2 or can be approximated suitably by an effective average value. Or, if K_p has been measured at two or more temperatures, an average value of ΔH^o can be found just as heats of vaporization are found from vapor pressures at several temperatures.

Analogous equations involving K_c are slightly different. By (6.15),

$$\ln K_p = \ln K_c + \Delta n_{(g)} \ln RT.$$

Whence

$$\frac{\partial \ln K_p}{\partial T} = \frac{\partial \ln K_c}{\partial T} + \frac{\Delta n_{(g)}}{T}.$$

By (6.45),

$$\frac{\Delta H^o}{RT^2} = \frac{\partial \ln K_c}{\partial T} + \frac{\Delta n_{(g)}}{T}$$

$$\frac{\partial \ln K_c}{\partial T} = \frac{\Delta H^o - \Delta n_{(g)} RT}{RT^2}.$$

But by (3.61)

$$\Delta H^o - \Delta n_{(g)} RT = \Delta E^o.$$

Hence,

$$\frac{\partial \ln K_c}{\partial T} = \frac{\Delta E^o}{RT^2}. \tag{6.47}$$

On definite integration with ΔE^o constant,

$$\int_{\ln K_{c_1}}^{\ln K_{c_2}} d(\ln K_c) = \int_{T_1}^{T_2} \frac{\Delta E^o}{RT^2} \, dT$$

$$\ln\left(\frac{K_{c_2}}{K_{c_1}}\right) = \frac{\Delta E^o(T_2 - T_1)}{RT_1 T_2}. \tag{6.48}$$

365

Equations like (6.47) and (6.48) are true even for changes that do not involve gases. When K_c applies to condensed phases, even at constant pressure the volume is almost constant and $\Delta E^\circ \approx \Delta H^\circ$.

Example 6.12. Gaseous iodine dissociates to atoms at high temperatures to such an extent that measurable deviations from the expected pressures are observed [M. L. Perlman and G. K. Rollefson, *Journal of Chemical Physics*, 9, 362 (1941)]. Observed pressures P and expected pressures P_o if there were no dissociation are listed below for several absolute temperatures. If the total pressure differences are due to dissociation, from these data calculate (a) the heat of dissociation of I_2, and (b) the standard free energy of an iodine atom at 25°C.

Absolute Temperature (°K)	Expected P_o (atm)	Observed P (atm)	K_p (atm)
973	0.0576	0.0624	0.175×10^{-2}
1073	0.0631	0.0750	1.108×10^{-2}
1173	0.0684	0.0918	4.87×10^{-2}
1274	0.0736	0.1122	17.05×10^{-2}

(a) The values of K_p in the table above have been calculated by the method of Example 6.3. Figure 6.1 is the plot of the logarithm of K_p vs. the reciprocal of T. The slope of the line is -8200. Since the equation of the line is of the form

$$\log K_p = -\frac{\Delta H}{2.303RT} + \frac{C_o}{2.303}$$

it follows that

$$\Delta H = -2.303R \text{ (slope)} = 37{,}500 \text{ cal}$$

for the reaction that corresponds to K_p, namely,

$$I_{2(g)} \rightleftharpoons 2\,I_{(g)}.$$

The true value at absolute zero as derived spectroscopically is 35.55 kcal (A. G. Gaydon, *Dissociation Energies and Spectra of Diatomic Molecules*. London: Chapman & Hall, Ltd., 1947, pp. 65, 209).

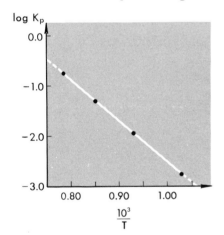

Fig. 6.1. *Logarithm of K_p for Dissociation of Iodine as a Function of Reciprocal Temperature.*

(b) ΔC_p for this reaction is about $\frac{3}{2}R$, since C_p of a perfect monatomic gas is $\frac{5}{2}R$ and is $\frac{7}{2}R$ for a perfect diatomic gas that is rigid. By (3.100) or (6.40),

$$\Delta H^\circ = \Delta H_o^\circ + \Delta C_P T$$
$$37{,}500 = \Delta H_o^\circ + \tfrac{3}{2}R \times 1000$$
$$\Delta H_o^\circ = 34{,}500$$

where an average temperature of $1000°K$ has been assumed to correspond to the graphical $\Delta H°$. At $T_1 = 1000°K$, $\log K_{p_1} = -2.52$ and

$$\Delta G_1^o = -RT_1 \ln K_{p1}$$
$$= -1.987 \times 1000 \times 2.303 \times (-2.52)$$
$$= +11,500 \text{ cal}.$$

By (6.42), with $\Delta C_P^{(1)} = \Delta C_P^{(2)} = 0$ and $T = 298.2$,

$$\Delta G^o = \frac{298.2 \times 11,500}{1000} - \frac{34,500(298.2 - 1000)}{1000}$$
$$- \frac{3}{2} R \times 298.2 \times 2.303 \times \log\left(\frac{298.2}{1000}\right)$$
$$= 3440 + 24,200 + 1080 = 28,720 \text{ cal}.$$

Since the standard free energy of $I_{2(g)}$ at $25°C$ is 4.63 kcal,

$$\Delta G^o = 2 \Delta G_f^o[I_{(g)}] - \Delta G_f^o[I_{2(g)}]$$
$$28.72 = 2 \Delta G_f^o[I_{(g)}] - 4.63$$
$$\Delta G_f^o[I_{(g)}] = 16.68 \text{ kcal mole}^{-1}.$$

The value reported in Circular 500 of the National Bureau of Standards is 16.766 kcal mole^{-1}.

Example 6.13. What partial pressure of NO is expected in air at equilibrium at $2000°K$? Assume that ΔC_P is zero.

For the reaction of interest at $25°C$,

$$N_{2(g)} + O_{2(g)} \rightleftharpoons 2 NO_{(g)}$$
$$\Delta H^o = 2 \Delta H_f^o(NO) = 2 \times 21,600 = 43,200 \text{ cal}$$

and $\qquad \Delta G^o = 2 \Delta G_f^o(NO) = 2 \times 20,719 = 41,438 \text{ cal}.$

Hence, at $25°C$,

$$\log K_p = -\frac{\Delta G^o}{2.303RT} = -\frac{41,438}{2.303 \times 1.987 \times 298.2}$$
$$= -30.37 = 0.63 - 31.00$$
$$K_p = 4.3 \times 10^{-31}.$$

By (6.46),

$$\log\left(\frac{K_p}{4.3 \times 10^{-31}}\right) = \frac{43,200(2000 - 298)}{2.303 \times 1.987 \times 2000 \times 298.2} = 26.95$$
$$K_p = 8.9 \times 10^{26} \times 4.3 \times 10^{-31} = 3.8 \times 10^{-4} \text{ at } 2000°K.$$

Let p_{NO} be the equilibrium partial pressure of NO at $2000°K$. Then, since 2 NO are formed for every N_2 or O_2 that reacts, the partial pressure of N_2 is $0.800 - (\frac{1}{2})p_{NO}$

and that of O_2 is $0.200 - (\frac{1}{2})p_{NO}$. The equilibrium constant relation serves to fix p_{NO} thus:

$$K_p = 3.8 \times 10^{-4} = \frac{p_{NO}^2}{\left(0.800 - \dfrac{p_{NO}}{2}\right)\left(0.200 - \dfrac{p_{NO}}{2}\right)}.$$

Since $p_{NO} \ll 0.4$, an approximate solution is readily found.

$$p_{NO}^2 \approx 3.8 \times 10^{-4} \times 0.80 \times 0.20 = 61 \times 10^{-6}$$

$$p_{NO} \approx 7.8 \times 10^{-3} (\ll 400 \times 10^{-3} = 0.4).$$

The partial pressure of NO is only 7.8×10^{-3} atm. A more accurate value is 7.837×10^{-3} atm [E. van Beek-Visser, *Journal of Chemical Physics*, **29**, 1358 (1958)].

Example 6.14. An excess of crystals of both pure ammonium thiohydroxide and pure ammonium carbamate are introduced into a vessel containing only pure gaseous hydrogen sulfide and pure gaseous carbon dioxide. These solids are completely dissociated in the gas phase thus:

$$NH_4SH_{(s)} \rightleftharpoons NH_{3(g)} + H_2S_{(g)}$$

$$NH_4OCONH_{2(s)} \rightleftharpoons 2\,NH_{3(g)} + CO_{2(g)}$$

If no solid solutions are formed and if H_2S and CO_2 do not react chemically with each other, (a) calculate the smallest number of independent variables that must be specified at 25°C in order to define completely the thermodynamic state of the system; and (b) what is the partial pressure of NH_3 at 25°C if reasonable values of the required number of variables are specified? The standard molar free energies of $NH_4SH_{(s)}$ and $NH_4OCONH_{2(s)}$ may be assumed to be -13.181 kcal and -105.80 kcal at 25°C.

(a) The system consists of three phases ($\mathbf{P} = 3$), namely two solids and gas. Each solid can be made from NH_3 and either H_2S or CO_2; hence, NH_3, H_2S, and CO_2 are the three components ($\mathbf{C} = 3$). At 25°C, $\mathbf{F} = \mathbf{C} - \mathbf{P} + 1 = 1$. One intensive variable must be specified to fix the state of the system at 25°C.

(b) From $\Delta G^{\circ} = -RT \ln K_p$, the usual calculation yields a value of K_p for each reaction, namely

$$K_p = p_{NH_3} \times p_{H_2S} = 0.109$$

$$K_p = p_{NH_3}^2 \times p_{CO_2} = 0.00238.$$

Specification of any one of these three equilibrium partial pressures fixes the others at 25°C while both solids remain. If p_{NH_3} is itself specified, the solids will dissociate until this specified value is attained provided the initial pressures of CO_2 and H_2S are small enough that the values of K_p can be satisfied at equilibrium. A more suitable intensive variable is the ratio of p_{H_2S} to p_{CO_2} at equilibrium. Then

$$p_{NH_3} = \left(\frac{0.00238}{0.109}\right)\left(\frac{p_{H_2S}}{p_{CO_2}}\right).$$

Example 6.15. At what temperature can metallic iron be generated from $Fe_2O_{3(s)}$ by reduction with hydrogen, as suggested in Example 4.20?

If the reaction is

$$3\,H_{2(g)} + Fe_2O_{3(s)} = 2\,Fe_{(s)} + 3\,H_2O_{(g)}$$

then it was shown in Example 4.20 that $\Delta G_1^{\circ} = 13.2$ kcal and $\Delta H_1^{\circ} = 23.1$ kcal at $T_1 = 298.2°K$.

As a start, let the reaction be called possible if $\Delta G^\circ = 0$ and $K_p = 1$ at the temperature T. If $\Delta C_P = 0$, then $\Delta H^\circ = \Delta H_1^\circ = 23.1$ kcal at all T and

$$-\frac{\Delta G^\circ}{T} + \frac{\Delta G_1^\circ}{T_1} = \frac{\Delta H_1^\circ(T - T_1)}{TT_1} \tag{6.39}$$

$$0 + \frac{13{,}200}{298.2} = \frac{23{,}100\ (T - 298.2)}{298.2\,T}$$

$$T = 696°\text{K}.$$

The reason why high temperatures favor this reaction is that ΔS° is greater than zero. At $T_1 = 298.2°\text{K}$, $\Delta S^\circ = 33.2$ cal deg^{-1}, greater than zero mainly because oxygen atoms are transferred from a condensed phase to the gaseous phase while H and Fe atoms do not change their kind of phase. Since $\Delta S^\circ > 0$, the term $-T\,\Delta S^\circ$ decreases ΔG° more and more as T increases.

If $\Delta C_P = 0$, it follows that ΔS° is independent of T; for by (4.53) as it applies to initial and final states at some temperature T,

$$\left(\frac{\partial S}{\partial T}\right)_P = \frac{C_P}{T}$$

$$\left(\frac{\partial \Delta S^\circ}{\partial T}\right)_P = \frac{\Delta C_P}{T}.$$

In other words, since $\Delta G^\circ = \Delta H_1^\circ - T\,\Delta S_1^\circ$ at all T when $\Delta C_P = 0$, $\Delta G^\circ = 0$ when

$$0 = 23{,}100 - T \times 33.2$$

$$T = \frac{23{,}100}{33.2} = 696°\text{K}.$$

Actually, ΔC_P is approximately -10 cal mole-deg^{-1} so that ΔS° decreases as T increases. The term $-T\,\Delta S^\circ$ is accordingly less effective in decreasing ΔG° than supposed above.

The condition that ΔG° be zero is rather severe. Maintaining a high pressure of H_2 and a low pressure of H_2O, perhaps by passing dry H_2 over heated Fe_2O_3, favors reduction. If p'_{H_2} equals rp'_{H_2O}, then for the change

$$3\ H_{2(g)}(p'_{H_2}) + Fe_2O_{3(s)} = 2\ Fe_{(s)} + 3\ H_2O_{(g)}(p'_{H_2O})$$

it follows from (6.26) that

$$\Delta G = \Delta G^\circ + RT \ln \frac{(p'_{H_2O})^3}{(p'_{H_2})^3} = \Delta G^\circ - 3RT \ln r.$$

As r increases, ΔG decreases, just as ΔG° decreases because of $-T\,\Delta S^\circ$. When $\Delta G = 0$, $\Delta G^\circ = 3RT \ln r$. If $\Delta C_P = -10$ cal deg^{-1}, by (6.40)

$$\Delta H_o^\circ = \Delta H_1^\circ - \Delta C_P T_1 = 23{,}100 + 10 \times 298 = 26{,}100 \text{ cal}.$$

Then, by (6.42), with $\Delta G^\circ = 3RT \ln r$,

$$3RT \ln r = \frac{13{,}200\,T}{298.2} - \frac{26{,}100(T - 298.2)}{298.2} + 10T \ln\left(\frac{T}{298.2}\right).$$

That is, the operating temperature T and r are not both independent. Simplification yields

$$\log r = -3.15 + \frac{1900}{T} + 1.676 \log\left(\frac{T}{298.2}\right).$$

If $T = 696°K$, log $r = 0.20$ and $r = 1.6$. If $T = 500°K$, log $r = 1.03$ and $r = 10.7$.

Although these calculations indicate that the reaction is possible at modest temperatures, they do not indicate its rate.

6.7   Free Energy from Calorimetric Data

A very simple and powerful method of performing thermodynamic calculations at arbitrary temperatures most expeditiously utilizes the free energy function and the heat content function.[1]   To the Gibbs free energy, to the entropy, and to the enthalpy are assigned absolute values G_T^o, S_T^o, and H_T^o for the standard states at the temperature T.   At absolute zero, the value of the enthalpy is H_o^o and the value of the entropy S_o^o is, by the third law, zero.   The free energy function is defined as $(G_T^o - H_o^o)/T$ and the heat content function as $(H_T^o - H_o^o)/T$.   These functions can be calculated from observed heat capacities C_P and enthalpies of transition ΔH_{tr}^o thus.   By the definition of G in (4.81), $G_T^o = H_T^o - TS_T^o$.   Hence,

$$G_T^o - H_o^o = H_T^o - H_o^o - TS_T^o$$

$$\frac{G_T^o - H_o^o}{T} = \frac{H_T^o - H_o^o}{T} - S_T^o .\qquad(6.49)$$

Table 6.2.   *Selected Values of Free Energy Function at Various Temperatures**
[*Tabulated values of* $-(G_T^o - H_o^o)/T$ (*cal mole*$^{-1}$ *deg*$^{-1}$)]

SUBSTANCE	ABSOLUTE TEMPERATURE					
	0°K	298.16°K	500°K	1000°K	1500°K	2000°K
$O_{(g)}$	0	33.078	35.840	39.460	41.539	43.002
$H_{(g)}$	0	22.425	24.993	28.436	30.451	31.880
$N_{(g)}$	0	31.646	34.215	37.658	39.673	41.102
$C_{(g)}$	0	32.533	35.207	38.730	40.772	42.215
$O_{2(g)}$	0	42.016	45.675	50.697	53.808	56.103
$H_{2(g)}$	0	24.423	27.950	32.738	35.590	37.669
$H_2O_{(g)}$	0	37.172	41.295	47.018	50.622	53.38
$N_{2(g)}$	0	38.817	42.415	47.306	50.284	52.478
$NO_{(g)}$	0	42.980	46.760	51.864	54.964	57.239
C(graphite)	0	0.517	1.146	2.771	4.181	—
$CO_{(g)}$	0	40.350	43.947	48.860	51.864	54.078
$CO_{2(g)}$	0	43.555	47.663	54.109	58.481	61.85
$CH_{4(g)}$	0	36.46	40.75	47.65	52.84	—
$C_2H_{6(g)}$	0	45.27	50.77	61.11	69.46	—
$C_2H_{4(g)}$	0	43.98	48.74	57.29	63.94	—
$C_2H_{2(g)}$	0	39.976	44.508	52.005	57.231	—
$C_6H_{6(g)}$	0	52.93	60.24	76.57	90.45	—

* Rossini, F. D., K. S. Pitzer, W. J. Taylor, J. P. Ebert, J. E. Kilpatrick, C. W. Beckett, M. G. Williams, and H. G. Werner, *Selected Values of Properties of Hydrocarbons.* Washington, D. C.: Circular of the National Bureau of Standards C 461, U. S. Government Printing Office (1947).

The quantity S_T^o is the absolute standard entropy of the substance at the temperature T. Values of S_T^o at $T = 298.16$ have been given in Table 4.1, and at any temperature, as in (4.74),

$$S_T^o = \int_0^{T_{tr}} \frac{C_P^{(\alpha)}}{T} dT + \frac{\Delta H_{tr}}{T_{tr}} + \int_{T_{tr}}^{T_f} \frac{C_P^{(\beta)}}{T} dT + \frac{\Delta H_f}{T_f}$$

$$+ \int_{T_f}^{T_v} \frac{C_P^{(1)}}{T} dT + \frac{\Delta H_v}{T_v} + \int_{T_v}^{T} \frac{C_P^{(g)}}{T'} dT' . \quad (6.50)$$

Similarly, since $H_T^o - H_o^o$ represents the increase in enthalpy suffered by a system as its temperature rises from the reference temperature at $T = 0$ to the temperature T at 1 atm, the second term of (6.49) is

$$\frac{H_T^o - H_o^o}{T} = \frac{1}{T} \left[\int_0^{T_{tr}} C_P^{(\alpha)} dT + \Delta H_{tr} + \int_{T_{tr}}^{T_f} C_P^{(\beta)} dT + \Delta H_f \right.$$

$$\left. + \int_{T_f}^{T_v} C_P^{(1)} dT + \Delta H_v + \int_{T_v}^{T} C_P^{(g)} dT' \right]. \quad (6.51)$$

Table 6.3. *Selected Values of Heat Content Function at Various Temperatures and Selected Values of Heats of Formation ΔH_o^o at Absolute Zero**

[*Tabulated values of* ΔH_o^o *(kcal mole^{-1}) and* $(H_T^o - H_o^o)/T$ *(cal mole^{-1} deg^{-1})*]

SUBSTANCE	ΔH_o^o	ABSOLUTE TEMPERATURE					
		0°K	298.16°K	500°K	1000°K	1500°K	2000°K
$O_{(g)}$	58.586	0	5.391	5.291	5.159	5.102	5.071
$H_{(g)}$	51.620	0	4.968	4.968	4.968	4.968	4.968
$N_{(g)}$	112.55†	0	4.968	4.968	4.968	4.968	4.968
$C_{(g)}$	170.60†	0	5.228	5.126	5.048	5.022	5.014
$O_{2(g)}$	0	0	6.942	7.048	7.497	7.850	8.109
$H_{2(g)}$	0	0	6.788	6.859	6.966	7.130	7.336
$H_2O_{(g)}$	−57.104	0	7.934	8.039	8.580	9.251	9.88
$N_{2(g)}$	0	0	6.950	6.970	7.202	7.502	7.750
$NO_{(g)}$	21.477	0	7.359	7.288	7.506	7.796	8.015
C(graphite)	0	0	0.844	1.642	3.075	3.876	—
$CO_{(g)}$	−27.202	0	6.951	6.980	7.256	7.572	7.818
$CO_{2(g)}$	−93.969	0	7.506	8.446	10.222	11.336	12.072
$CH_{4(g)}$	−15.987	0	8.039	8.730	11.56	14.09	—
$C_2H_{6(g)}$	−16.517	0	9.578	12.02	18.28	23.00	—
$C_2H_{4(g)}$	14.522	0	8.47	10.23	14.76	18.07	—
$C_2H_{2(g)}$	54.329	0	8.021	9.582	12.090	13.694	—
$C_6H_{6(g)}$	24.000	0	11.41	17.50	30.16	38.24	—

* All values taken from reference to Table 6.2 except those marked with dagger (†); these latter are from Gaydon, A. G., *Dissociation Energies and Spectra of Diatomic Molecules.* London: Chapman and Hall, Ltd., 1947; or Brewer, L. and A. W. Searcy, "High Temperature Chemistry" in *Annual Review of Physical Chemistry,* 7, 269 (1956).

When the substance is not a gas at T, some of the last terms of (6.50) and (6.51) are not evaluated. Values of the free energy function are then evaluated by (6.49) with known values of C_P, ΔH_{tr}, and so on. The selected values of the free energy function of Table 6.2 have been derived in this and other ways. Table 6.3 contains similar selected values of the heat content function and ΔH_o^o. Since these functions vary only slowly with temperature, graphical or analytical interpolation yields accurate values of these functions at any temperature. Circular C 641 contains data at intervals of 100°.

A value of ΔG^o for a reaction is calculated at some temperature T in this way from tabulated or interpolated values.

$$\Delta \left(\frac{G_T^o - H_o^o}{T} \right) = \sum_{products} \left(\frac{G_T^o - H_o^o}{T} \right) - \sum_{reactants} \left(\frac{G_T^o - H_o^o}{T} \right). \quad (6.52)$$

But since T is fixed,

$$\Delta \left(\frac{G_T^o - H_o^o}{T} \right) = \frac{\Delta G^o}{T} - \frac{\Delta H_o^o}{T}.$$

Whence
$$\Delta G^o = \Delta H_o^o + T \, \Delta \left(\frac{G_T^o - H_o^o}{T} \right) \quad (6.53)$$

where ΔH_o^o, the heat of reaction at absolute zero, is calculated from the second column of Table 6.3. These values of ΔH_o^o are the real values at 0°K, for the heat capacities of (6.50) and (6.51) are the really observed values at the temperatures involved. Once ΔG^o is known, (6.29) and (6.34) furnish the equilibrium constant at once. On the other hand, it is not generally recognized that only one measurement of an equilibrium constant or ΔG^o at one temperature can yield through (6.53) a value of ΔH_o^o that is often much more accurate than a value of ΔH^o determined from a plot of $\log K$ vs. $1/T$. All that is required for this last type of calculation are the free energy functions of reactants and products at the temperature T. If these are not available, they are often readily guessed with good accuracy.

The heat content functions of Table 6.3 are useful in calculating the increase in enthalpy of a change of state at any temperature without the use of equations like (3.100) and (3.101). Let the diagram be this.

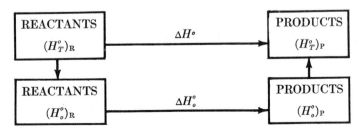

Then, for the alternate routes from reactants to products at the temperature T,

$$\Delta H^\circ = [(H_o^\circ)_R - (H_T^\circ)_R] + \Delta H_o^\circ + [(H_T^\circ)_P - (H_o^\circ)_P]$$

$$= \Delta H_o^\circ + [(H_T^\circ - H_o^\circ)_P - (H_T^\circ - H_o^\circ)_R]$$

$$= \Delta H_o^\circ + \sum_P \left[T\left(\frac{H_T^\circ - H_o^\circ}{T}\right) \right] - \sum_R \left[T\left(\frac{H_T^\circ - H_o^\circ}{T}\right) \right].$$

That is,

$$\Delta H^\circ = \Delta H_o^\circ + T \Delta\left(\frac{H_T^\circ - H_o^\circ}{T}\right). \tag{6.54}$$

All the quantities on the right of (6.54) are listed in Table 6.3.

Example 6.16. With the data of Tables 6.2 and 6.3, calculate the equilibrium constant at $2000°K$ for the reaction

$$N_{2(g)} + O_{2(g)} \rightleftharpoons 2\,NO_{(g)}.$$

From Table 6.3, $\Delta H_o^\circ = 2(21,477)$ cal $= 42,954$ cal. By (6.53) with data from Table 6.2,

$$\Delta G^\circ = \Delta H_o^\circ + T \Delta\left(\frac{G_T^\circ - H_o^\circ}{T}\right) \tag{6.53}$$

$$= 42,954 + 2000\,[2(-57.239) - (-52.478) - (-56.103)]$$

$$= 42,954 + 2000(-5.897) = 31,160.$$

By the equivalent of (6.29),

$$\log K_p = -\frac{\Delta G^\circ}{2.303RT}$$

$$= -\frac{31,160}{2.303 \times 1.987 \times 2000}$$

$$= -3.405 = 0.595 - 4.000$$

$$K_p = 3.94 \times 10^{-4}.$$

The value calculated in Example 6.13 is 3.8×10^{-4}, and a rather accurate value is 3.770×10^{-4} [calculated from E. van Beek-Visser, *Journal of Chemical Physics*, **29**, 1358 (1958)].

Example 6.17. Calculate the fraction of methane decomposed at equilibrium at one atm total pressure at $1000°K$ if the only reaction is

$$CH_{4(g)} \rightleftharpoons C_{(s)} + 2\,H_{2(g)}.$$

By (6.53), at $1000°K$,

$$\Delta G^\circ = 15,987 + 1000\,[(-2.771) + 2(-32.738) - (-47.65)]$$

$$= 15,987 + 1000\,(-20.60) = -4610\ \text{cal}.$$

373

By (6.29),

$$\log K_p = -\frac{\Delta G^o}{2.303RT} = -\frac{-4610}{2.303 \times 1.987 \times 1000} = 1.007$$

$$K_p = 10.16 = \frac{p_{H_2}^2}{p_{CH_4}}.$$

Since the total pressure is one atm, $P = p_{H_2} + p_{CH_4} = 1$. Then, on substitution into K_p,

$$10.16 = \frac{(1 - p_{CH_4})^2}{p_{CH_4}}$$

$$p^2 - 12.16p + 1 = 0$$

$$p = 0.08 \text{ atm}.$$

If α is the fraction of CH_4 decomposed, then at equilibrium the number of molecules is $1 - \alpha + 2\alpha = 1 + \alpha$ and

$$p_{CH_4} = \left(\frac{1 - \alpha}{1 + \alpha}\right) P$$

$$0.08 = \left(\frac{1 - \alpha}{1 + \alpha}\right) 1$$

$$\alpha = 0.85.$$

Methane at equilibrium at one atm at $1000°K$ is 85% decomposed by the reaction above.

Example 6.18. At $2257°K$ at one atm total pressure, water is 1.77% dissociated at equilibrium [von Wartenberg (1906)]. With neglect of the pressure of OH that exists through the reaction $2 H_2O \rightleftharpoons H_2 + 2 OH$, calculate the value of $\Delta H°$ at absolute zero for the reaction

$$2 H_{2(g)} + O_{2(g)} \rightleftharpoons 2 H_2O_{(g)}.$$

At $2257°K$, the free energy functions of $H_{2(g)}$, $O_{2(g)}$, and $H_2O_{(g)}$ are -38.56, -57.08, and -54.60 cal deg^{-1}, respectively [interpolated values from F. D. Rossini, et al., Circular of the National Bureau of Standards C 461 (1947)].

If $\alpha = 0.0177$ in the dissociation reaction

$$2 H_2O_{(g)} \rightleftharpoons 2 H_{2(g)} + O_{2(g)}$$
$$2(1 - \alpha) \qquad 2\alpha \qquad \alpha$$

then, since the total pressure P is one atm and the total number of molecules is $2(1 - \alpha) + 2\alpha + \alpha = 2 + \alpha$,

$$p_{H_2O} = \left(\frac{2 - 2\alpha}{2 + \alpha}\right) P = \frac{2 - 0.0354}{2.0177} = 0.9737 \text{ atm}$$

$$p_{O_2} = \left(\frac{\alpha}{2 + \alpha}\right) P = \frac{0.0177}{2.0177} = 0.00878 \text{ atm}$$

$$p_{H_2} = 2p_{O_2} = 0.0176 \text{ atm}$$

$$K_p = \frac{p_{H_2}^2 \, p_{O_2}}{p_{H_2O}^2} = \frac{(1.76 \times 10^{-2})^2(8.78 \times 10^{-3})}{(9.74 \times 10^{-1})^2} = 2.87 \times 10^{-6}.$$

At 2257°K,

$$\Delta G^\circ = -RT \ln K_p$$
$$= -1.987 \times 2257 \times 2.303 \times \log (2.87 \times 10^{-6})$$
$$= -1.987 \times 2257 \times 2.303 \times (0.458 - 6.000)$$
$$= +57,240 \text{ cal}.$$

Hence, for the combination reaction

$$\Delta H_o^\circ = \Delta G^\circ - T \Delta \left(\frac{G_T^\circ - H_o^\circ}{T} \right) \tag{6.53}$$
$$= -57,240 - 2257[2(-54.60) - 2(-38.56) - (-57.08)]$$
$$= -57,240 - 2257 \times 25.00 = -113,660 \text{ cal}.$$

The value from Table 6.3 is $2(-57.104)$, or $-114,208$ cal.

Example 6.19. With the aid of the heat content functions of Table 6.3 and the fact that at 25°C the heat of formation of $H_2O_{(g)}$ is $-57,797.9$ cal mole^{-1} (Table 3.3), evaluate ΔH_o° for the reaction

$$2 H_{2(g)} + O_{2(g)} \rightleftharpoons 2 H_2O_{(g)}.$$

By (6.54),

$$\Delta H_o^\circ = \Delta H^\circ - T \Delta \left(\frac{H_T^\circ - H_o^\circ}{T} \right)$$
$$= 2(-57,797.9) - 298.16[2(7.934) - 2(6.788) - 6.942]$$
$$= 2(-57,797.9) - 298.16(-4.650) = -114,209.4 \text{ cal}.$$

6.8 Free Energy from Statistical Mechanics

The calculation of free energies and equilibrium constants from heats of reaction, heat capacities, and the third law is essentially an experimental thermodynamic approach to chemical equilibrium.   It is remarkable in that no equilibrium measurement is required; only thermal measurements are required to predict chemical equilibrium states.   By the methods of statistical mechanics, however, it is possible to proceed from microscopic properties like molecular structure and the laws of mechanics of molecules and, by a suitable mathematical process of averaging, to calculate macroscopic thermodynamic properties directly observable on a molar basis.   The average or observable property generally involves the mechanical behavior of the order of 10^{20} to 10^{24} particles.   It is because of these huge numbers of particles that visible macroscopic thermodynamic properties appear quite uniform and continuous.

Each atom in a system has three Cartesian coordinates of position and three components of linear momentum along the x, y, z axes.   Each atom, then, has six mechanical variables the specification of which at any time allows the prediction of the mechanical state of that atom at any past or future time if the laws of classical mechanics adequately describe its mechanical behavior. Quantum mechanics explicitly admits that the exact mechanical state of a system cannot be observed or predicted in this way, but for the present it is not necessary to dwell upon these limits imposed by quantum mechanics. In a system of N atoms there are, then, $3N$ position coordinates and $3N$ momentum coordinates. These $6N$ coordinates specify exactly the mechanical state of the system in so far as classical mechanics is a valid approximation of quantum mechanics. In order to describe the behavior of these N atoms there is conceived a γ-phase space of $6N$ dimensions, half specifying positions q and half specifying momenta p (compare Section 1.12).

The preparation of a system in a certain thermodynamic state corresponds to sampling one system in a definite dynamical state (i.e., at a definite point in phase space) from a statistical population of systems. For this statistical population or ensemble of systems there exists in phase space a certain probability density $f(p, q, t)$. The function $f(p, q, t)$ is a measure of the number of systems in the region of the point (p, q) at the time t. If $f(p, q, t)$ is independent of time, then it can be shown that f depends only on the energy of the system.

With a suitable but sometimes rather complicated choice of coordinates p and q, it is possible to write in a very simple way the differential equations that describe the classico-mechanical behavior of any system. Although every book of theoretical physics contains a description of this method, called the *Hamiltonian method*, it is necessary here only to know that the energy E of the system is equal to its Hamiltonian $\mathcal{H}$, which is a function of the $3N$ momenta p and the $3N$ coordinates q and certain parameters x_i that can be fixed exactly by the experimenter. That is, for an isolated system, $E = \mathcal{H}(p, q, x_i)$. Such a system is constrained to move on a "surface" of constant energy in phase space.

For a system in equilibrium with an isothermal heat reservoir, it is necessary to take an average value of the energy. The probability that a certain sampling of a system from the ensemble will yield a system of energy $\mathcal{H}(p, q, x_i)$ is $f(p, q)$. The average energy expected is just the sum of the expected values of energy, namely,

$$E = \iint \mathcal{H}(p, q, x_i)\, f(p, q)\, dp\, dq \qquad (6.55)$$

where the summation is an integral over all possible places (or choices) in phase space. For (6.55) to be dimensionally homogeneous, $f(p, q)$ is a probability per unit volume, where $dp\, dq$ is the element of volume in phase space. Any sampling inevitably yields just one system so that the sum of these probabilities everywhere in phase space is unity. That is,

$$1 = \iint f(p, q)\, dp\, dq . \qquad (6.56)$$

Equation (6.56) is called *normalization*. Baseball batting averages are normalized to 1.000 or 1000 so that, barring walks and so on, the probability of a hit plus the probability of a nonhit is unity. Here E, the average number of bases per time at bat, equals the sum of five terms involving the hit function $\mathcal{H}$ (which assumes values of 0, 1, 2, 3, 4) times the probability f of a nonhit, single, double, triple, or home run.

Since the criterion of equilibrium

$$(\delta E)_{S,V} \geqslant 0 \tag{4.128}$$

involves the volume V and entropy S, it is necessary to obtain some average value of each in order to apply this criterion. The parameters x_i that can be specified by the operator correspond to the volume V, for the operator can limit the possible values of q by suitable constraints. The entropy, however, requires somewhat more insight. It is postulated that

$$S = -k \iint \text{f} \ln \text{f} \, dp \, dq \,. \tag{6.57}$$

The constant k establishes the correct dimensions and magnitude, and the double integration over momentum and position coordinates is really a summation. This entropy postulate is analogous to the expression for the entropy of mixing

$$\overline{\Delta S} = -R \sum_{i=1}^{\mathbf{c}} N_i \ln N_i \tag{5.46}$$

if mole fraction N_i is interpreted as a probability of sampling species i from a mixture of several species.

The new criterion of equilibrium

$$(\delta E)_{S,x_i} \geqslant 0 \tag{6.58}$$

requires that the energy E assume a stationary value (a minimum or at least constant value) when the entropy S and parameters of external force x_i are held constant. Lagrange's method of undetermined multipliers is well suited to accomplish this. Since $\mathcal{H}$ is constant for a point in phase space, any virtual change in E can be effected only through a change in f. That is, by (6.55)

$$\delta E = \iint \mathcal{H}(p, q, x_i) \, \delta \text{f}(p, q) \, dp \, dq$$

$$\delta E = \iint \mathcal{H} \, \delta \text{f} \, dp \, dq \,. \tag{6.59}$$

Such a variation of f in (6.56) yields

$$\delta(1) = \iint \delta \text{f}(p, q) \, dp \, dq$$

$$0 = \iint \delta \text{f} \, dp \, dq \,. \tag{6.60}$$

Such a variation of f in (6.57) yields

$$\delta S = -k \iint f\,\delta(\ln f)\,dp\,dq - k \iint \delta f \ln f\,dp\,dq$$
$$= -k \iint f\left(\frac{\delta f}{f}\right) dp\,dq - k \iint \delta f \ln f\,dp\,dq$$
$$= -k \iint \delta f\,dp\,dq - k \iint \delta f \ln f\,dp\,dq$$
$$= -k \iint \delta f \ln f\,dp\,dq \tag{6.61}$$

where (6.60) has been used to simplify δS. Lagrange's method finds a stationary value of E by choosing constant multipliers $(-A)$ and $-(1/\beta k)$ that can be determined later and setting the variations equal to zero thus:

$$\delta E - A\,\delta(1) - \left(\frac{1}{\beta k}\right)\delta S = 0 . \tag{6.62}$$

Substitution from (6.59), (6.60), and (6.61) yields

$$\iint \left(\mathcal{H} - A + \frac{1}{\beta}\ln f\right)\delta f\,dp\,dq = 0 . \tag{6.63}$$

If the integral (6.63) is to be zero for any change δf in the probability density function, then

$$\mathcal{H} - A + \frac{1}{\beta}\ln f = 0$$

$$A - \mathcal{H} = \frac{1}{\beta}\ln f$$

$$f = e^{\beta(A-\mathcal{H})} . \tag{6.64}$$

The values of the undetermined multipliers $(-A)$ and $-(1/\beta k)$ are fixed by the requirements that E in (6.55) be the energy, that f be normalized as in (6.56), and that the thermodynamic temperature be given, as in (4.88), by

$$T = \left(\frac{\partial E}{\partial S}\right)_{x_i} . \tag{6.65}$$

By (6.56),

$$1 = \iint e^{\beta(A-\mathcal{H})}\,dp\,dq = e^{\beta A}\iint e^{-\beta\mathcal{H}}\,dp\,dq$$
$$e^{-\beta A} = \iint e^{-\beta\mathcal{H}}\,dp\,dq . \tag{6.66}$$

By (6.57),

$$S = -k \iint f[\beta(A - \mathcal{H})]\,dp\,dq$$
$$= -k\beta A \iint f\,dp\,dq + k\beta \iint \mathcal{H}f\,dp\,dq .$$

But by (6.56) and (6.55), it follows that the entropy S is

$$S = -k\beta A + k\beta E .$$

Whence,

$$E = A + \left(\frac{1}{k\beta}\right) S . \tag{6.67}$$

By (6.65),

$$T = \left(\frac{\partial E}{\partial S}\right)_{x_i} = \left[\frac{\partial}{\partial S}\left(A + \frac{1}{k\beta} S\right)\right]_{x_i} = \frac{1}{k\beta}$$

$$\beta = \frac{1}{kT} . \tag{1.117} \tag{6.68}$$

Then, by (6.67) it is clear that A is the Helmholtz free energy, for

$$A = E - TS . \tag{4.79}$$

Now that A, E, T, and S are identified with certain average values of the mechanical properties of the ensemble of systems, it is a simple matter to evaluate by the usual thermodynamic means the several other thermodynamic variables of interest. For example, the pressure P is given by

$$P = -\left(\frac{\partial A}{\partial V}\right)_T .$$

The actual calculation of numerical values is facilitated by the definition of a partition function Q.

$$Q = e^{-\beta A} . \tag{6.69}$$

Since the Hamiltonian $\mathcal{H}(p, q)$ is known for the system, Q is calculated thus:

$$Q = \int\!\int e^{-\beta \mathcal{H}(p,q,x_i)} \, dp \, aq \tag{6.70}$$

where (6.66) was used to obtain (6.70) from (6.69).

From (6.69), the Helmholtz free energy A is

$$A = -kT \ln Q . \tag{6.71}$$

By (6.55), the energy of the ensemble is

$$E = \int\!\int \mathcal{H} \mathfrak{f} \, dp \, dq$$
$$= \int\!\int \mathcal{H} e^{\beta(A - \mathcal{H})} \, dp \, dq$$
$$= e^{\beta A} \int\!\int \mathcal{H} e^{-\beta \mathcal{H}} \, dp \, dq$$
$$= \frac{1}{Q}\left(-\frac{\partial Q}{\partial \beta}\right)_{x_i} .$$

That is,

$$E = -\left(\frac{\partial \ln Q}{\partial \beta}\right)_{x_i} . \tag{6.72}$$

Again, by (4.79), (6.71), and (6.72),

$$S = \frac{E - A}{T}$$

$$= \frac{1}{T}\left[-\left(\frac{\partial \ln Q}{\partial \beta}\right)_{xi} + kT \ln Q\right].$$

Since $\beta = \dfrac{1}{kT}$ it follows that

$$S = k\left[\ln Q - \beta\left(\frac{\partial \ln Q}{\partial \beta}\right)_{xi}\right]. \tag{6.73}$$

Other thermodynamic functions are derived from Q by similar methods. Equations (6.71), (6.72), and (6.73) are the key relations.

Explicit evaluation of the partition function Q in terms of structural variables can be a tedious process and some of the methods are given in Chapter 9. The Hamiltonian must be evaluated and the integration performed, often with approximations of various kinds. It is clear, however, that Q depends upon the mechanical nature of the systems of the ensemble and that thermodynamic properties can indeed be calculated from the mechanical behavior of the particles of a system. Most of the values of Tables 6.2 and 6.3 have been calculated by statistical mechanics.

Example 6.20. Express the heat capacity C_V in terms of the partition function.

$$C_V = \left(\frac{\partial E}{\partial T}\right)_V \tag{3.26}$$

$$= \left(\frac{\partial E}{\partial \beta}\right)_{xi}\left(\frac{\partial \beta}{\partial T}\right)_{xi}$$

$$= \left[\frac{\partial}{\partial \beta}\left(-\frac{\partial \ln Q}{\partial \beta}\right)_{xi}\right]_{xi} \times \left[\frac{\partial}{\partial T}\left(\frac{1}{kT}\right)\right]_{xi}$$

$$= -\left(\frac{\partial^2 \ln Q}{\partial \beta^2}\right)_{xi} \times \left(-\frac{1}{kT^2}\right)$$

$$= + k\beta^2\left(\frac{\partial^2 \ln Q}{\partial \beta^2}\right)_{xi}.$$

REFERENCES

Gaydon, A. G., *Dissociation Energies and Spectra of Diatomic Molecules*. London: Chapman & Hall, Ltd., 1947.

Guggenheim, E. A., *Thermodynamics, An Advanced Treatment for Chemists and Physicists*. Amsterdam: North-Holland Publishing Co., 1957.

Tolman, R. C., *The Principles of Statistical Mechanics*. New York: Oxford University Press, 1938.

PROBLEMS

1. At 28°C the equilibrium constant for the reaction

$$BF_{3(g)} + BCl_{3(g)} \rightleftharpoons BFCl_{2(g)} + BF_2Cl_{(g)}$$

is 0.53 [T. H. S. Higgins, E. C. Leisegang, C. J. G. Raw, and A. J. Rossouw, *Journal of Chemical Physics*, **23**, 1544 (1955)]. Calculate the partial pressure of $BFCl_2$ at equilibrium if the initial pressures of BF_3 and BCl_3 are 300 mm Hg and 200 mm Hg. *Answer:* 102 mm Hg.

2. If pressures are known within 0.001 atm, what is the smallest value of K_p certainly known to be greater than zero at a total pressure of 1 atm for a reaction of the type $A_{2(g)} \rightleftharpoons 2 A_{(g)}$?

3. At 3500°K, K_p for the reaction $C_2N_{2(g)} \rightleftharpoons 2 CN_{(g)}$ is 2.50 [E. Rutner, W. H. McLain, Jr., and K. Scheller, *Journal of Chemical Physics*, **24**, 173 (1956)]. What percentage by volume is not dissociated at one atm? *Answer:* 38.0%.

4. For $PH_{3(g)}$ at 25°C, $\Delta G_f^o = 4360$ cal mole^{-1} [F. D. Rossini *et al.*, Circular of the National Bureau of Standards 500 (1952)]. What percentage of $PH_{3(g)}$ is dissociated into elements at one atm at 25°C at equilibrium? (Assume $P_{4(s)}$ is stable.)

5. Which of these oxides can react spontaneously with gaseous hydrogen at 1.000 atm at 25°C to yield the solid metal and liquid water at 25°C? $Ag_2O_{(s)}$; $OsO_{4(s)}$; $Fe_2O_{3(s)}$; $Fe_3O_{4(s)}$; $Al_2O_{3(s)}$. *Answer:* Ag_2O; OsO_4.

6. Calculate the pressure of $H_2O_{(g)}$ in equilibrium with $ZnSO_4 \cdot H_2O_{(s)}$ and $ZnSO_4 \cdot 6 H_2O_{(s)}$ at 25°C.

7. Which of the two forms of solid OsO_4 is more stable at 25°C? What are their vapor pressures at 25°C?

8. What is the solubility product constant of ZnS at 25°C? *Answer:* 9.5×10^{-25}.

9. If steam at one atm is 1.77% dissociated at 2257°K and 1.18% dissociated at 2155°K, find ΔH^o for the formation of 1 mole $H_2O_{(g)}$ at 2200°K.

10. It is common to express the dependence of ΔG^o upon temperature in the form

$$\Delta G^o = A + BT$$

where A and B are constants. Justify this form and identify A and B in terms of thermodynamic variables.

11. Values of K_p for the reaction $C_2N_{2(g)} \rightleftharpoons 2 CN_{(g)}$ are given for several temperatures [E. Rutner, W. H. McLain, Jr., and K. Scheller, *Journal of Chemical Physics*. **24**, 173 (1956)]. Find ΔG^o, ΔH^o, and ΔS^o for this reaction at 1500°K and 2500°K, and explain the differences in values. Estimate ΔH^o at 0°K.

$T(°K)$	K_p	$T(°K)$	K_p
1400	2.16×10^{-10}	2400	4.28×10^{-3}
1500	3.23×10^{-9}	2500	1.08×10^{-2}
1600	3.17×10^{-8}	2600	2.56×10^{-2}

381

12. It is sometimes said that all gases are less soluble in water as the temperature rises. Discuss.

13. For the reaction

$$TiCl_{3(s)} + HCl_{(g)} \rightleftharpoons TiCl_{4(g)} + \tfrac{1}{2} H_{2(g)}$$

$K_p = 2.74$ at 400°C and $K_p = 4.80$ at 450°C [W. F. Krieve and D. M. Mason, *Journal of Chemical Physics*, 25, 524 (1956)]. If $\Delta C_P = -6$ cal deg^{-1}, find $\Delta H°$ at 25°C for this reaction. What will be the partial pressure of $TiCl_{4(g)}$ if HCl at an initial pressure of one atm in a closed rigid vessel comes to equilibrium with excess $TiCl_{3(s)}$ at 500°C? *Answer:* $\Delta H° = 13{,}240$ cal; 0.919 atm.

14. Calculate K_p at 298°K and 500°K for the reaction $C_2H_{4(g)} + H_{2(g)} \rightleftharpoons C_2H_{6(g)}$.

15. Calculate the equilibrium constant at 1000°C for the reaction

$$3 C_2H_{2(g)} \rightleftharpoons C_6H_{6(g)}.$$

Answer: 1.7×10^6.

---

16. Consider these equilibria in the same vessel:

$$Ag_2O_{(s)} \rightleftharpoons 2 Ag_{(s)} + \tfrac{1}{2}O_{2(g)}$$

$$Ag_2CO_{3(s)} \rightleftharpoons Ag_2O_{(s)} + CO_{2(g)}.$$

In what way does the presence of $Ag_2O_{(s)}$ restrict the pressures of CO_2 and O_2? Under what circumstances could Ag_2O disappear? Are the pressures of CO_2 and O_2 independent?

17. At 133°C, the density of gaseous acetic acid is 2.78 g l^{-1} at one atm [*International Critical Tables III*, p. 437]. Calculate the percentage by weight that exists as dimer and calculate K_p for the reaction $(CH_3COOH)_{2(g)} \rightleftharpoons 2 CH_3COOH_{(g)}$.

18. Calculate ΔG and ΔH at 25°C for the changes:
(a) $H_{2(g)}$ (0.10 atm) $+ Cl_{2(g)}$ (0.90 atm) $\rightarrow 2 HCl_{(g)}$ (1.00 atm).
(b) $H_{2(g)}$ (0.10 atm) $+ Cl_{2(g)}$ (0.50 atm) $\rightarrow 2 HCl_{(g)}$ (0.20 atm).

19. Is 0.20 molar AgF a saturated solution at 25°C if $\Delta G_f°$ of $AgF_{(s)}$ is -44.2 kcal mole^{-1} (F. D. Rossini *et al.*, Circular 500 NBS.)? *Answer:* No.

20. The solubility product constant of CaF_2 at 25°C is 4.0×10^{-11}. Calculate $\Delta G_f°$ of Ca_{aq}^{++} if $\Delta G_f°$ of $CaF_{2(s)}$ is -277.7 kcal mole^{-1} (F. D. Rossini *et al.*, Circular 500 N.B.S.). *Answer:* -131.3 kcal mole^{-1}.

21. What is the ionization constant of NH_4OH at 25°C and the partial pressure of $NH_{3(g)}$ above 0.100 molal NH_4OH at 25°C?

22. Calculate K_p at 298°K for the dissociation of $HI_{(g)}$ into $H_{2(g)}$ and $I_{2(g)}$. What percentage is dissociated at 298°K? *Answer:* In absence of $I_{2(s)}$, 6.76%.

23. At what temperature will $NaHCO_{3(s)}$ decompose at a total pressure of 1 atm if C_P for $Na_2CO_{3(s)}$ and $NaHCO_{3(s)}$ are 26.5 and 21.0 cal deg^{-1} per gram-formula weight? The reaction is

$$2 NaHCO_{3(s)} \rightleftharpoons Na_2CO_{3(s)} + H_2O_{(g)} + CO_{2(g)}.$$

At 25°C, $\Delta H° = 31.0$ kcal.

24. At 50°C, the partial pressures p_{SO_2} of SO_2, the total molalities m_{SO_2} of dissolved SO_2, and the molalities m_+ of H^+ are [H. F. Johnstone and P. W. Leppla, *Journal of the American Chemical Society*, **56**, 2233 (1934)]:

p_{SO_2} (atm $\times 10^3$)	$m_{SO_2} \times 10^3$	$m_+ \times 10^3$
2.30	4.67	3.42
3.83	6.37	4.28
5.38	8.38	5.21
8.79	10.57	6.20

Calculate, from these data and those in Example 5.6, the heat of solution of SO_2 in water, the heat of ionization of H_2SO_3, and the first ionization constant of H_2SO_3 at 25°C and 50°C.

25. Equilibrium constants for the reaction $2\ NOCl_{(g)} \rightleftharpoons 2\ NO_{(g)} + Cl_{2(g)}$ were calculated from the initial pressures p^o_{NOCl}, p^o_{NO}, and $p^o_{Cl_2}$ in a rigid vessel and the final observed total pressure P [J. K. Dixon, *Zeitschrift für physikalische Chemie, Bodenstein Festband*, 679 (1931)]. Some of the data, with pressures (mm Hg), are:

$T(°C)$	P	p^o_{NOCl}	p^o_{NO}	$p^o_{Cl_2}$
230	539.0	208.7	0	312.4
308	648.4	241.0	0	360.6
399	781.2	278.5	0	416.9
279	676.8	441.5	163.4	0
377	867.1	519.6	192.3	0
465	1027.7	589.6	218.2	0

From these data calculate:
(a) K_p and K_c at each temperature.
(b) $\Delta H°$ for the dissociation reaction.
(c) ΔG_f^o of $NOCl_{(g)}$ at 25°C if $\Delta C_P = 0$.

26. Which is least stable at 1000°K relative to the elements: $C_2H_{2(g)}$, $C_2H_{4(g)}$, or $C_2H_{6(g)}$?

27. The strongest bonds in diatomic molecules like N_2 and CO require about 225 kcal mole^{-1} for dissociation to atoms at absolute zero. The temperature at which $\Delta G°$ is zero for such dissociations may be considered the upper limit of temperature for chemistry. Estimate this limit.
Answer: 7000°K.

28. At elevated temperatures, gaseous hydrogen reduces $CuO_{(s)}$ to $Cu_2O_{(s)}$ and/or $Cu_{(s)}$. If pure CuO and pure H_2 are heated together at equilibrium, how many intensive variables can be specified at will (and explain in terms of equilibrium constants)? If solid Cu is then added, what changes can be made?

29. At 502.2°K, K_p for the reaction $PCl_{3(g)} + Cl_{2(g)} \rightleftharpoons PCl_{5(g)}$ is 1.752 [D. P. Stevenson and D. M. Yost, *Journal of Chemical Physics*, **9**, 403 (1941)]. Calculate the percentage of PCl_5 dissociated:
(a) At one atm total pressure.
(b) At ten atm total pressure.
(c) At one atm in a mixture that was made of equal numbers of moles of $Cl_{2(g)}$ and $PCl_{5(g)}$.

30. At 25°C the equilibrium constant for the reaction $2\ BrCl_{(g)} \rightleftharpoons Br_{2(g)} + Cl_{2(g)}$ is 0.15 [H. C. Mattrow, C. F. Pachucki, and N. J. Hawkins, *Journal of Chemical Physics*, **22**, 1117 (1954)] and the vapor pressure of Br_2 is 0.30 atm.
(a)   What is the partial pressure of BrCl in a vessel of 30.0 l containing 0.500 moles $Cl_{2(g)}$ initially and excess liquid Br_2 if Cl_2 does not dissolve in $Br_{2(l)}$ and if the reaction above is the only possible one?
(b)   What is ΔG_f° of $BrCl_{(g)}$?

31.   Calculate the first and second ionization constants at 25°C of H_2CrO_4 and the equilibrium constant for the reaction $Cr_2O_{7(aq)}^- + H_2O_{(l)} \rightleftharpoons 2\ CrO_{4(aq)}^- + 2\ H_{(aq)}^+$. *Answer:* $K_1 = 0.19$; $K_2 = 4.2 \times 10^{-7}$; $K_{eq} = 4 \times 10^{-15}$.

32.   At 115.5°C, the pressure of $NO_{(g)}$ above a mixture of $Ag_{(s)}$, $AgNO_{2(s)}$, and $AgNO_{3(s)}$ is 0.395 atm, while at 142.6°C it is 1.530 atm [M. Randall, G. G. Manov, and O. L. I. Brown, *Journal of the American Chemical Society*, **60**, 694 (1938)].   Predict the pressure of $NO_{(g)}$ above the same three solids at 100.0°C if the reaction is $2\ AgNO_{2(s)} \rightleftharpoons Ag_{(s)} + AgNO_{3(s)} + NO_{(g)}$.   Can this same reaction occur if pure $AgNO_{2(s)}$ is placed in a continuously evacuated chamber at 100°C?   Explain. *Answer:* 0.167 atm; yes, for phase rule applies only at equilibrium.

33.   Equilibrium constants K_p for the reaction $\frac{1}{2} N_{2(g)} + \frac{3}{2} H_{2(g)} \rightleftharpoons NH_{3(g)}$ at several temperatures and total pressures are reported below [A. T. Larson and R. L. Dodge, *Journal of the American Chemical Society*, **45**, 2918 (1923); A. T. Larson, *Journal of the American Chemical Society*, **46**, 367 (1924)].

Total Pressure	350°C	400°C	450°C	500°C
10 atm	26.6×10^{-3}	12.9×10^{-3}	6.59×10^{-3}	3.81×10^{-3}
50 atm	27.8×10^{-3}	13.0×10^{-3}	6.90×10^{-3}	3.88×10^{-3}
100 atm	—	13.7×10^{-3}	7.25×10^{-3}	4.02×10^{-3}
300 atm	—	—	8.84×10^{-3}	4.98×10^{-3}
600 atm	—	—	12.94×10^{-3}	6.51×10^{-3}
1000 atm	—	—	23.28×10^{-3}	—

(a)   Suggest reasons why K_p depends upon pressure at constant temperature.
(b)   Calculate $\Delta H°$ at 400°C by using data at 350°C, 400°C and 450°C.
(c)   With values of C_P from Table 3.1, find $\Delta G°$ as a function of temperature.
(d)   Calculate the standard free energy of formation of $NH_{3(g)}$ at 298.16°K.
(e)   What percentage of $NH_{3(g)}$ is dissociated at equilibrium at a total pressure of 200 atm at 450°C?
(f)   Find ΔG at 450°C for the change $N_{2(g)}$ (75.0 atm) $+ 3\ H_{2(g)}$ (150.0 atm) $\rightarrow 2\ NH_{3(g)}$ (75.0 atm).

34.   Analysis of the vapors effusing from a small hole in a heated chamber containing $TiCl_{2(s)}$ yielded these results [M. Farber and A. J. Darnell, *Journal of Chemical Physics*, **25**, 526 (1956)] (rounded) for equilibrium pressures above $TiCl_{2(s)}$:

T(°K)	p(TiCl₄) (atm)	p(TiCl₃) (atm)	p(TiCl₂) (atm)
797	3.5×10^{-7}	7.5×10^{-6}	4.6×10^{-7}
828	9.4×10^{-7}	2.1×10^{-5}	1.4×10^{-6}
862	3.0×10^{-6}	5.6×10^{-5}	4.4×10^{-6}
893	9.2×10^{-6}	1.5×10^{-4}	1.2×10^{-5}

From these data find ΔH^o ΔG^o, and ΔS^o at 850°K for the reactions:
(a) $2 \ TiCl_{2(s)} \rightleftharpoons TiCl_{4(g)} + Ti_{(s)}$.
(b) $3 \ TiCl_{2(s)} \rightleftharpoons 2 \ TiCl_{3(g)} + Ti_{(s)}$.
(c) $TiCl_{2(s)} \rightleftharpoons TiCl_{2(g)}$.
Calculate ΔH^o and ΔG^o at 850°K for the reaction

$$Ti_{(s)} + 3 \ TiCl_{4(g)} \rightleftharpoons 4 \ TiCl_{3(g)}.$$

35. From the heat content function of graphite in Table 6.3, find an expression for C_P of graphite of the form $C_P^{(0)} + C_P^{(1)} T + C_P^{(2)} T^2$ above 298°K. Then, with the aid of heat capacities from Table 3.1, find ΔG^o as a function of temperature for the reactions

$$C_{(s)} + CO_{2(g)} \rightleftharpoons 2 \ CO_{(g)}$$

$$C_{(s)} + H_2O_{(g)} \rightleftharpoons CO_{(g)} + H_{2(g)}.$$

36. At 2000°K, the partial pressure of $C_{(g)}$ in equilibrium with graphite is 3.3×10^{-11} atm [L. Brewer and A. W. Searcy, "High Temperature Chemistry," *Annual Review of Physical Chemistry*, **7**, 268 (1956)]. Calculate the heat of sublimation of graphite at absolute zero.
Answer: $\Delta H_o^o = 170$ kcal mole^{-1}.

37. The partition function Q for N monatomic gas molecules each of mass m in a total volume V at temperature T is given by the expression

$$\ln Q = N \left[\ln \left(\frac{V}{N} \right) + \ln \left(\frac{2\pi mkT}{h^2} \right)^{3/2} e \right]. \tag{9.26}$$

The constant h has the value 6.624×10^{-27} erg-sec molecule^{-1} and k is the gas constant per molecule. Find:
(a) E, A, S, P, C_V, C_P, and G for this system.
(b) The standard absolute entropies at 298.16°K at 1 atm (1.01325×10^6 dyne cm^{-2}) of Ar (atomic weight = 39.944) and gaseous Hg (atomic weight = 200.61). The observed values [F. D. Rossini, *et al.*, Circular of the National Bureau of Standards 500 (1952)] are 36.983 and 41.80 cal mole^{-1} deg^{-1}.

FOOTNOTES

1. Margrave, J. L., *Journal of Chemical Education*, **32** (1955), 520.

7 / ELECTROCHEMISTRY

A. MIGRATION OF CHARGED SPECIES

7.1 Electrical Units

The electrical behavior of matter and its chemical implications have been mentioned briefly with regard to the structures of ionic lattices, thermodynamic work, and thermodynamic functions of ions in Tables 3.3, 4.1, and 6.1. In this chapter, these anticipations of electrochemistry are to be integrated into a systematic exposition of the importance of electricity to many chemical concepts. While modern theoretical chemistry focuses its attention upon the electron, and thus upon the electrical nature of substances, early chemistry and indeed alchemy could ignore electrical phenomena. Distillations, determinations of equivalent and atomic weights, and the discovery of elements needed little theoretical basis, and the rapid growth of organic chemistry seemed to lead chemistry away from physics and electricity. Physics was firmly based upon an electrical theory of matter by Maxwell through his electromagnetic theory of radiation and by Thomson, Bohr, and Rutherford through their work on the electron and atom. Chemistry had to follow the lead of physics. Ionic reactions in aqueous solution and theories of electrolytic conductance were first. Then in rapid succession came Moseley's atomic numbers, Lewis's electron-pair bond, and quantum mechanics.

One of the simplest laws of electricity, Ohm's law, describes the time rate of transfer of electric charge. This law says that $\mathcal{J}$, the electric charge carried per second through an electric conductor, is proportional to the potential difference $\mathscr{E}$ which causes the flow and is inversely proportional to the resistance $\mathscr{R}$ which opposes the flow. Mathematically, it is (7.1).

$$\mathscr{I} = k \, \frac{\mathscr{E}}{\mathscr{R}} \, . \tag{7.1}$$

This law is an empirical observation of the electrical behavior of steady currents in many substances.

In the now outmoded international system of electrical units, the international ampere was defined as that constant current which would deposit 0.00111800 g Ag sec^{-1} from an aqueous solution of silver nitrate. The international ohm was defined as the resistance of pure Hg at 0°C in a column of uniform cross section, the column containing 14.4521 g Hg in a length of 106.300 cm. The international volt was the unit of potential difference $\mathscr{E}$ and was chosen to make the proportionality factor k in (7.1) unity. That is, with $\mathscr{I}$ expressed in *amperes*, $\mathscr{E}$ in *volts*, and $\mathscr{R}$ in *ohms*, Ohm's law was (7.2).

$$\mathscr{E} = \mathscr{I}\mathscr{R} \, . \tag{7.2}$$

In 1948, the National Bureau of Standards established the absolute ampere, ohm, and volt as the legal standards. The absolute system of units is derived from electromagnetic units. As the conversion factors of Appendix C indicate, only in very accurate work is the difference in systems noticeable. Ohm's law retains the proportionality factor of unity when the absolute system is used.

Since the current $\mathscr{I}$ is the time rate of movement of charge Q, it follows that

$$\mathscr{I} = \frac{dQ}{dt} \, . \tag{7.3}$$

If the current $\mathscr{I}$ flows for a finite time t, the total charge Q that passes a fixed point in the circuit is

$$Q = \int_0^t \mathscr{I} \, dt' \, . \tag{7.4}$$

When the current $\mathscr{I}$ is steady,

$$Q = \mathscr{I} \int_0^t dt'$$
$$= \mathscr{I}t \, . \tag{7.5}$$

If $\mathscr{I}$ is measured in amperes and t in *seconds*, the unit that measures Q is the *coulomb*. Since the units of time are the same in the absolute and international systems, the conversion factor for charge in coulombs is the same as that for current in amperes.

387

The infinitesimal work dw that must be done in generating a charge dQ at a potential $\mathcal{E}$ or in moving a charge dQ through a potential difference $\mathcal{E}$ is given by (3.4).

$$dw = +\mathcal{E}\,dQ. \tag{3.4}$$

The convention on the signs of $\mathcal{E}$ and Q requires the positive sign. If the charge dQ is so small that it does not noticeably disturb the value of $\mathcal{E}$, then this electric work is independent of the path by which the charge is generated or moved, just as movement of mass in the potential of a gravitational field requires work that is independent of the path. The finite amount of work w done on a system when a finite amount of charge is generated or moved is the sum of the many infinitesimal changes.

$$w = +\int \mathcal{E}\,dQ. \tag{7.6}$$

If $\mathcal{E}$ is constant for the charge Q,

$$w = +\mathcal{E}\int_0^Q dQ'$$
$$= +\mathcal{E}Q. \tag{7.7}$$

The unit of electric work is the *joule* and is the product of potential difference $\mathcal{E}$ in volts and charge Q in coulombs. The *thermochemical calorie* is defined in terms of electric energy in joules. Exactly 1 cal is equivalent to 4.18400 absolute joules, and a method of comparing thermal and electric energies was discussed in Example 3.4.

7.2 Electrolysis

Electrolysis is the process by which chemical changes are caused by the flow of electric current. Ordinary metallic conductors carry electric charges as an organized movement of electrons. A metal is conceived as a kind of electron-fluid in which metallic ions are regularly arranged. The chemical changes of electrolysis are effected by these electrons as they are transferred to or from the chemicals by electrodes. The electrodes may partake in the chemical changes, or they may be inert and function merely as a source or sink of electrons. The electrode that is connected to the negative terminal of the external source of electricity furnishes electrons to the electrolytic cell and is called the *cathode*. The cathode has an excess of electrons relative to the other electrode, called the *anode*, which is connected to the positive terminal of the external source of electricity.

Some of the typical chemical changes caused by a flow of electrons are listed in Table 7.1. The various electrolytes, the chemicals undergoing changes, conduct an electric current by virtue of the chemical changes that occur at the electrodes and by virtue of the movement of charge carriers called *ions* within the chemical electrolyte that separates the electrodes. Generally there is one predominant chemical change at each electrode, although concentration changes may influence the kind of change that occurs just as the natures of electrode and electrolyte do.

Table 7.1. *Chemical Changes Caused by Electrolysis*

CATHODE	MAIN CATHODE REACTION	AQUEOUS ELECTROLYTE	MAIN ANODE REACTION	ANODE
Pt	$e^- + H^+ \rightleftharpoons \frac{1}{2} H_2$	H_2SO_4	$OH^- \rightleftharpoons \frac{1}{4} O_2 + \frac{1}{2} H_2O + e^-$	Pt
Pt	$e^- + H^+ \rightleftharpoons \frac{1}{2} H_2$	dil HCl	$OH^- \rightleftharpoons \frac{1}{4} O_2 + \frac{1}{2} H_2O + e^-$	Pt
Pt	$e^- + H^+ \rightleftharpoons \frac{1}{2} H_2$	con HCl	$Cl^- \rightleftharpoons \frac{1}{2} Cl_2 + e^-$	Pt
Ag	$e^- + H^+ \rightleftharpoons \frac{1}{2} H_2$	HCl	$Cl^- + Ag \rightleftharpoons AgCl + e^-$	Ag
Pt	$e^- + Ag^+ \rightleftharpoons Ag$	$AgNO_3$	$OH^- \rightleftharpoons \frac{1}{4} O_2 + \frac{1}{2} H_2O + e^-$	Pt
Ag	$e^- + Ag^+ \rightleftharpoons Ag$	$AgNO_3$	$Ag \rightleftharpoons Ag^+ + e^-$	Ag
Pt	$e^- + \frac{1}{2} Hg_2^{++} \rightleftharpoons Hg$	Hg_2SO_4	$\frac{1}{2} Hg_2^{++} \rightleftharpoons Hg^{++} + e^-$	Pt
Pb, $PbSO_4$	$e^- + \frac{1}{2} PbSO_4 \rightleftharpoons \frac{1}{2} Pb + \frac{1}{2} SO_4^{--}$	H_2SO_4	$\frac{1}{2} PbSO_4 + H_2O \rightleftharpoons \frac{1}{2} PbO_2 + 2 H^+ + \frac{1}{2} SO_4^{--} + e^-$	Pb, $PbSO_4$, PbO_2

The last pair of reactions in Table 7.1 describes the process of charging a lead storage battery. If the external source of electricity were disconnected, the electrode that was the cathode in electrolysis would be found to be negative relative to the electrode that was anode. Discharging a storage cell, then, allows the reverse reactions to occur and Pb and PbO_2 become $PbSO_4$. Any of the cells in Table 7.1 behave in the same way. The third cell would produce electrons at the cathode by virtue of the combination of H_2 and Cl_2 to produce HCl. If the products of electrolysis were, however, allowed to mix, their potential chemical energy would not appear as electric energy but would appear as heat, light, and so on.

In order to continue electrolyzing the electrolyte, the external source of electricity must impose a potential difference not less than that developed by the cell if it were disconnected and used as a source of electricity. These potential differences are of course opposed during electrolysis. Thus, even inert electrodes become active as products of electrolysis collect around them.

In 1834, Faraday stated the exact mathematical relation between the amounts of electricity and chemicals produced during electrolysis in two laws: (1) The mass of a substance generated at an electrode is proportional to the amount of electricity passed during electrolysis. (2) The masses of substances generated at several electrodes in series in a single electrolysis are directly proportional to their chemical equivalent weights.

Suppose that two electrolytic cells were connected in series as in Figure 7.1. At the cathode of the first cell, which contains aqueous $ZnBr_2$, there would be deposited metallic zinc, and at the same time elemental bromine would be generated at the inert anode. In the second cell, hydrogen would be generated at the cathode by electrolysis of dilute sulfuric acid and oxygen would be freed at the anode. Since the only route for the transfer of charge is around the singly connected loop that goes from external source $\mathcal{E}$ through the $ZnBr_2$ cell and then through the H_2SO_4 cell, the same amount of charge passes through each electrode. Faraday's second law then says: (a) If all the Zn and Br_2 produced were mixed and allowed to react, pure $ZnBr_2$ would be produced without any Zn or Br_2 left over. (b) Similarly, if all the H_2 produced were burned in all the O_2 produced, pure H_2O would be produced and no H_2 or O_2 would remain. (c) If all the Zn produced were dissolved in acid, it would yield exactly the same amount of H_2 as was produced in the electrolysis. (d) If all the Zn produced by electrolysis were burned in the O_2 produced by electrolysis, only pure ZnO would be made and no Zn or O_2 would remain unused. (e) If the H_2 and Br_2 produced from these cells were combined, pure HBr would be the sole product. (f) And so on.

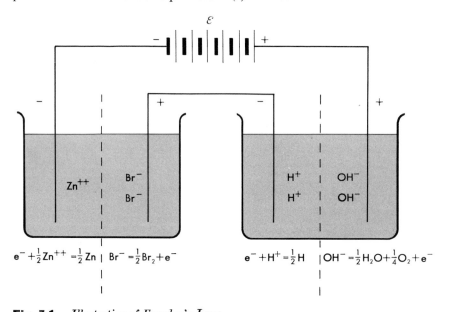

Fig. 7.1. *Illustration of Faraday's Laws.*

The quantity of charge that will generate exactly 1 gram equivalent weight of any chemical is called a *faraday*. The international ampere was defined in terms of the reaction

$$e^- + Ag^+ \rightleftharpoons Ag_{(s)} .$$

Since 1 mole of electrons is equivalent to 1 gram-atom Ag, the equivalent weight of Ag is here equal to its atomic weight, 107.880. Since a current of 1 international ampere deposits 0.00111800 g Ag sec^{-1}, 107.880/0.00111800 sec would be required to deposit 107.880 g. But 107.880/0.00111800 amp-sec are just 96,494 international coulombs. The best value is, however, 96,493.1

absolute coulombs per equivalent [see Appendix C]. Both of Faraday's laws are stated most simply thus: exactly 1 gram-equivalent of any substance is produced or destroyed by electrolysis by 96,493.1 absolute coulombs of electricity.

Example 7.1. From the fact that the charge on one electron is 1.60186×10^{-19} coulomb, evaluate Avogadro's number N.

Since the generation of 1 gram-equivalent of a substance involves the transfer of N electrons,

$$N = \frac{\mathcal{F}}{e} = \frac{96,493}{1.60186 \times 10^{-19}}$$

$$= 6.0238 \times 10^{23} \text{ electrons equivalent}^{-1}$$

$$= 6.0238 \times 10^{23} \text{ molecules mole}^{-1}.$$

Example 7.2. How long will it take to deposit exactly 1 g Cu from a solution of $CuSO_4$ with a constant current of 3.000 amp if the only reaction is

$$2e^- + Cu^{++} \rightleftharpoons Cu \ ?$$

The equation says that 2 faradays are required to deposit 1 atomic weight Cu or 63.54 g. That is, the equivalent weight is 31.77 g. Since charge and mass are in direct proportion by Faraday's first law and since $Q = \mathcal{I}t$,

$$\frac{1.000}{63.54} = \frac{3.000t}{2 \times 96,493}$$

$$t = 1012 \text{ sec}.$$

7.3 Transference Numbers from Concentration Changes at Electrodes

Although chemically equivalent amounts of substances are generated by electrolysis at each electrode, the concentration changes at each electrode depend upon the speeds with which ions can move through the electrolyte to maintain electroneutrality of the electrolyte near the electrode. Too rapid electrolysis may even exhaust the supply of ions and lead to alternate reactions or to cessation of electrolysis. Being negatively charged, the cathode attracts positively charged ions. The anode attracts negative ions. That is, the electrostatic field that exists in the electrolyte because of the externally imposed potential difference accelerates ions so that negative ions move to the anode and positive ions move to the cathode. The terminal velocity reached under this acceleration depends upon the size and charge of the ion and its interactions with the solution. Within the electrolyte, part of the current is carried by positive ions and part is carried by negative ions.

The formation of complex ions or interaction with the solvent may yield unusual changes in ionic concentration. For example, in solutions of halides of zinc and cadmium, there is a net transfer of metal to the *anode* when the halide ion concentration is great. The reason is that complex ions like $ZnCl_3^-$, $ZnCl_4^{--}$, CdI_3^-, and CdI_4^{--} are more plentiful and carry a larger fraction of the total current than do ions like Zn^{++}, $ZnCl^+$, Cd^{++}, and CdI^+.

Or again, the speed of hydrogen ions in aqueous solutions is so great that it is obvious that hydrogen ions that appear at the cathode could not be the same ones that existed throughout the solution as electrolysis began. Since protons are indistinguishable from each other, a cooperative exchange of them among water molecules throughout the water structure could yield hydrogen at the cathode with only a very small displacement of individual protons. That is, any one proton need move only from its position near an oxygen atom to the equivalent position near the oxygen to which it had been hydrogen-bonded. A thorough comparison of theory with results of experiments in water, in mixtures of water and alcohols, and in isotopically substituted water favors the following mechanism of proton transfer.[1] At any H_3O^+ ion there exists a proton that cannot be accommodated by the usual structure of water (see Section 2.18). In particular, near H_3O^+ there are two protons along one line joining adjacent oxygen atoms, but there should be only one proton. This unfavorable configuration causes the awkwardly oriented H_2O to rotate in the field of the H_3O^+ ion. After rotation, with three adjacent oxygen atoms available to receive one of its extra protons, the H_3O^+ is free to transfer a proton to one of its neighboring H_2O molecules and thus transform it into H_3O^+. The transfer occurs swiftly by a process peculiar to individual particles of small mass like electrons and protons. The proton suddenly disappears from its position near the H_3O^+ and reappears near an H_2O. It has, by a quantum mechanical "tunneling" movement (see Section 8.10), penetrated the barrier between its twofold set of equilibrium positions without proceeding over the barrier as a mountain climber, subject to the laws of classical mechanics, must tediously and breathlessly toil up and over a mountain pass. The quantum mechanical tunneling requires only about one one-hundredth as long as the rotation of an adjacent H_2O. A rotated H_2O that has become H_3O^+ is, like the first H_3O^+, surrounded by four H_2O molecules one of which is unfavorably oriented. And so the process is repeated again and again, each time by a new proton; rotate, tunnel; rotate, tunnel; rotate, tunnel; .... In an electric field, the movement is given a preferred direction.

It is possibilities like these that suggest that identification and characterization of the actually existing ionic species that carry part of the current in both directions may be quite difficult. A swift nondestructive sampling technique like a spectroscopic method that does not disturb the equilibriums involving the several partially dissociated complex ions, might allow the identification of the actual charge carriers. But a chemical analysis for the total amount of Zn or Cd by precipitation of ZnS or CdS will displace equilibriums involving $ZnCl_4^{--}$ or CdI_3^- and thus yield only the total amount of metal present. Since this last kind of analysis is the only one generally available, the discussion and definition of transference numbers must allow for these awkward possibilities.

Of the several ways of defining transference numbers, the following is accurate and sufficient for this discussion.[2] The transference number of an ion constituent is the net number of equivalents of the ion constituent that crosses an imaginary plane fixed to the solvent when 1 faraday of charge passes across that plane. It is the fraction of the current carried by the ion constituent. The ion constituents of an electrolyte are those ions which can be combined in various proportions to produce the ions that really exist in the electrolyte. The ion constituents of a solution of $ZnCl_2$ and NaCl are Zn^{++}, Na^+, and Cl^-, or some other set of ions that can be mixed to yield the final solution. The ion constituents may be only minor species in the electrolyte, as Zn^{++} is in concentrated solutions of $ZnCl_2$. However, concentration changes of an ion constituent are readily determined by ordinary chemical methods.

When the solute is completely dissociated into ions such that no partially dissociated complex ions exist, the ion constituents are the really existing charge carriers. Throughout the discussions that follow, complete dissociation into two oppositely charged ion constituents will be assumed. Simple electrolytes like NaCl, $AgClO_4$, and NH_4NO_3 behave in this way. Since the ionic molality $m_\pm$ measures the number of moles of ions per kilogram of solvent, the number of equivalents of an ion per kilogram of solvent is $z_\pm m_\pm$, where $z_\pm$ is the number of positive or negative charges per ion. Per kilogram of solvent, the number of equivalents that pass a plane fixed to the solvent is proportional to the velocity $v_\pm$ of the ions relative to the fixed solvent. The number of equivalents of cations that pass on their way to the cathode is proportional to $z_+ m_+ v_+$, while the number of equivalents of anions is proportional to $|z_-| m_- v_-$. The proportionality constants are equal because the electric field, the gradient of the potential difference, is the same for both ions at this plane. The fraction of the charge carried by the ions is just the ratio of the number of equivalents of either kind to the total number of equivalents. By the definition of the transference number $t_\pm$,

$$t_\pm = \frac{z_\pm m_\pm v_\pm}{z_+ m_+ v_+ + |z_-| m_- v_-}. \tag{7.8}$$

However, since the solution is electrically neutral, the number of positive charges equals the number of negative charges and

$$z_+ m_+ = |z_-| m_-$$

hence,

$$t_\pm = \frac{v_\pm}{v_+ + v_-}. \tag{7.9}$$

In (7.8) and (7.9), all upper signs are used for t_+; all lower, for t_-. From this it follows at once that

$$t_+ + t_- = \frac{v_+}{v_+ + v_-} + \frac{v_-}{v_+ + v_-} = 1 . \tag{7.10}$$

Equation (7.10) follows from the fact that, except for charge carried by electrons or by the solvent itself, it is the solute ions that carry all the electric charge. The ratio of transference numbers not only gives the ratio of ion velocities but also gives the ratios of charge carried and of current carried. That is,

$$\frac{t_+}{t_-} = \frac{v_+}{v_-} = \frac{Q_+}{Q_-} = \frac{\mathcal{I}_+}{\mathcal{I}_-} . \tag{7.11}$$

The Hittorf method of measuring transference numbers involves analysis by ordinary chemical means of the electrolyte near each electrode and in a region between the electrodes that suffers no net change in concentration. Relative to a given mass of solvent, the number of equivalents of an ion constituent present near an electrode after electrolysis is equal to the number present initially plus those generated at the electrode minus those lost by migration to the central compartment. Since the electrode reaction may lead to a loss of equivalents while migration may lead to a partial replacement of this loss, this statement of the number of equivalents η at an electrode after electrolysis is (7.12),

$$\eta = \eta_o \pm \eta_e \mp \eta_m . \tag{7.12}$$

where η_o is the number of equivalents initially present, η_e is the total number of faradays passed through the cell (exclusive of electrons and solvent conduction), and η_m is the number of equivalents that migrate across the boundary between the region around the electrode and the unchanged region between electrodes.

The use of (7.12) is exemplified in the electrolysis of a solution of $AgNO_3$. If the cathode is Ag or Pt, the equivalents of Ag^+ near the cathode decrease due to plating of Ag on the cathode, but some of the loss is offset by migration of Ag^+ toward the cathode. If the anode is Ag, more Ag^+ dissolves in the solution because of electrolysis than is lost by migration away from the anode. If the anode is Pt, electrolysis yields oxygen gas and hydrogen ions, some of which migrate away. In other words, for this solution in these circumstances: the lower signs are used at the cathode; the upper signs are used at the anode of Ag; and at the inert anode, if the analysis is for Ag^+, $\eta = \eta_o - \eta_m$. It is not necessary, however, that both upper or both lower signs in (7.12) be used together. For example, at a platinum anode in a solution of Fe^{++}, the anode destroys Fe^{++} and yet Fe^{++} migrates out of the anode chamber so that both signs are negative.

Equation (7.12) aids in interpreting data meant to fix transference numbers, for

$$t_+ = \frac{\text{no. of equiv. of cation constituent lost by migration from anode}}{\text{total no. of faradays carried thru cell by solute}} \quad (7.13)$$

The numerator is proportional to v_+; the denominator, to $v_+ + v_-$. Similarly,

$$t_- = \frac{\text{no. of equiv. of anion constituent lost by migration from cathode}}{\text{total no. of faradays carried thru cell by solute}} \quad (7.14)$$

These equations are illustrated by the electrolysis of aqueous LiCl in which the highly solvated lithium ion moves only about one-half as fast as the smaller chloride ion. Figure 7.2 illustrates the situations with regard to Li^+ and Cl^- ions before and after electrolysis between Ag, AgCl electrodes. The central chamber has the same composition before and after electrolysis, but the anode and cathode chambers suffer changes even though the net reaction for the cell is nil. The passage of 3 faradays charge yields three equivalents of Cl^- at the cathode; two of these migrate to the central compartment while one Li^+ enters the cathode compartment from the central one. The central compartment gains one Li^+ from the anode compartment and gives it two Cl^- in an attempt to compensate for the loss of three Cl^- at the anode due to electrolysis. If the cathode had been inert, the reaction would have been

$$e^- + H^+ \rightleftharpoons \tfrac{1}{2} H_2$$

if the anode were inert, its reaction would have been

$$OH^- \rightleftharpoons \tfrac{1}{2} H_2O + \tfrac{1}{4} O_2 + e^- .$$

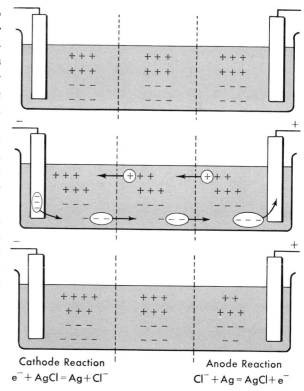

Cathode Reaction
$e^- + AgCl = Ag + Cl^-$

Anode Reaction
$Cl^- + Ag = AgCl + e^-$

Fig. 7.2. *Transference in LiCl.*

As long as the H^+ and OH^- ions do not reach the central compartment, the charges are carried by Li^+ and Cl^- across the compartment boundaries and the presence of H^+ near the anode and OH^- near the cathode is without effect upon the transference numbers. It may be important to know the nature of the electrodes, however, in interpreting the results, for inert electrodes give a different cell reaction from that of Figure 7.2. If only one electrode were

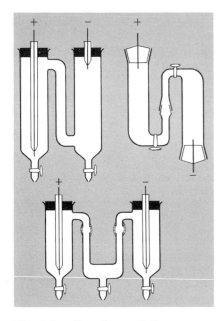

Fig. 7.3. *Transference Cells.*

inert, the total amount of Cl^- in the three compartments would change, but the transference numbers calculated from the data would not.

Three common kinds of transference cells are shown in Figure 7.3. In series with the transference cell and the external source of electricity is a coulometer that measures accurately the amount of charge sent through the cell by the weight of silver deposited on a weighted platinum cup from an aqueous solution of $AgNO_3$. Table 7.2 lists transference numbers for several electrolytes. The influence of temperature is small and more important than the influence of concentration on transference numbers.

Example 7.3. An aqueous solution of $CuSO_4$ was electrolyzed between copper electrodes. After the passage of 1.350×10^{-3} faraday charge, the 25.01 g of solution from the cathode compartment had a molality of 0.0330. The molality of the initial solution and that of the central compartment after electrolysis were 0.0500. Calculate the transference number of cupric ion in this solution.

The amount of water in the cathode compartment after electrolysis must be found in order to relate the molalities, which do not indicate the size of the experiment or the chambers, to the number of faradays charge, which measure the number of ions discharged at the cathode. Since the equivalent weight of $CuSO_4$ is 159.63/2, the grams of water x and the number of

Table 7.2. *Transference Numbers of Cations by the Gravimetric Method**

ELECTROLYTE	TEMPERATURE (°C)	NORMALITY (equivalents per liter)					
		0.010	0.020	0.050	0.100	0.200	1.000
HCl	0	0.846	0.844	0.839			
	18	0.833	0.833	0.834	0.835	0.837	0.844
	30	0.822	0.822	0.822			
	96	0.748					
KCl	0	0.493	0.493	0.493	0.492	0.491	
	18	0.496	0.496	0.496	0.495	0.494	0.490
	30	0.498	0.498	0.498	0.497	0.496	
NaCl	0	0.387	0.387	0.386	0.385		
	18	0.397	0.396	0.393	0.390	0.385	0.365
	30	0.404	0.404	0.404	0.403		
	96			0.442	0.442	0.442	
H_2SO_4	8		0.835	0.835	0.835		
	20		0.822	0.822	0.822		0.812
	32		0.808	0.808	0.808		

* *International Critical Tables VI*, p. 310.

equivalents y of $CuSO_4$ in the cathode compartment are found by solving the simultaneous equations for mass and molality:

$$25.01 = x + y \left(\frac{159.63}{2} \right)$$

$$2 \times 0.0330 = \frac{y}{x \times 10^{-3}}$$

$$25.01 = x + \frac{159.63}{2} \times 6.60 \times 10^{-5} \times x$$

$$x = \frac{25.01}{1.0053} \approx 25.01(1 - 0.0053)$$

$$= 24.88 \text{ g } H_2O .$$

Hence,

$$y = 0.0660 \times 24.88 \times 10^{-3}$$

$$= 1.640 \times 10^{-3} \text{ equivalent } CuSO_4 .$$

Initially, 24.88 g water contained 2.488×10^{-3} equivalent $CuSO_4$. Since Cu^{++} migrates into the cathode compartment while Cu^{++} ions are removed at the cathode, by (7.12),

$$1.640 = 2.488 - 1.350 + \eta_m$$

$$\eta_m = 0.502 .$$

Since the cathode compartment gains what the anode compartment loses by migration to the unchanged central compartment, by (7.13),

$$t_+ = \frac{0.502}{1.350} = 0.372 .$$

The equivalents of solute are referred to a fixed amount of solvent, 24.88 g water, because movement relative to a plane fixed in the solvent means that the amount of water in each chamber is constant.

7.4 Transference Numbers from Position of Moving Boundary

The Hittorf method of measuring transference numbers is tediously slow and may yield values of transference numbers precise to about 0.001. Hydration of ions may cause observed transference numbers to differ from true ones by 0.026 or less, but the addition of a nonmigrant like a sugar permits a correction for this by analysis for solvent moved by ions that are hydrated. The Hittorf method is being replaced by other methods, one of which is the very accurate moving-boundary method. Direct observation of a boundary that moves with the velocity of one of the ions permits the evaluation of the ion's transference number.

The essential feature of a moving-boundary cell is a tube of uniform cross-sectional area as diagramed in Figure 7.4. Two solutions with a common ion are placed in the cell without mixing. In order to keep the boundary between the solutions sharp during electrolysis, the denser solution is placed on the bottom and the boundary is caused to move into the solution containing the swifter noncommon ion. Since the resistance of an electrolyte increases as its ability to transfer charge decreases, the resistance of the solution containing the slower ion is greater than that containing the swifter ion. Since the current density along the tube is constant, the potential difference per unit length along the tube is greater in the solution of high resistance and slow ions. If any swift ions should lag behind the boundary, this increased field would accelerate them until they reached the boundary. Similarly, should a slow ion diffuse ahead of the boundary, the lower field in the leading solution would allow it to lag until it was once again in the boundary between the leading and indicating solutions. Thus, the boundary remains sharp and may be followed by noting the position of the discontinuity in index of refraction or some visible chemical change.

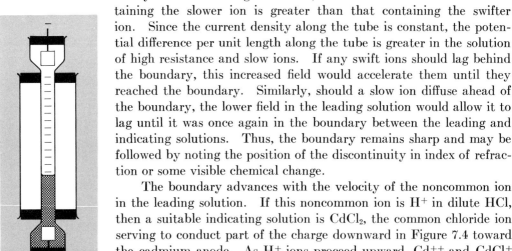

The boundary advances with the velocity of the noncommon ion in the leading solution. If this noncommon ion is H+ in dilute HCl, then a suitable indicating solution is CdCl$_2$, the common chloride ion serving to conduct part of the charge downward in Figure 7.4 toward the cadmium anode. As H+ ions proceed upward, Cd++ and CdCl+ ions take their places and form a solution of CdCl$_2$ somewhat more dilute than the initial indicating solutions. Hydrogen gas is generated at the cathode, and cadmium dissolves at the anode to replace the lost H+ ions. The volume ΔV generated by the boundary as it moves a distance z along the tube of constant cross-

Fig. 7.4. *Moving Boundary Transference Cell.*

Table 7.3. *Transference Numbers of Cations at 25°C by the Moving-Boundary Method**[*]

ELECTROLYTE	NORMALITY (equivalents per liter)				
	0.01	0.02	0.05	0.10	0.20
HCl	0.8251	0.8266	0.8292	0.8314	0.834
KCl	0.4902	0.4901	0.4899	0.4898	0.489
NaCl	0.3918	0.3902	0.3876	0.3854	0.382
LiCl	0.3289	0.3261	0.3211	0.3168	0.311
NH$_4$Cl	0.4907	0.4906	0.4905	0.4907	0.491
KBr	0.4833	0.4832	0.4831	0.4833	0.484
KI	0.4884	0.4883	0.4882	0.4883	0.489
KNO$_3$	0.5084	0.5087	0.5093	0.5103	0.512
AgNO$_3$	0.4648	0.4652	0.4664	0.4682	—
NaC$_2$H$_3$O$_2$	0.5537	0.5550	0.5573	0.5594	0.561
CaCl$_2$	0.4264	0.4220	0.4140	0.4060	0.395
Na$_2$SO$_4$	0.3848	0.3836	0.3829	0.3828	0.383
LaCl$_3$	0.4625	0.4576	0.4482	0.4375	0.4233

* Longsworth, L. G., *Journal of the American Chemical Society,* **54**, 2741 (1932); **57**, 1185 (1935); Longsworth, L. G. and D. A. MacInnes, *Journal of the American Chemical Society,* **60**, 3070 (1938).

section $\mathcal{C}$ is $\mathcal{C}z$. The number of gram-equivalents in a volume ΔV is $N_{\pm}\Delta V \times 10^{-3}$. Here $N_{\pm}$ is the normality of the leading solution and ΔV is measured in milliliters. The number of coulombs of charge carried by the leading ion is, then, $N_{\pm} \times \Delta V \times \mathcal{F} \times 10^{-3}$. For a constant current $\mathcal{I}$ that flows a time Δt, the total charge in coulombs passed through the electrolytes is $\mathcal{I}\Delta t$. Since the transference number is the fraction of the total charge carried by an ion constituent,

$$t_{\pm} = \frac{N_{\pm} \times \mathcal{F} \times \Delta V}{10^3 \times \mathcal{I} \times \Delta t}. \tag{7.15}$$

Some values of cation transference numbers determined by the moving-boundary method are listed in Table 7.3. As the table indicates, transference numbers are almost independent of concentration.

Example 7.4. The table contains some data of L. G. Longsworth [*Journal of the American Chemical Society*, 54, 2745 (1932)] in the determination of the transference number of Na^+ in 0.02 $N_{\pm}$ NaCl at 25°C. The anode was Cd; the following solution, $CdCl_2$; the cathode, Ag-AgCl; the regulated constant current, 0.001600 amp; the cross-sectional area of the tube, 0.1113 cm². (A small correction is to be added to the mean.) The values of the third column of this table have been calculated from (7.15).

VERTICAL DISTANCE MOVED (cm)	TIME (SECONDS)	t_+ (7.15)
0.000	0	—
2.000	689	0.3897
4.000	1380	0.3891
6.000	2070	0.3891
8.000	2757	0.3895
10.000	3453	0.3888
	MEAN	0.3893

7.5 Electrophoresis

It is possible to purify and characterize pure substances and to characterize and separate complex mixtures by the moving boundary technique. The process by which dissolved or suspended colloidal particles move under the

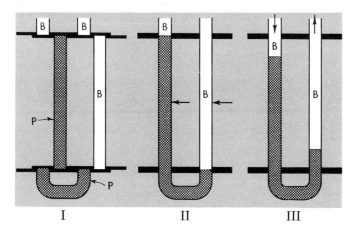

Fig. 7.5. *Diagram of Electrophoretic Cell.*

influence of an electric field is called *electrophoresis*. First observed by accident in 1807 by Reuss, the phenomenon became of analytical importance only in 1937 when Tiselius succeeded in building an apparatus that simplified the precise separation of colloids like proteins and other biological species.

Modern electrophoretic apparatus contains many refinements that permit routine measurements. The optical cell is made in three pieces so that two sharp boundaries can be generated between a buffer and a buffered colloidal dispersion. These sharp boundaries are made by slipping laterally one part into line with another, as in Figure 7.5. The cell parts are filled with solutions of protein (P) and of buffer (B) as in I; after equilibration in a thermostat, the boundaries are produced as in II; then the boundaries are moved into the optical path as in III. The Ag-AgCl electrodes are next connected to the arms of the cell in a way that prevents movement of buffer to the electrode. The thermostat operates at about 1°C so that the rise in temperature due to the electric work done on the cell contents does not greatly change the density of the solutions and blur the boundary by mixing, for near 4°C water and dilute aqueous solutions have their maximum densities and thus exhibit only very small changes in density for a few degrees rise in temperature.

By means of complex optical devices, the rate of change of index of refraction with respect to vertical distance is recorded photographically. Under the action of the potential difference, the charged colloidal particles rise in the right leg and fall in the left. The fastest-moving species can be isolated from the ascending side by withdrawal through a capillary into a syringe, and the slowest-moving species can similarly be withdrawn from the descending leg. Isolation of some other species requires a change of buffer that changes the relative velocities of the several species. Figure 7.6 shows a typical record of the rates of change of index of refraction at some particular time in the electrophoresis. The area of the peaks is related to the amount of a species present, and the width of a peak is related to the homogeneity of its species and its tendency to diffuse. Many of these and other details of typical procedure have been described in the literature.[3]

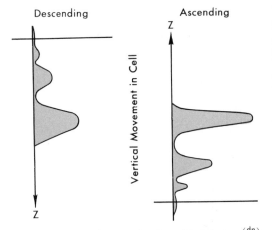

Fig. 7.6. *Typical Electrophoretic Patterns.*

Complex organic molecules like proteins migrate because they contain ionic groups. Acidic groups in proteins are due to the carboxyl groups of glutamic and aspartic acids; basic groups, to lysine, histidine, and arginine. At its isoelectric point, a protein does not migrate because its net charge due to acidic and basic sites that have lost or gained protons is zero. This acid strength is an important characteristic of a protein, just as its rate of movement in an electric field is. In order to reduce all velocities of migration to a common basis of field intensity, the term *mobility* is used. The mobility is the velocity attained in a steady state under the influence of a potential gradient (or field) of 1 volt cm^{-1}. That is, the mobility u is

$$u = \frac{v}{(\mathcal{E}/l)} \qquad (7.16)$$

where v is the velocity attained because of a potential difference $\mathcal{E}$ applied along a distance l. Equation (7.16) applies to colloids and ions alike. The mobility of colloids and ions is about 5×10^{-4} cm^2 volt^{-1} sec^{-1}, but H$^+$ and OH$^-$ have unusually great mobilities of 36.2×10^{-4} and 20.5×10^{-4} cm^2 volt^{-1} sec^{-1}.

It is possible to observe the electrophoretic behavior of small samples of colloids through a microscope. Although colloidal particles range in size from fifty to a few thousand Angstroms and are not directly visible with light, they do scatter light (the Tyndall effect) because of the difference in indexes of refraction of dispersed and dispersing phase. In an ultramicroscope, the direct beam of a powerful source of light can not enter the objective lens, but the light scattered from this beam by the colloidal particles can be seen and used to locate the colloidal particles as individuals. The rate of movement of the colloidal particles can be observed by noting the time required to traverse a standard path of known length.

Table 7.4. *Typical Behavior of Colloids*

LYOPHILIC COLLOIDS	PROPERTY	LYOPHOBIC COLLOIDS
Often not well defined.	Particle size.	About 50 A to about 2000 A.
Particles distinguished as individuals only with difficulty if at all.	Scattering of light (Tyndall effect).	Particles readily seen as individuals in ultramicroscope.
Direction of migration easily changed; particles may have charges of both signs or no charge at all.	Behavior in electric field.	All particles migrate in same direction and have same kind of charge.
Almost nil.	Colligative properties.	Almost nil.
Much greater than dispersing phase.	Viscosity.	Almost same as dispersing phase.
Small amounts have little effect; much may cause dispersed phase to "salt out."	Action of electrolytes.	Small amounts cause precipitation, especially when ion of high valence has charge of sign opposite to dispersed phase.
High molecular weight species: proteins; gels; glue; biological systems.	Typical examples.	Aqueous dispersions of slightly soluble species; aerosols; airborne dust.

7.6 Electrokinetic Potential

The physicochemical properties of the colloidal state are ultimately caused by the state of subdivision of the colloid and the way in which it interacts with its dispersing phase. Table 7.4 lists the characteristics of the two classifications of colloid: *lyophilic* and *lyophobic*.

Because of the large surface area due to a colloid's state of division, surface properties are of utmost importance. The very existence of a lyophobic colloid depends upon the mutual electrical repulsion of particles that might achieve a state of lower free energy by agglomeration. Indeed, all unlike phases develop a difference in potential on contact. The potential gradient (rate of change of potential with respect to distance perpendicular to the interphase boundary) is great within a distance of one ion of the dispersed phase of a colloid, but farther out into the dispersing medium the potential gradient is less and may even change sign. The first layer of ions adsorbed is very tightly bonded, but the more diffuse layer, where the potential gradient is less, is less uniform and rigid. The difference in potential between the outer fixed layer of adsorbate and the bulk of the dispersing medium is called the *electrokinetic potential*. In Figure 7.7, which illustrates the dependence of potential on distance, the electrokinetic potential ζ, often called merely the *zeta-potential*, has the sign of the charge of the tightly adsorbed ions. The value $\zeta = -0.05$ volt commonly observed for glass-water interfaces is interpreted in terms of adsorption of hydroxyl ions by the glass. It is quite generally true for all substances in contact with aqueous acids and bases that increasing the hydroxide ion concentration lowers ζ while increasing the acidity increases ζ. Addition of ions of high valence and of sign opposite to that of the dispersed phase is very effective in decreasing ζ, often to such an extent that the colloidal particles no longer repel each other to prevent agglomeration and precipitation. Even mixing colloids of opposite charge will cause their mutual precipitation.

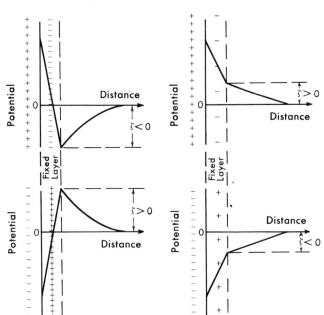

Fig. 7.7. *Electrokinetic Potential (ζ) and Double Layer Potential as Functions of Distance from Surface of Dispersed Phase.*

The magnitude and effects of the electrokinetic potential are observable in four ways: (1) by *electroosmosis*, in which a potential difference, applied to two parts of a liquid separated by a porous membrane or set of capillaries, causes a flow of liquid through the membrane because of the zeta-potential developed between membrane and liquid; (2) by the *streaming potential*, in which a potential difference between parts of a liquid on two sides of a membrane is caused by forced flow through that membrane (reverse of electroosmosis); (3) by the *Dorn effect*, in which particles falling through a fluid acquire a potential different from that of the surrounding fluid; and (4) by *electrophoresis*, in which colloidal particles migrate in an external electric field because they have a potential and charge different from the surrounding fluid (reverse of Dorn effect).

The electrokinetic potential ζ developed by a colloidal particle because of a uniform surface density of electric charge σ is related to its mobility u in an electric field E. The accelerating force on the charge σ per unit area is σE. The opposing force is due to the viscosity η of the dispersing phase. The force F required to move unit areas distant by dr past each other with a difference in velocity dv is, by (2.43) when $\mathcal{C} = 1$,

$$F = \eta \frac{dv}{dr}. \tag{7.17}$$

Since $v' = 0$ at the surface of the double layer and $v' = v$ at a distance d far out in the dispersing phase, by (7.17),

$$\int_0^d F \, dr = \int_0^v \eta \, dv' .$$

The effective opposing force F is, then,

$$F = \eta \frac{v}{d}. \tag{7.18}$$

At the steady state, the accelerating electric force is balanced by the opposing viscous force F; hence, by (7.18),

$$\sigma E = \eta \frac{v}{d}. \tag{7.19}$$

The charge σ per unit area in the double layer is directly related to ζ by Gauss's law of electrostatics. This law says that the total flux of electric displacement **D** through any closed surface is equal to 4π times the free charge enclosed by that surface. For a closed surface surrounding unit area of the double layer, Gauss's law reads $D = 4\pi\sigma$. The gradient of the potential difference ζ is ζ/d and the dielectric constant is κ, so that

$$\kappa \frac{\zeta}{d} = 4\pi\sigma . \tag{7.20}$$

403

Since $v = uE$ by (7.16), elimination of σ from (7.19) and (7.20) yields the relation of ζ to the mobility u. The thickness d of the double layer also disappears.

$$\frac{\kappa\zeta}{4\pi d} = \frac{\eta v}{Ed}$$

$$\zeta = \frac{4\pi\eta u}{\kappa}. \tag{7.21}$$

If κ, η, and u are expressed in cgs units, then ζ as expressed in practical (absolute or international) volts is

$$\zeta = \frac{4\pi(300)^2}{\kappa}\eta u. \tag{7.22}$$

Example 7.5. As viewed in an ultramicroscope, particles of a silica-alumina cracking catalyst suspended in water traversed a standard distance of 0.33 mm between cross hairs toward the positive electrode in 38.2 sec in a potential gradient of 3.2 volts cm^{-1}. If the viscosity of the suspension was 0.0090 dyne sec cm^{-2} and if its dielectric constant was 78, what was the electrokinetic potential of the catalyst particles in water?

Since the velocity of the particles is

$$v = \frac{0.033 \text{ cm}}{38.2 \text{ sec}} = 8.6 \times 10^{-4} \text{ cm sec}^{-1}$$

by (7.16)

$$u = \frac{8.6 \times 10^{-4}}{3.2} = 2.7 \times 10^{-4} \text{ cm}^2 \text{ volt}^{-1} \text{ sec}^{-1}.$$

Then, by (7.22) with account of the direction of migration,

$$\zeta = -\frac{4\pi(300)^2}{78} \times 9.0 \times 10^{-3} \times 2.7 \times 10^{-4} = -0.035 \text{ volt}.$$

The negative sign on ζ indicates that the particles migrated toward the anode and had a net negative charge.

B. CONDUCTIVITY

7.7 Specific Conductivity

The electrical conductivity of a substance is a direct measure of its ability to carry an electric current. The conductivity L of a substance with a resistance $\mathcal{R}$ is given by (7.23).

$$L = \frac{1}{\mathcal{R}}. \tag{7.23}$$

The specific conductivity L_{sp} of a conductor with a cross-sectional area $\mathcal{Q}$ and length l is that proportionality factor which links L, $\mathcal{Q}$, and l for a certain substance. All other things being equal, the conductivity of a substance is directly proportional to its cross section $\mathcal{Q}$ and inversely proportional to its length l; that is,

$$L = L_{sp} \left(\frac{\mathcal{Q}}{l} \right). \qquad (7.24)$$

The specific conductivity L_{sp} is, therefore, numerically equal to the current that flows through a conductor 1 cm long with a cross section of 1 cm² under a potential difference of 1 volt. The unit of conductivity is the reciprocal ohm, or mho. Substances are classified as insulators if their specific conductivities are less than 10^{-13} mho cm^{-1}, as semiconductors if their specific conductivities

Table 7.5. *Specific Conductances of Aqueous* KCl* (international mho cm^{-1})

DEMAL CONCENTRATION	GRAMS KCl PER 1000 GRAMS SOLUTION	SPECIFIC CONDUCTANCE (L_{sp})		
		0°	18°	25°
0.01000	0.745263	0.00077364	0.00122052	0.00140877
0.10000	7.41913	0.0071379	0.0111667	0.0128560
1.00000	71.1352	0.065176	0.097838	0.111342

range from 10^2 to 10^{-10} mho cm^{-1}, and as good conductors if they are about 10^5 mho cm^{-1}. The specific conductivities of aqueous solutions of strong electrolytes like KCl, AgNO$_3$, and CuSO$_4$ in mho cm^{-1} are numerically about one-tenth of their normalities. The specific conductances of three KCl solutions at 0°C, 18°C, and 25°C are listed in Table 7.5. The conductivities of many aqueous solutions increase by about 2% deg^{-1} as these solutions of KCl do. The demal units of concentration measure the number of gram formula weights of KCl in exactly 1000 cc of solution at 0°C. These solutions of KCl are used as reference standards; their conductivities were measured very exactly with electrodes of known area $\mathcal{Q}$ and known separation l.

In order to determine the specific conductance of any solution it is necessary to measure accurately its resistance in a cell of known $\mathcal{Q}$ and l. For a particular cell, an effective value of $\mathcal{Q}/l$ can be found through (7.24) by measuring L for a solution of KCl of known L_{sp}. Here L can be found accurately by use of a Wheatstone bridge, diagramed in Figure 7.8. When the

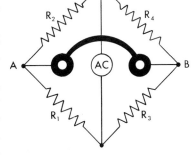

Fig. 7.8. *Wheatstone Bridge.*

bridge is balanced, no current flows through the earphones and they do not hum. If $\mathcal{I}_{12}$ is the current through impedances $\mathcal{R}_1$ and $\mathcal{R}_2$ and if $\mathcal{I}_{34}$ is that

* Jones, G. and B. C. Bradshaw, *Journal of the American Chemical Society*, **55**, 1799 (1933).

through $\mathcal{R}_3$ and $\mathcal{R}_4$ at balance, then, because there is no potential difference between A and B, $\mathcal{I}_{12}\mathcal{R}_1 = \mathcal{I}_{34}\mathcal{R}_3$ and $\mathcal{I}_{12}\mathcal{R}_2 = \mathcal{I}_{34}\mathcal{R}_4$. Division of these equations yields

$$\frac{\mathcal{R}_1}{\mathcal{R}_2} = \frac{\mathcal{R}_3}{\mathcal{R}_4}. \tag{7.25}$$

If B is a sliding contact along a uniform resistance wire with total resistance $\mathcal{R}_3 + \mathcal{R}_4$, the ratio of lengths yields $\mathcal{R}_3/\mathcal{R}_4$. If $\mathcal{R}_2$ is a standard impedance, $\mathcal{R}_1$ is fixed accurately by (7.25). If $\mathcal{R}_1$ is the impedance of a conductivity cell filled with KCl of known L_{sp}, it follows that the cell constant of that cell is, by (7.23) and (7.24),

$$\frac{\alpha}{l} = \frac{1}{\mathcal{R}_1 L_{sp}}. \tag{7.26}$$

With a solution of unknown specific conductivity L'_{sp} in the same cell, a second measurement of impedance $\mathcal{R}'_1$ yields

$$L'_{sp} = \frac{1}{\mathcal{R}'_1}\left(\frac{l}{\alpha}\right)$$

$$= \left(\frac{\mathcal{R}_1}{\mathcal{R}'_1}\right) L_{sp}. \tag{7.27}$$

Example 7.6. At 25°C, a 0.1000 demal KCl solution had an impedance of 97.36 ohms in a certain conductivity cell. Filled with 0.100 normal NaCl, the same cell had an impedance of 117.18 ohms. Calculate the specific conductivity of the NaCl solution.

According to Appendix C, one ohm is 0.999505 international ohm, so that the specific conductivity of 0.1000 demal KCl at 25°C is

$$L_{sp} = 0.0128560 \times 0.999505 \text{ mho cm}^{-1} = 0.0128496 \text{ mho cm}^{-1}.$$

The cell constant is, by (7.26),

$$\frac{\alpha}{l} = \frac{1}{97.36 \times 0.0128496}.$$

Then, by (7.27), the specific conductivity of the NaCl solution is

$$L'_{sp} = \frac{97.36 \times 0.0128496}{117.18} = 0.010676 \text{ mho cm}^{-1}.$$

7.8 Equivalent Conductivity

The equivalent conductivity of a solution is the conductivity of that volume of solution which contains one gram-equivalent of electrolyte when the spacing between electrodes is one cm. In a solution of normality $N_{\pm}$, the volume that contains one equivalent is $(1000/N_{\pm})$ ml. If the distance l between electrodes is one cm, the area $\mathcal{Q}$ of the electrodes is $1000/N_\pm$. By analogy with (7.24), the equivalent conductivity Λ is, by definition,

$$\Lambda = \left(\frac{1000}{N_\pm}\right) L_{\mathrm{sp}}. \tag{7.28}$$

In terms of directly observed variables, (7.28), as transformed by (7.23) and (7.24), reads

$$\Lambda = \left(\frac{1000}{N_\pm}\right)\left(\frac{1}{\mathcal{R}_1}\right)\left(\frac{l}{\mathcal{Q}}\right). \tag{7.29}$$

While specific conductivity varies greatly with chemical concentration, the equivalent conductivity of a strong electrolyte like a salt dissolved in water depends only slightly upon concentration. In the spirit of the Debye-Huckel theory, this weak dependence upon concentration is linear in the square root of the normality in dilute solutions. Because of the interference due to the other ions, equivalent conductance decreases as concentration increases; hence,

$$\Lambda = \Lambda_o - C\sqrt{N_\pm} \tag{7.30}$$

where $\qquad \Lambda_o = \lim_{\sqrt{N_\pm}\to 0}(\Lambda).$ $\qquad$ (7.31)

The limit Λ_o at infinite dilution is conveniently found by graphical extrapolation as in Figure 7.9.

Onsager has shown theoretically that (7.30) is of the correct form. Three things oppose the movement of an ion: the viscosity of the solution, the distortion of the ion atmosphere due to movements of ions in the opposite direction, the flow of solvent held by ions of opposite charge as they move in the opposite direction. On equating the sum of these three opposing forces to the electric force in a steady state, Onsager found that

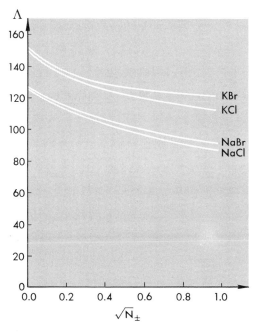

Fig. 7.9. *Dependence of Equivalent Conductance on Concentration* $(25°C)$. *(Int. Crit. Tables VI, pp. 233–35).*

$$\Lambda = \Lambda_o - (C_1 + C_2\Lambda_o)\sqrt{I}.$$

Both C_1 and C_2 depend upon T, z_+, z_-, e, and κ; C_1 depends also upon $\mathcal{F}$ and the viscosity, while C_2 depends also upon equivalent ionic conductances. Theoretical values of C_1 and C_2 agree well with experiment in aqueous and non-aqueous solutions.

In about 1875, Kohlrausch advanced the hypothesis that at infinite dilution, where interionic attractions and repulsions are negligible, each ion migrates independently. The reproducible differences between Λ_o for the chlorides and bromides of sodium and potassium of Figure 7.9 are examples in support of this hypothesis. Mathematically, if l_+^o and l_-^o are the equivalent conductances of cation and anion at infinite dilution,

$$\Lambda_o = l_+^o + l_-^o . \qquad (7.32)$$

The total conductance Λ_o is apportioned between ions according to their transference numbers; hence,

$$\Lambda_o = t_+^o \Lambda_o + t_-^o \Lambda_o \qquad (7.33)$$

where $t_\pm^o$ is the transference number at infinite dilution. A comparison of (7.32) and (7.33) yields a simple expression for ionic conductances, namely, (7.34).

$$l_\pm^o = t_\pm^o \Lambda_o . \qquad (7.34)$$

Table 7.6 lists values of $l_\pm^o$ for several common ions.

Table 7.6. *Equivalent Conductances of Ions at Infinite Dilution* * (25°C)

CATION	l^o_+	ANION	l^o_-
H^+	349.82	OH^-	198.
Li^+	38.69	Cl^-	76.34
Na^+	50.11	Br^-	78.4
K^+	73.52	I^-	76.8
NH_4^+	73.4	NO_3^-	71.44
Ag^+	61.92	$C_2H_3O_2^-$	40.9
Tl^+	74.7	$C_2H_2ClO_2^-$	39.7
$\frac{1}{2} Ba^{++}$	63.64	ClO_4^-	68.0
$\frac{1}{3} La^{+++}$	69.6	$\frac{1}{2} SO_4^{--}$	79.8

7.9 Weak and Strong Electrolytes

The equivalent conductivities of aqueous solutions of NaOH and HCl vary according to (7.30) at low concentrations. However, in the same range of low concentrations, the equivalent conductivities of aqueous solutions of NH_4OH and $HC_2H_3O_2$ are far below the limit Λ_o calculated from their equivalent ionic conductivities. The reason is that NH_4OH and $HC_2H_3O_2$ are only partly ionized even at the low concentrations where the conductivity of water itself begins to contribute to the conductivity of the solution. Figure 7.10 illustrates the behavior typical of strong and weak electrolytes. Because extrapolation of a curve for a weak electrolyte would not yield an accurate limit at $\sqrt{N_\pm} = 0$, Λ_o is calculated by (7.32) from ionic conductances found for salt solutions like NH_4Cl or $NaC_2H_3O_2$, which are completely ionized at all concentrations.

If C_i is the molarity of a solution of a weak electrolyte A_aB_b of which the fraction α is ionized to cations of charge z_+ and anions of charge z_-, then

$$A_aB_b \rightleftharpoons a\,A^{z_+} + b\,B^{z_-}$$
$$(1-\alpha)C_i, \qquad a\alpha C_i \qquad b\alpha C_i . \qquad (7.35)$$

---

* MacInnes, D. A., *Principles of Electrochemistry*. New York: Reinhold Publishing Corporation, 1939, p. 342.

The actual molarity of cations is $a\alpha C_i$ that of anions, $b\alpha C_i$. If there is no other source of these ions, as from a salt in the same solution, then electroneutrality requires that

$$a\alpha C_i z_+ + b\alpha C_i z_- = 0 \qquad (7.36)$$

where z_- is a negative integer. Also,

$$N_\pm = z_+ a C_i = |z_-| \, b C_i . \qquad (7.37)$$

Since Ohm's law fails for solutions only at very great potential gradients, for a solution with resistance $\mathcal{R}$, the time rate of transfer of charge through migration of ions is

$$\mathcal{I} = \frac{\mathcal{E}}{\mathcal{R}} . \qquad (7.38)$$

The number of equivalents of ions per liter is $\alpha N_\pm$ and the time rate of traversal of volume by cations is $\mathcal{Q} v_+$ while that by anions if $\mathcal{Q} v_-$ cm^3 sec^{-1}. Accordingly, the current in amperes, or coulombs per second, is

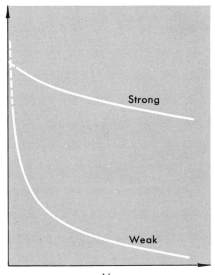

Fig. 7.10. *Typical Dependence of Equivalent Conductivities of Strong and Weak Electrolytes.*

$$\mathcal{I} = \alpha N_\pm \mathcal{F} \mathcal{Q} (v_+ + v_-) \times 10^{-3} . \qquad (7.39)$$

By (7.38), (7.39) yields

$$\alpha \mathcal{F} (v_+ + v_-) = \frac{\mathcal{I} \times 10^3}{N_\pm \mathcal{Q}} = \frac{\mathcal{E} \times 10^3}{\mathcal{R} N_\pm \mathcal{Q}} \times \left(\frac{l}{l}\right) = \left(\frac{\mathcal{E}}{l}\right)\left(\frac{1000 \times l}{N_\pm \mathcal{R} \mathcal{Q}}\right) .$$

Whence, by (7.16) and (7.29), for weak electrolytes

$$\alpha \mathcal{F} (u_+ + u_-) = \Lambda . \qquad (7.40)$$

Since α approaches unity as $\sqrt{N_\pm}$ approaches zero,

$$\lim_{\sqrt{N_\pm} \to 0} [\alpha \mathcal{F} (u_+ + u_-)] = \lim_{\sqrt{N_\pm} \to 0} [\Lambda] .$$

Or,

$$\mathcal{F} (u_+^o + u_-^o) = \Lambda_o . \qquad (7.41)$$

Equation (7.41) applies to both weak and strong electrolytes. An equation like (7.41) holds for strong electrolytes even at finite concentrations; that is,

$$\mathcal{F} (u_+ + u_-) = \Lambda . \qquad (7.42)$$

Even at finite, nonzero concentrations it is reasonable to suppose that by analogy with (7.32) and (7.33)

$$\Lambda = l_+ + l_- = t_+ \Lambda + t_- \Lambda . \qquad (7.43)$$

409

Term-for-term comparison of (7.32), (7.33), and (7.43) with (7.40), (7.41), and (7.42) yields several relations among $l_\pm$, $t_\pm$, $u_\pm$, and Λ. For weak and strong electrolytes,

$$\mathscr{F} u_\pm^o = l_\pm^o . \tag{7.44}$$

For weak electrolytes,

$$\alpha \mathscr{F} u_\pm = l_\pm . \tag{7.45}$$

For strong electrolytes,

$$\mathscr{F} u_\pm = l_\pm = t_\pm \Lambda . \tag{7.46}$$

By analogy with (7.9) and (7.34) it follows that for strong electrolytes

$$t_\pm = \frac{l_\pm}{l_+ + l_-} . \tag{7.47}$$

The degree of ionization of a weak electrolyte can be estimated through measurement of a colligative property or through a measurement of conductivity. If $(u_+^o + u_-^o)$ is approximately equal to $(u_+ + u_-)$, then division of (7.40) by (7.41) yields a simple expression for α, namely,

$$\alpha = \frac{\Lambda}{\Lambda_o} . \tag{7.48}$$

While (7.48) is approximately true, it is more accurate to calculate α by (7.48) when Λ and Λ_o are measured at the same ionic strength.

Example 7.7. If the equivalent conductance of dichloroacetic acid at infinite dilution at 25°C is 388.5 (*International Critical Tables VI*, p. 262), with the aid of data in Example 5.20 estimate the conductivity of 0.100 molal chloroacetic acid. Determine also the equivalent conductance of the anion at infinite dilution.

Since l_+^o of H^+ is 349.8 by Table 7.6, it follows from (7.32) that the equivalent conductance of chloroacetate ion at infinite dilution is

$$l_-^o = \Lambda_o - l_+^o = 388.5 - 349.8 = 38.7 .$$

The degree of ionization as judged from the freezing point depressions in Example 5.20 is 0.61; hence, by (7.48),

$$\Lambda = \alpha \Lambda_o = 0.61 \times 388.5 = 237 .$$

Then, by (7.28) the specific conductivity L_{sp} is

$$L_{sp} = \left(\frac{N_\pm}{1000} \right) \times \Lambda = \frac{0.100}{1000} \times 237 = 2.37 \times 10^{-2} \text{ mho cm}^{-1} .$$

Example 7.8. Calculate the effective mobility of a proton in water.

From Table 7.6, the equivalent conductance of H^+ is 349.82. By (7.44), its mobility is

$$u_+ = \frac{l_+^o}{\mathscr{F}} = \frac{349.82}{96{,}493.1} = 36.253 \times 10^{-4} \text{ cm}^2 \text{ volt}^{-1} \text{ sec}^{-1} .$$

410

7.10 Uses of Conductivity

Measurements of conductivity can yield information about the degree of ionization of a weak electrolyte, as discussed in the preceding section. Simple extension of such methods furnishes information about the degree of hydrolysis of salts and the stability of complex ions. On the other hand, conductivity measurements can characterize the solvent. Figure 7.11 indicates how the equivalent conductivities of KCl, KBr, and KI depend upon concentration in water and in liquid sulfur dioxide at 0°C. In SO_2 these halides are weak electrolytes. They are only partly ionized mainly because the dielectric constant of SO_2 is only about one-sixth as large as that of water. In water, however, where the dielectric constant is great, the attraction among unlike ions is small and ionization is complete. Liquid hydrogen fluoride, which is of importance in the production of fluorine, has a dielectric constant almost equal to that of water and is similar in many ways to water.

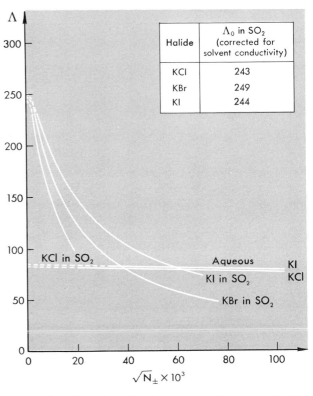

The solvent properties of liquid ammonia are well known and have been investigated in goodly detail.[4] Many metathetical reactions occur in NH_3 but not in water because the solubilities of salts differ. For example, AgI is quite soluble in NH_3, but MgI_2 and KCl are rather insoluble. The most remarkable solutions in liquid ammonia are,

Fig. 7.11. *Equivalent Conductances of Potassium Halides in Water and in Liquid Sulfur Dioxide at 0°C.* *

however, the solutions of alkali and alkaline earth metals. A saturated solution of Na or K in NH_3 has a mole fraction of metal of about 0.15 below 0°C. Such solutions are reddish in color and have a metallic appearance. The specific conductivity of a saturated solution of Na in NH_3 is about 0.5×10^4 mho cm^{-1}, of the same order of magnitude as metals. The transference number of the carrier of negative charge is ten to a few hundred times that of the positive carrier. Conduction is mainly by electrons that are almost free to move anywhere in the solution.

* N. N. Lichtin and H. P. Leftin, *J. Phys. Chem.* **60**, 160 (1956); *Int. Crit. Tables VI*, pp. 234–35.

The production of Al, Mg, Na, and other metals by electrolysis of their molten salts is of great economic importance. The specific conductivities of molten salts is of the order of 10^0 mho cm^{-1}. Conduction occurs by ions freed from their lattice sites by fusion, but in certain situations, especially in molten sulfides, conduction may be electronic also. The specific conductivities of many solids are very sensitive to the presence of impurities and even to the intensity of light that falls on them. In these cases, electrons carry negative charge and holes (electrons that might have been) carry positive charge, but ions themselves generally remain fixed at their lattice sites. Typical metallic conduction also involves movement of electrons through an orderly array of fixed positive ions.

Since a measurement of conductivity with alternating current generally causes little electrolysis and decomposition of a sample, it is an excellent means of swift, nondestructive analysis. Rates of chemical reactions can be followed and the composition of a stream in an industrial flow process can be monitored continuously. Conductivity measurement aids in the manufacture of paper and sugar, in vat dyeing, in following the course of fractional distillation or chemical reaction, in stream pollution studies, in estimating the hardness of water, in soil studies, in detecting the adulteration of milk, in following chromatographic separations, in detecting the extent of disease in plant leaves, and in many other ways.

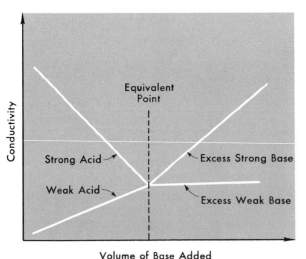

Fig. 7.12. *Conductimetric Titrations.*

The end point of a chemical reaction in solution can be determined conductimetrically if there is a characteristic change in conductivity at the stoichiometric point. Acid-base titrations in water can be done this way because at the equivalence point speedy H^+ and OH^- ions are few. Even though the salt produced by neutralization is present, the conductivity is a minimum when chemically equivalent amounts of acid and base have reacted. In order to minimize dilution effects, the added reagent is concentrated. When a weak acid or base is titrated, a sharp change but not a minimum in conductivity is produced at the equivalent point. Precipitation of a slightly soluble compound or any reaction that withdraws ions from solution can be followed in this way. The end point is found graphically, as in Figure 7.12.

Measurement of the specific conductivity of a saturated solution of a slightly soluble substance permits calculation of its solubility product constant

K_{sp}. Such a solution is usually so dilute that its equivalent conductance is almost equal to Λ_o, provided of course that the electrolyte is strong and therefore totally ionized. Then, as in (7.28),

$$N_{\pm} = \left(\frac{1000}{\Lambda_o}\right) L_{sp} . \tag{7.49}$$

From $N_{\pm}$ the value of K_{sp} is readily found.

Example 7.9. At 25°C, the specific conductivity of a saturated aqueous solution of TlBr is 295.2×10^{-6} mho cm^{-1} [C. R. Johnson and G. A. Hulett, *Journal of the American Chemical Society*, **57**, 256 (1935)]. The water used had a specific conductivity of 0.2×10^{-6} mho cm^{-1}. Calculate the solubility product constant of TlBr and compare with the value calculated from the following standard free energies [F. D. Rossini, *et al.*, National Bureau of Standards Circular 500]: $\Delta G_f^o[\text{Tl}^+_{(aq)}] = -7.8$ kcal mole^{-1}; $\Delta G_f^o[\text{Br}^-_{(aq)}] = -24.6$ kcal mole^{-1}; $\Delta G_f^o[\text{TlBr}_{(s)}] = -39.7$ kcal mole^{-1}.

The equivalent conductance Λ_o of aqueous TlBr at infinite dilution is, by Table 7.6 and (7.32),

$$\Lambda_o = 74.7 + 78.4 = 153.1 .$$

The conductivity of the water is due to the presence of H$^+$, OH$^-$, and impurities; hence, it is necessary to correct the specific conductivity of the saturated solution by 0.2×10^{-6} mho cm^{-1}. Then, by (7.49),

$$N_{\pm} = \frac{1000}{153.1} \times (295.2 - 0.2) \times 10^{-6} = 1.927 \times 10^{-3} .$$

Then, since $N_{\pm} = C_{\text{Tl}^+} = C_{\text{Br}^-}$,

$$K_{sp} = (1.927 \times 10^{-3})(1.927 \times 10^{-3}) = 3.71 \times 10^{-6} .$$

Thermodynamically, as in Section 6.5, for the reaction

$$\text{TlBr}_{(s)} \rightleftharpoons \text{Tl}^+_{(aq)} + \text{Br}^-_{(aq)}$$
$$\Delta G^o = -7.8 - 24.6 - (-39.7) = 7.3 \text{ kcal} .$$

But $\Delta G^o = -RT \ln K$; whence

$$\log K_{sp} = -\frac{\Delta G^o}{2.303RT} = -\frac{7300}{2.303 \times 1.987 \times 298.2}$$
$$= -5.35 = 0.65 - 6.00$$
$$K_{sp} = 4.5 \times 10^{-6} .$$

C. IONIC EQUILIBRIUMS

7.11 Ionization of Water

The purest water that can be prepared has a specific conductivity of 6.2×10^{-8} mho cm^{-1} at 25°C. This and values at other temperatures found by Kohlrausch and Heydweiller[5] are listed in Table 7.7. Since the specific conductivities of liquid hydrocarbons and other insulators are less than 10^{-13} mho cm^{-1}, water itself is a source of ions. Ionization is said to proceed thus:

Table 7.7. *Specific Conductivity of Water*

Temperature (°C)	0	18	25	34	50
L_{sp} (mho cm^{-1}) $\times 10^8$	1.5	4.3	6.2	9.5	18.7

$$H_2O_{(l)} + H_2O_{(l)} \rightleftharpoons H_3O^+_{(aq)} + OH^-_{(aq)} \, .$$

According to (7.32) and the data of Table 7.6, Λ_o of H_2O at 25°C is 349.8 + 198 = 548. It follows then from (7.49) that the concentration of H_3O^+ or OH$^-$ at 25°C is

$$N_{\pm} = \left(\frac{1000}{\Lambda_o}\right) L_{sp} \tag{7.49}$$

$$= \frac{1000}{548} \times 6.2 \times 10^{-8} = 1.13 \times 10^{-7} \text{ mole l}^{-1} \, .$$

Because the concentration of H_2O in pure water or dilute solutions is essentially constant at 55.5 moles l^{-1}, it is convenient to use the relation

$$K_W = a_{H_3O^+} a_{OH^-} \, . \tag{7.50}$$

Numerically, if concentrations are activities,

$$K_W = (1.13 \times 10^{-7})^2$$

$$= 1.28 \times 10^{-14} \, . \tag{7.51}$$

Thermodynamic calculation with the data of Table 6.1 yields $K_W = 1.009 \times 10^{-14}$. The difference in results is due in part to neglect of activity coefficients in this dilute solution. Equation (7.50) expresses a condition upon possible concentrations of H_3O^+ and OH$^-$ in dilute solutions.

Analogous ionizations are thought to account for the conductivities and physicochemical behavior of nonaqueous solvents. For example,

$$NH_{3(l)} + NH_{3(l)} \rightleftharpoons NH_4^+ + NH_2^-$$

and

$$SO_{2(l)} + SO_{2(l)} \rightleftharpoons SO^{++} + SO_3^{--} \, .$$

The specific conductivities of liquid NH_3 and SO_2 are of the order of 10^{-8} mho cm^{-1}.

7.12 Theories of Acids and Bases

There are two general kinds of theory of acids and bases. In one, an acid is a source of protons; in the other, a base is a source of electrons.

The most general protonic theory of acids is that of Lowry and Bronsted. This theory applies equally well to aqueous solutions, nonaqueous solutions, liquids, gases, or solids. An *acid* is defined as a *proton donor;* a *base*, as a *proton acceptor.* Acid-base reactions are viewed as competition for protons. The general reaction of acid HA with base B^- to produce weaker acid HB and weaker base A^- is

$$HA + B^- \rightleftharpoons A^- + HB . \quad (7.52)$$

Here HA and A^- are conjugate acid and base, as are HB and B^-. Table 7.8 lists several examples of acid-base behavior. Generally neutralization reactions are conceived as occurring in a solvent, but this is not necessary according to the definitions. The main fault of this view is that extreme preoccupation with the proton prevents an adequate treatment of salts. The simpler Arrhenius theory, though limited to aqueous solutions, does provide that a salt and water result from neutralization of a protonic acid by a hydroxide base.

Table 7.8. *Acid-Base Reactions Involving Protons*

SOLVENT	ACID	+ BASE	$\rightleftharpoons$ ACID	+ BASE
H_2O	H^+Cl^-	$+ OH^-$	$\rightleftharpoons HOH$	$+ Cl^-$
H_2O	NH_4^+	$+ CO_3^{--}$	$\rightleftharpoons HCO_3^-$	$+ NH_3$
H_2O	$H_2PO_4^-$	$+ PO_4^{---}$	$\rightleftharpoons HPO_4^{--}$	$+ HPO_4^{--}$
H_2O	H_2O	$+ H_2O$	$\rightleftharpoons H_3O^+$	$+ OH^-$
H_2O	H_2O	$+ CO_3^{--}$	$\rightleftharpoons HCO_3^-$	$+ OH^-$
NH_3	NH_4^+	$+ NH_2^-$	$\rightleftharpoons NH_3$	$+ NH_3$
NH_3	NH_3	$+ H^-$	$\rightleftharpoons H_2$	$+ NH_2^-$
None	H_2^+	$+ D$	$\rightleftharpoons HD^+$	$+ H$

The second general theory of acids and bases is electronic and thus in the limit treats all chemical reactions, even oxidation-reduction reactions, as neutralization of acid and base. A *base* offers *electrons* or their equivalent to an acid. In a solution, the equivalent of an electron is often an anion. An acid can therefore be an electron-acceptor, an anion-acceptor, or a cation-donor. Salts are the products of neutralization of an acid and a base. Table 7.9 illustrates the universality of neutralization reactions as viewed by the electronic theory.

A subset of these kinds of reaction is described by the Lewis theory of acids and bases. A Lewis base is a donor of a *pair of electrons*, and a Lewis acid is any species capable of accepting a pair of electrons. Neutralization is conceived as the formation of a coordinate covalent bond. The first four reactions of Table 7.9 exemplify Lewis neutralizations.

Table 7.9. *Acid-Base Reactions Involving Electrons*

SOLVENT	ACID	+ BASE	$\rightleftharpoons$ SALT	+ SALT
H_2O	H^+Cl^-	$+ Na^+OH^-$	$\rightleftharpoons Na^+Cl^-$	$+ HOH$
None	CO_2	$+ CaO$	$\rightleftharpoons CaCO_3$	
H_2O	$FeCl_3$	$+ Cl^-$	$\rightleftharpoons FeCl_4^-$	
None	BF_3	$+ NH_3$	$\rightleftharpoons H_3NBF_3$	
SO_2	$SO^{++}Br_2^-$	$+ Na_2^+SO_3^{--}$	$\rightleftharpoons 2 Na^+Br^-$	$+ 2 SO_2$
None	S	$+ Zn$	$\rightleftharpoons ZnS$	
NH_3	$2 NH_3$	$+ 2 Na$	$\rightleftharpoons 2 Na^+NH_2^-$	$+ H_2$
None	Cl_2	$+ 2 Na$	$\rightleftharpoons NaCl$	$+ NaCl$

The main defect in the electronic theory is its utter universality. Although the analogy of oxidation-reduction reactions to neutralization may at times be of value, the terms *acid* and *base* should perhaps be reserved for some species less general than any chemical substance.

415

7.13 Ionization Constants of Weak Acids

The strongest acid in dilute aqueous solution is H_3O^+ because stronger acids react with H_2O to produce H_3O^+. Acids weaker than H_3O^+ are common. A weak acid HA and its conjugate base A^- react with water thus:

$$HA + H_2O \rightleftharpoons H_3O^+ + A^- \tag{7.53a}$$

$$H_2O + A^- \rightleftharpoons HA + OH^-. \tag{7.54a}$$

For (7.53a), the acid ionization constant K_A, which differs from the equilibrium constant by the factor a_{H_2O}, is defined by (7.53b).

$$K_A = \frac{(a_{H_3O^+}) \times (a_{A^-})}{a_{HA}}. \tag{7.53b}$$

Similarly, for (7.54a),

$$K_B = \frac{(a_{HA}) \times (a_{OH^-})}{a_{A^-}}. \tag{7.54b}$$

Whence it follows by (7.50) that

$$K_A K_B = a_{H_3O^+} \times a_{OH^-} = K_W. \tag{7.55}$$

Example 7.10. Verify (7.55) when HA is NH_4^+. For (7.54), one writes at 25°C

$$H_2O + NH_3 \rightleftharpoons NH_4^+ + OH^-$$

$$K_B = \frac{a_{NH_4^+} \, a_{OH^-}}{a_{NH_3}} = 1.8 \times 10^{-5}.$$

For (7.53),

$$NH_4^+ + H_2O \rightleftharpoons H_3O^+ + NH_3$$

$$K_A = \frac{a_{H_3O^+} \times a_{NH_3}}{a_{NH_4^+}} \times \frac{a_{OH^-}}{a_{OH^-}} = \frac{K_W}{K_B}.$$

Whence (7.55) is obviously true.

For a dibasic acid H_2A three equilibriums are involved in aqueous solutions.

$$H_2A + H_2O \rightleftharpoons H_3O^+ + HA^-, \qquad K_{A1} = \frac{a_{H_3O^+} \, a_{HA^-}}{a_{H_2A}} \tag{7.56}$$

$$HA^- + H_2O \rightleftharpoons H_3O^+ + A^{--}, \qquad K_{A2} = \frac{a_{H_3O^+} a_{A^{--}}}{a_{HA^-}} \tag{7.57}$$

$$H_2O + H_2O \rightleftharpoons H_3O^+ + OH^-, \qquad K_W = a_{H_3O^+} a_{OH^-}. \tag{7.58}$$

There are three sources of H_3O^+ ions. If equilibrium is reached by ionization of H_2A,

$$C_{H_3O^+} = C_{OH^-} + C_{A^{--}} + C_{HA^-} \tag{7.59}$$

because each ionization produces one H_3O^+ for every OH^-, A^{--}, or HA^- ion produced. With the expressions for K_{A1}, K_{A2}, and K_W above, if $a_i = C_i$,

$$C_{H_3O^+} = \frac{K_W}{C_{H_3O^+}} + \frac{K_{A2}C_{HA^-}}{C_{H_3O^+}} + \frac{K_{A1}C_{H_2A}}{C_{H_3O^+}}$$

$$= \frac{K_W}{C_{H_3O^+}} + \frac{K_{A2}K_{A1}C_{H_2A}}{C_{H_3O^+}^2} + \frac{K_{A1}C_{H_2A}}{C_{H_3O^+}}.$$

That is,

$$C_{H_3O^+} = \left[K_W + K_{A1}C_{H_2A}\left(1 + \frac{K_{A2}}{C_{H_3O^+}}\right)\right]^{1/2}. \tag{7.60}$$

If H_2A is a weak acid, C_{HA^-} is generally less than $C_{H_2A} \times 10^{-2}$. Since generally $K_{A2} \sim K_{A1} \times 10^{-5}$, it follows from above that in these circumstances

$$\frac{K_{A2}}{C_{H_3O^+}} = \frac{C_{A^{--}}}{C_{HA^-}} = \frac{K_{A2}C_{HA^-}}{K_{A1}C_{H_2A}} = (<10^{-2})(10^{-5}) < 10^{-7}.$$

Hence, (7.60) with $C_o = C_{H_2A}$ becomes

$$C_{H_3O^+} = [K_W + K_{A1}C_o]^{1/2}. \tag{7.61}$$

If $K_W \ll K_{A1}C_o$, the species H_2A is a weak acid and

$$C_{H_3O^+} = \sqrt{K_{A1}C_o}. \tag{7.62}$$

That is, for the reaction

$$H_2A + H_2O \rightleftharpoons H_3O^+ + HA^-$$

since ionization of one H_2A yields one each of H_3O^+ and HA^-,

$$K_{A1} = \frac{C_{H_3O^+}C_{HA^-}}{C_{H_2A}} = \frac{C_{H_3O^+}^2}{C_o - C_{H_3O^+}}.$$

With $C_{H_3O^+} \ll C_o$, this leads at once to (7.62).

Example 7.11. Calculate the hydrogen ion concentration in 0.10 molar H_3BO_3 if $K_{A1} = 6 \times 10^{-10}$.

Since $C_o = 1.0 \times 10^{-1}$, $C_o K_{A1} = 6 \times 10^{-11}$, which is very small compared to K_W. Hence, by (7.62),

$$C_{H_3O^+} = \sqrt{6 \times 10^{-10} \times 1.0 \times 10^{-1}} = \sqrt{60 \times 10^{-12}} = 8 \times 10^{-6}.$$

7.14 Hydrolysis

Hydrolysis is a chemical reaction in which water is decomposed. In particular, it is the ionization of water caused by a solute. For example, NaSH hydrolyzes thus:

$$Na^+SH^- + H_2O \rightleftharpoons H_2S + Na^+OH^- .$$

Mathematical description of hydrolysis in terms of (7.56), (7.57), and (7.58) begins with a solution of a salt containing HA^- ions of initial concentration C_o. Since $C_{H_3O^+}$ increases as H_2O and HA^- ionize but decreases as HA^- hydrolyzes,

$$C_{H_3O^+} = C_{OH^-} + C_{A^{--}} - C_{H_2A}$$

$$= \frac{K_W}{C_{H_3O^+}} + \frac{K_{A2}C_{HA^-}}{C_{H_3O^+}} - \frac{C_{H_3O^+}C_{HA^-}}{K_{A1}}$$

$$C_{H_3O^+}^2\left(1 + \frac{C_{HA^-}}{K_{A1}}\right) = K_W + K_{A2}C_{HA^-}$$

$$C_{H_3O^+} = \left(\frac{K_W K_{A1} + K_{A1}K_{A2}C_{HA^-}}{K_{A1} + C_{HA^-}}\right)^{1/2}. \tag{7.63}$$

Equation (7.63) assumes several approximate forms. If $C_{HA^-} \gg K_{A1}$, it reads

$$C_{H_3O^+} = \left[K_{A1}\left(\frac{K_W}{C_{HA^-}} + K_{A2}\right)\right]^{1/2}. \tag{7.64}$$

If in addition, $K_W C_{HA^-}^{-1} \gg K_{A2}$ and $C_{HA^-} \gg C_{H_2A} + C_{A^{--}}$,

$$C_{H_3O^+} = \sqrt{\frac{K_{A1}K_W}{C_o}}. \tag{7.65}$$

On the other hand, if C_{HA^-} is not only great relative to K_{A1} and $C_{H_2A} + C_{A^{--}}$ but also great relative to $K_W K_{A2}^{-1}$, (7.64) becomes (7.66).

$$C_{H_3O^+} = \sqrt{K_{A1}K_{A2}}. \tag{7.66}$$

Example 7.12. Describe the orders of magnitude of K_{A1} and K_{A2} for which (7.65) and (7.66) can be applied to a 0.10 molar solution of HA^- in water. Give particular examples of anions HA^- that fit these criteria.

Since $C_{HA^-} \gg K_{A1}$ for both equations, with 1% error, $K_{A1} < C_{HA^-} \times 10^{-2}$. Since HA^- is the main solute containing A in order that $C_o = C_{HA^-} \gg C_{H_2A} + C_{A^{--}}$, $K_{A1} < 10^{-3}$ and HA^- must hydrolyze and ionize weakly. In particular, within 1%,

$$\frac{C_{H_2A}}{C_{HA^-}} = \frac{C_{H_3O^+}}{K_{A1}} < 10^{-2}$$

and

$$\frac{C_{A^{--}}}{C_{HA^-}} = \frac{K_{A2}}{C_{H_3O^+}} < 10^{-2}.$$

That is, on multiplication,

$$\frac{K_{A2}}{K_{A1}} < 10^{-4}.$$

Since $K_{A1} < 10^{-3}$, K_{A2} must be less than 10^{-7}.

Equation (7.65) obtains when, besides these limitations on K_{A1} and K_{A2}, it also happens that

$$K_{A2} \ll \frac{K_W}{0.10} \sim 10^{-13}.$$

Equation (7.65) thus applies to HS^-.

Equation (7.66) obtains when, besides the limitations on K_{A1} and K_{A2}, it also happens that

$$K_{A2} \gg \frac{K_W}{0.10} \sim 10^{-13}.$$

Equation (7.66) thus applies to HCO_3^-.

The hydrolysis of the salt of a weak base BOH is described by the equation

$$B^+ + 2\,H_2O \rightleftharpoons BOH + H_3O^+.$$

If hydrolysis diminishes C_{B+} only slightly from the initial value C_o, and if $C_{BOH} = C_{H_3O^+}$,

$$\frac{C_{BOH}C_{H_3O^+}}{C_{B+}} \times \frac{C_{OH^-}}{C_{OH^-}} = \frac{K_W}{K_{B1}} = \frac{C_{H_3O^+}^2}{C_o}.$$

Whence,

$$C_{H_3O^+} = \sqrt{\frac{K_W C_o}{K_{B1}}}. \tag{7.67}$$

Equation (7.67) results from (7.63) when K_{A1} approaches infinity, when $K_{A2}K_{B1} = K_W$, and when $C_o \gg K_B$.

7.15 Common Ion Effect

When there are two sources of an ion in a solution, for example from ionization of a weak electrolyte and from a fully ionized salt, the ionization of the weak electrolyte is repressed. When the weak acid HA ionizes, $C_{H_3O^+}$ is no longer equal to C_{A^-}; when the weak base BOH ionizes, C_{B+} is no longer equal to C_{OH^-}.

Example 7.13. What is the hydrogen ion concentration in a solution prepared by mixing 25.0 ml 0.100 molar acetic acid ($K_{A1} = 1.8 \times 10^{-5}$) and 20.0 ml 0.100 molar NaOH?

As a zero approximation, the final 45.0 ml of solution will contain 2.00 millimoles sodium acetate and 0.50 millimole acetic acid. In first approximation, if x millimoles of the remaining acetic acid ionize, the concentrations of the various species will be $C_{H_3O^+} = x/45.0$; $C_{C_2H_3O_2^-} = (2.00 + x)/45.0$; $C_{HC_2H_3O_2} = (0.50 - x)/45.0$. Then, as in (7.53),

$$1.8 \times 10^{-5} = \frac{(x/45.0)[(2.00 + x)/45.0]}{(0.50 - x)/45.0}.$$

If $x \ll 0.50$,

$$8.1 \times 10^{-4} \approx \frac{2.00x}{0.50}$$

$$x \approx 2.0 \times 10^{-4} (\ll 5 \times 10^{-1}).$$

Hence,

$$C_{H_3O^+} = \frac{2.00 \times 10^{-4}}{45.0} = 4.4 \times 10^{-6} \text{ moles l}^{-1}.$$

Buffered solutions are an important class of solution involving the common ion effect. Buffers resist changes in acidity upon the addition of even strong base or strong acid. The rate of change of the hydrogen ion activity is a minimum when conjugate acid and base are equal in concentration. In order to show this, let C_1 be the initial concentration of weak acid HA and let C_2 be that of A^-. After the addition of x moles of strong acid or base followed by ionization of y moles of HA,

$$\left.\begin{array}{l} C_{HA} = C_1 \pm x - y \\ C_{H_3O^+} = y \\ C_{A^-} = C_2 \mp x + y \end{array}\right\} \tag{7.68}$$

where the upper signs apply to added acid and lower signs apply to added base. For the reaction

$$HA + H_2O \rightleftharpoons H_3O^+ + A^-$$

$$K_A = \frac{y(C_2 \mp x + y)}{(C_1 \pm x - y)}. \tag{7.69}$$

As can be shown by solving for y and setting its second partial derivative with respect to x equal to zero, the rate of change of y with respect to x is a minimum when $C_1 = C_2 \mp 2x$. If x and y are negligible relative to C_1 and C_2, and if $C_1 = C_2$, then by (7.69)

$$y = C_{H_3O^+} = K_A. \tag{7.70}$$

Similarly, for a buffer composed of BOH and B^+, where K_B is the ionization constant for the reaction

$$BOH \rightleftharpoons B^+ + OH^-$$

the buffer is most efficient in resisting changes in C_{OH^-} or $C_{H_3O^+}$ when $C_{BOH} = C_{B^+}$ and when $C_{OH^-} = K_B$.

7.16 *p*H

When electrical measurements are used to determine the concentration of H_3O^+ in a solution, it is convenient to use the function *p*H, potential of hydrogen. It is defined in terms of a measurement of the potential of a hydrogen electrode dipping into the solution relative to the potential of a reference electrode. Because the measured potentials depend upon variables for which only approximate corrections can be made, *p*H is reported only to the nearest hundredth of a *p*H unit. The cell is of such construction that, approximately,

$$pH = -\log a_{H_3O^+} . \tag{7.71}$$

In dilute solutions,

$$pH = -\log C_{H_3O^+} . \tag{7.72}$$

In pure water, $a_{H_3O^+} = a_{OH^-} = K_W$. Since $K_W = 1.009 \times 10^{-14}$ at 25°C, the *p*H of pure water is given by (7.73).

$$
\begin{aligned}
pH &= -\log (1.009 \times 10^{-14})^{1/2} \\
&= -\tfrac{1}{2} \log 1.009 - \tfrac{1}{2} \log 10^{-14} \\
&= 7.00, \qquad (H_2O, 25°C) .
\end{aligned}
\tag{7.73}
$$

Example 7.14. (a) Calculate the *p*H of a solution in which the activity of H_3O^+ is 2.4×10^{-4}. (b) Calculate the activity of H_3O^+ in a buffer of *p*H = 11.54.
(a) According to (7.71),

$$
\begin{aligned}
pH &= -\log 2.4 \times 10^{-4} = -\log 2.4 - \log 10^{-4} \\
&= -0.38 - (-4.00) = 3.62 .
\end{aligned}
$$

(b) If *p*H = 11.54, $-pH = -11.54$ and by (7.71)

$$\log a_{H_3O^+} = -11.54 = 0.46 - 12.00$$
$$a_{H_3O^+} = 2.9 \times 10^{-12} .$$

D. ELECTRIC WORK AND FREE ENERGY

7.17 Measurement of Potential Difference

Any measurement of the state of a system involves contact with the system from the surroundings, and this demands an exchange of energy. For example, the temperature of a body is measured by inserting a thermometer that can absorb heat from the system. The heat absorbed by a mercury thermometer causes the mercury to expand into the stem, and the extent of expansion is a measure of the temperature finally achieved by system and thermometer. A large mercury thermometer would absorb more heat per degree rise in the temperature of the thermometer than a tiny single-junction thermocouple, which in turn would disturb the system more than reading its temperature with an optical pyrometer. The measured temperature differs from the initial temperature of the system because of the disturbance. The measurement itself causes an uncertainty in temperature and a lower limit of precision.

The ideal method of measurement involves a null measurement. In the limit, the difference in the property of the test body and that of the system approaches zero. Thus, a temperature measurement even with a large mercury thermometer could be made quite accurate if the temperature of the thermometer were adjusted to be almost equal to that of the system before its insertion into the system.

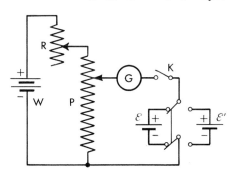

Fig. 7.13. *Balancing Potentiometer.*

Potential difference is readily measured by a null method. The circuit is shown in Figure 7.13 without refinements peculiar to particular instruments. A working cell W establishes a potential difference across resistors R and P. With the double switch to the left, the resistance of R is varied until the scale on P reads the standard cell potential difference $\mathcal{E}$ when the galvanometer G reads zero. When no current flows through G, $\mathcal{E}$ of the cell is undisturbed, except of course for a small discharge not noted by the galvanometer. The key K prevents more than momentary discharges in the stochastic process of attaining balance. Since the standard cell should never be subjected to a current of more than 0.0001 amp, the circuit should contain high resistances in the early stages of finding balance. Then, with the double switch in the right-hand position, the unknown potential $\mathcal{E}'$ is measured by leaving R fixed as above and varying the contact to P until the current through G is zero. If the scale of P is linear and if the potential of W has remained constant, the scale reading of P is $\mathcal{E}'$ in the units of $\mathcal{E}$. With a mechanical galvanometer, precision of the order of one part in a million is attainable, and this can be improved by taking an average of several measurements or by using an ultrasensitive galvanometer. Measurements made in this way are made essentially at equilibrium, for at thermodynamic equilibrium the flow of current is zero.

7.18 Chemical Potential and Electric Work

The potential difference $\mathcal{E}$ measured by the experimenter in the surroundings is the difference in electrostatic potentials $\Phi^{(i)}$ of two pieces of metal connected to the electrodes of the chemical cell. These pieces of metal are commonly the copper wire used to connect the cell to the potentiometer. The two pieces of metal must be of the same substance, for only if these contacts to the potentiometer are alike chemically is the potential difference meaningful.

The value of $\mathcal{E}$ is given by (7.74).

$$\mathcal{E} = \Phi^{(2)} - \Phi^{(1)} . \tag{7.74}$$

If $\Phi^{(2)}$ exceeds $\Phi^{(1)}$, $\mathcal{E}$ is positive. In order to transfer a positive charge dQ from phase 1 of potential $\Phi^{(1)}$ to phase 2 of potential $\Phi^{(2)}$, a positive amount of electric work dw_E must be done on the cell. That is, as in Equation (3.4),

$$dw_E = +\mathcal{E}\, dQ . \tag{7.75}$$

The total amount of work dw done on the cell may also include expansion work dw_{PV}; hence, the first law reads

$$dE = dq + dw \tag{3.31}$$

$$dE = dq + dw_{PV} + dw_E . \tag{7.76}$$

By the usual methods of Section 4.13, (7.76) becomes

$$dG \leqslant -S\, dT + V\, dP + dw_E . \tag{7.77}$$

For a reversible process at constant temperature $(dT = 0)$ and constant pressure $(dP = 0)$,

$$dG = dw_E . \tag{7.78}$$

That is, for a reversible isothermal isobaric process that may involve only expansion and electric work, the increase in free energy dG is equal to the electric work dw_E done on the system. In general, in any reversible isothermal isobaric process, the increase in Gibbs free energy in the system is equal to all the nonexpansion work done on the system.

Electric charge is carried within and through the cell by massive chemical species called ions. The increase in energy $dE^{(j)}$ of phase j within the system is appropriately described in terms of (5.11) for an open subsystem j (or phase j), with, however, the addition of dw_E as in (7.76). If phase j is at a potential $\Phi^{(j)}$ relative to some arbitrary zero level of potential, then

$$dE^{(j)} = T\, dS^{(j)} - P\, dV^{(j)} + \Phi^{(j)}\, dQ^{(j)} + \sum_{i=1}^{C} \mu_i^{(j)}\, dn_i^{(j)} . \tag{7.79}$$

Here C is the number of independently variable components, at least one of which must carry an electric charge. The condition of electroneutrality is relaxed to allow for the transfer of electric charge, but deviations from strict electroneutrality cannot be observed by chemical analysis. An excess of 10^{-10} millimole of singly charged ions per milliliter would have a potential relative to neutral regions of the order of 10^6 volts!

If phase j contains $n_i^{(j)}$ moles of species i with charge $z_i\mathcal{F}$, then the net charge $Q^{(j)}$ on the phase is

$$Q^{(j)} = \sum_{i=1}^{C} z_i n_i^{(j)} \mathcal{F} . \tag{7.80}$$

Since

$$dQ^{(j)} = \sum_{i=1}^{C} z_i \mathcal{F}\, dn_i^{(j)}$$

Equation (7.79) becomes

$$dE^{(j)} = T\, dS^{(j)} - P\, dV^{(j)} + \sum_{i=1}^{C} [\mu_i^{(j)} + z_i \mathcal{F} \Phi^{(j)}] dn_i^{(j)} . \tag{7.81}$$

According to (5.16), the definition of chemical potential, the chemical potential $\boldsymbol{\mu}_i^{(j)}$ of species i is

$$\boldsymbol{\mu}_i^{(j)} = \mu_i^{(j)} + z_i \mathcal{F} \Phi^{(j)} . \tag{7.82}$$

If the phase is at zero potential ($\Phi^{(j)} = 0$) or if species i is electrically neutral ($z_i = 0$), $\boldsymbol{\mu}_i^{(j)} = \mu_i^{(j)}$. Because $\boldsymbol{\mu}_i^{(j)}$ seems experimentally to be independent of $\Phi^{(j)}$, except perhaps at potentials of the order of 10^6 volts, $\mu_i^{(j)}$ may be assumed to be the value long used in previous chapters. However, $\boldsymbol{\mu}_i^{(j)}$ is the only true and observable chemical potential.

By methods analogous to those of Section 5.3, it can be shown that at equilibrium the temperatures and pressures in all phases of an electrochemical system are equal. For any species i that exists in and can be exchanged between phases j and k, at equilibrium, $\boldsymbol{\mu}_i^{(j)} = \boldsymbol{\mu}_i^{(k)}$. However, if a component cannot move between phases, its value of $\boldsymbol{\mu}_i$ need not be the same in both phases.

The difference in electrostatic potential between phases j and k is defined only when these phases are chemically alike. If in addition to chemical likeness it happens that $\mu_i^{(j)} = \mu_i^{(k)}$, as seems experimentally to be true at modest potentials, then by (7.82) and (7.74)

$$\boldsymbol{\mu}_i^{(j)} - \boldsymbol{\mu}_i^{(k)} = z_i \mathcal{F} [\Phi^{(j)} - \Phi^{(k)}]$$
$$= z_i \mathcal{F} \mathcal{E} . \tag{7.83}$$

If phase j differs chemically from phase k, the value of $\mathcal{E} = \Delta\Phi$ is not meaningful even though a reading could be registered on an instrument meant to measure potential difference.

7.19 An Electrochemical Cell

A conglomeration of chemicals develops a finite electric potential difference between phases because one or more charged components cannot be exchanged between certain phases. This barrier to exchange may be a selective membrane, but generally it is mere physical separation in space.

A very simple cell consists of a hydrogen electrode and a silver-silver chloride electrode both immersed in the same solution of hydrochloric acid. The hydrogen electrode consists of a piece of platinum that catalyzes the equilibrium between hydrogen ions of the solution and gaseous hydrogen continuously furnished to the electrode. The other electrode is a piece of platinum connected to a piece of solid silver on which solid silver chloride is deposited. Figure 7.14 is a sketch of this cell. The piece of platinum in contact with the silver electrode is at a higher electrostatic potential than the piece of platinum of the hydrogen electrode.

The conventional cell diagram of this cell is this:

$$(\text{Pt})\text{H}_{2(g)}(f_{\text{H}_2}) \mid \text{H}^+(a_{\text{H}^+}),\ \text{Cl}^-(a_{\text{Cl}^-}) \mid \text{AgCl}_{(s)} \mid \text{Ag}_{(s)}(\text{Pt})\ .$$

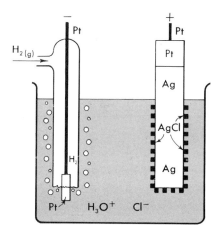

Fig. 7.14. *Sketch of a Simple Cell.*

Since the platinum does not partake in the overall chemical change, it is enclosed in parentheses. A comma separates species in one phase and a single vertical line separates phases such as electrode and electrolyte. The activities or fugacities are enclosed in parentheses immediately after the species to which they refer.

The potential difference $\mathcal{E}$ of the cell is given the sign of the potential of the right-hand electrode relative to the left-hand one, which is at zero potential. For this cell, $\mathcal{E} > 0$ because the right-hand electrode is at a higher potential $\Phi^{(2)}$ than the left-hand one at $\Phi^{(1)}$. Table 7.10 lists the observed values of $\mathcal{E}$ as a function of molality of HCl at 20°C, 25°C, and 30°C.

If this cell were short-circuited, electrons would flow spontaneously from the hydrogen electrode through the external circuit to the Ag-AgCl electrode. At the left-hand electrode, the hydrogen would give up electrons to the platinum metal and would dissolve as ions according to the electrode (or half-cell) reaction

$$\tfrac{1}{2}\,\text{H}_{2(g)} \rightleftharpoons \text{H}^+ + e^-\ . \tag{7.84a}$$

Upon entering the silver electrode from the external circuit, these electrons would transform AgCl into Ag according to the electrode (or half-cell) reaction

$$e^- + \text{AgCl}_{(s)} \rightleftharpoons \text{Ag}_{ss)} + \text{Cl}^-\ . \tag{7.84b}$$

The net reaction of the entire cell is the sum of (7.84a) and (7.84b), namely,

$$\tfrac{1}{2}\,\text{H}_{2(g)} + \text{AgCl}_{(s)} \rightleftharpoons \text{Ag}_{(s)} + \text{H}^+ + \text{Cl}^-\ . \tag{7.85}$$

The electrons transferred from H_2 to AgCl in this reaction are forced to proceed through the external circuit because the H_2 is separated in space from the AgCl. To be sure, the trace of AgCl dissolved in the acid can contact the H_2 at the hydrogen electrode and the trace of H_2 dissolved in the acid can contact the AgCl at the Ag-AgCl electrode. But these internal short-circuits are small because H_2 and AgCl dissolve only slightly. The effect is small, as is attested by the finite and reproducible potential difference developed by the cell.

The electric work $-dw_E$ done reversibly by this cell on the potentiometer at balance when reaction (7.85) occurs as written involves the transfer of 1 mole of electrons from the hydrogen electrode to the Ag-AgCl electrode. Since the charge on the electrons is negative, $dQ = -\mathcal{F} dn$, where dn is the infinitesimal number of moles of electrons transferred from left to right in the external circuit. By (7.75),

$$-dw_E = -\mathcal{E}(-\mathcal{F}\ dn)$$

$$-w_E = +\int_0^1 \mathcal{E}\mathcal{F}\ dn = \mathcal{E}\mathcal{F}\ .$$

Table 7.10. *Potential Differences $\mathcal{E}$ of the Cell* $(Pt)H_{2(g)}(1\ atm) \mid HCl\ (m) \mid AgCl_{(s)} \mid Ag_{(s)}(Pt)*$

m	$\mathcal{E}$ (international volts)		
	20°C	25°C	30°C
0.00500	0.49690	0.49844	0.49983
0.00600	0.48800	0.48940	0.49065
0.00700	0.48050	0.48178	0.48289
0.00800	0.47399	0.47518	0.47617
0.00900	0.46828	0.46937	0.47026
0.01000	0.46319	0.46419	0.46499
0.02000	0.42978	0.43022	0.43049
0.03000	0.41041	0.41056	0.41050
0.04000	0.39673	0.39666	0.39638
0.05000	0.38614	0.38589	0.38543
0.06000	0.37749	0.37709	0.37648
0.07000	0.37017	0.36965	0.36890
0.08000	0.36382	0.36320	0.36285
0.09000	0.35823	0.35751	0.35658
0.10000	0.35321	0.35240	0.35140
0.33187	0.29521	0.29347	0.29160
0.60585	0.26422	0.26204	0.25968
0.83640	0.24627	0.24387	0.24130
0.98615	0.23661	0.23410	0.23147
1.5872	0.20604	0.20328	0.20033
1.7983	0.19721	0.19427	0.19123
1.9789	0.19015	0.18716	0.18405

Whence, by (7.78), $\Delta G = -\mathcal{E}\mathcal{F}$.

In general, as a cell works reversibly on its balancing potentiometer, it does work $-dw_E$ at constant potential difference $\mathcal{E}$. If it transfers n moles of electrons from left to right in the external circuit, $Q = -n\mathcal{F}$ and, by (7.75),

$$-w_E = -\int_0^Q \mathcal{E}\ dQ' = -\mathcal{E}Q = n\mathcal{F}\mathcal{E}\ .$$

But $\Delta G = w_E$ by (7.78); hence,

$$\Delta G = -n\mathcal{F}\mathcal{E}\ . \tag{7.86}$$

The value of ΔG is for the cell reaction as written, and n is the number of faradays associated with either electrode reaction.

Example 7.15. Calculate the increase ΔG in free energy at 25°C and 1 atm for the reaction

$$H_{2(g)} + 2\ AgCl_{(s)} \rightleftharpoons 2\ Ag_{(s)} + 2\ H^+Cl^-$$

when the H_2 is at 1 atm and the HCl is 0.100 molal.

---

* Harned, H. S. and R. W. Ehlers, *Journal of the American Chemical Society,* **54,** 1350 (1932); **55,** 2179 (1933).

For the reaction as written, two faradays are involved in each electrode reaction; hence, $n = 2$. Table 7.10 lists $\mathscr{E} = +0.35240$ international volt, or $+0.35252$ absolute volt. By (7.86),

$$\Delta G = -2 \times 96{,}493.1 \times 0.35252 = -68{,}030 \text{ absolute joules.}$$

For (7.85), ΔG would be half as great.

7.20 Entropy and Enthalpy Changes from Potential Differences

When the cell potential difference is measured reversibly in a balancing potentiometer, only an infinitesimal number of electrons passes through the external circuit. An infinitesimal change in potential could stop or reverse the infinitesimal flow of current at balance. The cell is at equilibrium with its surroundings. At equilibrium at constant temperature and pressure,

$$(\delta G)_{P,T} \geqslant 0 . \tag{4.131}$$

But this criterion of equilibrium is derived from the condition

$$(\delta E)_{S,V} \geqslant 0 . \tag{4.128}$$

Thus, for the system consisting of the whole chemical cell, (4.128) and (7.81) require that

$$\sum_{j=1}^{P} \sum_{i=1}^{C} [\mu_i^{(j)} + z_i \mathscr{F} \Phi^{(j)}] \, \delta n_i^{(j)} \geqslant 0 . \tag{7.87}$$

Equation (7.87) is quite general; it can be simplified in two ways. It ordinarily happens that each neutral component occurs in only one phase; hence, the summation upon j leads to only one term for each value of i and is thus superfluous. Moreover, it is customary and always possible to choose only the electron as the charged component with $z_e = -1$. All other components are chosen as neutral with $z_i = 0$. If the flow of n moles of electrons through the external circuit from phase 1 with potential $\Phi^{(1)}$ to phase 2 with potential $\Phi^{(2)}$ would lead to the formation of n_i moles of component i, then the progress of the change in the system can be followed by a progress variable ξ. For neutral components,

$$\delta n_i^{(j)} = n_i \, \delta\xi . \tag{7.88a}$$

For products, $n_i > 0$; for reactants, $n_i < 0$. For electrons, which are generated chemically in phase 1 and are destroyed chemically in phase 2 as the cell reaction proceeds,

$$\delta n_e^{(1)} = -\delta n_e^{(2)} = n \, \delta\xi . \tag{7.88b}$$

Since electrons as such do not pass through the cell, $\delta n_e^{(j)} = 0$ for $1 \neq j \neq 2$.

Hence, substitution of (7.88a) and (7.88b) into (7.87) yields

$$\left[\sum_{i=1}^{C-1} n_i\mu_i + (-1)n\mathcal{F}\Phi^{(1)} + (-1)(-n)\mathcal{F}\Phi^{(2)}\right]\delta\xi \geq 0 .$$

For arbitrary values of $\delta\xi$,

$$\sum_{i=1}^{C-1} n_i\mu_i + n\mathcal{F}(\Phi^{(2)} - \Phi^{(1)}) = 0 . \qquad (7.89)$$

According to Equations (6.1) to (6.4), this summation is ΔG for the cell reaction, and by (7.74), (7.86) follows at once.

$$\Delta G = -n\mathcal{F}\mathcal{E} . \qquad (7.86)$$

If reactants and products are in their usual standard states,

$$\Delta G^\circ = -n\mathcal{F}\mathcal{E}^\circ . \qquad (7.90)$$

The Gibbs-Helmholtz equation (4.153) permits a calculation of ΔS for a change of state if ΔG is known as a function of temperature. Since $\mathcal{E}$ is the only variable upon which ΔG depends in (7.86), a knowledge of $\mathcal{E}$ as a function of temperature yields ΔS, for by (4.153)

$$\Delta S = -\left(\frac{\partial \Delta G}{\partial T}\right)_P$$

$$= n\mathcal{F}\left(\frac{\partial \mathcal{E}}{\partial T}\right)_P . \qquad (7.91)$$

The value of ΔH can similarly be calculated from electrical measurements, for

$$\Delta H = \Delta G + T\,\Delta S$$

$$= -n\mathcal{F}\mathcal{E} + T\left[n\mathcal{F}\left(\frac{\partial \mathcal{E}}{\partial T}\right)_P\right]$$

$$= n\mathcal{F}\left[T\left(\frac{\partial \mathcal{E}}{\partial T}\right)_P - \mathcal{E}\right] . \qquad (7.92)$$

Example 7.16. Calculate ΔS and ΔH for the reaction of Example 7.15.

Since (7.91) requires the isobaric temperature coefficient of cell potential difference, an average value must be found from Table 7.10. Between 20°C and 25°C,

$$\frac{\Delta\mathcal{E}}{\Delta T} = \frac{0.35240 - 0.35321}{298.12 - 293.12} = -1.62 \times 10^{-4} \text{ volt deg}^{-1} .$$

Between 25°C and 30°C,

$$\frac{\Delta\mathcal{E}}{\Delta T} = \frac{0.35140 - 0.35240}{303.12 - 298.12} = -2.00 \times 10^{-4} \text{ volt deg}^{-1} .$$

Hence, the average value at 25°C is -1.81×10^{-4} volt deg^{-1}. By (7.91),

$$\Delta S = 2 \times 96{,}493.1 \times (-1.81 \times 10^{-4}) = -34.9 \text{ joules deg}^{-1}.$$

By (7.92),

$$\Delta H = 2 \times 96{,}493.1 \,[298.16(-1.81 \times 10^{-4}) - 0.35252] = -78{,}450 \text{ joules}.$$

Example 7.17. Explain in words the significance of the equation $\Delta H = \Delta G + T\,\Delta S$ as it applies to isothermal isobaric cell reactions.

For any isothermal reversible process, the second law requires that $q_{rev} = T\,\Delta S$. On the other hand, when both expansion and electric work are possible, (3.24) says $\Delta H = q_P + w_E$, whether the process is reversible or not. Since $\Delta G = w_{E(rev)} =$ the reversible isothermal isobaric work done on the system, it follows that at constant temperature and pressure

$$q_P + w_E = w_{E(rev)} + q_{rev}.$$

That is, the heat absorbed by the system plus the electric work done on the system equals the reversible electric work done on the system plus the heat absorbed reversibly by the system. However, the isothermal isobaric electric work done on the system irreversibly exceeds that done reversibly because of (7.77) and (7.78), for

$$dw_E \geqslant dG = dw_{E(rev)}.$$

Since $w_{E(rev)}$ exceeds $w_{E(rev)}$, q_{rev} exceeds q_P. Hence, $-q_P$ exceeds $-q_{rev}$ so that an exothermic cell reaction evolves more heat irreversibly than reversibly for the same change of state at constant temperature and pressure. Most heat is evolved when no electric work is done ($w_E = 0$); least, when the electric work is reversible.

7.21 Equilibrium Constants from Potential Differences

If a cell were allowed really to discharge, the concentrations of some components would change as the accompanying cell reaction occurred. In the cell of the previous sections, hydrochloric acid would be generated. But $\mathcal{E}$ decreases as acid forms in this cell. Finally when $\mathcal{E}$ became zero no current would flow and ΔG would be zero. A state of equilibrium would exist with all components at the same potential. In general, at equilibrium at constant temperature and pressure, $\mathcal{E}$ is zero, as required by (7.86) when $\Delta G = 0$.

The dependence of $\mathcal{E}$ upon activities and fugacities follows at once on substituting (7.86) and (7.90) into (6.26) or (6.33).

$$\Delta G = \Delta G^\circ + RT \ln Q \qquad (6.26;\ 6.33)$$

$$-n\mathcal{F}\mathcal{E} = -n\mathcal{F}\mathcal{E}^\circ + RT \ln Q$$

$$\mathcal{E} = \mathcal{E}^\circ - \frac{RT}{n\mathcal{F}} \ln Q. \qquad (7.93)$$

Equation (7.93) is the well-known Nernst equation. When $\mathcal{E} = 0$ at equilibrium,

$$-n\mathcal{F}\mathcal{E}^\circ = -RT \ln K. \qquad (7.94)$$

This is a special form of (6.29) and (6.34), which read $\Delta G^\circ = -RT \ln K$.

Table 7.11. *Cell Notation and Reactions of Varied Cell Types*

CELL NOTATION	REACTIONS
$(Pt)Na(Hg)(0.2\%) \mid Na^+(a_1), Cl^-(a_2) \mid Cl_{2(g)} (pCl_2)(Pt)$	$Na(Hg) \rightleftharpoons Na^+ + e^-$ $e^- + \frac{1}{2} Cl_{2(g)} \rightleftharpoons Cl^-$ $Na(Hg) + \frac{1}{2} Cl_{2(g)} \rightleftharpoons Na^+ + Cl^-$
$(Pt)Zn_{(s)} \mid Zn^{++}(a_1) \mid Fe^{+++}(a_2), Fe^{++}(a_3) \mid (Pt)$	$\frac{1}{2} Zn_{(s)} \rightleftharpoons \frac{1}{2} Zn^{++} + e^-$ $e^- + Fe^{+++} \rightleftharpoons Fe^{++}$ $\frac{1}{2} Zn_{(s)} + Fe^{+++} \rightleftharpoons \frac{1}{2} Zn^{++} + Fe^{++}$
$(Pt)Hg_{(l)} \mid Hg_2Cl_{2(s)} \mid Cl^-(a_1) \parallel I^-(a_2) \mid I_{2(s)}(Pt)$	$Hg_{(l)} + Cl^- \rightleftharpoons \frac{1}{2} Hg_2Cl_{2(s)} + e^-$ $e^- + \frac{1}{2} I_{2(s)} \rightleftharpoons I^-$ $Hg_{(l)} + Cl^- + \frac{1}{2} I_2 \rightleftharpoons \frac{1}{2} Hg_2Cl_{2(s)} + I^-$
$(Pt)Zn_{(s)} \mid ZnO_2^{--}(a_1) \parallel$ $MnO_4^{--}(a_2), MnO_4^-(a_3) \mid (Pt)$	$\frac{1}{2} Zn_{(s)} + 2 OH^- \rightleftharpoons \frac{1}{2} ZnO_2^{--} + H_2O_{(l)} + e^-$ $e^- + MnO_4^- \rightleftharpoons MnO_4^{--}$ $\frac{1}{2} Zn_{(s)} + 2 OH^- + MnO_4^- \rightleftharpoons MnO_4^{--} + H_2O_{(l)} + \frac{1}{2} ZnO_2^{--}$
$(Pt) \mid VO^{++}(a_1), V(OH)_4^+(a_2) \parallel$ $Ce^{+++}(a_3), Ce^{++++}(a_4) \mid (Pt)$	$VO^{++} + 3 H_2O \rightleftharpoons V(OH)_4^+ + 2 H^+ + e^-$ $e^- + Ce^{++++} \rightleftharpoons Ce^{+++}$ $VO^{++} + 3 H_2O + Ce^{++++} \rightleftharpoons V(OH)_4^+ + 2 H^+ + Ce^{+++}$

E. ELECTROCHEMICAL CELLS

7.22 Cell Notation

Before applying the Nernst equation, a brief summary of cell types and their description is necessary. Electrode reactions may involve either anions or cations, and both oxidized and reduced forms of the active species may occur with variable activity. Pure condensed phases exhibit constant activities taken as unity. Table 7.11 lists electrode and cell reactions of various types of cells. As above, an inert electrode is within parentheses; a single vertical line indicates a change of phase; a comma separates species in one phase.

The standard cell of known potential fixes the scale of the potentiometer by fixing R in Figure 7.13. Although several types of standard cell have been used, the most common is the unsaturated Weston cell. Its cell diagram is this.

$$(Pt)Cd(Hg) \mid Cd^{++}SO_4^{--} \mid Hg_2SO_{4(s)} \mid Hg_{(l)}(Pt) .$$

The amalgam Cd(Hg) contains 12.5% by weight Cd; the aqueous solution of $CdSO_4$ is that solution which is saturated with $CdSO_4 \cdot \frac{8}{3} H_2O_{(s)}$ at 4°C; the right-hand electrode is a paste of Hg_2SO_4 and Hg in contact with $Hg_{(l)}$. The standard form of this cell is shown in Figure 7.15. The potential difference of a cell like this is about 1.01904 volts at 25°C. For highest accuracy, the value for a particular cell should be redetermined every year or two by the National Bureau of Standards. This type of cell should be kept at temperatures between 4°C and 40°C. Although its temperature coefficient is less than 10 microvolts deg^{-1}, it should be at the same temperature throughout and should never be subjected to rapid changes of temperature, for these may cause temporary changes in potential difference of a few thousandths of a volt.

The normal (or saturated) Weston cell has this cell diagram.

$$(Pt)Cd(Hg) \mid CdSO_4 . \tfrac{8}{3} H_2O_{(s)} \mid Cd^{++}SO_4^{--} \mid Hg_2SO_{4(s)} \mid Hg_{(l)}(Pt) .$$

It differs from the unsaturated Weston cell in having an electrolyte saturated with respect to $CdSO_4 \cdot \tfrac{8}{3} H_2O_{(s)}$ at the temperature of use. Its potential difference at 25°C is 1.018386 volts. It is used less often than the unsaturated Weston cell because its temperature coefficient is about -45 microvolts deg^{-1} near 25°C.

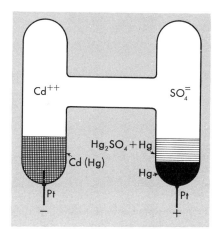

A single vertical line in a cell diagram indicates a change in phase. If this change involves solutions the cell is said to exhibit *transference*. The first cell of Table 7.11 is without transference; the second is a cell with transference. In such a cell, no correction is made for the potential due to the contact of dissimilar solutions, such as that between the solution of zinc ions and that of ferrous and ferric ions. A double vertical line indicates that this junction potential has been eliminated. Experimentally to reduce a junction potential calls for a salt bridge (containing a solution of KCl, NH$_4$NO$_3$, or other salt). To eliminate it calls for a double cell of the type

Fig. 7.15. *Unsaturated Weston Cell.*

$$(Pt)H_{2(g)}(p_1) \mid H^+(a_1), Cl^-(a_3) \mid AgCl_{(s)} \mid Ag_{(s)} \mid AgCl_{(s)} \mid Cl^-(a_4),$$
$$H^+(a_2) \mid H_{2(g)}(p_2) (Pt) .$$

If $a_3 = a_4$, this double cell would have the same potential difference and same cell reaction as the following seemingly simpler cell:

$$(Pt)H_{2(g)}(p_1) \mid H^+(a_1) \parallel H^+(a_2) \mid H_{2(g)}(p_2) (Pt) .$$

Example 7.18. With the aid of opposed cells like the double cell just mentioned, calculate the free energy of dilution of hydrochloric acid at 25°C from 0.9862 molal to 0.1000 molal. See Table 7.10 for data.

The cell reaction is to be

$$H^+Cl^- (m = 0.9862) \rightleftharpoons H^+Cl^- (m = 0.1000) .$$

The reaction in the left-hand cell must produce the more dilute acid in view of (7.85). Since the two cells are opposed, their total potential difference is $+0.35240 - (+0.23410) = 0.11830$ international volt, or 0.11834 absolute volt. Hence, by (7.86)

$$\Delta G = -1 \times 96,493.1 \times 0.11834 = -11,419 \text{ joules} .$$

431

A negative value of ΔG indicates that dilution is a spontaneous process. If the ratio of activities is the ratio of concentrations, (5.21) yields for both ions

$$\Delta G = 8.3144 \times 298.16 \times \ln \left(\frac{0.100}{0.9862} \right)^2 = -11,347 \text{ joules}.$$

Example 7.19. Calculate the potential difference expected at 25°C from the cell

$$(Pt)Zn_xHg \mid Zn^{++}, SO_4^{--} \mid Zn_yHg(Pt)$$

if $x = 6.13 \times 10^{-3}$ and $y = 3.17 \times 10^{-6}$. The value observed by Crenshaw [*Journal of Physical Chemistry*, 14, 158 (1910)] is 0.09773 volt.

If x and y were equal the electrodes would be alike and the cell reaction would be nil. Hence, $\mathcal{E}^o$ is zero and, by (7.93),

$$\mathcal{E} = -\frac{RT}{n\mathcal{F}} \ln \left(\frac{N_2}{N_1} \right).$$

Here N_1 and N_2 are the mole fractions of Zn in the amalgams and are approximately equal to x and y because x and y are small compared to unity. Since the cell reaction for 2 faradays involves the transfer of 1 g formula weight of Zn from Zn_xHg to Zn_yHg, $N_1 = 6.13 \times 10^{-3}$ and $N_2 = 3.17 \times 10^{-6}$. Thus,

$$\mathcal{E} = -\frac{8.3144 \times 298.16 \times 2.3026}{2 \times 96,493} \log \left(\frac{3.17 \times 10^{-6}}{6.13 \times 10^{-3}} \right)$$

$$= -\frac{0.059155 \times (-3.286)}{2} = +0.09719 \text{ volt}.$$

Example 7.20. If $\mathcal{E}^o = +0.84$ volt at 25°C for the cell $(Pt) \mid Fe^{++}, Fe^{+++} \parallel Ce^{+++}, Ce^{++++} \mid (Pt)$ calculate the equilibrium constant of the cell reaction.

The cell reaction is $Fe^{++} + Ce^{++++} \rightleftharpoons Fe^{+++} + Ce^{+++}$. By (7.94),

$$\ln K = \frac{0.84 \times 1 \times 96,500}{8.314 \times 298} = 32.7$$

$$K = \frac{a_{Fe^{+++}}a_{Ce^{+++}}}{a_{Fe^{++}}a_{Ce^{++++}}} = 1.6 \times 10^{14}.$$

Example 7.21. Calculate the equilibrium constant for the reaction $Ag_{(s)} + Fe^{+++} \rightleftharpoons Ag^+ + Fe^{++}$ from these facts. For the cell

$$Ag_{(s)} \mid Ag^+(0.100 \ N) \mid K^+NO_3^-(0.1 \ N) \mid K^+Cl^-(1 \ N) \mid Hg_2Cl_{2(s)} \mid Hg(Ag)$$

$\mathcal{E} = -0.4523$ volt at 25°C; and, at 25°C, $\mathcal{E} = -0.4494$ volt for the cell

$$(Pt) \mid Fe^{++}(0.0500 \ N), Fe^{+++}(0.0500 \ N) \mid K^+Cl^-(sat.) \mid K^+Cl^-(1 \ N)$$
$$\mid Hg_2Cl_{2(s)} \mid Hg(Pt).$$

With these and other data, Noyes and Brann [*Journal of the American Chemical Society*, 34, 1016 (1912)] found $K = 0.100$; by analytical methods they found $K = 0.128$.

If the common normal calomel electrode at the right of each cell is removed and the remainders of the cells are joined, there results the cell

$$(Pt)Ag_{(s)} \mid Ag^+(0.1 \ N) \parallel Fe^{++}(0.0500 \ N), Fe^{+++}(0.0500 \ N) \mid (Pt).$$

Since the $Ag_{(s)}$ is at a higher potential than (Pt) when compared to the calomel electrode, for this last cell $\mathcal{E} = -0.4523 - (-0.4494) = -0.0029$ volt. Its cell reaction is the one desired.

Since K can be found if $\mathcal{E}^\circ$ is known, (7.93) must be used. If concentrations equal activities,

$$\mathcal{E} = \mathcal{E}^\circ - \frac{RT}{n\mathcal{F}} \ln Q \qquad (7.93)$$

$$-0.0029 = \mathcal{E}^\circ - \frac{0.05916}{1} \log\left(\frac{0.100 \times 0.0500}{1 \times 0.0500}\right)$$

$$\mathcal{E}^\circ = -0.0029 + 0.05916 \log (0.100)$$

$$= -0.0029 - 0.0592 = -0.0621 \text{ volt}.$$

Then, by (7.94),

$$\ln K = \frac{-0.0621 \times 96{,}500}{8.314 \times 298} = -2.42$$

$$\log K = -1.05 = 0.95 - 2.00$$

$$K = 8.9 \times 10^{-2}.$$

7.23 Standard Electrode Potentials

The electric potential of an electrode is the electric potential difference measurable between it and a reference electrode. As for any cell, the measurement is made between chemically identical pieces of metal joined to the electrodes. The reference electrode at zero potential is the standard hydrogen electrode. This electrode consists of a piece of platinum in contact with hydrogen gas at unit fugacity (1 atm) and an aqueous solution in which the hydronium ion activity is unity. The standard electrode potential $\mathbf{V}^\circ$ of this electrode is zero at all temperatures.

The electrical potential of an electrode is the measurable potential difference of a cell in which the left-hand electrode is a standard hydrogen electrode. This measurable potential difference is called the *electrode potential* of the right-hand electrode. It is referred to the standard hydrogen electrode at the left at zero potential $[\Phi^{(1)} = \mathbf{V}^\circ(\mathrm{H}_2) = 0]$. The electrode potential of the Ag-AgCl electrode is the potential difference of the cell

$$(\mathrm{Pt})\mathrm{H}_{2(g)}(f_{\mathrm{H}_2} = 1) \mid \mathrm{H}^+(a_{\mathrm{H}^+} = 1), \mathrm{Cl}^-(a_{\mathrm{Cl}^-}) \mid \mathrm{AgCl}_{(s)} \mid \mathrm{Ag}_{(s)}(\mathrm{Pt}).$$

The electrode potential of the Zn-Zn^{++} electrode is the potential difference of the cell

$$(\mathrm{Pt})\mathrm{H}_{2(g)}(f_{\mathrm{H}_2} = 1) \mid \mathrm{H}^+(a_{\mathrm{H}^+} = 1) \parallel \mathrm{Zn}^{++}(a_{\mathrm{Zn}^{++}}) \mid \mathrm{Zn}(\mathrm{Pt}).$$

If the species that partake in an electrode reaction are in their standard states, the electrode potential $\mathbf{V}$ becomes a standard electrode potential $\mathbf{V}^\circ$. The standard electrode potential of the Zn-Zn^{++} electrode is the measured potential difference of the cell

$$(\mathrm{Pt})\mathrm{H}_{2(g)}(f_{\mathrm{H}_2} = 1) \mid \mathrm{H}^+(a_{\mathrm{H}^+} = 1) \parallel \mathrm{Zn}^{++}(a_{\mathrm{Zn}^{++}} = 1) \mid \mathrm{Zn}_{(s)}(\mathrm{Pt}).$$

433

The measured value is -0.763 volt. The standard electrode potential of the Cu-Cu^{++} electrode is $+0.337$ volt, for this is the measured potential difference of the cell

$$(Pt)H_{2(g)}(f_{H_2} = 1) \mid H^+(a_{H^+} = 1) \parallel Cu^{++}(a_{Cu^{++}} = 1) \mid Cu_{(s)}(Pt).$$

Tables 7.12 and 7.13 list standard electrode potentials in aqueous solution and the electrode reactions. Many of the values listed for acidic solutions can be used also in basic solutions. Table 7.14 lists standard electrode potentials for a few metals in solutions in liquid ammonia. In liquid ammonia, K, Na, and Pb are less vigorous reducing agents than in water.

Table 7.12. *Standard Electrode Potentials in Acidic Aqueous Solution**

ELECTRODE REACTION		$V°$ (volts)
$e^- + \frac{1}{2} Ca^{++}$	$\rightleftarrows Ca_{(s)}$	-2.87
$e^- + Na^+$	$\rightleftarrows Na_{(s)}$	-2.714
$e^- + \frac{1}{3} AlF_6^{---}$	$\rightleftarrows \frac{1}{3} Al_{(s)} + 2 F^-$	-2.07
$e^- + \frac{1}{3} Al^{+++}$	$\rightleftarrows \frac{1}{3} Al_{(s)}$	-1.66
$e^- + \frac{1}{2} Mn^{++}$	$\rightleftarrows \frac{1}{2} Mn_{(s)}$	-1.18
$e^- + \frac{1}{2} V^{++}$	$\rightleftarrows \frac{1}{2} V_{(s)}$	-1.18
$e^- + \frac{1}{2} Zn^{++}$	$\rightleftarrows \frac{1}{2} Zn_{(s)}$	-0.763
$e^- + Tl\ I_{(s)}$	$\rightleftarrows Tl + I^-$	-0.753
$e^- + TlBr_{(s)}$	$\rightleftarrows Tl + Br^-$	-0.658
$e^- + \frac{1}{2} Fe^{++}$	$\rightleftarrows \frac{1}{2} Fe_{(s)}$	-0.440
$e^- + \frac{1}{2} Cd^{++}$	$\rightleftarrows \frac{1}{2} Cd_{(s)}$	-0.403
$e^- + Ti^{+++}$	$\rightleftarrows Ti^{++}$	-0.37
$e^- + Tl^+$	$\rightleftarrows Tl_{(s)}$	-0.3363
$e^- + V^{+++}$	$\rightleftarrows V^{++}$	-0.255
$e^- + AgI_{(s)}$	$\rightleftarrows Ag_{(s)} + I^-$	-0.151
$e^- + \frac{1}{2} Pb^{++}$	$\rightleftarrows \frac{1}{2} Pb_{(s)}$	-0.126
$e^- + H^+$	$\rightleftarrows \frac{1}{2} H_{2(g)}$	0.0000
$e^- + AgCl_{(s)}$	$\rightleftarrows Ag_{(s)} + Cl^-$	0.222
$e^- + \frac{1}{2} Cu^{++}$	$\rightleftarrows \frac{1}{2} Cu_{(s)}$	0.337
$e^- + 2 H^+ + VO^{++}$	$\rightleftarrows V^{+++} + H_2O_{(l)}$	0.361
$e^- + \frac{1}{2} Ag_2CrO_{4(s)}$	$\rightleftarrows \frac{1}{2} CrO_4^{--} + Ag_{(s)}$	0.446
$e^- + \frac{1}{2} I_{2(s)}$	$\rightleftarrows I^-$	0.5355
$e^- + \frac{1}{2} I_3^-$	$\rightleftarrows \frac{3}{2} I^-$	0.536
$e^- + H^+ + \frac{1}{2} O_2$	$\rightleftarrows \frac{1}{2} H_2O_2$	0.682
$e^- + Fe^{+++}$	$\rightleftarrows Fe^{++}$	0.771
$e^- + Ag^+$	$\rightleftarrows Ag_{(s)}$	0.7991
$e^- + 2 H^+ + V(OH)_4^+$	$\rightleftarrows VO^{++} + 3 H_2O$	1.00
$e^- + \frac{1}{2} Br_{2(l)}$	$\rightleftarrows Br^-$	1.0652
$e^- + H^+ + \frac{1}{4} O_2$	$\rightleftarrows \frac{1}{2} H_2O_{(l)}$	1.229
$e^- + \frac{1}{2} Tl^{+++}$	$\rightleftarrows \frac{1}{2} Tl^+$	1.25
$e^- + \frac{1}{2} Cl_{2(g)}$	$\rightleftarrows Cl^-$	1.3595
$e^- + \frac{1}{3} Au^{+++}$	$\rightleftarrows Au_{(s)}$	1.50
$e^- + \frac{8}{5} H^+ + \frac{1}{5} MnO_4^-$	$\rightleftarrows \frac{1}{5} Mn^{++} + \frac{4}{5} H_2O_{(l)}$	1.51
$e^- + Au^+$	$\rightleftarrows Au_{(s)}$	1.68
$e^- + \frac{8}{3} H^+ + FeO_4^{--}$	$\rightleftarrows \frac{1}{3} Fe^{+++} + \frac{4}{3} H_2O_{(l)}$	1.9
$e^- + \frac{1}{2} F_{2(g)}$	$\rightleftarrows F^-$	2.87

* Latimer, Wendell M., *Oxidation States of the Elements and Their Potentials in Aqueous Solutions,* 2nd. ed. Englewood Cliffs, N. J.: Prentice-Hall, Inc., Copyright 1938, 1952.

Just as tables of ΔH_f^o, S^o, and ΔG_f^o tersely summarize much chemistry, these three tables of standard electrode potentials summarize in briefest form much electrochemistry. From standard electrode potentials can be calculated cell potentials and free energies of cell reactions. For example, the cell potential of the cell

$$(Pt)Zn_{(s)} \mid Zn^{++}(a_{Zn^{++}} = 1) \parallel Cu^{++}(a_{Cu^{++}} = 1) \mid Cu_{(s)}(Pt)$$

is equal to the cell potential of the double cell (with all species in standard states)

$$(Pt)Zn \mid Zn^{++} \parallel H^+ \mid H_2(Pt) - (Pt)H_2 \mid H^+ \parallel Cu^{++} \mid Cu(Pt) .$$

Table 7.13. *Standard Electrode Potentials in Basic Aqueous Solution**

ELECTRODE REACTION	V^o (volts)
$e^- + \frac{1}{2} ZnS \rightleftharpoons \frac{1}{2} Zn_{(s)} + \frac{1}{2} S^{--}$	−1.44
$e^- + \frac{1}{2} CdS_{(s)} \rightleftharpoons \frac{1}{2} Cd_{(s)} + \frac{1}{2} S^{--}$	−1.21
$e^- + \frac{1}{2} Tl_2S \rightleftharpoons Tl_{(s)} + \frac{1}{2} S^{--}$	−0.96
$e^- + H_2O_{(l)} \rightleftharpoons \frac{1}{2} H_2(g) + OH^-$	−0.828
$e^- + \frac{1}{2} Ag_2S_{(s)} \rightleftharpoons Ag_{(s)} + \frac{1}{2} S^{--}$	−0.69
$e^- + \frac{1}{2} S_{(s)} \rightleftharpoons \frac{1}{2} S^{--}$	−0.48
$e^- + TlOH_{(s)} \rightleftharpoons Tl_{(s)} + OH^-$	−0.3445
$e^- + Ag(NH_3)_2^+ \rightleftharpoons Ag_{(s)} + 2\,NH_{3(aq)}$	0.373

Table 7.14. *Standard Electrode Potentials in Liquid Ammonia at 20°C (referred to the normal aqueous hydrogen electrode)†*

V^o IN NH_3	ELECTRODE REACTION
−2.73	$e^- + K^+ \rightleftharpoons K_{(s)}$
−2.59	$e^- + Na^+ \rightleftharpoons Na_{(s)}$
−1.27	$e^- + \frac{1}{2} Zn^{++} \rightleftharpoons \frac{1}{2} Zn_{(s)}$
−0.93	$e^- + \frac{1}{2} Cd^{++} \rightleftharpoons \frac{1}{2} Cd_{(s)}$
−0.75	$e^- + H^+ \rightleftharpoons \frac{1}{2} H_{2(g)}$
−0.42	$e^- + \frac{1}{2} Pb^{++} \rightleftharpoons \frac{1}{2} Pb_{(s)}$
−0.32	$e^- + \frac{1}{2} Cu^{++} \rightleftharpoons \frac{1}{2} Cu_{(s)}$
0.00	$e^- + \frac{1}{2} Hg^{++} \rightleftharpoons \frac{1}{2} Hg_{(l)}$
+0.08	$e^- + Ag^+ \rightleftharpoons Ag_{(s)}$

Because the hydrogen electrodes are alike and opposed, their effect is nil. Since the electrodes of the left part of this double cell are interchanged, the cell reaction of the left part is reversed and its potential difference is +0.763 volt. The total potential difference of the double cell is, then, +0.763 + (+0.337) = +1.100 volt. This same result is obtained from (7.74) when V^o is substituted for Φ. That is, for the cell (with all species in standard states)

$$(Pt)Zn \mid Zn^{++} \parallel Cu^{++} \mid Cu(Pt)$$

the electrode and cell reactions are

left electrode $\qquad\qquad \frac{1}{2} Zn_{(s)} \rightleftharpoons \frac{1}{2} Zn^{++} + e^-$

right electrode $\qquad\qquad e^- + \frac{1}{2} Cu^{++} \rightleftharpoons \frac{1}{2} Cu_{(s)}$

whole cell $\qquad\qquad \frac{1}{2} Zn_{(s)} + \frac{1}{2} Cu^{++} \rightleftharpoons \frac{1}{2} Zn^{++} + \frac{1}{2} Cu_{(s)} .$

* Latimer, Wendell M., *Oxidation States of the Elements and Their Potentials In Aqueous Solutions*, 2nd. ed. Englewood Cliffs, N. J.: Prentice-Hall, Inc., Copyright 1938, 1952.
† Cappel, N. O. and G. W. Watt, *Journal of Chemical Education*, **13**, 231 (1936).

By (7.74), which is always true for any cell,

$$\mathcal{E} = \Phi^{(2)} - \Phi^{(1)} \tag{7.74}$$

$$= \mathbf{V}^{(\text{right})} - \mathbf{V}^{(\text{left})} . \tag{7.95}$$

For this cell,

$$\mathcal{E}^o = \Phi^{(\text{Cu})} - \Phi^{(\text{Zn})} = \mathbf{V}^o_{(\text{Cu})} - \mathbf{V}^o_{(\text{Zn})}$$

$$= +0.337 - (-0.763) = +1.100 \text{ volts} .$$

The positive value of $\mathcal{E}^o$ means that the piece of Pt joined to the copper electrode is at a higher electrostatic potential than the piece of Pt joined to the zinc electrode. If this cell were short circuited, electrons would flow spontaneously from zinc to copper through the external circuit.

Similarly, for the cell (with all species in standard states)

$$(\text{Pt})\text{Cu} \mid \text{Cu}^{++} \parallel \text{Zn}^{++} \mid \text{Zn}\,(\text{Pt})$$

the electrode and cell reactions are

$$\tfrac{1}{2}\,\text{Cu}_{(s)} \rightleftharpoons \tfrac{1}{2}\,\text{Cu}^{++} + e^-$$

$$\underline{e^- + \tfrac{1}{2}\,\text{Zn}^{++} \rightleftharpoons \tfrac{1}{2}\,\text{Zn}_{(s)}}$$

$$\tfrac{1}{2}\,\text{Cu}_{(s)} + \tfrac{1}{2}\,\text{Zn}^{++} \rightleftharpoons \tfrac{1}{2}\,\text{Cu}^{++} + \tfrac{1}{2}\,\text{Zn}_{(s)} .$$

By (7.74),

$$\mathcal{E}^o = \Phi^{(\text{Zn})} - \Phi^{(\text{Cu})} = \mathbf{V}^o_{(\text{Zn})} - \mathbf{V}^o_{(\text{Cu})}$$

$$= -0.763 - (+0.337) = -1.100 \text{ volts} .$$

The negative value of $\mathcal{E}^o$ means that the piece of Pt joined to the zinc electrode is at a lower electrostatic potential than the piece of Pt joined to the copper electrode. If this cell were short circuited, electrons would flow spontaneously from zinc to copper through the external circuit.

The sign convention described here is the one originally chosen by Gibbs. It is sometimes called the *European convention* to distinguish it from the American[6] convention popularized by Lewis. Licht and de Bethune[6] have very clearly explained and compared these two conventions concerning signs. The main advantage of the European convention used here is that the sign associated with the electrode potential is invariant. Moreover, (7.74) is always true and a negative sign is associated with electrodes that tend to donate electrons to the external circuit. The so-called European convention is that sign convention adopted in 1953 at Stockholm by the International Union of Pure and Applied Chemistry. The statement of the I.U.P.A.C. follows:[7]

The Electromotive Force of a Cell

The cell should be represented by a diagram, e.g.,

$$\text{Zn} \mid \text{Zn}^{++} \parallel \text{Cu}^{++} \mid \text{Cu} .$$

The electromotive force is equal in sign and magnitude to the electrical potential of the metallic conducting lead on the right when that of the similar lead on the left is taken as zero, the cell being open.

When the reaction of the cell is written as

$$\tfrac{1}{2}\,Zn + \tfrac{1}{2}\,Cu^{++} \rightarrow \tfrac{1}{2}\,Zn^{++} + \tfrac{1}{2}\,Cu$$

this implies a diagram so drawn that this reaction takes place when positive electricity flows through the cell from left to right. If this is the direction of the current when the cell is short-circuited, as in the present example, the electromotive force will be positive (unless the ratio Cu^{++}/Zn^{++} is extremely small). If, however, the reaction is written as:

$$\tfrac{1}{2}\,Cu + \tfrac{1}{2}\,Zn^{++} \rightarrow \tfrac{1}{2}\,Cu^{++} + \tfrac{1}{2}\,Zn$$

this implies the diagram

$$Cu \mid Cu^{++} \parallel Zn^{++} \mid Zn$$

and the electromotive force of the cell so specified will be negative (unless the ratio Cu^{++}/Zn^{++} is extremely small).

The Electromotive Force of a Half-Cell and the So-called 'Electrode Potential'

When we speak of the electromotive forces of the half-cells:

$$Zn^{++} \mid Zn$$
$$Cl^{-} \mid Cl_2, Pt$$
$$Cl^{-} \mid AgCl, Ag$$
$$Fe^{++}, Fe^{+++} \mid Pt$$

we mean the electromotive forces of the cells

$Pt, H_2 \mid H^{+} \parallel Zn^{++} \mid Zn$		$\tfrac{1}{2}\,H_2 + \tfrac{1}{2}\,Zn^{++} \rightarrow H^{+} + \tfrac{1}{2}\,Zn$
$Pt, H_2 \mid H^{+} \parallel Cl^{-} \mid Cl_2, Pt$	implying	$\tfrac{1}{2}\,H_2 + \tfrac{1}{2}\,Cl_2 \rightarrow H^{+} + Cl^{-}$
$Pt, H_2 \mid H^{+} \parallel Cl^{-} \mid AgCl, Ag$	the	$\tfrac{1}{2}\,H_2 + AgCl \rightarrow H^{+} + Cl^{-} + Ag$
$Pt, H_2 \mid H^{+} \parallel Fe^{++}, Fe^{+++} \mid Pt$	reaction	$\tfrac{1}{2}\,H_2 + Fe^{+++} \rightarrow H^{+} + Fe^{++}$

where the electrode on the left is a *standard hydrogen electrode.*

These electromotive forces may also be called *relative electrode potentials* or, in brief, *electrode potentials.*

When, on the other hand, we speak of the electromotive forces of the half-cells:

$$Zn \mid Zn^{++}$$
$$Pt, Cl_2 \mid Cl^{-}$$
$$Ag, AgCl \mid Cl^{-}$$
$$Pt \mid Fe^{++}, Fe^{+++}$$

we mean the electromotive forces of the cells

$Zn \mid Zn^{++} \parallel H^{+} \mid H_2, Pt$		$\tfrac{1}{2}\,Zn + H^{+} \rightarrow \tfrac{1}{2}\,Zn^{++} + \tfrac{1}{2}\,H_2$
$Pt, Cl_2 \mid Cl^{-} \parallel H^{+} \mid H_2, Pt$	implying	$Cl^{-} + H^{+} \rightarrow \tfrac{1}{2}\,Cl_2 + \tfrac{1}{2}\,H_2$
$Ag, AgCl \mid Cl^{-} \parallel H^{+} \mid H_2, Pt$	the	$Ag + Cl^{-} + H^{+} \rightarrow AgCl + \tfrac{1}{2}\,H_2$
$Pt \mid Fe^{++}, Fe^{+++} \parallel H^{+} \mid H_2, Pt$	reaction	$Fe^{++} + H^{+} \rightarrow Fe^{+++} + \tfrac{1}{2}\,H_2$

where the electrode on the right is a *standard hydrogen electrode.*

These electromotive forces should NOT be called electrode potentials.

Example 7.22. If the decinormal calomel electrode, with electrode reaction $e^- + \frac{1}{2} Hg_2Cl_{2(s)} \rightleftharpoons Hg_{(l)} + Cl^-(0.1\ N)$, has $\mathbf{V} = +0.3338$ volt at $25°C$, calculate the standard electrode potential of the chlorine electrode if $\mathcal{E} = 1.0508$ volts for the cell

$$(Pt)Hg_{(l)} \mid Hg_2Cl_{2(s)} \mid HCl(0.1\ N) \mid Cl_{2(g)}(0.0490\ \text{atm})(Pt)\ .$$

[G. N. Lewis and F. F. Rupert, *Journal of the American Chemical Society*, **33**, 299 (1911).]

The cell reaction is found thus.

$$Hg_{(l)} + Cl^-(0.1\ N) \rightarrow \frac{1}{2} Hg_2Cl_{2(s)} + e^-$$
$$\frac{e^- + \frac{1}{2} Cl_{2(g)}(0.0490\ \text{atm}) \rightarrow Cl^-(0.1\ N)}{Hg_{(l)} + \frac{1}{2} Cl_{2(g)}(0.0490\ \text{atm}) + Cl^-(0.1\ N) \rightarrow Cl^-(0.1\ N) + \frac{1}{2} Hg_2Cl_{2(s)}\ .}$$

If $\mathbf{V}^o$ is the standard electrode potential of the chlorine electrode, (7.95) requires that $\mathcal{E}^o = \mathbf{V}^o - (+0.3338)$ volt for the cell

$$(Pt)Hg_{(l)} \mid Hg_2Cl_{2(s)} \mid Cl^-(0.1\ N) \parallel Cl^-(a_{Cl^-} = 1) \mid Cl_{2(g)}(1\ \text{atm})(Pt)\ .$$

For the cell observed, (7.93) reads

$$1.0508 = \mathbf{V}^o - 0.3338 - \frac{RT}{\mathcal{F}} \ln \left(\frac{a_{Cl^-}}{f_{Cl_2}^{1/2}} \right).$$

The activity of chloride ion appears in this equation because $\mathbf{V} = +0.3338$ for the decinormal calomel cell includes a term of the form $(RT/\mathcal{F}) \ln a_{Cl^-}$, for Cl^- is part of the decinormal calomel electrode reaction. Since $a_{Cl^-} = 0.0796$ in $0.1\ N$ HCl (see Section 7.24), and since the pressure is low enough to assume that fugacity and pressure are equal, it follows that

$$\mathbf{V}^o = 1.0508 + 0.3338 + 0.05916 \log \left(\frac{0.0796}{0.0490^{1/2}} \right)$$

$$= 1.0508 + 0.3338 - 0.0263 = 1.3583\ \text{volts}\ .$$

Example 7.23. Calculate the standard molar free energy of formation of the chloride ion in aqueous solution.

For the cell

$$(Pt)H_{2(g)}(1\ \text{atm}) \mid H^+(a_{H^+} = 1) \parallel Cl^-(a_{Cl^-} = 1) \mid Cl_{2(g)}(1\ \text{atm})(Pt)$$

the cell potential is, by Table 7.12 and (7.95),

$$\mathcal{E}^o = \mathbf{V}^o_{(Cl_2)} - \mathbf{V}^o_{(H_2)} = 1.3595 - 0 = 1.3595\ \text{volts}\ .$$

For the cell reaction,

$$\frac{1}{2} H_{2(g)} + \frac{1}{2} Cl_{2(g)} \rightarrow H^+ + Cl^-$$

by (7.90),

$$\Delta G^o = -1 \times 96,493 \times 1.3595 = -131,180\ \text{joules} = -30,640\ \text{cal}\ .$$

This is also the standard molar free energy of formation of $Cl^-_{(aq)}$ since all other species in the cell reaction are in standard states for which $\Delta G^o_f = 0$. The value in Table 6.1 is $-31,350$ cal.

Example 7.24. At 25°C, $\mathcal{E}$ = 1.05080 volts for the cell

$$(Pt)H_{2(g)} \text{ (1 atm) } | \; Na^+OH^-(a_1), \; Na^+Cl^-(a_1) \; | \; AgCl_{(s)} \; | \; Ag_{(s)}(Pt)$$

[E. J. Roberts, *Journal of the American Chemical Society*, **52**, 3877 (1930)].

With the aid of data from Table 7.10 for the cell

$$(Pt)H_{2(g)}(1 \text{ atm}) \; | \; HCl(m) \; | \; AgCl_{(s)} \; | \; Ag_{(s)}(Pt)$$

calculate the ion product K_W of water at 25°C. Estimate mean molal activity coefficients by (5.120).

$$-\log \gamma_\pm = 0.509 z_+ \, | \, z_- | \, \sqrt{I} \, . \tag{5.120}$$

If $m_\pm$ = 0.0050 in Table 7.10, by (7.93) for the cell reaction (7.85),

$$0.49844 = \mathcal{E}^o - \frac{2.303RT}{\mathcal{F}} \log a_{H^+} \times a_{Cl^-}$$

$$\mathcal{E}^o = 0.49844 + 0.05916 \log (\gamma_\pm m_\pm)^2$$

$$= 0.49844 + 0.11832[\log m_\pm + \log \gamma_\pm]$$

$$= 0.49844 + 0.11832 \log 0.0050 + 0.11832 \log \gamma_\pm$$

$$= 0.49844 - 0.27225 - 0.11832 \times 0.509 \times \sqrt{I}$$

$$= 0.22619 - 0.0602 \sqrt{I} \, .$$

But

$$I = \tfrac{1}{2} \sum_i z_i^2 m_i \tag{5.108}$$

$$= \tfrac{1}{2} (1^2 \times 0.0050 + 1^2 \times 0.0050)$$

$$= 0.0050 \, .$$

Hence

$$\mathcal{E}^o = 0.22619 - 0.0602 \sqrt{0.0050}$$

$$= 0.22193 \text{ international volt} \, .$$

For the basic cell, the electrode and cell reactions are these.

$$\tfrac{1}{2} H_{2(g)} + OH^- \rightleftharpoons H_2O_{(1)} + e^-$$

$$e^- + AgCl_{(s)} \rightleftharpoons Ag_{(s)} + Cl^-$$

$$\overline{\tfrac{1}{2} H_{2(g)} + AgCl_{(s)} + OH^- \rightleftharpoons Ag_{(s)} + Cl^- + H_2O_{(1)}} \, .$$

Since the activities of OH^- and Cl^- are equal, and since all other species are in their standard states, $\mathcal{E} = \mathcal{E}^o$ = 1.05080 international volts.

If a double cell were formed by joining Ag-AgCl electrodes of these cells, the basic cell being reversed, the result would be essentially the same as

$$(Pt)H_{2(g)} \; | \; H^+ \; \| \; OH^- \; | \; H_{2(g)}(Pt) \, .$$

The standard cell potential of this cell is

$$\mathcal{E}^o = +0.22193 - (+1.05080)$$

$$= -0.82887 \text{ international volt}$$

$$= -0.82914 \text{ absolute volt} \, .$$

The electrode and cell reactions are

$$\frac{1}{2} H_{2(g)} \rightleftharpoons H^+ + e^-$$
$$e^- + H_2O_{(1)} \rightleftharpoons OH^- + \frac{1}{2} H_{2(g)}$$
$$\overline{H_2O_{(1)} \rightleftharpoons H^+ + OH^-}.$$

But the equilibrium constant for this reaction is K_W; therefore, by (7.94)

$$\log K_W = \frac{-0.82914 \times 1 \times 96,493}{2.3026 \times 8.3144 \times 298.16} = -14.051$$

$$K_W = 0.889 \times 10^{-14}.$$

Roberts' more elegant method of finding $\mathcal{E}^\circ$ yielded a somewhat greater value of K_W.

Example 7.25. Calculate the solubility product constant of TlBr at 25°C and compare the values found in Example 7.9.

Since the solubility product constant K_{sp} is the equilibrium constant of the reaction $TlBr_{(s)} \rightleftharpoons Tl^+ + Br^-$, this same reaction must be the cell reaction of the cell chosen. Two suitable electrode reactions are

$$Tl_{(s)} \rightleftharpoons Tl^+ + e^-$$
$$e^- + TlBr_{(s)} \rightleftharpoons Tl_{(s)} + Br^-.$$

For the cell $Tl_{(s)} \mid Tl^+ \parallel Br^- \mid TlBr_{(s)} \mid Tl_{(s)}$ it follows from (7.95) and Table 7.12 that

$$\mathcal{E}^\circ = -0.658 - (-0.3363) = -0.322 \text{ volt}.$$

By (7.94),
$$\log K_{sp} = \frac{-0.322 \times 1 \times 96,493}{2.303 \times 8.314 \times 298.2}$$

$$= -5.44 = 0.56 - 6.00$$

$$K_{sp} = 3.6 \times 10^{-6}.$$

Example 7.26. Calculate the cell potential of the cell $(Pt) \mid Ti^{++}$ $(a = 0.200)$, Ti^{+++} $(a = 0.0200) \parallel H^+$ $(a = 0.0100) \mid H_{2(g)}(730 \text{ mm Hg})(Pt)$. The cell reaction, if electrons proceed from left to right through the external circuit, is

$$Ti^{++} + H^+ \rightleftharpoons \frac{1}{2} H_2 + Ti^{+++}.$$

By (7.93) and (7.95) and Table 7.12,

$$\mathcal{E} = \mathcal{E}^\circ - \frac{RT}{\mathcal{F}} \log \left(\frac{a_{Ti^{+++}} a_{H_2}^{1/2}}{a_{H^+} a_{Ti^{++}}} \right)$$

$$= [0.00 - (-0.37)] - 0.05916 \log \left[\frac{0.0200 \times (730/760)^{1/2}}{0.0100 \times 0.200} \right]$$

$$= 0.37 - 0.05916 \log 9.80 = 0.37 - 0.06 = 0.31 \text{ volt}.$$

Example 7.27. Calculate V° for the Fe-Fe^{+++} electrode at 25°C.

From Table 7.12,

$$e^- + \frac{1}{2} Fe^{++} \rightleftharpoons \frac{1}{2} Fe_{(s)}, \qquad V^\circ = -0.440 \text{ volt}.$$
$$e^- + Fe^{+++} \rightleftharpoons Fe^{++}, \qquad V^\circ = +0.771 \text{ volt}.$$

For the reaction $2e^- + Fe^{++} \rightleftharpoons Fe_{(s)}$, by an expression analogous to (7.90),

$$\Delta G^o = -2 \times 96{,}500 \times (-0.440) = +84{,}900 \text{ joules}.$$

For the reaction $e^- + Fe^{+++} \rightleftharpoons Fe^{++}$,

$$\Delta G^o = -1 \times 96{,}500 \times 0.771 = -74{,}400 \text{ joules}.$$

Since G^o is a function of state, for the reaction $3e^- + Fe^{+++} \rightleftharpoons Fe_{(s)}$, namely, the sum of these last two reactions,

$$\Delta G^o = +84{,}900 + (-74{,}400) = 10{,}500 \text{ joules}.$$

Whence,

$$\mathbf{V}^o = \frac{\Delta G^o}{-n\mathcal{F}} = \frac{10{,}500}{-3 \times 96{,}500} = -0.0363 \text{ volt}.$$

7.24 Activity Coefficients From Cell Potentials

Observed cell potentials of suitably chosen electrochemical cells provide a direct and simple means of measuring ionic activities and activity coefficients. The various kinds of activities and activity coefficients have been defined in Section 5.23. This discussion deals with mean molal activities $a_{\pm}$ and mean molal activity coefficients $\gamma_{\pm}$.

The method of calculation is readily illustrated by the cell

$$(Pt)H_{2(g)}(a = 1) \mid H^+(a_+), Cl^-(a_-) \mid AgCl_{(s)} \mid Ag_{(s)}(Pt).$$

Since the cell reaction is

$$\tfrac{1}{2} H_{2(g)} + AgCl_{(s)} \rightleftharpoons Ag_{(s)} + H^+ + Cl^- \tag{7.85}$$

it follows at once from (7.93) that

$$\mathcal{E} = \mathcal{E}^o - \frac{RT}{\mathcal{F}} \ln (a_+ a_-). \tag{7.96}$$

But by (5.112), $a_{HCl} = a_+ a_- = a_{\pm}^2$; and by (5.113), $a_{\pm} = \gamma_{\pm} m_{\pm}$. Since $m_{\pm} = m_{HCl} = m$, (7.96) reads

$$\mathcal{E} = \mathcal{E}^o - \frac{RT}{\mathcal{F}} \ln (\gamma_{\pm} m)^2$$

$$= \mathcal{E}^o - \frac{2RT}{\mathcal{F}} \ln \gamma_{\pm} - \frac{2RT}{\mathcal{F}} \ln m. \tag{7.97}$$

As m approaches zero, $\gamma_{\pm}$ approaches unity and $\ln \gamma_{\pm}$ approaches zero. Hence,

$$\lim_{\sqrt{m} \to 0} \left[\mathcal{E} + \frac{2RT}{\mathcal{F}} \ln m \right] = \mathcal{E}^o. \tag{7.98}$$

Inasmuch as $[\mathscr{E} + (2RT/\mathscr{F}) \ln m]$ can be calculated from directly observed values of $\mathscr{E}$, m, and T, extrapolation to the limit at $\sqrt{m} = 0$ yields $\mathscr{E}^\circ$. Unfortunately the extrapolation is not linear in this case so that an accurate value of the standard cell potential is not forthcoming.

The limiting form of the Debye-Huckel equations fails at about 0.001 molal. In the range of low concentrations $(m < 0.2)$ for which $\mathscr{E}$ and m are known for this cell,

$$-\log \gamma_\pm = A\sqrt{m} + Bm. \qquad (7.99)$$

Here B is an empirical constant independent of m. Substitution of (7.99) into (7.97) yields

$$\mathscr{E} + \frac{2RT}{\mathscr{F}} \ln m - \frac{2RT}{\mathscr{F}} A\sqrt{m}$$
$$= \mathscr{E}^\circ + \frac{2RT}{\mathscr{F}} Bm.$$

Since $A = 0.509$ at $T = 298.16$,

$$\mathscr{E} + 0.11831 \log m - 0.0602\sqrt{m}$$
$$= \mathscr{E}^\circ + B'm \qquad (7.100)$$

where B' is some empirical constant. Extrapolation of the left-hand member of (7.100) to $m = 0$ is, however, linear in m and is accordingly an accurate method of finding $\mathscr{E}^\circ$. Figure 7.16 shows the extrapolation with data of Tables 7.10 and 7.15 at 25°C. The value of $\mathscr{E}^\circ$, 0.22252 absolute volt, is almost the same as the value of 0.22239 international volt found by Harned and Ehlers.[8]

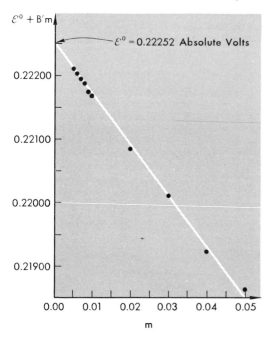

Fig. 7.16. *Standard Electrode Potential of Silver-Silver Chloride Electrode at 25°C.*

Table 7.15. *Calculations for Figure 7.16*

m	$\mathscr{E}$ (INT. VOLTS)	$\mathscr{E}$ (ABS. VOLTS)	$+ 0.11831 \log m$	$+ 0.0602\sqrt{m}$	$\mathscr{E}^\circ + B'm$
0.005	0.49844	0.49860	−0.27223	0.00426	0.22211
0.006	0.48940	0.48956	−0.26286	0.00467	0.22203
0.007	0.48178	0.48194	−0.25495	0.00504	0.22195
0.008	0.47518	0.47534	−0.24808	0.00538	0.22188
0.009	0.46937	0.46952	−0.24204	0.00571	0.22177
0.010	0.46419	0.46434	−0.23662	0.00602	0.22170
0.020	0.43022	0.43036	−0.20100	0.00851	0.22085
0.030	0.41056	0.41070	−0.18017	0.01042	0.22011
0.040	0.39666	0.39679	−0.16539	0.01204	0.21923
0.050	0.38589	0.38602	−0.15392	0.01346	0.21864

With $\mathcal{E}^\circ$ known, mean molal activity coefficients follow at once from (7.97) or (7.101) for each value of m.

$$\ln \gamma_\pm = \frac{\mathcal{F}(\mathcal{E}^\circ - \mathcal{E})}{2RT} - \ln m .\qquad(7.101)$$

In particular, at $m = 0.1000$ where $\mathcal{E} = 0.35252$,

$$\log \gamma_\pm = \frac{(0.22252 - 0.35252)}{2 \times 0.059155} - \log 0.1000$$

$$= -1.0988 + 1 = 0.9012 - 1$$

$$\gamma_\pm = 0.7965 .$$

This is the value used in Example 7.22.

7.25 Concentration Cell Without Transference

Cells without transference are so made that solutions of different concentration are not in direct contact. Such cells have no salt bridges and have no need for them. Cells without transference are of two types. (a) One electrode is reversible with respect to a cation of the common electrolyte, while the other electrode is reversible with respect to an anion of the common electrolyte. Examples are:

$$(Pt)H_{2(g)} \mid H^+,\ Cl^- \mid AgCl_{(s)} \mid Ag_{(s)}(Pt)$$

$$(Pt)Hg_{(l)} \mid Hg_2Cl_{2(s)} \mid Cl^- \mid Cl_{2(g)}(Pt) .$$

(b) The electrodes contacting the common electrolyte have different activities of the species that can become either an anion or cation of the common electrolyte. Examples are:

$$(Pt)Zn_xHg \mid Zn^{++} \mid Zn_yHg(Pt), \qquad (x \neq y)$$

$$(Pt)Cl_2(p_1) \mid Cl^- \mid Cl_2(p_2)(Pt), \qquad (p_1 \neq p_2) .$$

Even these cells are only approximations to an ideal cell, for the separation of reactive species is not perfect. The concentrations of Ag^+ and H_2, of Hg_2^{++} and Cl_2, of Zn and Hg, and of Cl_2 in the common electrolyte are not zero. Fortunately they are negligible.

A concentration cell is a cell that exhibits a potential difference because of a difference in concentrations at the electrodes. Cells of type (b) above are concentration cells without transference.

443

Example 7.28. Calculate the cell potential at 25°C of the cell

$$(Pt)H_{2(g)}(1.000\ atm)\ |\ H^+(0.1\ N)\ |\ H_{2(g)}(386.6\ atm)(Pt)\ .$$

Since $V°$ is zero for both electrodes and since the cell reaction is $H_{2(k)}(1.000\ atm) \rightleftharpoons H_{2(g)}(386.6\ atm)$, by (7.93)

$$\mathcal{E} = -\frac{RT}{\mathcal{F}}\ln\left(\frac{386.6^{1/2}}{1.000^{1/2}}\right)$$

$$= -\frac{0.05916}{2}\log 386.6 = -0.0765\ volt\ .$$

The observed value [W. R. Hainesworth, H. J. Rowley and D. A. MacInnes, *Journal of the American Chemical Society*, 46, 1437 (1924)] is -0.0794 volt. The deviation is probably due to nonideal behavior of H_2. The fact that $\mathcal{E}$ is less than zero indicates that the cell reaction is not spontaneous, for ΔG is greater than zero.

7.26 Concentration Cell With Transference Eliminated

Cells with transference have solutions of differing concentration directly in contact with each other. Ions tend to diffuse from solution to solution because they differ in nature and mobility and concentration. The slight deviations from electroneutrality that result at the interface between solutions cause a measurable potential difference. This potential difference is called a *diffusion potential* or *junction potential*. Cells with transference are of two types. (a) Both electrodes are reversible with respect to different cations or different anions. Examples are:

$$(Pt)Zn_{(s)}\ |\ Zn^{++}\ |\ Cu^{++}\ |\ Cu_{(s)}(Pt)$$

$$(Pt)Zn_{(s)}\ |\ Zn^{++}\ |\ Fe^{++},\ Fe^{+++}\ |\ (Pt)$$

$$(Pt)Br_{2(l)}\ |\ Br^-\ |\ Cl^-\ |\ Cl_{2(g)}(Pt)$$

(b) Similar electrodes are in contact with electrolytes of different ionic activity. Examples are:

$$Zn_{(s)}\ |\ Zn^{++}(a_2)\ |\ Zn^{++}(a_1)\ |\ Zn_{(s)}$$

$$(Pt)H_{2(g)}\ |\ H^+(a_2)\ |\ H^+(a_1)\ |\ H_{2(g)}(Pt)$$

$$(Pt)Cl_{2(g)}\ |\ Cl^-(a_1)\ |\ Cl^-(a_2)\ |\ Cl_{2(g)}(Pt)$$

$$Ag_{(s)}\ |\ AgCl_{(s)}\ |\ Cl^-(a_1)\ |\ Cl^-(a_2)\ |\ AgCl_{(s)}\ |\ Ag_{(s)}\ .$$

Since cells of type (b) exhibit a potential difference because a_1 is not equal to a_2, they are concentration cells with transference.

The junction potential caused by the change in concentration can be decreased by connecting the solutions of differing concentration with a salt bridge. Solutions of KCl or, when K^+ or Cl^- ions would interfere with electrode reactions, NH_4NO_3 are commonly used. Although the junction potential can seldom be eliminated completely, it can be decreased sufficiently in many cases so that calculations with the Nernst equation are meaningful.

A salt bridge, which is considered to reduce the junction potential to zero, is indicated by two vertical lines. For example,

$$Zn_{(s)} \mid Zn^{++}(a_2) \parallel Zn^{++}(a_1) \mid Zn_{(s)}$$

$$(Pt)Cl_{2(g)} \mid Cl^-(a_1) \parallel Cl^-(a_2) \mid Cl_{2(g)}(Pt) \ .$$

It is often possible to arrange a battery of cells without transference that has as its net reaction the same change of state effected in a concentration cell with transference. For example, for the last zinc concentration cell, the cell reaction is $Zn^{++}(a_1) \rightleftharpoons Zn^{++}(a_2)$. But this is the over-all reaction of the double cell

$$Ag \mid AgCl \mid Cl^-, \ Zn^{++}(a_1) \mid Zn \mid Zn^{++}(a_2), \ Cl^- \mid AgCl \mid Ag \ .$$

The cell reaction of the last chlorine concentration cell, $Cl^-(a_1) \rightleftharpoons Cl^-(a_2)$, is the net reaction of the double cell

$$(Pt)H_{2(g)} \mid H^+(a), \ Cl^-(a_2) \mid AgCl_{(s)} \mid Ag_{(s)} - Ag_{(s)} \mid AgCl_{(s)} \mid Cl^-(a_1),$$
$$Na^+(a'), \ H^+(a) \mid H_{2(g)}(Pt) \ .$$

The dilution of HCl in a cell of this type was discussed in Example 7.18.

Example 7.29. Calculate the cell potential at 25°C of the cell

$$(Pt)H_{2(g)}(a = 1) \mid H^+(a = 10^{-7}) \parallel H^+(a = 1) \mid H_{2(g)}(a = 1)(Pt) \ .$$

Since the cell reaction is $H^+(a = 1) \rightleftharpoons H^+(a = 10^{-7})$, by (7.93)

$$\mathcal{E} = 0.0000 - \frac{0.05916}{1} \log \left(\frac{10^{-7}}{1} \right) = +0.41412 \text{ volt} \ .$$

Electrons tend to flow spontaneously from left to right through the external circuit in this cell because there are more protons at the right ready to accept the electrons than there are protons at the left.

7.27 Junction Potentials

As 1 faraday of negative electric charge flows from left to right through the external circuit, 1 faraday of negative charge seems to flow from right to left through the cell to complete the circuit. Really the flow in the cell is due to movement of positive and negative ions. Anions carry negative charge to the left while cations carry positive charge to the right. Cations carry only part of the charge; anions carry the rest. However, the changes that occur at each electrode involve 1 faraday.

As a cell with transference discharges, ions diffuse between solutions not only because they carry charge but also because there exist concentration changes at the interface. The two solution phases are not at equilibrium. Because mobilities and rates of diffusion differ, the contacting solutions deviate from electroneutrality. A salt bridge between unlike solutions acts to minimize these electrical disturbances.

The three calomel electrodes (saturated, normal, and decinormal) are generally used in such a way that their solutions of KCl function as salt bridges. Since pH is defined in terms of measured cell potentials in a cell like

$$(Pt)H_{2(g)} \mid H^+, Cl^- \mid K^+, Cl^- \mid Hg_2Cl_{2(s)} \mid Hg_{(l)}(Pt)$$

it is of interest to investigate the junction potential caused at the HCl-KCl interface. The question is really how precisely pH can be measured or predicted despite the inevitable junction potential where the KCl solution meets the solution of unknown hydrogen ion activity. If $\mathcal{E}^\circ$ is the cell potential when the H^+ activity is unity, then by definition, when the potential of the cell above is $\mathcal{E}_t$, the subscript t indicating the influence of transference,

$$pH = \frac{\mathcal{F}(\mathcal{E}_t - \mathcal{E}^\circ)}{2.3026RT}. \tag{7.102}$$

If the cell is thermostated at constant pressure, equilibrium at the hydrogen electrode requires that

$$\mu_{H^+}^{(H_2)} = \mu_{H^+}^{(HCl)}. \tag{7.103}$$

Similarly, at the KCl-Hg$_2$Cl$_2$ interface,

$$\mu_{Cl^-}^{(KCl)} = \mu_{Cl^-}^{(Hg_2Cl_2)}. \tag{7.104}$$

Moreover, at the Hg$_2$Cl$_2$-Hg interface,

$$\mu_{Hg_2^{2+}}^{(Hg_2Cl_2)} = \mu_{Hg_2^{2+}}^{(Hg)}. \tag{7.105}$$

The inert Pt electrodes do not partake directly in the cell reaction and can be ignored. Since equilibrium does not obtain at the liquid junction, only these three equilibrium conditions exist. For the cell reaction

$$\tfrac{1}{2} H_{2(g)} + \tfrac{1}{2} Hg_2Cl_{2(s)} \rightleftharpoons Hg_{(l)} + H^+ + Cl^-$$

it follows from (5.18) that

$$\Delta G = \mu_{Hg}^{(Hg)} + \mu_{H^+}^{(HCl)} + \mu_{Cl^-}^{(KCl)} - \tfrac{1}{2}\mu_{H_2}^{(H_2)} - \tfrac{1}{2}\mu_{Hg_2Cl_2}^{(Hg_2Cl_2)}. \tag{7.106}$$

But $\mu_i^{(j)} = \mu_i^{(j)}$ for neutral components as required by (7.82); hence,

$$\left. \begin{aligned}
\mu_{HCl}^{(HCl)} &= \mu_{H^+}^{(HCl)} + \mu_{Cl^-}^{(HCl)} = \mu_{H^+}^{(HCl)} + \mu_{Cl^-}^{(HCl)} \\
\mu_{Hg}^{(Hg)} &= \tfrac{1}{2}\mu_{Hg_2^{2+}}^{(Hg)} + \mu_{e^-}^{(Hg)} = \tfrac{1}{2}\mu_{Hg_2^{2+}}^{(Hg)} + \mu_{e^-}^{(Hg)} \\
\tfrac{1}{2}\mu_{H_2}^{(H_2)} &= \mu_{H^+}^{(H_2)} + \mu_{e^-}^{(H_2)} = \mu_{H^+}^{(H_2)} + \mu_{e^-}^{(H_2)} \\
\tfrac{1}{2}\mu_{Hg_2Cl_2}^{(Hg_2Cl_2)} &= \tfrac{1}{2}\mu_{Hg_2^{2+}}^{(Hg_2Cl_2)} + \mu_{Cl^-}^{(Hg_2Cl_2)} = \tfrac{1}{2}\mu_{Hg_2^{2+}}^{(Hg_2Cl_2)} + \mu_{Cl^-}^{(Hg_2Cl_2)}.
\end{aligned} \right\} \tag{7.107}$$

Substitution of (7.107) into (7.106) yields

$$\Delta G = [\tfrac{1}{2}\mu_{Hg_2^{2+}}^{(Hg)} + \mu_{e^-}^{(Hg)}] + [\mu_{H^+}^{(HCl)} + \mu_{Cl^-}^{(HCl)} - \mu_{Cl^-}^{(HCl)}] + \mu_{Cl^-}^{(KCl)}$$
$$- [\mu_{H^+}^{(H_2)} + \mu_{e^-}^{(H_2)}] - [\tfrac{1}{2}\mu_{Hg_2^{2+}}^{(Hg_2Cl_2)} + \mu_{Cl^-}^{(Hg_2Cl_2)}] \,.$$

Simplification with (7.103), (7.104), and (7.105) then gives

$$\Delta G = [\mu_{e^-}^{(Hg)} - \mu_{e^-}^{(H_2)}] + [\mu_{Cl^-}^{(HCl)} - \mu_{Cl^-}^{(HCl)}] - [\mu_{Cl^-}^{(KCl)} - \mu_{Cl^-}^{(KCl)}] \,. \tag{7.108}$$

But $\mu_{e^-}^{(Hg)} - \mu_{e^-}^{(H_2)} = -\mathscr{F}[\Phi^{(Hg)} - \Phi^{(H_2)}] = -\mathscr{E}_t\mathscr{F}$, while by (7.82) $\mu_{Cl^-}^{(j)} = \mu_{Cl^-}^{(j)} - \mathscr{F}\Phi^{(j)}$; hence, (7.108) reads

$$\Delta G = -\mathscr{E}_t\mathscr{F} - \mathscr{F}[\Phi^{(HCl)} - \Phi^{(KCl)}] \,. \tag{7.109}$$

The junction potential $\mathscr{E}_j$ for this cell is

$$\mathscr{E}_j = \Phi^{(KCl)} - \Phi^{(HCl)} \,. \tag{7.110}$$

The sign of $\mathscr{E}_j$ follows the usual convention of right minus left. With (7.110), Equation (7.109) for the total cell reaction that actually occurs is

$$\Delta G = -\mathscr{F}(\mathscr{E}_t - \mathscr{E}_j) \,. \tag{7.111}$$

The value of $-\Delta G$ in (7.111) is less than the isothermal isobaric reversible electric work $\mathscr{F}\mathscr{E}_t$ that might have been done by the cell if transference were eliminated. The movement of ions through the interface is irreversible. As 1 faraday of positive charge passes through the liquid junction from left to right, H^+ ions enter the KCl solution and Cl^- ions enter the HCl solution. The liquid junction is not a real discontinuity in concentrations, but the gradient in concentrations may be great. At some surface in this region of rapidly varying concentration, the electric work done on these ions is dG_j, where

$$dG_j = t_+\, dG_+ + t_-\, dG_- \,. \tag{7.112}$$

The transference numbers t_+ and t_- depend upon the concentrations of ions in the various regions of the liquid junction. The quantity dG_+ or dG_- represents the infinitesimal increase in free energy when one equivalent of cation or anion passes the boundary. If the net transfer of ions across the liquid junction has a free energy increase of ΔG_j per faraday passed through the external circuit, and if $\Delta G_j = -\mathscr{F}\mathscr{E}_j$, then

$$\mathscr{E}_j = -\frac{1}{\mathscr{F}} \int_{(1)}^{(2)} (t_+\, dG_+ + t_-\, dG_-) \,. \tag{7.113}$$

If several charged species pass the liquid junction, (7.113) becomes (7.114), where the summation is over all charged species.

$$\mathscr{E}_j = -\frac{1}{\mathscr{F}} \sum_i \int_{(1)}^{(2)} \frac{t_i}{z_i}\, d\mu_i \,. \tag{7.114}$$

The line integrals in (7.113) and (7.114) can be evaluated if t_i and $d\mu_i$ are known as a function of some parameter such as the position in the liquid junction. The integration is carried out from left to right within the cell from phase (1) to phase (2). If the concentration of each ion changes linearly with the parameter of integration, if the two electrolytes are uni-univalent and have a common ion such as Cl^-, if the solutions are so dilute that ionic conductances are equal to those at infinite dilution, and if the concentrations of the two solutions are equal, then (7.114) for uni-univalent electrolytes becomes (tediously)

$$\mathcal{E}_j = -\frac{RT}{\mathcal{F}} \ln \left(\frac{\Lambda_o^{(2)}}{\Lambda_o^{(1)}}\right). \tag{7.115}$$

The equivalent conductance of the right-hand solution at infinite dilution is $\Lambda_o^{(2)}$. This is similar to the Lewis and Sargent formula:

$$\mathcal{E}_j = -\frac{RT}{\mathcal{F}} \ln \left(\frac{\Lambda^{(2)}}{\Lambda^{(1)}}\right). \tag{7.116}$$

For dilute solutions in contact with a saturated solution of KCl, $\mathcal{E}_j$ is of the order of 0.003 volt. The size of $\mathcal{E}_j$ is greater than this for unsaturated KCl solutions or for most other salt bridges. Because of $\mathcal{E}_j$ the measurement of pH is uncertain to about ± 0.05 unit, for by (7.102),

$$pH = \frac{\mathcal{E}_t \pm 0.003 - \mathcal{E}^o}{0.05916} = \frac{\mathcal{E}_t - \mathcal{E}^o}{0.05916} \pm \frac{0.003}{0.06} = \frac{\mathcal{E}_t - \mathcal{E}^o}{0.05916} \pm 0.05 .$$

When pH is measured with a glass electrode with membrane G and a calomel electrode, the complete cell diagram reads

$$Ag \mid AgCl \mid H^+Cl^-(a_o) \mid G \mid H^+(a = ?) \mid K^+Cl^- \mid Hg_2Cl_{2(s)} \mid Hg_{(1)}(Ag)$$

where a_o is fixed as part of the glass electrode. The liquid junction here is between the KCl solution and the solution of unknown pH. When the glass electrode is used, the potential difference is read with the glass and calomel electrodes dipping into a solution of known pH. This fixes $\mathcal{E}^o$ for the cell so that when the unknown solution replaces the solution of known pH, (7.102) defines its pH.

Example 7.30. By means of the Lewis and Sargent formula, estimate the junction potential between 0.1 N HCl and 0.1 N KCl. The equivalent conductivities of these solutions at 25°C are 391 and 129.

By (7.116),

$$\mathcal{E}_j = -0.05915 \log \left(\frac{129}{391}\right) = +0.05915 \times 0.482 = +0.0285 \text{ volt} .$$

7.28 Overvoltage

As soon as electrolysis begins, the decomposition products formed at the electrodes convert the electrodes and electrolyte into a chemical cell.   The newly
created cell potential is opposed to the externally imposed potential difference
that causes the electrolysis and can be calculated by methods already described.   If the electrolysis is to proceed irreversibly, as it must if measurable
electrolysis occurs, the externally imposed potential difference $\mathcal{E}'$ must exceed
the newly created cell potential $\mathcal{E}$.   Part of the irreversible work done on the
cell is converted into heat.   The current $\mathcal{I}$ through the cell is related to the
conductivity L and to $\mathcal{E}'$ and $\mathcal{E}$ by (7.117).

$$\mathcal{I} = L(\mathcal{E}' - \mathcal{E}) . \tag{7.117}$$

Measurement with a balancing potentiometer is done when $\mathcal{I}$ is zero and $\mathcal{E}'$,
the potential difference of the potentiometer, equals $\mathcal{E}$.

The minimum potential $\mathcal{E}'$ required to effect electrolysis often exceeds the
measured or predicted cell potential $\mathcal{E}$.   This excess potential difference $\mathcal{E}_o$
is called the *overvoltage*.   In general, as in (7.117),

$$\mathcal{I} = L(\mathcal{E}' - \mathcal{E}_o - \mathcal{E}) . \tag{7.118}$$

Overvoltage is not simply an extraordinary value of $\mathcal{E}$ because the concentrations of decomposition products at the electrodes are not known; nor is it due
to a decrease in conductivity due to changes in the electrolyte or bubbles of
newly generated gases that adhere to the electrodes and reduce their exposed
surface.   Rather, $\mathcal{E}_o$ is a surface phenomenon the magnitude of which depends
in part upon how ions are discharged at the electrodes and in part upon the
rate at which they are discharged.

An empirical equation that often describes $\mathcal{E}_o$ caused by an irreversible
electrode is

$$\mathcal{E}_o = C + B \log \left(\frac{\mathcal{I}}{\mathcal{Q}}\right) \tag{7.119}$$

where $\mathcal{I}$ is the current, $\mathcal{Q}$ is the area of the electrode, and C and B are empirical
constants.   Here C is of the order of 1 volt for H_2 deposited on C, Ag, or Hg;
C is of the order of 0.5 volt for O_2 deposited on Pt, C, Ag, and other metals;
B is sometimes proportional to the absolute temperature and approximately
equal to $2RT/n\mathcal{F}$.

Because many metals have small or zero values of overvoltage when
deposited from aqueous solution, it is possible to deposit them even though
hydrogen might theoretically be expected.   By decreasing the activity of H^+
and by using electrodes that exhibit large values of $\mathcal{E}_o$ for deposition of H_2,
very active metals can be removed from aqueous solution.   Pure zinc can be
removed from solution by electrolysis, and even metallic sodium can be

generated from aqueous NaCl provided the cathode is an amalgam in which the newly generated Na can dissolve and thereby achieve a lower activity than that of the pure metal.

REFERENCES

Guggenheim, E. A., *Thermodynamics, An Advanced Treatment for Chemists and Physicists.* Amsterdam: North-Holland Publishing Co., 1957.

Harned, H. S., and B. B. Owen, *The Physical Chemistry of Electrolytic Solutions,* 3rd Ed. New York: Reinhold Publishing Corp., 1958.

Kortum, G., and J. O'M. Bockris, *Textbook of Electrochemistry.* New York: Elsevier Publishing Co., 1951.

Latimer, W. M., *Oxidation States of the Elements and Their Potentials in Aqueous Solutions.* Englewood Cliffs, N. J.: Prentice-Hall, Inc., 1952.

MacInnes, D. A., *Principles of Electrochemistry.* New York: Reinhold Publishing Corp., 1939.

Robinson, R. A., and R. H. Stokes, *Electrolyte Solutions.* London: Butterworth & Co., 1955.

PROBLEMS

1. How many faradays are transferred when a potential difference of 3.21 volts is applied across a resistance of 1052 ohms for two hours?
Answer: 2.28×10^{-4}.

2. In three electrolytic cells connected in series, 0.473 g metallic Cu was deposited in the first cell in exactly 10 hours of operation at constant current. If the first cell contained excess aqueous $CuSO_4$:
(a) How much metallic Fe was deposited in the second cell if the only change there was $3e^- + Fe^{+++} \to Fe$?
(b) How much metallic Tl was deposited from a solution containing excess Tl^+?
(c) What steady current flowed?
Answer: 0.277 g Fe.

3. How many grams of KI will be in 50.00 g of the solution near the cathode if 85.3 coulombs are passed through the solution by means of electrodes reversible with respect to iodide ions? The initial molality of KI was 0.1047.

4. Before electrolysis, the cathode chamber of an electrolytic cell had 0.1473 mg-equivalent of $CuSO_4$ per g H_2O and after electrolysis by 1.372×10^{-3} faradays it contained 0.1183 mg-equivalent $CuSO_4$ per g H_2O. If the cathode chamber held 30.0 g H_2O before and after electrolysis, what is the transference number of cupric ion?
Answer: 0.366.

5. Calculate the final concentration of cupric ion in the anode chamber, which holds 28.0 g H_2O, for the experiment of the previous problem if:
(a) The anode was inert.
(b) The anode was copper.
Answer: (a) 0.0647 molal; (b) 0.0892 molal.

6. In a certain moving boundary experiment with 0.132 N HCl followed by $CdCl_2$ solution, the boundary indicated by an indicator advanced at a rate of 2.09 cm hour^{-1} with a current of 1.375 milliamperes. If the cross-sectional area of the tube was 0.153 cm^2, what was the observed transference number of H^+ in HCl?
Answer: 0.823.

7. Predict the flow of water caused by electroosmosis if a potential difference of 50 volts exists between the ends of a glass capillary tube that is 1.29 cm long and 0.083 cm in diameter. The electrokinetic potential of water and glass is -0.05 volt and for H_2O $\kappa = 80$ and $\eta = 0.010$ dyne sec cm^{-2}.

8. A solution with a specific conductivity of 0.0426 mho cm^{-1} had a resistance of 102.6 ohms in a certain conductivity cell. A second solution in the same cell had a resistance of 82.6 ohms. What was its specific conductivity?

9. Graphically find Λ_o of LiCl at 25°C from these data [K. A. Krieger and M. Kilpatrick, *Journal of the American Chemical Society*, **59**, 1878 (1937)] and compare with the sum of ionic conductivities:

$N_\pm \times 10^4$	0.52613	1.1271	1.8787	3.4888	6.5987	12.694	21.683	30.191	37.533
Λ	114.40	114.02	113.79	113.44	112.73	111.93	111.11	110.58	110.05

Answer: 114.97.

10. At 25°C, a saturated solution of TlI in water has a specific conductivity of 36.6×10^{-6} mho cm^{-1} [C. R. Johnson and G. A. Hulett, *Journal of the American Chemical Society*, **57**, 256 (1935)] if the pure water used has a specific conductivity of 0.3×10^{-6} mho cm^{-1}. What is K_{sp} for TlI?

11. From the free energies of formation of H^+ and OH^-, calculate the specific conductivity of water at 25°C. Then calculate the ion product of water at 37°C.
Answer: 0.552×10^{-7} mho cm^{-1}.

12. Label acid and base in these reactions and explain why:
(a) $Al(OH)_3 + H_2O \rightleftharpoons Al(OH)_4^- + H^+$.
(b) $2\,Na + 2\,NH_3 \rightarrow 2\,NaNH_2 + H_2$.
(c) $CaO + SO_3 \rightarrow CaSO_4$.
(d) $Cu^{++} + 4\,NH_3 \rightleftharpoons Cu(NH_3)_4^{++}$.
(e) $CdCl_2 + 2\,Cl^- \rightleftharpoons CdCl_4^{--}$.
(f) $S + SnS \rightarrow SnS_2$.
(g) $P_4O_{10} + 6\,H_2O \rightleftharpoons 4\,H_3PO_4$.
(h) $TiCl_4 + 2\,Mg \rightleftharpoons Ti + 2\,MgCl_2$.

13. If $K_{A1} = 1.2 \times 10^{-10}$ for phenol in water, calculate the hydrogen ion concentration in a solution containing 0.70 mole phenol l^{-1}.

14. Calculate the hydrogen ion concentration in 0.100 molar $NaHCO_3$ if $K_{A1} = 3 \times 10^{-7}$ and $K_{A2} = 6 \times 10^{-11}$.

15. Calculate the pH of 0.060 molal NaOCl if the ionization constant of HClO is 4×10^{-8}.
Answer: 10.1.

16. A buffered solution with $pH = 8.40$ must be prepared. The only chemicals available are acetic acid ($K_{A1} = 1.8 \times 10^{-5}$); ammonium hydroxide ($K_{B1} = 1.8 \times 10^{-5}$); HCl; NaOH; H_2O. Explain how to prepare 100 ml of the buffer without having any solute species more concentrated than 1 molar.

17. Calculate the pH of solutions which have hydrogen ion activities of:
(a) 1.43×10^{-2}.
(b) 6.42×10^{-11}.

18. Calculate the hydrogen ion activity of solutions with pH of:
(a) 6.47.
(b) 11.29.

19. Is any realizable electrochemical cell capable of being run in a truly reversible manner? Explain with specific examples.

20. Diagram an electrochemical cell that has these equations as net cell reaction:
(a) $AgCl_{(s)} + I^-_{(aq)} \rightleftharpoons AgI_{(s)} + Cl^-_{(aq)}$.
(b) $Zn_{(s)} + H_2SO_{4(aq)} \rightleftharpoons ZnSO_{4(aq)} + H_{2(g)}$.
(c) $10\ FeSO_{4(aq)} + 2\ KMnO_{4(aq)} + 8\ H_2SO_{4(aq)} \rightleftharpoons K_2SO_{4(aq)} + 2\ MnSO_{4(aq)} + 5\ Fe_2(SO_4)_{3(aq)} + 8\ H_2O_{(l)}$.
(d) $Fe_{(s)} + Cl_{2(g)} \rightleftharpoons FeCl_{2(aq)}$.

21. Justify the value -0.828 volt for V^o of the half-cell in basic solution: $e^- + H_2O_{(l)} \rightleftharpoons \frac{1}{2} H_{2(g)} + OH^-$.

22. Calculate the cell potential of the cell
$$(Pt)H_{2(g)}\ (0.127\ atm)\ |\ H^+,\ Cl^-\ |\ H_2\ (6.43\ atm)\ (Pt).$$
Answer: -0.0504 volt.

23. Calculate the solubility product constant of Ag_2CrO_4 at $25°C$.

24. Calculate the solubility product constants of Ag_2S and $TlOH$ at $25°C$.

25. What is the standard potential of the electrode reaction $e^- + \frac{1}{3} Tl^{+++} \rightleftharpoons \frac{1}{3} Tl_{(s)}$?
Answer: $+0.72$ volt.

26. Calculate V^o for the half-cell $e^- + \frac{1}{2} Sn^{++} \rightleftharpoons Sn_{(s)}$ if $\mathcal{E} = -0.643$ volt at $25°C$ for the cell $(Zn)Sn_{(s)}\ |\ Sn^{++}\ (a = 0.347)\ \|\ Zn^{++}\ (a = 0.100)\ |\ Zn_{(s)}$.
Answer: -0.136 volt.

27. With the aid of Tables 3.3 and 4.1, find V^o of $e^- + AgBr_{(s)} \rightleftharpoons Ag_{(s)} + Br^-$.

28. List in order elements in the electrochemical series in liquid ammonia and compare to the series in acidic aqueous solutions.

29. What is the minimum voltage necessary to electrolyze 1.00 molal $ZnBr_2$ to produce Zn and Br_2?
Answer: 1.810 volts.

30. If the standard electrode potential for the decinormal calomel electrode is $+0.3338$ volt at $25°C$ as in Example 7.22, calculate $\mathcal{E}$ for the cells:
(a) $(Pt)Hg_{(1)}\ |\ Hg_2Cl_{2(s)}\ |\ KCl(0.1\ N)\ \|\ Zn^{++}(a = 0.732)\ |\ Zn_{(s)}(Pt)$.
(b) $(Pt)Hg_{(1)}\ |\ Hg_2Cl_{2(s)}\ |\ KCl(0.1\ N)\ \|\ HCl\ (0.1N)\ |\ H_{2(2)}(1\ atm)\ (Pt)$.

31. What unnoticed change in hydrogen pressure will cause an error of $0.01\ pH$ unit when pH is measured with a hydrogen electrode at $25°C$ at laboratory pressures?
Answer: 36 mm Hg.

32. Active metals that cannot be deposited by electrolysis directly from aqueous solution can usually be removed at a liquid mercury cathode. Explain.

---

33. What volume of H_2 at $25°C$ at 1.000 atm and how many tons of liquid chlorine are expected from ten tons NaCl if electrolysis is performed with 1000 faradays charge?

34. How much Cu was plated out of a solution of $NaCu(CN)_2$ if 0.422 g Ag was deposited from $AgNO_3$ in a coulometer in series with the $NaCu(CN)_2$ cell?

35. At 32°C, 0.0500 molal H_2SO_4 was electrolyzed by a current of 10.0 milliamperes for 1000 sec. What volume of dry H_2 was released at 32°C at 0.980 atm and what was the H^+ concentration of the cathode chamber if it held 40.0 g of solution?

36. During electrolysis of 0.0514 molal aqueous $AgNO_3$ between silver electrodes, 69.3 coulombs charge was carried by the solute ions. If the solution from the anode weighed 28.64 g after electrolysis and contained 1.839 mg-equivalents Ag, what was the transference number of Ag^+?

37. What distance will the boundary between 0.10 $N_\pm$ KBr and a following solution of $CdBr_2$ move in a moving-boundary experiment determining transference numbers at 25°C if a current of 2.00 milliamperes flows 843 sec through a tube of cross section 0.1372 cm²?

38. What flow of water is possible through a diaphragm of clay ($\zeta = -0.03$ volt) if electrodes at a potential difference of 1000 volts are 10.0 cm apart with the diaphragm between them? The water levels are initially at the same height.
Answer: 0.02 cm sec⁻¹.

39. Explain the effect, if any, of a horizontal electric field upon the motion of glass beads falling through water.

40. When 0.1000 demal KCl solution at 18°C is placed in a certain conductivity cell, its resistance is 926 ohms.
(a) If the electrodes are of equal area and 5.00 cm apart, what is the area of one electrode?
(b) What resistance is expected of a solution with $L_{sp} = 0.00862$ mho cm⁻¹ in this same cell?
Answer: (a) 0.484 cm²; (b) 1200 ohms.

41. At 25°C, the equivalent conductivities of solutions of $MgSO_4$ depend upon normality as follows (*International Critical Tables VI*, p. 234):

$N_\pm$	0.0005	0.001	0.002	0.005	0.010	0.020
Λ	123.2	117.6	110.9	98.8	88.9	79.0

What is the equivalent conductance of magnesium ion at infinite dilution?

42. With data in Tables 7.6 and 7.7 and the fact that a saturated solution of $BaSO_4$ in water at 25°C has a specific conductivity of 3.00×10^{-6} mho cm⁻¹ [A. C. Melcher, *Journal of the American Chemical Society*, **32**, 54 (1910)], find K_{sp} of $BaSO_4$.

43. Suggest ionizations that account for the electrical conductivity of:
(a) Liquid N_2O_4.
(b) $AlCl_3$ dissolved in liquid $COCl_2$.
(c) KF in liquid HF.
(d) HNO_3 in liquid HF.

44. The equivalent conductance of 0.03 N trichloroacetic acid is 346 at 25°C and is 387 at infinite dilution at 25°C (*International Critical Tables VI*, p. 261). What is the ionization constant of this acid?

45. What kind of solvent must be used to characterize the relative strengths of acids stronger than H_3O^+?

46. From Example 5.6, find K_{A1} of H_2SO_3 and calculate the acidity of 100 ml of a solution containing 0.0020 moles NaOH and 0.0030 moles (total) SO_2.
Answer: $C_{H^+} = 3.8 \times 10^{-4}$.

47. Calculate the hydrogen ion concentration of 0.100 molar Na_2CO_3. For carbonic acid, $K_{A1} = 3 \times 10^{-7}$ and $K_{A2} = 6 \times 10^{-11}$.

48. If K_{A1} of HF is of the order of 10^{-3}, predict whether or not hydrolysis of a saturated solution of CaF_2 ($K_{sp} = 4 \times 10^{-11}$) is great enough to affect greatly a calculation of K_{sp} of this salt from a knowledge of the amount dissolved per liter of unbuffered pure water.

49. Calculate the pH of a solution with a hydrogen ion concentration of 2.38×10^{-5}:
(a) If concentration equals activity.
(b) According to the Debye-Huckel theory if the solution is an acetic acid-sodium acetate buffer with an acetic acid concentration of 0.04 molar.

50. Calculate ΔA at 25°C for the change

$$Cl_{2(g)} \ (0.100 \ atm) + Ca_{(s)} \rightarrow Ca^{++}(a = 1) + 2 \ Cl^-(a = 1).$$

51. In what circumstances is it possible to obtain more energy from chemicals as electric work than as evolved heat?

52. Calculate an electrochemical value of ΔH for the cell reaction of the cell $Tl \mid TlCl_{(s)} \mid KCl(1 \ N) \mid Hg_2Cl_{2(s)} \mid Hg_{(1)}$ if $\mathscr{E} = 0.7290$ v at 25°C and if $\mathscr{E}$ increases by 0.75 millivolt per degree rise in temperature [G. Jones and W. C. Schumb, *Proceedings of the American Academy of Arts and Sciences*, **56**, 199 (1919); by permission of the American Academy of Arts and Sciences].
Answer: $-41,500$ joules.

53. What will be the potential at 50°C of this cell?

$$(Ag)Pb_{(s)} \mid Pb^{++}(a = 1.07 \times 10^{-4}) \parallel Cl^-(a = 0.100) \mid AgCl_{(s)} \mid Ag_{(s)}.$$

Assume entropies of dilution are ideal.

54. Two identical electrochemical cells are allowed to generate 1 mole H_2 from H_2SO_4. One does so reversibly and the other does so irreversibly. Explain qualitatively the differences noted in the final states of the cell, acid solution, H_2, and so on.

55. Diagram two electrochemical cells for each pair of reactants that could convert the chemical potential energy of these reactants into useful electric energy:
(a) H_2 and Cl_2.
(b) Ag^+ and Cl^-.

56. Calculate ideally the free energy change upon diluting 1 mole NaCl from 0.020 m to 0.0010 m at 25°C and design an electrochemical battery without transference for measuring ΔG.
Answer: $-14,840$ joules.

57. Diagram two batteries in which the free energy of dilution of aqueous solutions of HCl might be measured without interference from junction potentials.

58. In this problem assume that the final concentrations of plentiful ionic species are 1 molar and that the final concentrations of rare ionic species are less than 0.001 molar. With the aid of Table 7.12, predict the final state of almost all vanadium at equilibrium if:
(a) The vanadium in solution is all reduced to V^{++} just before the solution is buffered at $pH = 0$.
(b) Excess metallic copper is added to a solution of V^{+++} buffered at $pH = 0$.
(c) A solution of Fe^{++} is added to a solution of $V(OH)_4^+$ buffered at $pH = 0$.
(d) A solution of Fe^{+++} is added to a solution of VO^{++} buffered at $pH = 0$.
(e) A solution of Cu^{++} is added to a solution of VO^{++} buffered at $pH = 0$.

59. Tabulated right are potential differences $\mathscr{E}$ in volts at 25°C as a function of molality m [W. G. Horsch, *Journal of the American Chemical Society*, 41, 1787 (1919)] for the cell $(Pt)Zn_{(s)} \mid ZnCl_2 (m) \mid AgCl_{(s)} \mid Ag_{(s)} (Pt)$. From these data find $\mathscr{E}°$ for the cell, $V°$ for the zinc electrode, and the mean ionic activities of the electrolyte at each concentration.
Answer: $\mathscr{E}° = 0.9813$ volt.

$m \times 10^3$	$\mathscr{E}$ (volts)
10.21	1.1558
6.022	1.1742
3.112	1.1953
1.453	1.2219
1.253	1.2289
0.772	1.2475
0.649	1.2497
0.3995	1.2699
0.3478	1.2701

60. Calculate the cell potentials at 25°C and reactions for the cells:
(a) $(Pt)Cu_{(s)} \mid Cu^{++}(a = 0.0010),\ Cl^-(a = 0.30) \mid Cl_{2(g)} (0.950\ atm) (Pt)$.
(b) $(Pt) \mid V^{++}(a = 0.242),\ V^{+++}(a = 0.0033) \parallel V^{++}(a = 0.425) \mid V_{(s)}(Pt)$.
(c) $(Pt)Cl_{2(g)} (1.12\ atm) \mid Cl^-(a = 0.526) \parallel I^-(a = 0.100) \mid AgI_{(s)} \mid Ag_{(s)}(Pt)$.
Answer: (a) 1.151 volts; (b) −0.82 volt; (c) −1.469 volts.

61. Calculate the equilibrium constant for the reaction $AlF_{6(aq)}^{---} \rightleftharpoons Al_{(aq)}^{+++} + 6\ F_{(aq)}^-$.
Answer: 1.6×10^{-21}.

62. What is the concentration of triiodide ion in equilibrium with excess solid iodine at 25°C in a solution in which the molality of iodide was 0.1000 before the addition of iodine?

63. Calculate the standard potential of the electrode reaction

$$e^- + \tfrac{1}{2} Au^{+++} \rightleftharpoons \tfrac{1}{2} Au^+.$$

64. Diagram a cell in which the solubility product constant of ZnS might be measured and calculate K_{sp} from standard electrode potentials.

65. Calculate the standard molar free energy of aqueous Pb^{++} and the potential of the cell $(Pt)H_{2(g)}(2.34\ atm) \mid H^+(a = 0.0022) \parallel Pb^{++}(a = 0.377) \mid Pb_{(s)}(Pt)$.

66. If the solubility product constant of Hg_2Cl_2 is 4.2×10^{-18} for the reaction $Hg_2Cl_{2(s)} \rightleftharpoons Hg_2^{++} + 2\ Cl^-$, and if the decinormal calomel electrode with half-cell reaction $e^- + \tfrac{1}{2} Hg_2Cl_{2(s)} \rightleftharpoons Cl^-(0.1\ N) + Hg_{(l)}$ has electrode potential of $+0.334$ volt, what is $V°$ of the half reaction $e^- + \tfrac{1}{2} Hg_2^{++} \rightleftharpoons Hg_{(l)}$?

67. In a cell consisting of glass electrode in solution with pH of 7.00 and a calomel electrode, the cell potential was 0.062 volt. When a solution of unknown pH replaced the standard buffer, the cell potential was 0.145 volt with the glass electrode negative. Calculate the unknown pH if, during the calibration, the glass electrode was:
(a) Negative.
(b) Positive.
Answer: (a) 8.40; (b) 10.5.

68. Quinhydrone $(Q \cdot QH_2)$, a compound of quinone $(Q = C_6H_4O_2)$ and hydroquinone $(QH_2 = C_6H_4(OH)_2)$ is slightly soluble in water. Because it provides equal numbers of moles of Q and QH_2, its half-cell reaction $e^- + H^+ + \tfrac{1}{2} Q_{(aq)} \rightleftharpoons \tfrac{1}{2} QH_{2(aq)}$ depends only upon the activity of H^+ in the presence of excess $Q \cdot QH_2$. If $V°$ of the quinhydrone electrode is $+0.6996$ v at 25°C, for the cell

$$(Pt)Q \cdot QH_{2(s)} \mid H^+ (pH = ?) \mid K^+Cl^- \mid Hg_2Cl_{2(s)} \mid Hg_{(l)}(Pt)$$

with a normal calomel electrode $(V° = +0.2802\ v)$, find:
(a) The $\mathscr{E}$ of cell when $pH = 5.00$.
(b) The pH when $\mathscr{E}$ of cell is zero.
(c) Which electrode is positive when $pH = 7.50$.

---

69. Electrolysis in two cells in series yielded 3.55 g Ag from $AgNO_3$ in one cell and 0.741 g Fe in the other. What fraction of the metallic iron was ferrous at the start of the electrolysis?

70. An aqueous solution of $CaCl_2$ was electrolyzed at 25°C between electrodes reversible with respect to chloride ions. From the cathode chamber came 32.78 g

solution that yielded 0.4351 g CaC_2O_4, while the central chamber yielded 0.3572 g of CaC_2O_4 from 28.66 g of solution. Calculate the transference numbers of calcium and chloride ions if 1.046×10^{-3} faraday was carried through the cell by the $CaCl_2$.

71. Suggest a mechanism that may account for the large mobility of hydroxide ions in aqueous solutions.

72. Estimate the thickness of the double-layer of a spherical protein molecule with $\zeta = -0.030$ volt, a diameter of 1000 A, and 10^3 acidic sites when all sites are ionized in water.
Answer: 40 A.

73. The freezing point of 0.500 molal $CdCl_2$ is $-1.48°C$. The equivalent conductivities of aqueous $CdCl_2$ depend upon normality thus (*International Critical Tables VI*, p. 232) at 0°C:

$N_\pm$	0.001	0.002	0.005	0.010	0.020
Λ	64.1	60.4	54.9	50.3	45.1
$N_\pm$	0.050	0.070	0.100	0.200	0.500
Λ	37.5	34.8	31.8	25.9	17.9

Calculate the degree of ionization of 0.5 N $CdCl_2$ by two methods and suggest reasons for any difference noted.

74. At 25°C the specific conductivity of a saturated aqueous solution of $CaSO_4$ is 2211.5×10^{-6} mho cm^{-1} when water with $L_{sp} = 0.6 \times 10^{-6}$ mho cm^{-1} is used [W. D. Harkins and H. M. Paine, *Journal of the American Chemical Society*, 41, 1155 (1919)]. What is K_{sp} for $CaSO_4$ if the equivalent conductivities of $CaSO_4$ solutions at 25°C are:

$N_\pm \times 10^3$	0.099955	0.19955	0.49795	0.9959
Λ	136.63	132.88	127.38	121.57

75. From the data of Table 7.7 find $\Delta H°$ for the reaction by which a proton in water reacts with a hydroxide ion in water to yield 1 mole water.

76. If the first and second ionization constants of salicylic acid are 1.0×10^{-3} and 1.0×10^{-13}, calculate the pH of 0.100 molar:
(a) HOC_6H_4COOH.
(b) HOC_6H_4COONa.
(c) $NaOC_6H_4COOH$.
(d) $NaOC_6H_4COONa$.
Answer: (a) 2.02; (b) and (c) 7.85; (d) 12.79.

77. Explain how to prepare a buffered solution with pH = 7.00 from H_3PO_4 and NaOH if the ionization constants of H_3PO_4 are 7.5×10^{-3}, 6.3×10^{-8}, and 3.6×10^{-13}.

78. Explain how mixing distinguishable species could yield electric work, and how electric work might unmix them.

79. Theoretically how much electric energy could be obtained at 1000°K and 1 atm by burning 1 mole CH_4 to H_2O and CO?
Answer: 604,290 joules.

80. Predict the potential at 10°C of the cell:

$$(Pt)H_{2(g)} \ (0.800 \text{ atm}) \mid H^+(a = 1), \ Cl^- \ (a = 1) \mid Cl_{2(g)} \ (1.00 \text{ atm}) \ (Pt).$$

81. For the cell $(Pt)H_{2(g)}(p \text{ atm}) \,|\, HCl \,(0.1 \, N) \,|\, H_2S(p \text{ atm}) \,|\, Ag_2S_{(s)} \,|\, Ag_{(s)}(Pt)$ $\mathcal{E} = -0.03779$ v at 10°C, -0.03670 v at 25°C, and -0.03584 v at 35°C [A. A. Noyes and E. S. Freed, *Journal of the American Chemical Society*, 42, 476 (1920)]. Calculate ΔG, ΔH, and ΔS for the cell reaction at 20°C and 25°C.

82. Calculate the potential difference between the electrodes and determine their signs at 25°C for the cell

$$Fe_{(s)} \,|\, Fe^{++} \,|\, Fe_{(s)} \text{ (compressed spring)} \,|\, Fe_{(s)}$$

if 10.0 cal reversible isothermal work were done in compressing the 1 lb coiled spring electrode at the right.
Answer: $\mathcal{E} = -26.6$ microvolts.

83. Derive an equation for the dependence of potential difference of an electrochemical cell upon total pressure if only condensed phases take part in the cell reaction.

84. If activities equal concentrations, what is the potential at 25°C of $(Pt)Na(0.200\% \text{ in Hg}) \,|\, NaCl \,(0.150 \, m) \,|\, AgCl_{(s)} \,|\, Ag_{(s)} \,|\, AgCl_{(s)} \,|\, NaCl \,(0.0372 \, m) \,|$ $Na \,(0.200\% \text{ in Hg})(Pt)$?

85. Although the standard hydrogen electrode has zero electrode potential at all temperatures, $\Delta S^\circ = \frac{1}{2} S^\circ(H_2)$ for the half-cell reaction of this electrode. Explain.

86. With the aid of Tables 3.3 and 4.1, find V° for each of these half cells:
(a) $e^- + \frac{1}{2} NO_{2(g)} + H^+ \rightleftharpoons \frac{1}{2} NO_{(g)} + \frac{1}{2} H_2O_{(l)}$.
(b) $e^- + \frac{1}{2} C_2H_{2(g)} + H^+ \rightleftharpoons \frac{1}{2} C_2H_{4(g)}$.

87. Calculate the partial equilibrium pressure of O_2 above 0.100 molal aqueous H_2O_2 at 25°C.
Answer: 10^{35} atm.

88. Calculate V° of the chlorine-chloride electrode at 37°C.

89. Predict the potential difference of the cell $(Pt)H_{2(g)} \,(0.970 \text{ atm}) \,|\, NaOH(0.332 \, N) \,|$ $Na(0.147\% \text{ mole amalgam})(Pt)$ at 25°C if activities equal concentrations.

90. For dilute aqueous NaOH, the cell $(Pt)H_{2(g)} \,(1 \text{ atm}) \,|\, Na^+OH^- \,|\, HgO_{(s)} \,|\, Hg_{(l)}(Pt)$ has a potential of 0.9264 v at 25°C [Ming Chow, *Journal of the American Chemical Society*, 42, 488 (1920)]. What is the standard free energy of formation of $HgO_{(s)}$?
Answer: $\Delta G_f^\circ = -13.97$ kcal mole^{-1}.

91. The solubility product constants of $PbSO_4$ and $BaSO_4$ are 1.35×10^{-8} and 1.35×10^{-9}, respectively. An electrode reversible to barium can be made by depositing $PbSO_4$ and $BaSO_4$ on an electrode of Pb. Explain its operation and find its standard electrode potential.
Answer: -0.096 volt.

92. If $\mathcal{E}$ is the cell potential of a concentration cell without transference in which the electrodes are reversible with respect to cations, show that the cell potential of the same concentration cell with transference is $t_-\mathcal{E}$, where t_- is the transference number of the anion. Show similarly for a concentration cell with electrodes reversible to anion that the cell potential with transference is $t_+\mathcal{E}$.

93. The equivalent conductivity of 0.20 m NaCl at 25°C is 101.6, while that of 0.010 m NaCl is 118.6 (*International Critical Tables VI*, p. 233). Estimate the magnitude and determine the sign of the junction potential between these two solutions:
(a) By the Lewis and Sargent formula.
(b) By graphical line integration with the transference numbers of Table 7.3 for some arbitrary reasonable-looking continuous change in concentration at the junction.

94. If the potential difference of the cell

$$(Pt)H_{2(g)} \ (p \ atm) \ | \ H^+ \ (a = 0.100) \ \| \ H^+(a = ?) \ | \ H_{2(g)}(p \ atm)(Pt)$$

is 0.0861 volt, what is the pH of the solution round the right-hand electrode if:
(a) It is positive at 25°C?
(b) It is negative at 25°C?
(c) It is negative at 0°C?

95. Estimate the minimum potential difference required at 500°C to produce solid metallic calcium and gaseous chlorine at 1 atm from fused $CaCl_2$ (containing some alkali halides) by electrolysis if for $CaCl_2$:
(a) C_P of liquid and solid = 18 cal deg^{-1} mole^{-1}.
(b) The molar heat of fusion is 6.78 kcal mole^{-1}.
(c) The molar heat of formation of the solid at 25°C is -190.0 kcal mole^{-1}.
(d) The standard free energy of formation of the solid at 25°C is -179.3 kcal mole^{-1}.
[Data from F. D. Rossini, *et al.*, Circular of the National Bureau of Standards 500 (1952)].
Answer: 3.77 volts.

96. Calculate the theoretical potential difference developed at 1000°K by the fuel cell

$$(Ag-Pt)H_{2(g)} \ (2.50 \ atm) \ | \ M_2CO_{3(l)} \ | \ O_{2(g)} \ (0.50 \ atm)(Ag).$$

Express the result as a function of H_2O pressure, and assume that p_{CO_2} is the same at both electrodes. What will the potential difference be during operation of the fuel cell?

FOOTNOTES

1. Conway, B. E., J. O'M. Bockris, and H. Linton, *Journal of Chemical Physics*, **24**, 834 (1956). See also: Eigen, M. and L. De Maeyer, *Journal of Chemical Physics*, **31**, 1134 (1959).

2. Spiro, M., *Journal of Chemical Education*, **33**, 464 (1956).

3. Alberty, R. A., *Journal of Chemical Education*, **25**, 426, 619 (1948).

4. Yost, Don M. and Horace Russell, Jr., *Systematic Inorganic Chemistry of the Fifth- and Sixth-Group Nonmetallic Elements.* Englewood Cliffs, N. J.: Prentice-Hall, Inc., 1944, Chapter 4. By permission.

5. Kohlrausch and Heydweiller, *Zeitschrift für physikalische Chemie*, **14**, 317 (1894).

6. Licht, T. S. and A. J. de Bethune, *Journal of Chemical Education*, **34**, 433 (1957).

7. Christiansen, J. A., *Manual of Physico-Chemical Symbols and Terminology.* London: Butterworth's Scientific Publications; copyright 1959 by International Union of Pure and Applied Chemistry; pp. 4, 6.

8. Harned, H. S. and R. W. Ehlers, *Journal of the American Chemical Society*, **55**, 2179 (1933).

8 / QUANTUM

CHEMISTRY

A. GENERAL QUANTUM MECHANICS

8.1 Energy Quanta

The kinetic and atomic theories seem to provide a suitable basis for the behavior of gases and crystalline solids and even of liquids; and thermodynamics, at least on the molar level, seems to explain a great deal of chemistry quite well.   Yet, with all their elegance, these theoretical bases of chemistry do not account for several things.   Why, for example, should the entropy of mixing depend upon the attitude or knowledge of the observer, as discussed in Section 5.6?   Or, why should the heat capacities of crystalline solids be observed to approach zero as absolute zero is approached?   As long as infinitesimal vibration of atoms is allowed, equipartition of energy requires that C_V equal $3R$ in a pure monatomic crystal at all temperatures regardless of how low they may be.   Conceivably C_V could decrease to $2R$, R, or even zero, but only if one, two, or all three degrees of freedom were completely lost.   Such discontinuous decreases are not in fact observed, nor is it reasonable to expect any body following the laws of classical mechanics utterly to stop moving at a finite temperature.

Before 1900 there was also no adequate explanation for the observed frequency-distribution of radiation emitted by a black body at a uniform temperature. To explain it, Planck in 1900 postulated that energy is radiated in discrete amounts called *quanta*. A quantum of energy is a bit or elementary unit of energy. The radiator was conceived as an assembly of oscillators each with a characteristic frequency ν. A quantum of energy ΔE is related to ν by a constant of proportionality called *Planck's constant h*.

$$\Delta E = h\nu .\tag{8.1}$$

This revolutionary view of energy also explains the observed gradual decreases in C_V at low temperatures. Although energy is absorbed and radiated in discrete amounts, the number of energized oscillators or atoms may vary. When their number is of the order of Avogadro's number, the energy of the crystalline assembly as viewed on a molar basis seems to be a continuous function of temperature with a derivative C_V that approaches zero continuously as absolute zero is approached.

In 1905, Einstein proposed that a quantum of radiation behaves like a particle. Light that falls on a metal, or in fact any kind of matter, may cause photoelectrons to be emitted with energies less than or equal to a certain maximum value that is a linear function of the frequency. This maximum energy is independent of intensity, some electrons being emitted with maximum energy at once when the radiation strikes, even in the weakest intensities. If radiation were a pure wave, such a concentration of energy at a point in ejecting the electron could occur only after absorption for some extended time over a large weakly irradiated area. In acting at once at a point, radiation thus behaves like a particle, more in accord with Newton's corpuscular theory of light than with its traditional role as wave.

The energy E of a photon, the particle of light, is related to its frequency ν by (8.2).

$$E = h\nu .\tag{8.2}$$

The maximum kinetic energy E of a photoelectron is

$$E = h\nu - E_o\tag{8.3}$$

where E_o is the minimum energy required to eject an electron from the irradiated substance. The actual energy of a photoelectron may differ from E because of external fields or because the photoelectron was not the least tightly bound electron in the irradiated substance.

Example 8.1. The energy required to remove the least tightly bound electron from the alkali metals is about two electron-volts (ev). With the aid of physical constants in Appendix C, find the longest wavelength of light just able to eject photoelectrons from the alkali metals.

If the radiation just ejects a photoelectron, E in (8.3) is about zero. Then, since $c = \lambda\nu$,

$$0 = h\nu - E_o$$

$$\lambda = \frac{hc}{E_o}.$$

One electron-volt is the kinetic energy acquired by an electron as it falls freely through a potential difference of 1 absolute volt. In cgs units, where 1 cgs volt equals 299.8 absolute volts, 1 ev is

$$\frac{4.802 \times 10^{-10}}{299.8} = 1.602 \times 10^{-12} \text{ erg}.$$

If $E_o = 2.00$ ev,

$$\lambda = \frac{6.624 \times 10^{-27} \times 2.998 \times 10^{10}}{2.00 \times 1.602 \times 10^{-12}} = 6.21 \times 10^{-5} \text{ cm} = 6210 \text{ A}.$$

Radiation in the green (5000 A) or blue (4000 A) is more energetic than that with $\lambda = 6210$ A (orange); hence green or blue light is expected to eject photoelectrons from alkali metals, but not red or infrared in one event.

8.2 Hydrogen Atom

Some of the early theoretical and experimental developments in the quantum theory are listed in Table 8.1. The three most important were those of Planck, Bohr, and the several physicists who originated matrix and wave mechanics.

Table 8.1. *Outline of Historical Origins of Quantum Theory*

DATE	INVESTIGATORS	CONTRIBUTIONS
1900	Planck	Radiation formula through energy quanta
1905	Einstein	Photoelectric effect through photons
1907–13	Einstein, Deybe, Born, von Karman	Specific heats of crystals near absolute zero
1911	Rutherford	Atom with small positive nucleus
1913	Bohr	Simple model of hydrogen atom
1914	Franck, Hertz	Atomic energy levels by electron bombardment
1915–16	Wilson, Sommerfeld	Rules of quantization in periodic systems
1923	Compton	Inelastic collision of photon and electron
1924	de Broglie	Wave nature of electron and matter
1925	Pauli	Exclusion principle
1926	Heisenberg, Born, Jordan, Schroedinger	Matrix and wave mechanics
1926	Uhlenbeck, Goudsmit, et al	Spinning electron
1927	Heisenberg	Uncertainty principle
1927	Davisson, Germer	Diffraction of electrons by crystal
1927–	Burrau, Heitler, London, et al.	Applications to H_2^+, H_2, chemistry

461

Bohr described a model of the hydrogen atom that accounted for its emission spectrum in terms of energy states that endured for a relatively long time. On transition from a state of energy E_1 to a state of energy E_2, a photon with energy $h\nu$ was absorbed or emitted. On absorption ($E_2 > E_1$),

$$E_2 - E_1 = h\nu \tag{8.4}$$

while on emission ($E_1 > E_2$)

$$E_1 - E_2 = h\nu . \tag{8.5}$$

Bohr imagined a hydrogen atom to be a massive, positively charged proton around which sped an electron that could have only discrete energies. These energies were fixed by specifying that the single electron could have angular momentum in its circular orbits of $n\hbar$, where $\hbar = h/2\pi$ and n is a positive real integer called a *quantum number*. That is, Bohr quantized the angular momentum of the electron. Some of the wavelengths of the emission spectrum of hydrogen that are quantitatively explained by this simple model are listed in Table 8.2. Equation (8.6) (from Landolt-Börnstein), which describes these wavelengths in terms of $\bar{\nu}$, a reciprocal wavelength proportional to an energy, is the most exact experimental equation of physics.

$$\bar{\nu} = 109{,}677.583 \left(\frac{1}{n^2} - \frac{1}{m^2} \right). \tag{8.6}$$

Table 8.2. *Some Wavelengths of Emission Spectrum of Hydrogen* (A)*

m	LYMAN (n = 1)	BALMER (n = 2)	PASCHEN (n = 3)	BRACKETT (n = 4)	PFUND (n = 5)
2	1215.68				
3	1025.83	6562.79			
4	972.54	4861.33	18,751.05		
5	949.74	4340.47	12,818.11	40,500.	
6	937.81	4101.74	10,938.	26,300.	74,000.
∞	911.76	3645.98			

Example 8.2. By the Bohr theory, derive the value of the numerical coefficient in (8.6).

Since the angular momentum of an electron circling around a proton at a distance r and at a uniform velocity v is $\mu v r$, where μ is the reduced mass of the two particles, the Bohr quantum condition is $\mu v r = n\hbar$. This circular orbit is stable if centrifugal force $\mu v^2/r$ is exactly balanced by coulombic attractive force e^2/r^2. That is, on equating forces, $\mu v^2 r = e^2$. Solution of these two equations for r and v^2 yields

$$v^2 = \frac{e^4}{n^2 \hbar^2} \quad \text{and} \quad r = \frac{n^2 \hbar^2}{\mu e^2}.$$

*Landolt-Börnstein, *Zahlenwerte und Funktionen I Band Atom-und Molekularphysik* 1. *Teil Atome und Ionen.* Berlin: Verlag Julius Springer, 1950, S. 51.

In center-of-mass coordinates, the energy of the system is therefore

$$E = \frac{\mu v^2}{2} - \frac{e^2}{r} = \frac{\mu e^4}{2n^2\hbar^2} - \frac{\mu e^4}{n^2\hbar^2} = - \frac{\mu e^4}{2n^2\hbar^2} .$$

For a change from state n to state m,

$$\Delta E = - \frac{\mu e^4}{2\hbar^2}\left(\frac{1}{m^2} - \frac{1}{n^2}\right) .$$

Since $\bar{\nu} = 1/\lambda = \nu/c = \Delta E/hc = \Delta E/2\pi\hbar c$, it follows that (8.6) is

$$\bar{\nu} = \frac{\mu e^4}{4\pi\hbar^3 c}\left(\frac{1}{n^2} - \frac{1}{m^2}\right)$$

with

$$\frac{\mu e^4}{4\pi\hbar^3 c} = 109,677.583 \text{ cm}^{-1}$$

for hydrogen.

8.3 Uncertainty Principle

After almost a decade of fruitful development, the simple Bohr theory was found to be inadequate in many ways.   In its refined form, it required half-integral quantum numbers in certain situations, made predictions contrary to experiment, and could not be made to predict things an adequate theory should.   In these straits, de Broglie made a masterful postulate.   If radiation is a photon, then material particles are radiation, the relation between momentum p and wavelength λ being

$$p\lambda = 2\pi\hbar = h . \tag{8.7}$$

This relation was fully vindicated by Davisson and Germer, who substituted a beam of uniformly accelerated electrons for a beam of X rays in a diffraction experiment with crystalline nickel.   Bragg-like diffraction occurred with the electron!   Whenever an experiment designed to measure the wave-nature of a particle is performed, it provides information that betrays the wave-nature of that particle.

The Heisenberg uncertainty principle is similar to (8.7).   If Δp_x is the minimum uncertainty in the observed x-component of linear momentum of a particle and if Δx is the minimum uncertainty in its observed x-component of position, it says

$$\Delta p_x \cdot \Delta x \geqslant \hbar . \tag{8.8}$$

All theoretical physicists agree that (8.8) applies to measurements as made, but some believe that (8.8) may not limit the real behavior of a particle. That is, some believe that a particle may really have an exact momentum and position even though they be simultaneously unmeasurable. However, all agree that (8.8) describes a real limit upon man's ability to measure x and p_x.

Equation (8.8) is really the result of a critical analysis of how a measurement of position is made. The position of a body can be found in many ways: by ear, by touch, by sight. A microscope appears to be best suited to locating a body small enough to be considered to lie at a point. However, microscopes are limited by the wavelength of light, just as location by ear is limited to the wavelength of sound. The minimum uncertainty Δx in position as determined by the best of microscopes is of the order of λ, the wavelength of light used.

It would appear, then, that a microscope using X rays or gamma rays, with very small λ, would be ideal. Unfortunately, photons behave like particles: they move the vanes of radiometers and generate the tails of comets by their collisions with matter. Photons with small λ have great energy $h\nu = hc/\lambda$ and great momentum. Although a photon with small λ could reduce the size of Δx on locating a body by collision and scattering into a microscope, it can transfer momentum to the body. On careful study, it happens that the uncertainty Δp_x in the located body's momentum is of the order of h/λ regardless of the degree of optical sophistication. As a result, the product of Δx and Δp_x is of the order of h, as (8.8) requires. With less care, Δx and Δp_x may of course be greater than the minimum.

A more general statement of (8.8) in terms of a generalized momentum p_i and its conjugate coordinate q_i is

$$\Delta p_i \cdot \Delta q_i \geqslant \hbar . \tag{8.9}$$

Three common pairs of conjugate mechanical variables are: linear momentum and position; angular momentum and angle; energy and time. In particular, some conjugate pairs are: p_x and x, p_y and y; p_z and z; in plane-polar coordinates, $mr^2\dot{\phi}$ and ϕ; E and t.

Example 8.3. Calculate the wavelength of (a) a 22-caliber bullet with a mass of 2.59 g and a muzzle velocity of 3.35×10^4 cm sec^{-1}; (b) an electron accelerated from rest by a potential difference of 40,000 volts, with neglect of relativistic effects.

(a) The linear momentum p of a particle is mv. For the bullet,

$$p = 2.59 \times 3.35 \times 10^4 = 8.68 \times 10^4 \text{ g cm sec}^{-1} .$$

By (8.7), with $h = 6.624 \times 10^{-27}$ erg-sec,

$$\lambda = \frac{6.624 \times 10^{-27}}{8.68 \times 10^4} = 7.63 \times 10^{-32} \text{ cm} .$$

(b) After acceleration by 40,000 volts, the kinetic energy of an electron is

$$E = \frac{p^2}{2m} = \frac{40,000}{300} \times 4.80 \times 10^{-10} = 6.40 \times 10^{-8} \text{ erg} .$$

Whence,

$$p = \sqrt{2mE} = \sqrt{2\left(\frac{1}{1836 \times 0.6024 \times 10^{24}}\right) \times 6.40 \times 10^{-8}}$$

$$= \sqrt{1.157 \times 10^{-34}} = 1.076 \times 10^{-17} \text{ g cm sec}^{-1}.$$

By (8.7),

$$\lambda = \frac{6.624 \times 10^{-27}}{1.076 \times 10^{-17}} = 6.16 \times 10^{-10} \text{ cm} = 0.0616 \text{ A}.$$

These examples indicate that wave-like behavior is likely to be observed only for very small particles because h is small.

8.4 Continuity of Entropy[1]

In section 5.6, the entropy of mixing of ideal gases was viewed as dependent upon the attitude or knowledge of the experimenter. Such subjectiveness in physical science is unusual; in this case, it leads to a paradox.

The paradox is best explained by the act of mixing two gases of kind A and kind B as in Section 5.6. If an observer in the surroundings sees no difference in the initial unmixed state and the final mixed state, he must report $\Delta S = 0$ because entropy is a function of state. He is here supposed to be ignorant because he did not know that the partition separating pure A and pure B was withdrawn and replaced or because he lacks suitably refined instruments for distinguishing A from B. But if another observer in the surroundings notes a difference in the initial and final states by distinguishing A from B, he must report $\Delta S > 0$ in accord with (5.45).

$$\overline{\Delta S} = -RN_A \ln N_A - RN_B \ln N_B. \tag{5.45}$$

Thus two honest observers state different results.

If A and B were really alike, the second observer would report $\Delta S = 0$. His report depends upon his decision; like or unlike. Regardless of how similar A and B may be, he is forced to decide on the basis of his analytical method whether ΔS is zero or the full value of $\overline{\Delta S}$ in (5.45). There is no in-between; he is limited to two choices: zero or $-R \sum N \ln N$. What is really troublesome is that he could base his decision upon a variable that changes continuously from A to B and thus could differ only infinitesimally in A and B. If his analysis were by length of molecule, as the difference in lengths of type A and type B approaches zero as a limit, $\overline{\Delta S}$ remains fixed by (5.45). However, when the limit itself is reached (that is, when he decides that type A and type B are alike or at least indistinguishable in length), ΔS is suddenly and discontinuously zero. Since entropy is an extensive property, the presence of the partition between chambers of like gases should be without effect, for the entropy of a system is the sum of the entropies of its parts.

465

Faced with this obnoxious discontinuity, A. Landé postulates continuity of entropy. Complete likeness or unlikeness is replaced by a fractional degree of likeness. As type A becomes less and less distinguishable from type B, $\overline{\Delta S}$ continuously approaches zero. In other words, the observer who must measure $\overline{\Delta S}$ is not always faced with the simple alternative, like or unlike.

The familiar macroscopic world presents no fractional likenesses; everything is either like or unlike. A mixture of molecules can be separated into groups of various length, the number of groups depending upon the accuracy with which the lengths are distinguished. Even in the microscopic world of fractional likeness, long molecules can be distinguished as completely unlike short molecules and completely like other long ones. But in the same microscopic world, when long pointed molecules must be distinguished from long rounded molecules by a test for bluntness, they often lose their length characteristics. That is, it may happen that a molecule cannot be termed long *and* pointed in the world of fractional likenesses. Rather, if long molecules are tested for bluntness, some will pass the test and be labeled blunt while the remainder are termed pointed. There is no predicting the outcome for a particular molecule; the result of the test for bluntness is the history of a chance event. The test for bluntness determines what fraction of the long molecules is blunt and rejects as fractionally unlike those which are found to be pointed. The acute student has probably guessed that exact values of conjugate mechanical variables subject to the uncertainty principle are really such fractionally like states.

8.5 Superposition of Probability Amplitudes[2]

In the familiar world of like and unlike, the probability of a sequence of chance events is the product of the probabilities of the events of the sequence. The probability of throwing heads with an unbiased coin is $\frac{1}{2}$ for each toss. To do so five times in a row has a probability of $(\frac{1}{2})^5$. Heads is completely unlike tails. Similarly, on a baseball team consisting of players who either strike out or hit a single, the probability that the first man at bat in an inning will get beyond first base is the sum of several terms. The first term is the product of his batting average times the probability that he can steal second. The second term is the product of his own batting average times the batting average of the batter who follows him. The third term is the product of his own batting average times that of the third batter; and so on, with every possible way contributing a term to the sum. In general, the probability q_{12} of achieving state 2 from state 1 via any one of n intermediate states i is

$$q_{12} = \sum_{i=1}^{n} q_{1i}q_{i2} \qquad (8.10)$$

where q_{1i} is the probability of achieving intermediate state i from state 1 and q_{i2} is the independent probability of achieving the final state 2 from state i.

In the unfamiliar world of fractional likenesses, (8.10) often errs. The only known rule that satisfies all the properties required of fractional likenesses q is

$$q_{12} = |\phi_{12}|^2 = \phi_{12}^* \phi_{12} \tag{8.11}$$

where

$$\phi_{12} = \sum_{i=1}^{n} \phi_{1i}\phi_{i2} . \tag{8.12}$$

In (8.12), the famous law of superposition of probability amplitudes, ϕ is called a *probability amplitude* because it yields a true probability when squared as in (8.11). It is generally a complex quantity, ϕ^* being the complex conjugate of ϕ. Equation (8.12) replaces (8.10) in the world of fractional likenesses. Its analogue in optics is the equation for the net amplitude of n waves; the analogue in optics of (8.11) is the equation that finds intensity (q) from amplitude (ϕ). Thus (8.12) describes a matter-wave, in accord with de Broglie's equation (8.7) and experiment.

A simple but definite example of the wave-nature of matter is the well-known diffraction experiment in which a particle penetrates a barrier with two holes. The experimentally observed facts are these. Suppose a barrier containing two holes is placed between a source of particles and a recording device such as a photographic plate. If the experimenter leaves both holes open and does not determine which hole the particle passes through (that is, if he does not determine that the particle really went through one hole), the record is a diffraction pattern characterized by intensity maxima out of line with source and holes and some intensity minima even on a direct line from source through holes to plate. This diffraction pattern is unaltered in kind even when the intensity is reduced so low that only one particle at a time passes the barrier. The recorded pattern is, however, changed in kind when the experimenter determines directly or indirectly which hole each particle uses. He can close one hole or put a very delicate counter in line with a hole and note whether or not the particle passes. However subtly he tries, a unique determination of position at the barrier by noting which hole is or is not used inevitably alters the very nature of the record. It is no longer a diffraction pattern; it becomes rather a particle pattern. The particle behaves like a particle if its exact trajectory is traced; it behaves like a wave if its path is not traced.

When only one hole is open (or known to be used), only one intermediate state i is possible. In going from source (state 1) to plate (state 2), by (8.11) and (8.12), $\phi_{12} = \phi_{1i}\phi_{i2}$ and the intensity of the recorded pattern is

$$q_{12} = \phi_{12}^*\phi_{12} = \phi_{1i}^*\phi_{i2}^*\phi_{1i}\phi_{i2}$$

$$= q_{1i}q_{i2} . \tag{8.13}$$

467

However, when both holes (a and b) are open, by (8.12),

$$\phi_{12} = \phi_{1a}\phi_{a2} + \phi_{1b}\phi_{b2}$$

and by (8.11), the intensity of the diffraction pattern is

$$q_{12} = (\phi_{1a}^{*}\phi_{a2}^{*} + \phi_{1b}^{*}\phi_{b2}^{*})\,(\phi_{1a}\phi_{a2} + \phi_{1b}\phi_{b2})$$

$$= q_{1a}q_{a2} + q_{1b}q_{b2} + \phi_{1a}^{*}\phi_{a2}^{*}\phi_{1b}\phi_{b2} + \phi_{1b}^{*}\phi_{b2}^{*}\phi_{1a}\phi_{a2}\,. \tag{8.14}$$

Even if the holes were opened alternately, (8.13) would be merely

$$q_{12} = q_{1a}q_{a2} + q_{1b}q_{b2}\,. \tag{8.15}$$

The last two terms of (8.14) set its q_{12} apart from the particle-like behavior of (8.13) or (8.15). These are the interference terms peculiar to waves.

8.6   The Wave Equation

There are several ways of stating the mathematical postulates of quantum mechanics. Landé chooses to develop the concept of continuity of entropy of mixing to yield more general equations like (8.11) and (8.12). Thence he proceeds even further by very general arguments. Feynman[3] begins with a more general form of (8.11) and (8.12) suitable to many intermediate states as his first postulate and, in his second postulate, specifies the functional form of ϕ. Regardless of the postulatory basis, it happens that the most convenient form for the formulation and solution of most chemical problems is a differential equation, the Schrödinger equation (8.16).

$$\mathbf{H}\psi = -\frac{\hbar}{i}\frac{\partial\psi}{\partial t}\,. \tag{8.16}$$

The Hamiltonian operator is based upon an analogy with the Hamiltonian appropriate to the corresponding problem of classical mechanics. For the purposes of this book, this operator is simply

$$\mathbf{H} = -\frac{\hbar^2}{2}\sum_{i}\frac{1}{m_i}\left(\frac{\partial^2}{\partial x_i^2} + \frac{\partial^2}{\partial y_i^2} + \frac{\partial^2}{\partial z_i^2}\right) + V\,. \tag{8.17}$$

The summation proceeds over all particles, each of mass m_i, and V is the potential energy of the system of particles stated as a function of coordinates. In general $\mathbf{H}$ may be much more complicated and may even depend explicitly upon time.

The wave function ψ is a function of position and time. It is the full and complete description of the system; no further knowledge could be found or verified by experiment.

8.7 Stationary Energy States

The probability that a system will achieve state 2 from state 1 is $q_{12} = \mid \phi_{12} \mid^2$, where ϕ_{12} is the probability amplitude for this change of state. Just as $\mid \phi_{12} \mid^2$ is the probability that the system lies somewhere between states 1 and 2, $\mid \psi(x_i, y_i, z_i, t) \mid^2$ is the probability at time t that the system is in the state described by $\psi(x_i, y_i, z_i, t)$ with position coordinates only infinitesimally different from x_i, y_i, z_i. That is, $\mid \psi(x_i, y_i, z_i, t) \mid^2$ is a probability density of matter in space at time t. If $\mid \psi \mid^2$ is independent of time (and if the state is such that a net flow of matter does not occur), then the state is a stationary (or steady) state. In stationary states, $\mathbf{H}$ is independent of time.

Stationary states have wave functions of the form

$$\psi(x_i, y_i, z_i, t) = u(x_i, y_i, z_i)f(t) . \tag{8.18}$$

The general form of $f(t)$ is found by substituting (8.18) into the wave equation (8.16). On the left,

$$\mathbf{H}\psi(x_i, y_i, z_i, t) = f(t)\mathbf{H}u(x_i, y_i, z_i)$$

and on the right,

$$-\frac{\hbar}{i} \frac{\partial \psi}{\partial t} = -\frac{\hbar}{i} u(x_i, y_i, z_i) \frac{df(t)}{dt} .$$

After equating these expressions and dividing by ψ,

$$\frac{1}{u} \mathbf{H}u = -\frac{\hbar}{if} \frac{df}{dt} . \tag{8.19}$$

Since the left-hand member of (8.19) is independent of t while the right-hand member is independent of positional coordinates, each side must be independent of x_i, y_i, z_i, and t for neither changes when these variables change. If E is a constant independent of these variables, then the right side of (8.19) yields

$$\frac{df(t)}{f(t)} = -\frac{iE}{\hbar} dt$$

and

$$f(t) = a \exp\left(-\frac{iEt}{\hbar}\right) . \tag{8.20}$$

From (8.19) come two equations, namely,

$$-\frac{\hbar}{i} \frac{\partial f(t)}{\partial t} = Ef(t) \tag{8.21}$$

$$\mathbf{H}u(x_i, y_i, z_i) = Eu(x_i, y_i, z_i) . \tag{8.22}$$

469

Mathematicians call equations like these *eigenvalue equations*. The constant E is a number, called an *eigenvalue*, and $f(t)$ and $u(x_i, y_i, z_i)$ are *eigenfunctions*. Often only a very special set of numbers $E_1, E_2, \ldots, E_n, \ldots$ can satisfy (8.21) and (8.22). Every observable quantity in quantum mechanics is an eigenvalue and each eigenvalue has an operator. For the energy E, the operator is $\mathbf{H}$ or $-(\hbar/i)(\partial/\partial t)$. An individual measurement of the energy of a quantum mechanical system in a stationary state would yield one of the values E_n. Each stationary state has its own wave function such that

$$\mathbf{H}\psi_n = -\frac{\hbar}{i}\frac{\partial\psi_n}{\partial t} \tag{8.23}$$

$$-\frac{\hbar}{i}\frac{df_n(t)}{dt} = E_n f_n(t) \tag{8.24}$$

$$\mathbf{H}u_n(x_i, y_i, z_i) = E_n u_n(x_i, y_i, z_i) \tag{8.25}$$

where
$$\psi_n = a_n u_n(x_i, y_i, z_i)e^{-iE_n t/\hbar} . \tag{8.26}$$

The constant a_n is adjusted so that the integral of $|\psi_n|^2$ over all space is normalized; hence, if $d\tau$ is the element of volume,

$$1 = \int \psi_n^* \psi_n \, d\tau = a_n^* a_n \int u_n^* u_n \, d\tau . \tag{8.27}$$

In order to be physically meaningful, ψ and its first derivatives must be continuous, finite, and single-valued everywhere. The general normalization condition

$$1 = \int \psi^* \psi \, d\tau \tag{8.28}$$

or the interpretation of $|\psi|^2 = \psi^*\psi$ as a probability density of matter somewhere this side of infinity generally requires also that ψ approach zero asymptotically for large values of its coordinates. As can be verified by substitution into (8.16), the most general solution of the wave equation in terms of eigenfunctions of the energy is

$$\psi(x_i, y_i, z_i, t) = \sum_n a_n u_n(x_i, y_i, z_i)e^{-iE_n t/\hbar} . \tag{8.29}$$

If several states have the same energy E_n, the state is called *degenerate*. Stationary states that are not degenerate have all but one a_n equal to zero.

Only long-lived states exhibit well-defined energies. In terms of the conjugate variables energy and time, the uncertainty principle reads

$$\Delta E \cdot \Delta t \geqslant \hbar . \tag{8.30}$$

A system in a stationary or long-lived state has a large value of Δt associated with it and a well-executed experiment can measure its energy within a correspondingly small uncertainty ΔE in energy.

Example 8.4. An excited state of a molecule is observed spectroscopically to have an uncertainty in energy of 5.0 cm^{-1}. Estimate the lifetime of this excited state.

Since $E = h\nu = hc/\lambda = hc\bar{\nu}$, $\Delta E = 6.6 \times 10^{-27} \times 3.0 \times 10^{10} \times 5.0$ erg. By (8.30),

$$\Delta t \geqslant \frac{\hbar}{\Delta E} = \frac{1}{2\pi \times 3.0 \times 10^{10} \times 5.0} \geqslant 1.0 \times 10^{-12} \text{ sec}.$$

The lifetime is about 1.0×10^{-12} sec.

Example 8.5. If the excited state of Example 8.4 is observed at room temperature at 1 atm, could deactivating collisions be the reason for the limited lifetime of the excited state?

If collisions were the main cause of decay of this excited state, the time between collisions must be of the order of the lifetime, 1×10^{-12} sec. The time between collisions is about equal to the mean free path l divided by the mean velocity $\bar{v}$, or, by (1.89),

$$\frac{1}{Z_1} = \frac{V}{4\sigma^2 N}\left(\frac{m}{\pi k T}\right)^{1/2}.$$

For a gas of molecular weight of 30 with $\sigma^2 = 10 \times 10^{-16}$ cm^2, at the stated conditions

$$\frac{1}{Z_1} = \frac{2.5 \times 10^4}{4 \times 10 \times 10^{-16} \times 0.60 \times 10^{24}}\left(\frac{30}{\pi \times 8.3 \times 10^7 \times 300}\right)^{1/2} = 2.0 \times 10^{-10} \text{ sec}.$$

Since the time between collisions is more than 100 times the lifetime, the main cause of decay is not collisions.

B. APPLICATIONS IN PHYSICS

8.8 Free Particle

A particle which is free to move throughout space has no potential energy; hence, $V(x, y, z) = 0$. On the other hand, it has no definite position so that Δx, the uncertainty in its position, can be very great. If Δx approaches infinity, then the uncertainty principle does not forbid an exact measurement of p_x, for by (8.8)

$$\Delta p_x \geqslant \frac{\hbar}{\Delta x} \to 0. \tag{8.31}$$

In a stationary state with $V = 0$, the Schrödinger equation without the time is $\mathbf{H}u = Eu$, in particular

$$-\frac{\hbar^2}{2m}\left(\frac{\partial^2 u}{\partial x^2} + \frac{\partial^2 u}{\partial y^2} + \frac{\partial^2 u}{\partial z^2}\right) = Eu. \tag{8.32}$$

A solution is of the form

$$u = \exp\left[\pm \frac{i}{\hbar}(p_x x + p_y y + p_z z)\right] \tag{8.33}$$

for

$$\frac{\partial u}{\partial x} = \pm \frac{i}{\hbar} p_x u , \qquad \text{and so on}$$

$$\frac{\partial^2 u}{\partial x^2} = - \frac{p_x^2}{\hbar^2} u , \qquad \text{and so on} .$$

On substitution into (8.32) the result is

$$\left(-\frac{\hbar^2}{2m} \right)\left(-\frac{p_x^2}{\hbar^2} - \frac{p_y^2}{\hbar^2} - \frac{p_z^2}{\hbar^2} \right) u = Eu .$$

If the particle exists, $u \neq 0$ and, as expected of a particle with only kinetic energy,

$$E = \frac{p_x^2 + p_y^2 + p_z^2}{2m} . \tag{8.34}$$

8.9 Particle In Box

The description of a particle free to move about in a finite region of space differs from the completely free particle in that the particle is not completely delocalized. That is, Δx, Δy, and Δz are restricted by the size of the box. Within the box, the potential energy $V(x, y, z)$ is zero; without, it is infinite. At the walls, $V(x, y, z)$ changes discontinuously from zero to infinity. Whenever the potential changes from a finite to an infinite value, the wave function at the boundary (here a box wall) must be zero if the wave function is not to become infinite in the region where V is finite. If the walls of the box are planes at $x = \pm a/2, y = \pm b/2$, and $z = \pm c/2$, then the condition on the wave function $u(x, y, z)$ at the box walls is $u(\pm a/2, \pm b/2, \pm c/2) = 0$. Moreover, the particle cannot escape from the box so that u is zero for $|x| > a/2, |y| > b/2, |z| > c/2$.

The wave equation within the box is

$$-\frac{\hbar^2}{2m}\left(\frac{\partial^2 u}{\partial x^2} + \frac{\partial^2 u}{\partial y^2} + \frac{\partial^2 u}{\partial z^2} \right) = Eu . \tag{8.35}$$

A solution, as for (8.32), is of the form

$$u = \exp\left[\pm \frac{i}{\hbar}(p_x x + p_y y + p_z z) \right]. \tag{8.36}$$

The solution (8.36) is subject, however, to the condition that $u = 0$ at the box walls so that

$$0 = \exp\left[\pm \frac{i}{\hbar}\left(\frac{p_x a}{2} + \frac{p_y b}{2} + \frac{p_z c}{2} \right) \right]. \tag{8.37}$$

Because of (8.37), only certain values of p_x, p_y, and p_z are allowed in a stationary state. Since $e^{i\theta} = \cos\theta \pm i \sin\theta$, the conditions that both real and imaginary parts of (8.37) vanish are

$$\frac{p_x a}{2\hbar} = (2n_x' + 1)\frac{\pi}{2}, \qquad (n_x' = 0, 1, 2, \cdots)$$

and

$$\frac{p_x a}{2\hbar} = (2n_x'')\frac{\pi}{2}, \qquad (n_x'' = 0, 1, 2, \cdots).$$

Similar relations limit p_y and p_z. As n' and n'' assume various integral values, all even integers are generated by $2n''$ and all odd integers by $2n' + 1$. The energy of the particle is thus

$$E = \frac{p_x^2 + p_y^2 + p_z^2}{2m}$$

$$= \frac{\pi^2\hbar^2}{2m}\left(\frac{n_x^2}{a^2} + \frac{n_y^2}{b^2} + \frac{n_z^2}{c^2}\right) \tag{8.38}$$

where n_x, n_y, and n_z may be any positive integers except zero. If any of these three quantum numbers were zero, u would vanish throughout the box and the particle would not be in the box.

Figure 8.1 illustrates in one dimension the one-dimensional wave function $X(x)$ for the first five stationary states. The "particle" behaves like a standing wave. The wave function may be zero at certain points within the box as well as at its walls. At these zeros, u^*u is zero so that where u is zero the probability of finding the particle is zero.

Example 8.6. Explain why the state with $n_x = n_y = n_z = 1$ has a reasonable energy in (8.38).

A classical particle could rest on the bottom of its box with zero energy, but the lowest energy of (8.38) is greater than zero. In any single direction, say, x, the lowest energy is

$$E_x = \frac{\pi^2\hbar^2}{2ma^2} > 0.$$

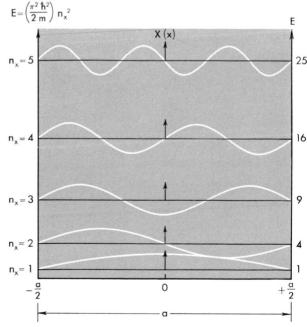

Fig. 8.1. *Wave Functions $X(x)$ of Particle in Box.*

473

Since the particle is somewhere in the box, a measures the uncertainty Δx in its position. If E_x is a measure of its uncertainty in energy, then the uncertainty in momentum is approximately

$$\Delta p_x = \sqrt{2mE_x} = \frac{\pi\hbar}{a}.$$

That is, $\Delta p_x \cdot \Delta x = \pi\hbar$, which is the uncertainty principle within a factor of π.

8.10   Tunnel Effect

Since $|X(x)|^2$ is the probability of finding a one-dimensional particle near x, a glance at Figure 8.1 will verify that there are $n_x - 1$ places within the box away from the walls where it cannot be found if it is in a stationary state n_x.

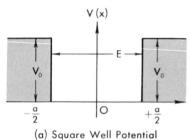

(a) Square Well Potential

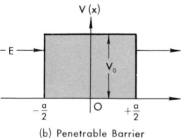

(b) Penetrable Barrier

Fig. 8.2.   *Some Simple Potentials.*

Similarly, in a three-dimensional box $|u(x, y, z)|^2$ has zeros where the particle is not. Still more amazing is the prediction that a particle can sometimes be found in a region where its total energy E is less than its potential energy V. Negative kinetic energy?

Figure 8.2(a) shows a particle in a one-dimensional box with sides where the potential energy $V(x)$ rises from zero to a finite value V_o for $|x| > a/2$. Where $V(x) = 0$, the wave function is of the form $\exp[\pm (i/\hbar) p_x x]$. If the particle has $E < V_o$ it can exist in at least one stationary energy state. If the well is wide enough and V_o is great enough, more than one such energy state may exist. For $E > V_o$ there is a continuous range of energies and the particle ranges from $x = -\infty$ to $x = +\infty$.

The wave equation for $|x| > a/2$ is

$$-\frac{\hbar^2}{2m}\frac{d^2u}{dx^2} + V_o u = Eu \tag{8.39}$$

$$\frac{d^2u}{dx^2} = \frac{2m(V_o - E)}{\hbar^2}\,u\,.$$

A solution when $E < V_o$ is

$$u = N_1 e^{Bx} + N_2 e^{-Bx}, \qquad B = \left(\frac{2m(V_o - E)}{\hbar^2}\right)^{1/2} \tag{8.40}$$

as substitution will show. Since $u \neq 0$ for $|x| > a/2$, $|u|^2$ has a finite value when $|x| > a/2$ and $E < V_o$. That is, the particle sometimes has $E < V_o$, which is impossible classically. Since $u(x)$ goes to zero for large x, $N_1 = 0$ when $x \geqslant a/2$ and $N_2 = 0$ when $x \leqslant -a/2$ and $|u|^2$ varies as $e^{-2B|x|}$ in the classically forbidden region.

Figure 8.2 (b) shows an analogous situation. A barrier of finite height V_o exists for $|x| \leqslant a/2$. If a particle of energy E comes to this barrier from the left, it can enter and even penetrate the barrier. For when $|x| \leqslant a/2$ its wave function is again (8.40) and $|u|^2$ is greater than zero. When $2ma^2(V_o - E) \gg \hbar^2$, the probability that a particle will be observed to tunnel through the barrier and appear at the right is proportional to e^{-2Ba}. Not only can the quantum mechanical particle penetrate the barrier, but its behavior near $x = 0$ when $E > V_o$ is disturbed, whereas classically the barrier would be without effect if $E > V_o$.

The probability of penetration increases as m, $(V_o - E)$, and a approach zero. Radioactive decay by alpha emission can be considered to be penetration of a narrow nuclear potential barrier by an alpha particle or its equivalent in the nucleus. Rotation of CH_3 against CH_3 in ethane, interconversion of optically active ammonias (Figure 2.39) by movement of a proton, and delocalization of electrons in resonance are a few examples of the tunnel effect.

8.11 Harmonic Oscillator

The one-dimensional harmonic oscillator has $V(x) = 2\pi^2 m \nu_o^2 x^2$. The wave equation is

$$-\frac{\hbar^2}{2m}\frac{d^2u(x)}{dx^2} + 2\pi^2 m\nu_o^2 x^2 u(x) = Eu(x) . \tag{8.41}$$

The solution[4] is

$$u_n(x) = N_n e^{-\xi^2/2} H_n(\xi) \tag{8.42}$$

where $\xi = (2\pi m\nu_o/\hbar)^{1/2}x$, N_n is a normalization constant, and $H_n(\xi)$ is a Hermite polynomial of degree n that satisfies the recursion formula

$$H_n(\xi) = 2\xi H_{n-1}(\xi) - 2(n - 1)H_{n-2}(\xi) . \tag{8.43}$$

Any value $H_n(\xi)$ can be calculated from (8.43) given

$$H_0(\xi) = 1 \tag{8.44}$$

and

$$H_1(\xi) = 2\xi . \tag{8.45}$$

The quantum number n originates quite naturally in the series solution of (8.41) if $u(x)$ is to approach zero for large x. In order to terminate the series and give polynomials $H_n(\xi)$ with a finite number of terms, it is necessary that

$$E_n = (n + \tfrac{1}{2})2\pi\hbar\nu_o, \qquad (n = 0, 1, 2, \cdots) . \tag{8.46}$$

The energy increases uniformly by $2\pi\hbar\nu_o$ when n increases by unity. In accord with the uncertainty principle, the lowest energy is $\pi\hbar\nu_o$, somewhat greater than zero. This minimum energy is called *zero-point energy*.

The harmonic oscillator is of paramount importance in discussing vibrations in molecules and crystals. In general, for f degrees of freedom, the wave function is a product of functions like (8.46) and

$$E = \sum_{i=1}^{f} E_{ni} = \sum_{i=1}^{f} (n_i + \tfrac{1}{2})2\pi\hbar\nu_{oi} . \tag{8.47}$$

If some of the ν_{oi} are alike for various degrees of freedom, some energies E are degenerate because the same value of E results from more than one choice of n_i's.

8.12 Hydrogen Atom Again

The hydrogen atom is important not only in its own right. It also is the prototype of all problems with a potential that depends only upon the radius r. The angular parts of its wave functions are useful in most atomic and valence problems, and its quantum numbers are applied to all atomic electrons of all atoms.

$V(r)$ for a positive nucleus of charge $+Ze$ and an electron of charge $-e$ is

$$V(r) = -\frac{Ze^2}{r}$$

Table 8.3. *Angular Wave Functions of Hydrogen Atom**
(a) $\Theta_{lm}(\theta)$

l	m	0	± 1	± 2
0		$\dfrac{\sqrt{2}}{2}$	NOT ALLOWED	NOT ALLOWED
1		$\dfrac{\sqrt{6}\cos\theta}{2}$	$\dfrac{\sqrt{3}\sin\theta}{2}$	NOT ALLOWED
2		$\dfrac{\sqrt{10}\,(3\cos^2\theta - 1)}{4}$	$\dfrac{\sqrt{15}\sin\theta\cos\theta}{2}$	$\dfrac{\sqrt{15}\sin^2\theta}{4}$

(b) $\Phi_m(\phi)$

$|m|$	0	1	2
$+$	$\dfrac{1}{\sqrt{2\pi}}$	$\dfrac{\cos\phi}{\sqrt{\pi}}$	$\dfrac{\cos 2\phi}{\sqrt{\pi}}$
$-$	$\dfrac{1}{\sqrt{2\pi}}$	$\dfrac{\sin\phi}{\sqrt{\pi}}$	$\dfrac{\sin 2\phi}{\sqrt{\pi}}$

* Pauling, L. and E. B. Wilson, Jr., *Introduction to Quantum Mechanics.* New York: McGraw-Hill Book Company, 1935, pp. 133-4.

where r is the distance between particles. If the nucleus of mass M is at X, Y, Z and the electron of mass m is at x, y, z, the wave equation is

$$-\frac{\hbar^2}{2M}\left(\frac{\partial^2 U}{\partial X^2} + \frac{\partial^2 U}{\partial Y^2} + \frac{\partial^2 U}{\partial Z^2}\right) - \frac{\hbar^2}{2m}\left(\frac{\partial^2 U}{\partial x^2} + \frac{\partial^2 U}{\partial y^2} + \frac{\partial^2 U}{\partial z^2}\right)$$
$$-\frac{Ze^2 U}{r} = E_{\text{total}} U . \tag{8.48}$$

Here $r = \sqrt{(X - x)^2 + (Y - y)^2 + (Z - z)^2}$ and E_{total} includes translational and all other energies. Exact solution in spherical polar coordinates r, θ, ϕ yields the angular wave functions of Table 8.3 as factors of the center-of-mass wave function

$$u(r, \theta, \phi) = R_{nl}(r)\Theta_{lm}(\theta)\Phi_m(\phi) . \tag{8.49}$$

The radial functions $R_{nl}(r)$ are polynomials in r modified by a factor exp $(-\mu Ze^2 r/n\hbar^2)$, where μ is the reduced mass of the two-particle system.

The quantum numbers n, l, m are the principal, azimuthal, and magnetic quantum numbers and take the values

$$\begin{array}{ll} n & 1, 2, 3, \cdots, \infty \\ l & 0, 1, 2, \cdots, (n - 1) \\ m & 0, \pm 1, \pm 2, \cdots, \pm l . \end{array} \right\} \tag{8.50}$$

These quantum numbers arise quite naturally in finding acceptable wave functions. The energy of the system relative to nucleus and electron infinitely separated at rest is

$$E = -\frac{\mu Z^2 e^4}{2\hbar^2 n^2} \tag{8.51}$$

The planar Bohr atom also yielded (8.51). The Schrödinger atom is, however, three dimensional. The absolute values of the angular parts of $u(r, \theta, \phi)$ are shown in Figure 8.3 for $l = 0, 1,$ and 2.

Since the main interest here is in energies and ideas and not in the techniques of solution and mathematical details of the wave equation, the student is referred to any quantum mechanics text for details.[5]

8.13   The Variation Method

The process of writing out the wave equation explicitly is almost always straightforward but solving it is generally impossible. Since chemists commonly deal with the most stable state of a system, its state of minimum energy, the variation method[6] of minimizing an approximate value of the energy is quite valuable.

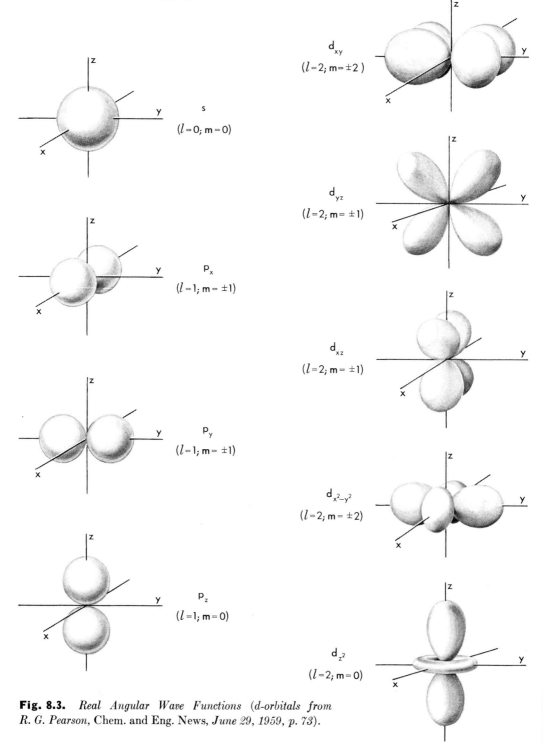

Fig. 8.3. *Real Angular Wave Functions (d-orbitals from R. G. Pearson*, Chem. and Eng. News, *June 29, 1959, p. 73).*

The variation method yields an energy that cannot be less than and may be quite close to the minimum energy really exhibited by the system. An approximate wave function $v(x_i, y_i, z_i)$ is guessed and with it an approximate value of energy E' is calculated by the formula

$$E' = \int v^*\mathbf{H}v \, d\tau . \tag{8.52}$$

Then E' is minimized with respect to certain parameters. This systematic search for the best possible wave function of the form $v(x_i, y_i, z_i)$ yields a value of E' that cannot be less than the lowest energy of the system. Although the calculational work may be extensive, a wise choice of v can reduce the difference between E' and the true energy to negligible size. The real system behaves as an analog computer in itself always getting a perfect wave function with lowest energy

$$E = \int u^*\mathbf{H}u \, d\tau .$$

8.14 Helium Atom

Despite the outstanding success of the Bohr theory in explaining the energies of the hydrogen atom, it could not yield reasonable energies for the helium atom. With comparative ease, beginning with wave functions similar to those for hydrogen, the variation method yielded an energy correct within one part in 50,000. The electron-electron repulsion is far from negligible, but even a simple variation function with one parameter a of the form $e^{-ar_1}e^{-ar_2}$ (where r_i is the distance from nucleus to electron i) yields E' within 6% of the observed value. Pauling and Wilson[7] list the results of several types of variation function.

8.15 Exclusion Principle

Besides important repulsions between electrons in polyelectronic atoms, there are certain combinations of electrons forbidden because of symmetry properties of electronic wave functions. Other fundamental particles also behave like electrons in these regards.

Electronic energies of atoms depend in general upon quantum numbers n and l. To account in detail for states of almost equal energies, Uhlenbeck and Goudsmit in 1926 attributed a magnetic moment to an electron. This moment was conceived as caused by the current associated with a spinning of the electron and its charge. The total magnetic moment of an electron or atom was then the vector sum of its orbital magnetic moment, due to movement round the nucleus, and its intrinsic magnetic moment, due to spin. Although the model of an actually spinning electron is obsolete, the magnetic moment exhibited by the electron is called its *spin*. Spin results automatically from Dirac's relativistically invariant wave equation of the electron.

Electronic spin introduces what is essentially a fourth electronic quantum number into the description of atomic electrons. Besides n, l, and m (hereafter called m_l because this magnetic moment comes from orbital motion), a spin quantum number m_s is needed. The component of spin angular momentum of an electron in the direction of a magnetic field is $m_s \hbar$, where $m_s = \pm \frac{1}{2}$.

Although matrix methods are particularly suitable for discussing all forms of angular momentum and especially spin, it is most convenient here to develop a mathematical description of spin as a function capable of two values: $\alpha(\omega)$ for $+\frac{1}{2}\hbar$ and $\beta(\omega)$ for $-\frac{1}{2}\hbar$.[8] These spin functions are orthogonal and normalized, for

$$\left. \begin{array}{c} \int \alpha(\omega)\alpha(\omega) \, d\omega = \int \beta(\omega)\beta(\omega) \, d\omega = 1 \\ \text{orthogonal:} \int \alpha(\omega)\beta(\omega) \, d\omega = 0 \, . \end{array} \right\} \tag{8.53}$$

In (8.53), ω is a variable formally like a position coordinate. Spin and its artificial variable ω differ, however, from position in that spin can assume only discrete values. A hydrogen-like electron with quantum numbers n, l, m_l, and $m_s = +\frac{1}{2}$ has a wave function $R_{nl}(r)\Theta_{lm_l}(\theta)\Phi_{m_l}(\phi)\alpha(\omega)$. If $m_s = -\frac{1}{2}$, $\beta(\omega)$ replaces $\alpha(\omega)$.

It is a matter of experience that particles with components of spin $\pm(n + \frac{1}{2})\hbar$ (where n is an integer) have antisymmetric wave functions. A wave function is antisymmetric if it changes algebraic sign when the coordinates of two identical particles are interchanged. Interchanging coordinates of identical particles leaves the algebraic sign of a symmetric wave function unchanged. Particles are identical if they would act alike in all experiments. This means essentially that a Hamiltonian operator that describes identical particles is symmetric, that is, unchanged in sign when positions of two identical particles are interchanged.

In general, the wave function of a stationary state involving two identical particles is either symmetric or antisymmetric, and remains so for all time despite changing interactions. Since the total wave function can be factored for discussing symmetry into a coordinate part and a spin part, it is possible to discuss each factor separately.

The spin functions of two electrons are: $\alpha(1)\alpha(2)$ and $\beta(1)\beta(2)$ if their spins are alike; $\alpha(1)\beta(2)$ and $\beta(1)\alpha(2)$ if their spins differ. There are three symmetric spin functions, namely,

$$\left. \begin{array}{c} \alpha(1)\alpha(2) \\[2mm] \dfrac{1}{\sqrt{2}} \left[\alpha(1)\beta(2) + \beta(1)\alpha(2) \right] \\[2mm] \beta(1)\beta(2) \, . \end{array} \right\} \tag{8.54}$$

Interchanging coordinates in each of (8.54) yields the same spin wave function, for example:

$$\frac{1}{\sqrt{2}}\left[\alpha(2)\beta(1) + \beta(2)\alpha(1)\right].$$

Only one antisymmetric spin wave function of two electrons exists:

$$\frac{1}{\sqrt{2}}\left[\alpha(1)\beta(2) - \beta(1)\alpha(2)\right]. \tag{8.55}$$

Interchanging coordinates yields

$$\frac{1}{\sqrt{2}}\left[\alpha(2)\beta(1) - \beta(2)\alpha(1)\right] = -\frac{1}{\sqrt{2}}\left[\alpha(1)\beta(2) - \beta(1)\alpha(2)\right].$$

This antisymmetric function is conveniently expressed in the form of a determinant

$$\frac{1}{\sqrt{2}}\begin{vmatrix} \alpha(1) & \beta(1) \\ \alpha(2) & \beta(2) \end{vmatrix}. \tag{8.56}$$

Since every electronic wave function must be antisymmetric, the spin of an electron being a half-integral value, a polyelectronic wave function is conveniently expressed in the form

$$u(1, 2, \cdots, n) = (n!)^{-1/2}\begin{vmatrix} u_a(1) & u_b(1) & \cdots & u_n(1) \\ u_a(2) & u_b(2) & \cdots & u_n(2) \\ \cdots & \cdots & & \cdots \\ u_a(n) & u_b(n) & \cdots & u_n(n) \end{vmatrix}. \tag{8.57}$$

In (8.57), the wave functions u_a, u_b, ..., u_n are functions of coordinates and spin. The wave function $u_a(1)$ might be $R_{nl}(r_1)\Theta_{lm_l}(\theta_1)\Phi_{m_l}(\phi_1)\alpha(1)$, the electron 1 being in state a, which is characterized by the quantum numbers n, l, m_l, and $m_s = +\frac{1}{2}$. Since interchanging rows or columns of a determinant changes its algebraic sign, $u(1, 2, \ldots, n)$ is completely antisymmetric, as required experimentally. The factor $(n!)^{-1/2}$ is a normalization factor.

The Pauli exclusion principle states that no two electrons can exist in the same quantum state. This is to say that no two columns of the determinant in (8.57) can be alike if $u(1, 2, \ldots, n)$ is not to vanish. When two rows or columns of a determinant are alike, the determinant is zero. For atoms, the Pauli exclusion principle says that no two atomic electrons can have the same four quantum numbers n, l, m_l, and m_s.

This principle accounts for the periodic table of elements. For historical reasons, electrons with $l = 0, 1, 2, 3, 4, 5, \ldots$ are labeled s, p, d, f, g, h, ... For a given value of n, only two s-electrons are possible, namely, n, $l = 0$,

$m_l = 0$, $m_s = +\frac{1}{2}$ and n, $l = 0$, $m_l = 0$, $m_s = -\frac{1}{2}$. For a given value of n, six p-electrons are possible, namely:

$$
\begin{array}{cccccc}
(1) & n & l = 1 & m_l = +1 & m_s = +\frac{1}{2} \\
(2) & n & l = 1 & m_l = +1 & m_s = -\frac{1}{2} \\
(3) & n & l = 1 & m_l = 0 & m_s = +\frac{1}{2} \\
(4) & n & l = 1 & m_l = 0 & m_s = -\frac{1}{2} \\
(5) & n & l = 1 & m_l = -1 & m_s = +\frac{1}{2} \\
(6) & n & l = 1 & m_l = -1 & m_s = -\frac{1}{2}
\end{array}
$$

Similarly, ten d-electrons, fourteen f-electrons, and so on are the maximum for fixed n. The change in electronic energy with a change in n is usually greater than that for a change in another quantum number. With these things in mind, a glance at a periodic table clearly shows the role of the exclusion principle in forcing electrons to assume greater and greater values of quantum numbers as the number of electrons increases.

Particles that exhibit spin in integral multiples of $\hbar$, including zero spin, have symmetric total wave functions. Any number of such particles can exist in the same state, whereas the number of particles with half-integral spin and antisymmetric wave functions in a state can be only one or zero. Table 8.4 lists some properties of elementary particles, including spin which fixes the symmetry or antisymmetry of the wave functions. Lately, two more hyperons, Σ^o and Ξ^o, have been reported.

Table 8.4. *Properties of Elementary Particles**

NAME	SYMBOL	RELATIVE REST MASS	DECAY PRODUCTS	MEAN LIFE (SEC)	SPIN
Light	γ^o	0	stable	∞	1
Neutrino	ν^o	$<5 \times 10^{-4}$	stable	∞	$\frac{1}{2}$
Electron	e^-	1	stable	∞	$\frac{1}{2}$
Positron	e^+	$1(\pm 0.0071\%)$	$e^+ + e^- \rightarrow n\gamma^o$	1.5×10^{-7}	$\frac{1}{2}$
L mesons $\{$	$\mu^{\pm}$	206.7	$e^{\pm} + \nu^o + \nu^o$	2.22×10^{-6}	$\frac{1}{2}$
	$\pi^{\pm}$	273	$\mu^{\pm} + \nu^o$	2.5×10^{-8}	0
	π^o	264.3	$\gamma^o + \gamma^o$, etc.	$\sim 10^{-15}$	0
K mesons $\{$	$\tau^{\pm}$	966.1	$\pi^{\pm} + \pi^{\pm} + \pi^{\mp}$, etc.	1.27×10^{-8}	0
	θ^o	965	$\pi^+ + \pi^-$	1.3×10^{-10}	Integral, $\neq 1$
Proton	p^+	1836.12	stable	∞	$\frac{1}{2}$
Antiproton	p^-	$1836.12(\pm 2\%)$			$\frac{1}{2}$
Neutron	n^o	1838.65	$p^+ + e^- + \nu^o$	1.11×10^3	$\frac{1}{2}$
Hyperons $\{$	Λ^o	2181.5	$p^+ + \pi^-$	3.7×10^{-10}	$\frac{1}{2}$ Integral
	Σ^+	2326.9	$p^+ + \pi^o$ or $n^o + \pi^+$	$\sim 3 \times 10^{-11}$	$\frac{1}{2}$ Integral
	Σ^-	2326.9	$n^o + \pi^-$	$\sim 3 \times 10^{-11}$	$\frac{1}{2}$ Integral
	Ξ^-	2586	$\Lambda^o + \pi^-$	$\sim 1 \times 10^{-10}$	$\frac{1}{2}$ Integral

* Selected from Shapiro, A. M., *Reviews of Modern Physics*, **28**, 164 (1956).

C. APPLICATIONS IN CHEMISTRY

8.16 Hydrogen Molecule Ion

The first chemical application of wave mechanics was to the hydrogen molecule ion H_2^+ (Burrau 1927). One electron near two protons separated by a distance R_{AB} has

$$V = -\frac{e^2}{r_A} - \frac{e^2}{r_B} + \frac{e^2}{R_{AB}} \qquad (8.58)$$

where r_A and r_B are the distances between electron and protons A and B. Because the protons are massive and localized compared to the electron, the wave equation can be written for just the electron in the field of stationary protons at a fixed distance R_{AB}. In this approximation of Born and Oppenheimer,

$$-\frac{\hbar^2}{2m}\left(\frac{\partial^2 u}{\partial x^2} + \frac{\partial^2 u}{\partial y^2} + \frac{\partial^2 u}{\partial z^2}\right) + Vu = Eu . \quad (8.59)$$

The position of the electron of mass m is x, y, z with the coordinate system fixed to the stationary protons.

As R_{AB} becomes either very small or very great, V assumes a simpler form. If the repulsion term for the protons is ignored as R_{AB} approaches zero, r_A approaches r_B and

$$V \approx -\frac{2e^2}{r} . \qquad (8.60)$$

On the other hand, as R_{AB} approaches infinity, if the electron is near one of the protons,

$$V \approx -\frac{e^2}{r} . \qquad (8.61)$$

In either limit the lone electron lies in a hydrogen-like potential and its wave function is also hydrogen-like. Just as the atomic problem is to find an atomic orbital for an atomic electron, the problem here is to find a molecular orbital, an orbital having more than one center.

As R_{AB} becomes great, the wave function of the electron becomes u_A when it is primarily under the influence of proton A and becomes u_B while near proton B. Since neither proton is to be preferred over the other, the law of superposition of probability amplitudes suggests a solution of (8.59) of the form

$$u = u_A \pm u_B . \qquad (8.62)$$

* Adapted from C. A. Coulson, *Valence*, Oxford (1952), p. 80.

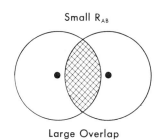

Small R_{AB}

Large Overlap

Large R_{AB}

Small Overlap

Fig. 8.4. *Overlap of 1s Orbitals.*

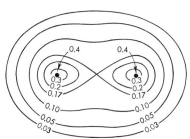

0.4   0.4
0.3   0.3
0.2   0.2
0.17   0.17
0.10   0.10
0.05   0.05
0.03   0.03

Binding: $|u_A + u_B|^2$

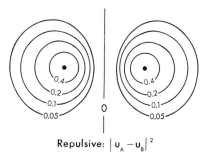

0.4   0.4
0.2   0.2
0.1   0.1
0.05   0.05
0

Repulsive: $|u_A - u_B|^2$

Fig. 8.5. *Contours of Constant Electron Density in H_2^+.*

Solution for the energy yields several terms. The first is due to nuclear repulsion. The second is due to the attraction between the electron and one of the protons as if the system were a proton and a hydrogen atom. The third term is due to the coulomb attraction between the bare proton and the electron on the other proton. The important term uniquely characteristic of quantum mechanics is similar to the interference terms of (8.14). It represents a coulomb-like effect of an electron on A and B simultaneously. The symmetric mode of existence on both nucleuses is a state of low energy — the stable state. A measure of the probability that the electron is on both nucleuses at once is the magnitude of the *overlap integral S*.

$$S = \int u_A^* u_B \, d\tau = \int u_B^* u_A \, d\tau . \tag{8.63}$$

The size of S or the amount of overlap for $1s$-hydrogen-like electronic orbitals as a function of R_{AB} is shown in Figure 8.4. The bounding circles indicate the distances at which the s-like function e^{-cr} reaches a small constant value.

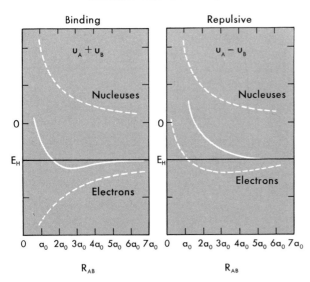

The stable state of H_2^+ has an electronic wave function that is symmetric $(u_A + u_B)$ in electron coordinates. For it the electron density is high between protons. The antisymmetric function $u_A - u_B$ represents a repulsive state in which the electron density is zero midway between protons, as shown in Figure 8.5.

Figure 8.6 describes the energies of these states as a function of R_{AB}, the distance between protons. The dashed curves labeled "electrons" are the energies calculated without nuclear repulsion. At large separation, the energy of the system is E_H (8.51), the energy of an atom and a proton. The net energy of H_2^+ includes nuclear repulsion and is the sum of the dashed curves. The strength of the bond is the energy difference between the minimum of the solid curve and E_H. These electronic orbitals of H_2^+ are the simplest molecular orbitals; and the bond, called a *one-electron bond*, is the simplest chemical bond.

Fig. 8.6. *Energy Curves of H_2^+.**

$$E_H = -\frac{e^2}{a_0} = -13.6 \text{ e.v.} \qquad a_0 = \frac{\hbar^2}{\mu e^2} = 0.529 \text{ A} .$$

* Adapted from C. A. Coulson, *Valence*, Oxford (1952), p. 79.

8.17 Hydrogen Molecule (Valence-Bond Method)

Calculating the chemically meaningful lowest energy of H_2 requires solving the wave equation for a system of two electrons and two protons in their most stable stationary state. The problem is difficult, for V has several awkward terms.

$$V = -\frac{e^2}{r_{1A}} - \frac{e^2}{r_{2B}} - \frac{e^2}{r_{2A}} - \frac{e^2}{r_{1B}} + \frac{e^2}{r_{12}} + \frac{e^2}{R_{AB}} \tag{8.64}$$

where R_{AB} is the distance between protons, r_{12} is the distance between electrons, and the other r's are electron-proton distances.

As R_{AB} becomes very small, r_{1A} becomes r_{1B} and r_{2A} becomes r_{2B}; wihtout proton-proton repulsion, (8.64) then suits He. Chemical intuition suggests, however, that the limit for large R_{AB} is more meaningful. As R_{AB} approaches infinity, if electron 1 stays on proton A and 2 stays on B,

$$V \approx -\frac{e^2}{r_{1A}} - \frac{e^2}{r_{2B}} \tag{8.65}$$

because r_{12}, r_{1B}, and r_{2A} approach infinity with R_{AB}. In this approximation of two hydrogen atoms, the wave function of H_2 is

$$u = u_A(1)u_B(2) \tag{8.66}$$

where $u_A(1)$ is a hydrogen-like wave function for electron 1 around proton A while $u_B(2)$ is for electron 2 around proton B.

Just as the nonclassical feature of the H_2^+ calculation was the identity of protons, here the identity of protons and electrons requires

$$u = u_A(1)u_B(2) \pm u_A(2)u_B(1) . \tag{8.67}$$

There is no telling which electron is on which proton or which belongs to which.

Energies calculated with (8.67) consist of several terms: nuclear repulsion (e^2/R_{AB}); energies of separated atoms $(2E_H)$; coulomb attraction terms (each proton for the other's electron); electron-electron repulsion terms; and finally, large terms of quantum mechanical nature. The coulomb attraction terms are of the form

$$\int \frac{u_A^*(2)e^2 u_A(2)}{r_{2B}} \, d\tau_2$$

indicating that electron 2 on A is attracted to B. Electron-electron repulsion terms are of the form

$$\iint \frac{u_A^*(1)u_B^*(2)e^2 u_A(1)u_B(2)}{r_{12}} \, d\tau_1 \, d\tau_2$$

indicating that electron 1 on A repels electron 2 on B. The terms of quantum mechanical nature are of the forms

$$\int u_A^*(1)u_B(1)\,d\tau_1 \int \frac{u_B^*(2)e^2u_A(2)}{r_{2A}}\,d\tau_2$$

and

$$\iint \frac{u_A^*(1)u_B^*(2)e^2u_A(2)u_B(1)}{r_{12}}\,d\tau_1\,d\tau_2\,.$$

These are called *exchange integrals* because the electrons are pictured as being exchanged between protons. The lowest energy calculated in this way is $2E_H - 3.14$ ev. That is, the energy for the dissociation of H_2 to atoms is calculated to be 3.14 ev. The observed value is 4.75 ev. This kind of solution is due to Heitler and London and is called the *valence-bond method*.

In this degree of approximation, the total antisymmetric electronic wave function for the state of H_2 of lowest energy is of the form

$$[u_A(1)u_B(2) + u_A(2)u_B(1)][\alpha(1)\beta(2) - \alpha(2)\beta(1)]\,.$$

The symmetric function of (8.67) becomes antisymmetric by virtue of spin. There is only one such spin state and thus only one state of lowest energy in H_2. As in He, the Pauli exclusion principle limits the number of electrons in this state to two. It can be shown that the electron-spins are opposed or paired in this simplest covalent bond.

8.18 Hydrogen Molecule (Molecular-Orbital Method)

Another kind of description of the bond in H_2 uses two molecular orbitals like (8.62) for H_2^+. The electronic wave function of H_2 in its most stable state is then

$$u = [u_A(1) + u_B(1)][u_A(2) + u_B(2)]\,. \tag{8.68}$$

This symmetric wave function must be combined with the one antisymmetric spin function to yield a total electronic wave function that is antisymmetric. That is, a molecular orbital can hold only two electrons, and these two must have opposed spins as in He. The binding energy $(E - 2E_H)$ calculated with (8.68) is -2.68 ev.

8.19 Comparison of Valence-Bond and Molecular-Orbital Methods

The molecular-orbital and valence-bond methods are approximations. Both describe the covalent bond in H_2 in terms of paired electrons shared by both protons. Although bond energies are calculated in terms of position coordinates and coulomb and exchange integrals, electron spin is a guide to allowed electron population. Pairing of electron spins in the molecular-orbital method is formally akin to pairing of electrons in atomic orbitals, but pairing in the valence-bond method is directly related to the antisymmetric nature of an electronic wave function. The energy of pairing itself is negligible; the main energy of the bond comes from the size of the exchange integral.

These two methods really approach the same observable limit if the wave functions are made more flexible. If the valence-bond variation function of H_2 is

$$u = [u_A(1)u_B(2) + u_A(2)u_B(1)] + a[u_A(1)u_A(2) + u_B(1)u_B(2)] \qquad (8.69)$$

a binding energy $(E - 2E_H)$ of -4.00 ev is achieved[9] for $a = 0.256$ and an effective atomic number of 1.193. The terms following a describe ionic structures A^-B^+ and A^+B^-. If a variable atomic number is included as a parameter in the simple molecular-orbital calculation,[10] $(E - 2E_H) = -3.47$ ev. The reason that this molecular orbital calculation does not yield a lower energy is that its wave function (8.68) requires $a = 1$ in (8.69), thus limiting the flexibility of the variation function and requiring that ionic structures be as important as purely covalent ones. As the variation functions are made more flexible and complex, the calculated energy approaches the observed energy within less than 1%.

In general, the molecular-orbital method places too much emphasis on ionic terms and too little on electron repulsion. It is poor at large internuclear separations because it often predicts wrong dissociation products, whereas the valence-bond method is superior at large distances and predicts correct dissociation products because the zero-order wave function suits large R_{AB}. The valence-bond method, however, underestimates ionic contributions and is generally less tractable mathematically. The molecular-orbital method deals with electrons as individuals, even in excited states, and describes in a simple and natural way the unusual one-electron bond of H_2^+. Since each method makes errors of the order of one or two electron volts in binding energy, neither is clearly to be preferred. Rather, if the use of both methods yields a particular prediction, one is safe in expecting the real situation to lie somewhere between these two extremes.[11]

8.20 Correlation Diagrams of Diatomic Molecules

The electron distributions in the lowest states of H_2^+ and H_2 are symmetrical about the internuclear axis. By analogy with spherically symmetrical atomic s-states, electronic states with cylindrical symmetry about the internuclear axis are called σ-states. If the two z-axes of two fluorine atoms, each in state $1s^2 2s^2 2p_x^2 2p_y^2 2p_z$, were along the internuclear axis as in Figure 8.7(a), a σ-bond could be formed due to the overlap of their $2p_z$-orbitals. The wave function would be of the form of (8.67) or (8.68) with $u_A = 2p_{Az}$ and $u_B = 2p_{Bz}$. The symbol σ indicates that the component of electronic orbital angular momentum along the internuclear axis is zero.

Two atomic p-states can form a bond involving considerable overlap of atomic wave functions in another way, shown in Figure 8.7(b). Since such an arrangement has net electronic orbital angular momentum of $\pm\hbar$ along the internuclear axis, the bond is called a π-bond by analogy with p atomic states. The internuclear axis is chosen as reference because it establishes a uniquely defined direction for atoms A and B.

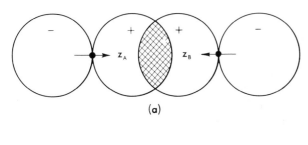

(a)

When atoms A and B are identical, the electronic wave function assumes symmetry appropriate to the molecule. In particular, since $|u|^2$ must be unchanged in sign when $+x$, $+y$, and $+z$, as measured from an origin midway between nucleuses, become $-x$, $-y$, and $-z$, the wave function itself must change from $+u$ to $\pm u$ for this same process, inversion. If $u = +u$ upon inversion, the state is labeled g (German: *gerade* = even); if u becomes $-u$, the state is labeled u (*ungerade*). The labels g and u have no meaning for heteronuclear molecules.

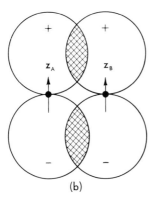

(b)

Fig. 8.7. *Overlap in p-p Bonds. (a) Sigma Bond. (b) Pi Bond.*

With these two bits of nomenclature, it is possible to classify the various electronic states of a diatomic molecule in terms of the electronic states of atoms for very small or very large internuclear separations. When identical atoms are far apart, they interact feebly to produce a g- and a u-state from each of the states they have when isolated. Moreover, this feeble interaction establishes a preferred direction in space along which angular momentum is quantized. These states of feeble interaction of separated atoms are listed with their origins at the right of Figure 8.8. For example, the even and odd s-states of the separated atoms can have no component of orbital angular momentum along the internuclear axis and so produce only σ-states. However, the even or odd p-states of the separated atoms have orbital angular momentum: if ± 1 along the axis, π-states result; if 0 along the axis, σ-states result.

At the left of Figure 8.8 levels are labeled σ and π because the incipient division of the nucleus into halves acts like an incipient electric field. If

$m_l = 0$, a σ-state results; if $m_l = \pm 1$, a π-state results. Here the s-, d-, ... states are g while the p-, f-, h-, ... states are u.

States with internuclear distances with intermediate values can be described in terms of these same quantum numbers. The quantum numbers, which indicate the symmetry and nature of the wave function, are conserved in going from united to separated atoms. That is, σ_g joins σ_g, σ_u joins σ_u, π_g joins π_g, π_u joins π_u, and so on, the correlation beginning at the bottom with the most stable states. Each correlation line describes a molecular orbital capable of holding two electrons with paired spins.

Bonding molecular orbitals usually have correlation lines that slope downward to the left. The scales of energy and distance in Figure 8.8 are, however, of only qualitative meaning. The most stable states of electrons in H_2^+, H_2, He_2, N_2, O_2, and F_2 are listed in the figure, paired arrows indicating paired spins. The state He_2 is nonbonding because the bonding effect of σ_g^2 is more than undone by the antibonding effect of σ_u^2. These two molecular orbitals hold the inert pairs in the K-shells. In N_2, with neglect of the two K-shells, the bonding electrons are $\sigma_g^2 \pi_u^4 \sigma_g^2$ while σ_u^2 are antibonding. Because a π-orbital may have angular momentum component of $+1$ or -1 along the axis, it can hold up to two pairs of electrons. The bond in N_2 is said to be a triple bond because there are a net of three pairs of bonding electrons, σ_g^2 and σ_u^2 having opposed effects. The electron structure in N_2 is cylindrically symmetric, for the π^4 electron distribution depends only upon the distance from the axis, while the σ^2 combinations are also symmetrical. Similarly, in F_2 the only pair of electrons in a bonding orbital not balanced by a similar nonbonding orbital of electrons is σ_g^2 of $2p$. These two electrons form the single σ-bond of F_2.

The most stable state of O_2 involves bonding electrons (neglecting K-electrons) in $\sigma_g^2 \pi_u^4 \sigma_g^2$ as in N_2 and F_2, but the antibonding electrons $\sigma_u^2 \pi_g^2$ are not all paired because the spins in π_g need not differ. The states π_u^4 and π_g^2 are of similar energy and are almost degenerate. These six electrons, with the net bonding effect of two electrons, are said to form two three-electron bonds, each with about half the strength of an electron-pair bond. The most stable state of O_2 is sometimes written thus: $: O \vDash O :$.

Although g and u have no meaning for heteronuclear diatomic molecules because $|u|^2$ need not be unchanged by inversion, the correlation rules σ to σ, π to π, ... remain. Figure 8.9 lists the states with a correlation that differs slightly from that in Figure 8.8 because of this change in rules. The general electronic structures of HD and CO remain like those of H_2 and N_2 except for even-odd character.

The electronic structure of NO is midway between those of N_2 and O_2. Without K-electrons, bonding electrons are $\sigma^2 \pi^4 \sigma^2$ and antibonding electrons are $\sigma^2 \pi$. The excess σ^2 orbital provides a single σ-bond, and the $\pi^4 \pi$ combination provides a single π-bond (π^2) and a three-electron bond ($\pi^2 \pi$). Without this unpaired antibonding π-electron, NO forms NO^+, as in the production

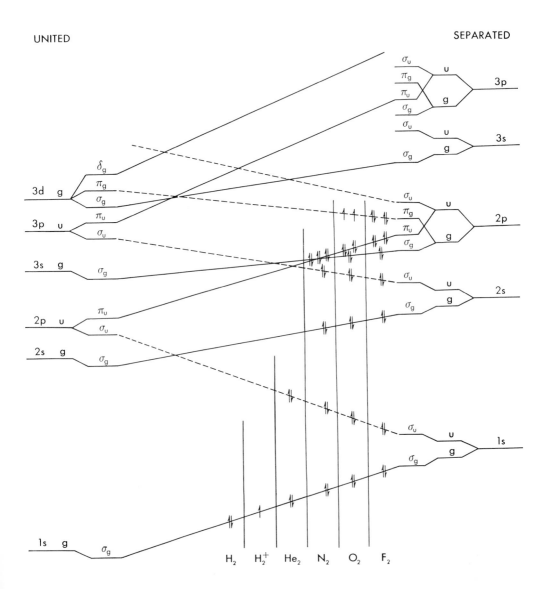

Fig. 8.8. *Correlation Diagram of Homonuclear Diatomic Molecules.* The correlation is $\sigma = \sigma$; $\pi = \pi$; . . .; and $g = g$; $u = u$. Bonding orbitals are solid lines; antibonding, dashed.*

* From R. S. Mulliken, *Rev. Mod. Phys.* **4**, 1 (1932).

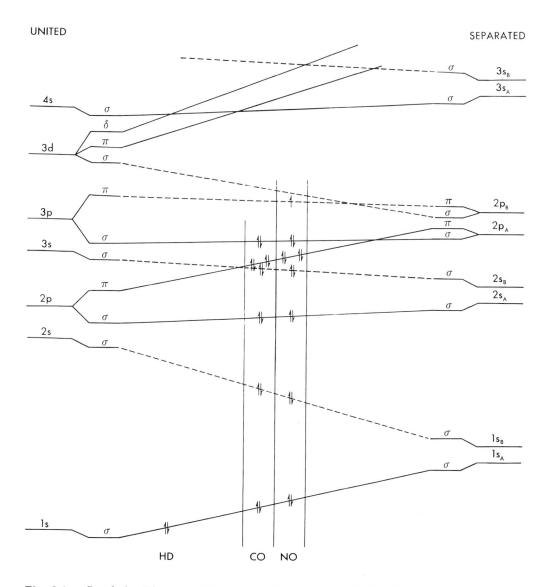

Fig. 8.9. *Correlation Diagram of Heteronuclear Diatomic Molecules.* * *The correlation is $\sigma = \sigma$; $\pi = \pi$; . . . . Bonding orbitals are solid lines; antibonding, dashed.*

* From R. S. Mulliken, *Rev. Mod. Phys.* **4**, 1 (1932).

of sulfuric acid by the lead chamber process. With a true triple bond, NO^+ is isoelectronic with CO and N_2. The stable form of NO with its three-electron bond is described chemically as $: N \equiv O :$. By this is really meant some quantum mechanical combination of structures like

$$: \overset{\uparrow}{N} = \overset{..}{O} : \quad \text{and} \quad : \overset{..}{\underset{-}{N}} = \overset{\uparrow}{\underset{+}{O}} :$$

These correlation diagrams are as important as the periodic table.

8.21 Energies of Diatomic Molecules

With internuclear separation R_{AB} as parameter, electronic energy E can in principle be calculated for any molecule. The calculations are excessively difficult even for H_2 and become almost impossible for more complex molecules. However, many empirical expressions for electronic energy as a function of internuclear separation have been developed.[12] Various spectroscopically observed constants are used to define the shapes of these energy curves, which are typically like Figure 8.10. Here D_e is the energy of dissociation from the minimum; D_o is the energy of dissociation from the state of lowest energy. Because of the uncertainty principle D_o differs from D_e, just as for a particle in a box or a harmonic oscillator the state of lowest energy is greater than zero. Here R_e is the equilibrium internuclear distance; R_o is the internuclear distance in the state of lowest energy; R_o exceeds R_e because the potential energy curve near the minimum is not quite symmetrical. As a result, the distribution of matter as calculated from the square of the wave function is skewed toward large R.

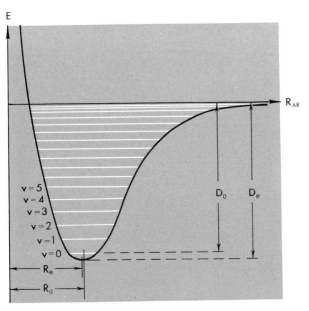

Fig. 8.10. *Vibrational Energies of an Electronic State of a Diatomic Molecule.*

Near the minimum molecules tend to behave like harmonic oscillators because the curve is almost parabolic. However, because the oscillator is slightly unharmonic, the various vibrational energies are given by a modified (8.46), namely,

$$E(v) = hc[\omega_e(v + \tfrac{1}{2}) - x_e\omega_e(v + \tfrac{1}{2})^2 + \cdots], \quad (v = 0, 1, 2, \cdots). \quad (8.70)$$

In (8.70), v is a vibrational quantum number and $x_e\omega_e$ is a small quantity that accounts for the gradual weakening of the bond as vibrational energy $E(v)$ increases. Figure 8.10 shows several vibrational energy levels superposed upon the electronic energy curve. The state of lowest energy has $v = 0$, but the zero of energy is at the minimum.

Just as vibrational energy is quantized, rotational energy $E(J)$ is also quantized in terms of a rotational quantum number $J = 0, 1, 2, \ldots$.

$$E(J) = hc[BJ(J + 1) - DJ^2(J + 1)^2 + \cdots]. \tag{8.71}$$

The rotational constants B and D depend slightly upon the vibrational state. For the unobserved equilibrium state,

$$B_e = \frac{\hbar}{4\pi c I_e} \tag{8.72}$$

where I_e is the molecule's moment of inertia. The rotational energies $E(J)$ are referred to a zero at each vibrational level and are small, relative to vibrational energies for modest values of v and J. These rotational energies are important because they fix the moment of inertia I_e through (8.72), and thus fix the internuclear distance R_e, for

$$I_e = \mu R_e^2 \tag{8.73}$$

where the reduced mass μ is related to the masses m_A and m_B of atoms by

$$\frac{1}{\mu} = \frac{1}{m_A} + \frac{1}{m_B} \tag{8.74}$$

Some spectroscopically observed vibrational and rotational constants are listed in Table 8.5. Several other kinds of molecular energies are known, but electronic, vibrational, and rotational are usually the most important.

Table 8.5. *Spectroscopic Constants of Diatomic Molecules in Their States of Lowest Energy**

MOLECULE	ω_e (cm^{-1})	$x_e\omega_e$ (cm^{-1})	B_e (cm^{-1})	D_0 (ev)
$Br^{79}Br^{81}$	323.2	1.07	0.08091	1.971
$C^{12}H^1$	2861.6	64.3	14.457	3.47
$Cl^{35}Cl^{35}$	564.9	4.0	0.2438	2.475
$C^{12}O^{16}$	2170.21	13.461	1.93139	11.11[†]
H^1H^1	4395.24	117.905	60.809	4.4763
H^1H^2	3817.09	94.958	45.655	4.5112
H^2H^2	3118.46	64.097	30.429	4.5536
H^1Cl^{35}	2989.74	52.05	10.5909	4.430
$N^{14}N^{14}$	2359.61	14.456	2.010	9.764[†]
$O^{16}O^{16}$	1530.361	12.0730	1.44567	5.080
$O^{16}H^1$	3735.21	82.81	18.871	4.35

* Herzberg, G., *Molecular Spectra and Molecular Structure I. Spectra of Diatomic Molecules.* Princeton, N. J.: D. Van Nostrand Company, Inc., 1950, Table 39, pp. 501-581.
† Gaydon, A. G., *Dissociation Energies and Spectra of Diatomic Molecules.* London: Chapman & Hall, Ltd., 1947.

Example 8.7. From the data of Table 8.5, calculate the internuclear distances in H_2, HD, and D_2.

By (8.72) and 8.73),

$$R_e = \sqrt{\frac{I_e}{\mu}} = \sqrt{\frac{\hbar}{4\pi c B_e \mu}} \cdot$$

Since $m_H = 1.00812$ and $m_D = 2.01471$, in atomic units (8.74) yields

$$\mu(H_2) = \frac{m_H m_H}{m_H + m_H} = \frac{m_H}{2} = 0.50406$$

$$\mu(HD) = \frac{m_H m_D}{m_H + m_D} = 0.67191$$

$$\mu(D_2) = \frac{m_D}{2} = 1.00736 \,.$$

In cgs units,

$$R_e(H_2) = \left(\frac{6.6238 \times 10^{-27} \times 6.0254 \times 10^{23}}{8 \times \pi^2 \times 2.9979 \times 10^{10} \times 60.809 \times 0.50406}\right)^{1/2} = 0.74168 \times 10^{-8} \text{ cm}\,.$$

Similarly, $R_e(HD) = 0.74138 \times 10^{-8}$ cm and $R_e(D_2) = 0.74166 \times 10^{-8}$ cm. Not all five significant figures have real meaning in the usual sense, for R_e as calculated is really a reciprocal root mean square distance, B_e being an average value of the reciprocal of the moment of inertia. Moreover, the uncertainty principle and the distinction between R_o and R_e must be considered. A meaningful distance would seem to be 0.742 A for H_2 and D_2 and 0.741 A for HD.

D. VALENCE THEORY

8.22 Bond Types

Of interest to chemists are diatomic molecules at high temperatures or in flames where molecules like OH and CN are among the main species. A few simple gases like N_2 and Cl_2 are also diatomic. In general, however, interest lies with polyatomic molecules. Because rigorous calculation is impractical and because the chemist finds empirically that the electron-pair bond localized between two particular atoms is often a good first approximation, the previous discussion of H_2^+, H_2, and diatomic molecules can be extended almost without modification to polyatomic molecules. It is merely necessary to view any molecule as an array of atoms joined by bonds that are almost independent of each other.

As for H_2^+ and H_2, wherever the atomic wave functions overlap greatly there is high electron density and a strong chemical bond. The greater the overlap, the stronger the bond. Since atomic s-orbitals are spherically symmetric, being independent of θ and ϕ, they show no preferred direction of bonding. Atomic p-orbitals are highly directional in nature as Figure 8.3 shows, and this preference for specific directions is shown by molecules like

PH_3 and H_2S. The HSH angle in H_2S is $92°$ because S has two $3p$-orbitals available for bonding. Any two of the three p-states of Figure 8.3 would make $90°$ the preferred angle. Similarly, P offers three mutually perpendicular atomic orbitals, the observed HPH angles being only a few degrees greater than $90°$.

In view of the peculiarities of wave mechanics, it is probably not surprising that an atom which has s- and p- and even d-electrons of similar energy in its valence shell will rearrange its electrons without regard to their atomic quantum states in order to minimize the molecular energy. Nor is it surprising that the result is often a hybrid of bonding orbitals less related to s-, p-, and d-orbitals than a mongrel dog is to its progenitors. Some of the many possible hybridizations are listed in Table 8.6. The hybrid orbitals form equivalent σ-bonds with maxima in directions that point to bonded atoms. The principal quantum number n and indeed the radial part of the wave function are assumed to be of secondary importance in determining the strength and symmetry of these hybrid combinations.

A simple exhibition of the meaning and use of these hybrid combinations involves the configurations expected in $Ni(CO)_4$ and $Ni(CN)_4^{--}$. A coordination number of four at once suggests tetrahedral arrangement as in carbon with sp^3 hybrid orbitals. The valence shell of neutral Ni is $3d^{10}$. This leaves a $4s$- and three $4p$-orbitals free to accept electron pairs from 4 CO; the arrangement is tetrahedral, with four equivalent sp^3-bonds. Dipositive Ni, however, has one stable $3d$-orbital vacant, and dsp^2-bonds form when 4 CN^- ions form coordinate covalent bonds with Ni^{++}. Pauling predicted $Ni(CN)_4^{--}$ and similar species to be planar on the basis of this kind of argument.[13]

Table 8.6. *Configurations of Hybrid Orbitals**

COORDINATION NUMBER	ATOMIC ORBITALS	GENERAL CONFIGURATION	STRONG $\pi-$ ORBITALS
2	sp	linear	p^2d^2
2	dp	linear	p^2d^2
3	sp^2	trigonal plane	pd^2
3	dp^2	trigonal plane	pd^2
3	d^2s	trigonal plane	pd^2
3	d^3	trigonal plane	pd^2
4	sp^3	tetrahedral	d^2
4	d^3s	tetrahedral	d^2
4	dsp^2	tetragonal plane	d^3p
4	d^2p^2	tetragonal plane	d^3p
6	d^2sp^3	octahedral	d^3
6	d^4sp	trigonal prism	—
6	d^5p	trigonal prism	—
6	d^3p^3	trigonal prism	—

* Kimball, G. E., *Journal of Chemical Physics,* **8,** 188 (1940).

Bonding in this kind of complex ion can be explained also in terms of molecular orbitals. Recently a third theory, the crystal field theory,[14] which explains many properties of complexes in terms of atomic electronic states perturbed by several coordinated groups, has been quite successful.

8.23 Multiple Bonds

While σ-bonds, hybrid or pure, determine the general configuration of a molecule, the actual internuclear distances are determined by the number of bonding electrons between atoms. The most typical multiple bonds occur in ethene and ethyne, whose structures are shown in Figure 2.38. The planar configuration of ethene is dominated by sp^2 hybridization on each carbon, with the carbon-carbon distance of 1.33 A such as to allow maximum overlap of the atomic p-orbitals perpendicular to the plane of the molecule. These p-orbitals form a π-bond or double bond. Again, the linear configuration of ethyne is dominated by sp hybridization on each carbon, while the carbon-carbon distance of 1.20 A is such as to allow maximum overlap of two pairs of atomic p-orbitals perpendicular to the axis of this linear molecule. These π^4-electrons form the second and third parts of ethyne's triple bond and are similar to the π^4 bonding electrons in N_2. Withdrawing two protons from nitrogen nucleuses would in fact transform $:N{\equiv}N:$ into $H-C{\equiv}C-H$ just as a united N atom can become separated CH atoms.

8.24 Resonance Energy

In classical mechanics, resonance occurs when the frequency of an externally impressed vibration equals a natural frequency of vibration of the undamped system upon which it is impressed. In quantum mechanics, resonance is said to occur when two or more arbitrarily chosen approximate wave functions combine as amplitudes to produce wave functions that represent more exactly the true state of the system.

Resonance of one electron between equivalent protons explains the stability of H_2^+ in the way characteristic of wave mechanics. The mutual exchange of electrons between equivalent hydrogen atoms similarly explains the stability of H_2. Resonance is in fact the characteristic feature of wave mechanics.

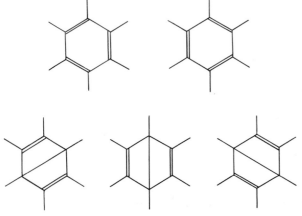

Fig. 8.11. *Some Resonating Structures of Benzene.*

In a more restricted sense, resonance is said to occur in molecules with several similar electrons or valence structures of comparable stability. The real valence or electron structures of such chemical species are found experimentally not to be explained simply in terms of these several simple structures. A nonadditive influence is at work. For example, benzene has five rather stable simple structures shown in Figure 8.11. Experimental chemists find only one kind of benzene with all carbon-carbon bonds and carbon-hydrogen bonds alike in reactivity. Structural chemists observe only one carbon-carbon bond distance and spectroscopists insist that the molecule is planar with sixfold symmetry. In terms of quantum mechanics, the true state of benzene is described by a superposition of wave functions for each of the rather arbitrary zero approximations of Figure 8.11. The result is a better approximation to the true wave function and true nature of real benzene.

Example 8.8. If the standard molar heats of formation of gaseous benzene, cyclohexene, and cyclohexane are 19.8 kcal, −0.8 kcal, and −29.4 kcal, calculate the resonance energy of benzene.

For the hydrogenation of cyclohexene

$$3 \; C_6H_{10(g)} + 3 \; H_{2(g)} \rightarrow 3 \; C_6H_{12(g)}, \qquad \Delta H^\circ = -85.8 \text{ kcal}.$$

For the hydrogenation of what seem to be three double bonds in benzene,

$$C_6H_{6(g)} + 3 \; H_{2(g)} \rightarrow C_6H_{12(g)}, \qquad \Delta H^\circ = -49.2 \text{ kcal}.$$

The difference of 36.6 kcal represents the extraordinary stability of benzene, its resonance energy.

8.25 Bond Lengths

Interionic distances in crystals do not of themselves yield ionic radii. Some method of apportioning the distance to anion and cation must be postulated. Covalent radii are easily found merely by halving the observed single-bond distance between like atoms. The carbon-carbon distance of 1.542 A in diamond yields at once a covalent single-bond radius of 0.771 A for carbon. This same distance of 1.54 A is also observed in saturated hydrocarbons. Similarly, all atoms have a characteristic single-bond radius that does not depend strongly upon environment. That is, in ordinary circumstances the single-bond distance between like atoms is a definite distance. Half of this distance is the element's single-bond radius r_i. Pauling's commonly used covalent atomic radii are listed in Table 8.7. The value for Cl, for example, is half the distance observed in Cl_2.

In general, these radii are additive, for the C-S bond length is observed to be about 1.82 A and the C-H bond length is observed to be about 1.09 A. When the atoms joined by a single bond of length R_{AB} differ considerably in electronegativity, additivity fails. Schomaker and Stevenson[15] have sug-

Table 8.7. *Covalent Atomic Radii (Å) and Some Electronegativities**

H 0.30																	H(2.1) 0.30
Li 1.225	Be 0.889	B 0.80											C(2.5) 0.771	N(3.0) 0.74	O(3.5) 0.74	F(4.0) 0.72	
Na 1.572	Mg 1.364	Al 1.248											Si(1.8) 1.173	P(2.1) 1.10	S(2.5) 1.04	Cl(3.0) 0.994	
K 2.025	Ca 1.736	Sc 1.439	Ti 1.324	V 1.224	Cr 1.172	Mn 1.168	Fe 1.165	Co 1.157	Ni 1.149	Cu 1.173	Zn 1.249	Ga 1.245	Ge(1.8) 1.223	As(2.0) 1.21	Se(2.4) 1.17	Br(2.8) 1.142	
Rb 2.16	Sr 1.914	Y 1.616	Zr 1.454	Nb 1.342	Mo 1.291	Tc	Ru 1.241	Rh 1.247	Pd 1.278	Ag 1.339	Cd 1.413	In 1.497	Sn 1.412	Sb 1.41	Te 1.37	I(2.5) 1.334	
Cs 2.35	Ba 1.981	La 1.690	Hf 1.442	Ta 1.343	W 1.299	Re 1.278	Os 1.255	Ir 1.260	Pt 1.290	Au 1.336	Hg 1.440	Tl 1.549	Pb 1.538	Bi 1.52	Po 1.53	At	

* Pauling, L., *Journal of the American Chemical Society*, **69**, 542 (1947); and *Nature of Chemical Bond*. Ithaca, N. Y.: Cornell University Press, 1960.

gested an empirical rule relating interatomic distance R_{AB} to atomic electronegativities x_A and x_B thus:

$$R_{AB} = r_A + r_B - 0.09 \mid x_A - x_B \mid . \qquad (8.75)$$

For example, gaseous and crystalline compounds have single Si-C bonds invariably close to 1.89 A in length, but additivity without correction for electronegativity difference predicts 1.94 A. Electronegativities of a few elements are given in parentheses in Table 8.7. Electronegativities of metals decrease smoothly from 1.8 near Fe and 1.7 near W to $0.8 = 0.2$ for the alkali metals. The observed As-F distance in pyramidal AsF_3 is 1.72 A, in agreement with the prediction of (8.75) that

$$\begin{aligned} R_{AsF} &= r_{As} + r_F - 0.09 \mid x_F - x_{As} \mid \\ &= 1.21 + 0.72 - 0.09 \, (4.0 - 2.0) = 1.75 \text{ A} . \end{aligned}$$

The length of a bond is a measure not only of the sizes of the atoms but also of the strength of the bond. The lengths of single, double, and triple C-C bonds are typically 1.54 A, 1.33 A, and 1.20 A. In terms of bond order n, somewhat greater than half the number of bonding electrons between atoms because of resonance stabilization, Pauling[16] finds that the interatomic distance $R(n)$ is related to the single-bond distance $R(1)$ by (8.76).

$$R(n) = R(1) - 0.706 \log_{10} n, \qquad (n > 1) . \qquad (8.76)$$

The values for C-C bonds fix the single empirical constant 0.706. Equation (8.76) is postulated for any bond between any atoms provided the bond order n is greater than unity. The bond between apparently singly bonded carbon atoms immediately adjacent to a triple bond is generally about 1.46 A in length. Because of various resonant forms, this bond has some π character; how much can be estimated from (8.76) thus:

$$1.46 = 1.54 - 0.706 \log_{10} n$$

$$\log_{10} n = \frac{0.08}{0.706} = \log 1.3 .$$

Although other bond-shortening influences may be at work, up to 30% double-bond character can be ascribed to this bond.

In graphite, where four bonds hold each carbon to its three neighbors in its layer, the bond number (half the number of bonding electrons) is $\frac{4}{3}$. Without distinction between bond number and bond order, $R(\frac{4}{3})$ is predicted to be $1.54 - 0.706 \log \frac{4}{3} = 1.45$ A. The observed value is less by 0.03 A because resonance greatly strengthens the bond. Similarly, the value predicted for benzene with $n = \frac{3}{2}$ is 1.42 A, longer than observed by 0.03 A.

When there are more stable bonding orbitals than bonding electrons, as in metals, $n < 1$ and (8.76) is modified to read

$$R(n) = R(1) - 0.600 \log_{10} n, \qquad (n < 1) . \qquad (8.77)$$

The new constant 0.600 automatically adjusts for the uninhibited resonance in electron-deficient substances. For them, n is the ratio of the number of valence electrons of a neutral atom to its coordination number. Equation (8.77) is the basis of a valence-bond theory of metals[17] and a unifying interpretation of the unusual structures of boron hydrides.[18]

Table 8.8. *Constant Energy Radii (A)**

C	N	O	F
			H
			0.84
1.22	1.12	1.12	1.11
Si	P	S	Cl
1.57	1.53	1.46	1.44
Ge	As	Se	Br
1.61	1.63	1.58	1.56
Sn	Sb	Te	I
1.80	1.83	1.79	1.73

Bond lengths have been related directly to the strength of a bond by Huggins' equation (8.78).

$$R = r_A^* + r_B^* - \tfrac{1}{2} \log_{10} D_{AB} \tag{8.78}$$

where D_{AB} is the dissociation energy (to atoms) of the bond between A and B and r_i^* is a constant energy distance characteristic of atom i. The energy D_{AB} is expressed in kilocalories per mole of bonds. Table 8.8 lists values of r_i^*, most of which are about 0.40 A greater than radii of Table 8.7.

Example 8.9. Discuss the bonding in Cl_2O and ClO_2 in view of the tabulated data [F. D. Rossini, *et al.*, Circular of the National Bureau of Standards 500 (1952); J. D. Dunitz and K. Hedberg, *Journal of the American Chemical Society*, **72**, 3108 (1950)]. The dissociation energies of Cl_2 and O_2 are 57.1 and 117.2 kcal mole^{-1}.

PROPERTY	Cl_2O	ClO_2
Heat of Formation (ΔH°_f)	18.2 kcal mole^{-1}	24.7 kcal mole^{-1}
Dipole moment	Small	Small
Cl-O distance	1.70A	1.49A
Angle between bonds	111°	116°

The Schomaker-Stevenson rule (8.75) predicts a single-bond Cl-O distance of $0.74 + 0.994 - 0.09 \times (3.5 - 3.0) = 1.69$ A in agreement with the observed value in Cl_2O. If two p-orbitals on O form angular p^2 σ-bonds, the deviation from the expected 90° is to be attributed to repulsion between Cl atoms. The mean dissociation energy D of a Cl-O bond in Cl_2O is 48.8 kcal, for

$$Cl_{2(g)} \rightarrow 2\ Cl_{(g)} \qquad \Delta H = +57.1 \text{ kcal}$$
$$\tfrac{1}{2} O_{2(g)} \rightarrow O_{(g)} \qquad \Delta H = +58.6 \text{ kcal}$$
$$\underline{Cl_2O_{(g)} \rightarrow Cl_{2(g)} + \tfrac{1}{2} O_{2(g)} \qquad \Delta H = -18.2 \text{ kcal}}$$
$$Cl_2O_{(g)} \rightarrow 2\ Cl_{(g)} + O_{(g)} \qquad \Delta H = +97.5 \text{ kcal} .$$

Rule (8.78) yields

$$R = 1.44 + 1.12 - \tfrac{1}{2} \log 48.8 = 1.71 \text{ A} .$$

For ClO_2, the mean dissociation energy per Cl-O bond is similarly found to be 60.6 kcal; hence, by (8.78), $R = 1.67$ A, far in excess of the observed 1.49 A. Rule (8.76) suggests that the Cl-O bonds are double bonds, for

$$1.49 = 1.69 - 0.706 \log n$$

$$\log n = \frac{0.20}{0.71} = \log 1.92 .$$

* Huggins, M. L., *Journal of the American Chemical Society*, **75**, 4126 (1953).

After some discussion and comparison with SO_2, Dunitz and Hedberg favor the electronic structure

$$:Cl\uparrow$$
$$\underset{:O \qquad\quad O:}{\diagup\!\diagup \qquad \diagdown\!\diagdown}$$

The chlorine atom uses six orbitals, some of which are $4s$ or $3d$ atomic orbitals. These and the stable $3p$-orbitals can form angular σ-bonds with strong π-bonds for the double bonds.

8.26 Hydrogen Bonds

A *hydrogen bond* is an essentially electrostatic attraction of a covalently bonded hydrogen toward a region of high electron density. This region of negative charge may be an ion or an unshared pair of electrons. Hydrogen bonds are linear, or almost so, and link only rather electronegative atoms, usually just N, O, and F. Small in size, the hydrogen can be coordinated with only two atoms. Because it has only one orbital stable enough to form a bond, the hydrogen cannot involve two covalent bonds. It remains covalently bonded to one atom at a single-bond distance, and commonly lies at a distance from the second atom which is about 0.8 A greater than that atom's single-bond radius. Thus, the proton is not symmetrically located between its two electronegative atoms. A notable exception is FHF^-, where the proton is exactly midway between fluoride ions which are about 2.26 A apart.

Hydrogen bonds are of paramount importance in biological systems. The configuration of proteins is controlled largely by hydrogen bonds. The packing of oxide and hydroxide ions in ionic crystals involves hydrogen bonds. Ice has a very low density because the formation of hydrogen bonds does not allow efficient packing of water molecules. Each oxygen in ice is surrounded tetrahedrally by only four other oxygens. A proton lies along each tetrahedral line, two covalently bonded and two from other water molecules held in line by hydrogen bonds.

The effects of hydrogen bonds on physical properties are manifest. Increased dielectric constants, viscosities, melting and boiling points, heats of vaporization and sublimation are common when hydrogen bonds link molecules. Intramolecular hydrogen bonds are, however, possible, as in salicaldehyde, where the phenolic hydrogen is hydrogen-bonded to the oxygen of the aldehyde group. Intramolecular hydrogen bonds generally cause increased solubility and volatility. Salicaldehyde can be steam distilled, but p-hydroxybenzaldehyde cannot because the crystal has intermolecular hydrogen bonds. Similarly, CH_4 is much more volatile than NH_3, H_2O, and HF.

Most hydrogen bonds have energies of about four to eight kilocalories per mole of bonds, a few have energies of 10 kcal, and that of FHF^- is about 27 kcal. The distance between electronegative atoms generally ranges from 2.7 A to 2.8 A, but the distance in FHF^- is only 2.26 A. Indeed, the distances in FHF^- are short enough and the bonds are ionic enough that, in addition to electrostatic attraction, resonance of the form $(F^- \cdots H\text{-}F;$ $F\text{-}H \cdots F^-)$ contributes significantly to the stability of the anion. In unsymmetrical hydrogen bonds the proton is too far from one atom to form a strong covalent bond with it, and yet it is too massive to tunnel between two positions 0.8 A apart at a rate approaching the "rate of movement" of electrons in resonating systems.

In ice, oxygen atoms lie 2.76 A apart. Since two hydrogen bonds are broken when one molecule of H_2O sublimes, the heat of sublimation of 12 kcal indicates a hydrogen bond with an energy of 6 kcal. Except for the requirement that each oxygen have two covalently bonded protons, the protons in ice are distributed at random between their twofold potential minima along O-O lines. With this disorder is associated residual entropy of ice at absolute zero.

E. SOLID STATE THEORY

8.27 Lattice Energy

The energy of an ionic crystal is mainly the coulomb energy of attraction and repulsion and the repulsion energy associated with the finite sizes of ions. Because the square of the electronic wave function of an ion approaches zero only asymptotically, the size of an ion is a matter of defining where $|u|^2$ becomes negligible. Because ions have an indefinite but finite size, calculating the energy of an ionic crystal would be difficult were it not for the spherical symmetry of many ions and the simplicity of ionic structures.

The lattice energy U_o of an ionic crystal is the energy required per gram formula weight to separate the ions and bring them to rest at infinity. For example,

$$NaCl_{(s)} \rightarrow Na^+_{(g)} + Cl^-_{(g)}, \qquad \Delta E = U_o .$$

In keeping with the usual development,[19] if R is the shortest interionic distance, the potential energy V of the crystal is

$$V = -\frac{Ae^2z^2}{R} + \frac{Be^2}{R^n} . \tag{8.79}$$

The constant A in the term that contains all coulombic interactions is the Madelung constant, a characteristic number that depends upon the nature of the lattice. The term containing B is a repulsive term, and n is of the order of ten. The value of z is the absolute value of the charge of the negative ions of the lattice. Table 8.9 lists values of the Madelung constants for some simple lattices.

At the observed equilibrium distance R_o, the potential energy is a minimum; hence,

$$\frac{dV}{dR} = 0 = \frac{Ae^2z^2}{R_o^2} - \frac{nBe^2}{R_o^{n+1}}$$

$$B = \left(\frac{z^2 R_o^{n-1}}{n}\right) A . \qquad (8.80)$$

Table 8.9. *Madelung Constants**

LATTICE TYPE	MADELUNG CONSTANT, A
NaCl	1.747558
CsCl	1.762670
CaF₂	5.03878
ZnS (cubic)	1.63806
ZnS (hexagonal)	1.641

Since n can be found experimentally from the compressibility of a crystal, B can be evaluated if R_o is also known from diffraction experiments. At equilibrium, substitution of (8.80) into (8.79) yields

$$V_o = -\frac{Ae^2z^2}{R_o}\left[1 - \frac{1}{n}\right]. \qquad (8.81)$$

For one gram formula weight, the lattice energy is

$$U_o = -NV_o = \frac{NAe^2z^2}{R_o}\left[1 - \frac{1}{n}\right]. \qquad (8.82)$$

The famous Born-Haber cycle relates the lattice energy to other quantities which can be calculated or observed. This isothermal cycle for a crystal $MX_{(s)}$ like NaCl is this:

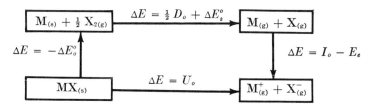

Here ΔE_o^o is the change in energy at absolute zero for the formation of $MX_{(s)}$ from the elements in standard states, D_o is the dissociation energy of $X_{2(g)}$, ΔE_s^o is the standard sublimation energy of $M_{(s)}$ at absolute zero, I_o is the ionization energy of $M_{(g)}$, and E_e is the electron affinity of $X_{(g)}$. Because ΔE is independent of the path,

$$U_o = -\Delta E_o^o + \tfrac{1}{2} D_o + \Delta E_s^o + I_o - E_e . \qquad (8.83)$$

Any one of the six energies in (8.83) can be calculated from the others; it also serves as a check if all are known.

* Sherman, J., *Chemical Reviews*, **11**, 93 (1932).

Example 8.10. Calculate the lattice energy of $NaCl_{(s)}$ if $n = 9$.

From Table 2.7, for NaCl, $a_o = 5.64$ A at room temperature. Since R_o is the distance of closest approach of ions, $R_o = 2.82$ A. By (8.82) with $z = 1$,

$$U_o = \frac{0.602 \times 10^{24} \times 1.748 \times (4.80 \times 10^{-10})^2}{2.82 \times 10^{-8}} \left[1 - \frac{1}{9} \right]$$

$$= 7.63 \times 10^{12} \text{ ergs mole}^{-1} = 182.2 \text{ kcal mole}^{-1}.$$

8.28 Band Theory

A crystal can be viewed either as an assembly of atoms into a macromolecule or as a periodic potential for electrons. Both views when fully developed require the crystal's electrons to have a range of almost continuously variable energies. Between these allowed ranges of energy there exist other ranges of energy forbidden to electrons in stationary states. These allowed and forbidden energy bands result from the wave-particle nature of the electron.

Viewed as a macromolecule, a crystal is the result of many interactions of many identical atoms. Since the interaction of just two atoms leads to states of slightly different energy, it is not surprising that the interaction of many atoms with discrete energies should lead to many states of similar energy with perhaps certain ranges of impossible energies. Figure 8.12 illustrates this smearing of the topmost atomic energy levels of Cu as the distance between copper atoms decreases. All the energy bands of Cu containing electrons are shown schematically in Figure 8.13 with the general density of electrons in each band. With N atoms, the s-bands can accommodate up to $2N$ electrons, the p-bands up to $6N$ electrons, the d-band up to $10N$ electrons, and so on.

If the crystal is viewed as a periodic potential of positively charged ions bathed in a sea of valence electrons, the electron energies are given approximately by (8.38) if a, b, and c are crystal edges.

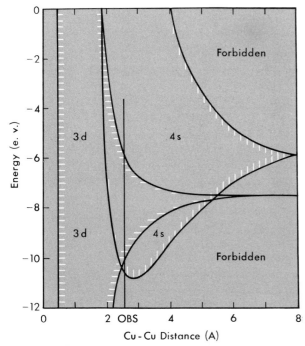

Fig. 8.12. *Bands of Energy in Crystalline Copper.*

$$E = \frac{\pi^2 \hbar^2}{2m} \left(\frac{n_x^2}{a^2} + \frac{n_y^2}{b^2} + \frac{n_z^2}{c^2} \right). \quad (8.38)$$

* Adapted from H. M. Krutter, *Phys. Rev.* **48**, 664 (1935).

Certain energies allowed to an electron in a box as large as the crystal are, however, forbidden to electrons in a periodic potential. Electrons with wavelengths that satisfy the Bragg relation $\lambda = 2d \sin \theta$ cannot exist in a stationary state within a crystal because they would be at once and continually diffracted and refracted. Such electrons cannot move through the crystal and thus do not exist. Equation (8.38) is approximately true for energies well removed from such forbidden energies.

A metal is a crystal containing vacant energy states infinitesimally removed in energy from states occupied by electrons. An electric field slightly changes the energies of the electrons and causes a preferential migration of electrons through use of these vacant energy states. In Cu, for example, conduction occurs mainly in states that are correlated with atomic 4s-states. Similarly, in Na, electrons in the periodic potential of sodium ions use 3s-like states for conduction.

Insulators resist the flow of electrons because there are no vacant energy states immediately joined to occupied states. Diamond is an insulator because its states correlated with atomic 1s-, 2s-, and 2p-states are completely filled, with 2N electrons of opposed spin in each s-band and 2N in the lowest p-band. Other 2p-states are separated from these occupied states by a forbidden energy of more than 150 kcal so that the vacant bands are not joined to the lower bands. Although elements like Mg and Ca also seem to be nonconductors because the configuration ns^2

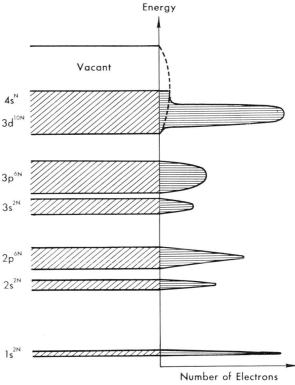

Fig. 8.13. *Distribution of Electrons of Various Energies in Copper.* (*Schematic.*)

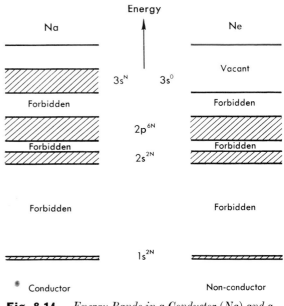

Fig. 8.14. *Energy Bands in a Conductor (Na) and a Non-Conductor (Ne).*

is complete, it happens that there are many states correlated with np atomic states with energies less than the most energetic ns-like states. As a result, as in Cu, electrons of highest energy exist in states of different symmetry. Since there are many free s- and p-states with energies infinitesimally different from energies of valence electrons in Mg and Ca, these elements have conducting crystals. Figure 8.14 contrasts the electron populations of conducting Na and nonconducting Ne. For further details, the student must read elsewhere.[20]

8.29 Semiconducting Silicon and Germanium

Semiconductors have conductivities intermediate between metals and insulators. Their conductivity is of two kinds: *intrinsic*, because of thermal excitation of electrons from the valence band across a narrow forbidden energy gap into the empty states of the conduction band; and *impurity*, because of a few energy states within the forbidden region between valence and conduction bands. Ordinarily intrinsic conductivity is important only at temperatures where the energy gap is of the order of RT. As the energy gap approaches zero, valence and conduction bands merge, and conduction becomes metallic when filled and vacant bands join.

Impurity conductivity is due to foreign atoms and lattice imperfections. Ultrapure Si and Ge are insulators at very low temperatures and conduct an electric current at higher temperatures because valence electrons from a filled band are excited thermally to a low-energy vacant band. Such Si and Ge, prepared by zone refining, can be transformed into impurity semiconductors by the deliberate and controlled addition of very small amounts of elements with similar sizes and chemical natures. If P or As is added to Si or Ge, the foreign atom is built right into the lattice in place of Si or Ge. The extra electron associated with each foreign atom remains nearby because of the extraordinary charge on the nucleus of the foreign atom. This extra electron cannot be accommodated in the usual valence band of crystalline Si or Ge. It seeks a state of low energy that may be in the range of energies forbidden to electrons in pure Si or Ge. This is an n-type (negative charge carrier) semiconductor.

If B, Al, or Ga were added as impurity to Si or Ge, the foreign atom would again substitute for Si or Ge. Lacking four valence electrons, each foreign atom has associated with it a "hole," namely, an electron energy state in the valence band that would have been filled if Si or Ge had been at the lattice site instead of the electron-deficient foreign atom. Because electrons are mobile, this hole can migrate about like an electron. However, if it leaves the foreign atom, that foreign atom has a negative charge associated with it because its octet of electrons is complete like Si or Ge. This is a p-type (positive charge carrier) semiconductor for positive holes carry the current.

The energies of electrons in an n-type semiconductor are shown schematically in Figure 8.15. These donor impurity levels lie near the top of the forbidden band and are indicated by short lines to suggest that they are localized near the impurity center. These levels are no longer forbidden because the structure is no longer perfect.

Some of the characteristics of electrons in impurity levels can be estimated by likening the state of such an electron near its positively charged foreign atom to a hydrogen-like electron near its proton. The lattice is supposed to act as a homogeneous dielectric. The various equations for hydrogen are readily modified to this situation provided that e^2 is replaced by e^2/κ (or $\mathbf{Z}$ by $\mathbf{Z}/\kappa$), where κ is the dielectric constant of the lattice.

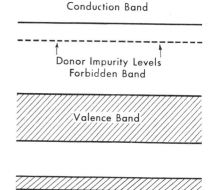

Fig. 8.15. *Electron Energy States in an n-Type Semiconductor.*

Example 8.11. Estimate the least energy required to transfer an electron from its most stable impurity level in n-type Si to the conduction band. The dielectric constant of Si is 13.

By (8.79) modified for a nonvacuum,

$$E = -\frac{\mu \mathbf{Z}^2 e^4}{2\hbar^2 n^2 \kappa^2}.$$

In the state of lowest energy, $n = 1$; hence, the least energy I to ionize an electron bound to an impurity center with $\mathbf{Z} = 1$ is

$$I = \left| \frac{\mu e^4}{2\hbar^2 \kappa^2} \right|$$

$$= \frac{\left(\dfrac{1}{1836 \times 0.602 \times 10^{24}} \right) \times (4.80 \times 10^{-10})^4}{2 \times \left(\dfrac{6.624 \times 10^{-27}}{2\pi} \right)^2 13^2}$$

$$= 1.28 \times 10^{-13} \text{ erg electron}^{-1}$$

$$= 1.84 \text{ kcal mole}^{-1} = 0.080 \text{ ev}.$$

8.30 Chemical Potential of Lattice Electrons

Lattice vibrations have energies of the order of RT. At room temperature, this is 600 cal mole^{-1} or about 0.025 ev. Only those electrons within about this energy of a vacant state are likely to be excited thermally into that vacant state. Since forbidden band gaps are of the order of 1 volt or more, very few electrons are available for conduction in insulators. Moreover, even in metals, where the highest energy electrons have vacant states only infinitesimally greater in energy, most of the electrons are in stable states well removed in energy from vacant bands and states. Only the electrons within 0.05 volt or so of the top are thermally active at room temperature.

The effective average energy of the electrons in thermal equilibrium with the surroundings is the *Fermi energy*. For metals, it is approximately the energy of the electrons that can be thermally promoted to a conduction state. At absolute zero in a metal, it is the energy of the most energetic electron. In insulators, the Fermi energy level lies about in the middle of the forbidden region above the topmost valence band. Thermal excitation of an insulator produces a few conduction electrons and an equal number of mobile holes in the valence band. The average energy of these current-carrying holes and electrons clearly lies in the energy gap that separates them.

The Fermi energy is the thermodynamically significant energy of lattice electrons. The thermodynamic name for this energy is the chemical potential of the electrons. That is to say, the chemical potential of electrons and the Fermi energy of those electrons are the same. Since phases in contact at equilibrium must have equal electronic chemical potentials, it follows at once that the Fermi energies of electrons in phases at equilibrium are equal. Achieving equilibrium often calls for considerable modification of band structure in the contact layer and incipient transfer of electrons through the phase boundaries.

Table 8.10. *Work Functions of Elements*[*]

ELEMENT	WORK FUNCTION (ϕ) (ev)
Na	2.28
K	2.25
Ca	3.20
V	4.11
Cr	4.45
W	4.53
Mn	3.95
Fe	4.63
Pt	5.36
Cu	4.48
Zn	4.27
Ga	4.16
Ge	4.62
Se	4.87

The energy required to take an electron with the Fermi energy to an infinite distance from a metal is called the *work function* ϕ of the metal. One way of evaluating ϕ is to measure the least energy of a photon that can cause emission of a photoelectron. Table 8.10 lists work functions for several elements.

8.31 Action of Light on Solids

Although electrons with energies of 0.5 ev less than the Fermi energy are little affected by ordinary temperature changes, any electron in any state can be affected by light of sufficiently short wavelength. Red light ($\lambda = 7000$ A) has an energy of about 1.8 ev, while blue light ($\lambda = 4000$ A) has an energy of 3.1 ev. Absorption of a photon of blue light can thus increase the energy of an electron by about 3 ev. If the final state of the electron be in the conduction band, the crystal becomes photoconductive.

There are many ways in which an excited electron can be stabilized. It may radiate its energy at once or bit by bit as it interacts with lattice

[*] Landolt-Börnstein, *Zahlenwerte und Funktionen I. Band. Atom-und Molekularphysik, 4. Teil Kristalle.* Berlin: Verlag Julius Springer 1955, pp. 759-61.

imperfections. If it happens to achieve a long-lived excited state, it is said to be *trapped*. The natures of traps vary greatly. The electron may remain in a trap with only a small probability of radiating or it may be obliged to await thermal excitation into a less stable state before radiating and achieving a state of low energy. Some excited states are not well localized in traps; an electron-hole pair may proceed through the structure much like a diffuse hydrogen atom until it collides with an imperfection and is destroyed or changed. The defects in photographically important silver halides are interstitial silver ions (Frenkel defects). Photoelectrons commonly are trapped by silver ions near grain boundaries or other lattice imperfections and form tiny crystals of metallic silver. These form a latent image, which is strengthened by development.

By far the best understood electron traps are the F, V, and F' centers in alkali halide crystals.[21] Although F and V centers are produced in equal numbers by radiation with photons or energetic electrons, each can be produced separately. Heating an alkali halide crystal in vapor of the alkali metal generates F centers; heating in halogen vapor generates V centers. Heating a crystal containing both F and V centers causes them and their characteristic purple colors to disappear. Crystals containing only one type of center are less affected by heating.

Much experimental evidence indicates that an F center is an electron in a halide ion vacancy (Schottky defect). Being smaller than chloride ion, an F center is free to roam from vacancy to vacancy. An electron excited from an F center can migrate and eventually settle down as another F center. Two such paired electrons in an anion vacancy constitute an F' center. Two F centers disappear when one F' center is formed, and they reappear when the F' center is destroyed.

Several types of V center exist. The simplest is a hole in a cation vacancy (Schottky defect). That is, there is the equivalent of one extra halogen atom near a V center. Like F centers, V centers can move readily because a hole has an effective mass and size of the same order of magnitude as an electron. The recombination of F and V centers is essentially the annihilation of an electron by a hole.

Example 8.12. Estimate the difference in energy of one F' center and two F centers in NaCl ($\kappa = 2.5$) if the first and second ionization potentials of He are 24.6 and 54.4 ev.

As in Example 8.11, the ionization energy in free space is κ^2 times as great as in the crystal. However, He and He$^+$ are analogous to F' and F only if $\mathbf{Z} = 2$ for the helium nucleus is reduced to $\mathbf{Z} = 1$ for the anion vacancy. Since the energy is proportional to $\mathbf{Z}^2$, it follows that the energy necessary to transfer an F-center electron into the conduction band of the crystal is

$$\frac{54.4}{2^2 \kappa^2} = \frac{54.4}{4 \times 2.5^2} = 2.18 \text{ ev} .$$

Similarly, the energy necessary to remove the first electron from an F' center and place it in the conduction band is

$$\frac{24.6}{2^2\kappa^2} = \frac{24.6}{4 \times 2.5^2} = 0.98 \text{ ev} .$$

The difference in energy of one F' center containing electrons of energy -0.98 ev and -2.18 ev and two F centers with energy -4.36 ev is therefore expected to be 1.20 ev.

REFERENCES

Coulson, C. A., *Valence*. New York: Oxford University Press, 1952.

Garner, W. E. (ed.), *The Chemistry of the Solid State*. London: Butterworth's Scientific Publications, 1955.

Gaydon, A. G., *Dissociation Energies and Spectra of Diatomic Molecules*. London: Chapman & Hall, Ltd., 1947.

Herzberg, G., *Molecular Spectra and Molecular Structure*. Princeton, N. J.: D. Van Nostrand Company, Inc. *Vol. I, Spectra of Diatomic Molecules* (1950); *Vol. II, Infrared and Raman Spectra of Polyatomic Molecules* (1945).

Kittel, C., *Introduction to Solid State Physics*. New York: John Wiley & Sons, Inc., 1953.

Landé, A., *Foundations of Quantum Theory, A Study in Continuity and Symmetry*. New Haven, Conn.: Yale University Press, 1955.

Margenau, H. and G. M. Murphy, *The Mathematics of Physics and Chemistry*. Princeton, N. J.: D. Van Nostrand Company, Inc., 1943.

Pauling, L., *The Nature of the Chemical Bond and the Structure of Molecules and Crystals*. Ithaca, N. Y.: Cornell University Press, 1960.

Pauling, L. and E. B. Wilson, Jr., *Introduction to Quantum Mechanics With Applications to Chemistry*. New York: McGraw-Hill Book Company, Inc., 1935.

Pinsker, Z. G., *Electron Diffraction* (tr. by J. A. Spink and E. Feigl). London: Butterworth's Scientific Publications, 1953.

Schiff, L. I., *Quantum Mechanics*. New York: McGraw-Hill Book Company, Inc., 1949.

Syrkin, Y. K., and M. E. Dyatkina, *Structure of Molecules and the Chemical Bond* (tr. and rev. by M. A. Partridge and D. O. Jordan). London: Butterworth's Scientific Publications, 1950.

PROBLEMS

1. The minimum energy required to eject the least tightly bound electron in many metals is 4 ev. At what wavelengths of light would such a metal emit photoelectrons? *Answer:* $\lambda < 3100$ A.

2. From the wavelengths of the Lyman series in the spectrum of monatomic hydrogen in Table 8.2, calculate the energies of the states of H in ev.

3. Find the Rydberg constant of Equation (8.6) for He^+ if $H^+ = 1.00757$ and $He^{++} = 4.00281$.

4. At what pressure can an uncertainty in energy of an excited state of 1.0 cm^{-1} be detected at room temperature in a gas with $\sigma^2 = 10 \times 10^{-16}$ cm^2 and $M = 30$?

5. Verify by substitution that $|\psi|^2$ is independent of time for states of a definite energy.

6. Show than $n_x = n_y = n_z = 0$ for a particle in a box yields an infinitely large wavelength or uncertainty in position.

7. Find the wave function and allowed energies of a three-dimensional harmonic oscillator.
Answer: $f = 3$ in (8.47).

8. Show that the hydrogen wave functions for $l = 1$ have maxima along the directions of the Cartesian axes.

9. Since angular momentum, including spin, must be conserved in any event, show that an odd number of neutrinos is involved in the decay of:
(a) A pi meson into a mu meson.
(b) A neutron into a proton and an electron.

10. List the elementary particles of Table 8.4 in two groups: those with symmetric wave functions and those with antisymmetric.

11. Write an electronic wave function for H_2 in an excited state.

12. Reproduce from memory correlation diagrams for homonuclear and heteronuclear diatomic molecules.

13. In terms of the valence-bond and molecular-orbital theories, describe and compare:
(a) N_2 and C_2H_2.
(b) Ne, HF, H_2O, NH_3, and CH_4.

14. Calculate the zero-point energy of a real diatomic molecule.

15. Describe the hybridized bonding orbitals on the central atom in:
(a) Octahedral SF_6.
(b) Linear HgX_2.
(c) Linear Hg_2X_2.

16. Write the resonating structures of CO_3^{--} and NO_3^{-}. Compare to BF_3.

17. Describe the electronic structures of SO_2 and SO_3 if $R(SO)$ is observed to be 1.43 A in each.

18. What is the expected effect upon the angle between sigma p^2-bonds as their s-character increases?
Answer: Angle increases.

19. Discuss electronic structures of ClO_2 in terms of three-electron bonds.

20. From data in Problem 6.17, and a hydrogen-bond energy of 6.0 kcal mole^{-1}, estimate the density of gaseous acetic acid at its normal boiling point of 118°C.

21. Calculate the lattice energy of $ZnS_{(s)}$ if $n = 9$.
Answer: 823 kcal mole^{-1}.

22. Draw a diagram of the energy bands in diamond and potassium.

23. Draw the actual population of electrons in conduction and valence bands for a pure insulator acting as an intrinsic conductor at an elevated temperature.

24. What is the temperature at which RT is 1 ev?
Answer: 11605°K.

25. Why are crystals containing transition elements in less than their maximum oxidation state often rather highly colored?

26. The minimum energy required to emit photoelectrons from $W_{(s)}$ is 4.5 ev. What potential difference is just sufficient to prevent photoelectrons from being ejected from $W_{(s)}$ by radiation with wavelength of 2000 Å?

27. By the Bohr theory calculate the Bohr distance a_o of electron from proton in H and show that $2\pi a_o = n\lambda$.
Answer: $a_o = 0.529$ Å.

28. By letting $\Delta E = mv \, \Delta v$, show that $\Delta E \times \Delta t \geqslant \hbar$ is equivalent to $\Delta p_x \cdot \Delta x \geqslant \hbar$.

29. By (8.52) calculate the energy of a system with ψ_n given by (8.26).

30. Discuss the symmetry of $X(x)$ in (8.60) and Figure 8.1 as regards a change in sign of x.

31. Show that the wave function of a particle with energy greater than the classical energy V_o of a potential barrier is influenced by the barrier, even though classically it would not be so influenced.

32. Justify the magnitude of the lowest energy of the one-dimensional harmonic oscillator in terms of the uncertainty principle.

33. Find the direction in which the angular wave functions of hydrogen for $l = 2$ have maxima.

34. With a variational function of the form ae^{-Ar} in center-of-mass coordinates, find the lowest energy of the hydrogen atom. Or do the same for the harmonic oscillator if $v = ae^{-cx^2}$.

35. Pi mesons are said to bind nucleuses together by converting neutrons into protons and vice versa. Suggest possible reactions of this kind that conserve charge and momentum.

36. Show that there are three real states of H_2 with coordinate electron wave function $u_A(1)u_B(2) - u_A(2)u_B(1)$.

37. By means of a correlation diagram with added electrons, describe the binding in BeO, Ne_2, and OH.

38. Describe the hybridized bonding orbitals on the central atom in:
(a) Planar BX_3, each X equivalent to the others.
(b) Tetrahedral SiF_4.
(c) Octahedral SiF_6^{--}.

39. Predict structures (configurations and interatomic distances) of PBr_3, C_2N_2, S_2Cl_2, and $VOCl_3$.

40. At 25°C, the heat of sublimation of $As_{(s)}$ to monatomic atoms is 50.74 kcal mole^{-1}, the dissociation energy of F_2 is 38.4 kcal mole^{-1}, and the heat of formation of $AsF_{3(g)}$ is -218.3 kcal mole^{-1} [F. D. Rossini, *et al.*, Circular of the National Bureau of Standards 500 (1952)]. By means of Table 8.8 and (8.78), predict the length of the As-F bond in AsF_3.

41. Discuss the bonding and probable bond lengths in these molecules if each be tetrahedral:
(a) CF_4.
(b) POF_3.
(c) OsO_4.

42. If the distance between fluorine nucleuses in HF_2^- is 2.26 Å and if the proton is midway between fluorines, discuss the bonding.

43. Calculate the electron affinity of sulfide ion if at $0°K$: the heat of formation of cubic ZnS is -48.5 kcal mole^{-1}; the heats of formation of gaseous atomic Zn and S are 30 kcal mole^{-1} and 52 kcal mole^{-1}; the energy to remove two electrons from $Zn_{(g)}$ to yield $Zn_{(g)}^{++}$ is 633 kcal mole^{-1}; $n = 9$.

44. Diagram the band energies of Mg and Al.

45. With the zero of energy at the top of the valence band, draw acceptor levels (hole energy levels) in the range of forbidden energies in a p-type semiconductor like Si.

46. The work function of Se in Table 8.10 is 4.87 ev and yet Se is a photoconductor in the presence of visible light. Explain .

47. What wavelength of light is perhaps absorbed by an F center in NaCl as light ionizes it?
Answer: 5700 A.

---

48. Calculate the wavelength of radiation that will cause positronium, an electron-positron pair, to go from its state of lowest energy to:
(a) Its next highest energy state.
(b) Complete separation of positron and electron.

49. Calculate the reversible isothermal work required to separate a mixture of molecules of kinds A, B, and C.

50. List the several states of a particle with energy $7\pi^2\hbar^2/ma^2$ in a cubic box of edge a.

51. If the wave function and its first space derivative are continuous at $x = \pm a/2$ where the potential energy is discontinuous as in Figure 8.2 (a), find solutions of the wave equation for a particle with $E < V_o$.

Answer: $E = E(V_o, a, m)$ where $\sqrt{\dfrac{V_o - E}{E}} = \tan\left(\dfrac{a\sqrt{2mE}}{2\hbar}\right) = -\operatorname{ctn}\left(\dfrac{a\sqrt{2mE}}{2\hbar}\right).$

52. Calculate $\overline{V}$ (the average value of the potential energy) of a one-dimensional harmonic oscillator for $n = 0$ and $n = 1$. Then find the average kinetic energy indirectly from this result and the total energy. The average value of the potential energy V is $\overline{V} = \int u_n^* V u_n \, d\tau$.

53. With a variational function v of the form axe^{-cx^2} find the lowest energy of the harmonic oscillator. In terms of symmetry of the wave function, explain why this energy is not $\pi\hbar\nu_o$.
Answer: $3\pi\hbar\nu_o$.

54. Show that a system of two weakly interacting alpha particles has a wave function that is approximately symmetric to interchange of alphas. Is this system's wave function really symmetric? Explain.

55. Discuss the valence-bond and molecular-orbital wave functions of HHe^+ after writing them out explicitly.

56. By means of a correlation diagram with added electrons, describe the free radicals CN, C_2, CH. Estimate internuclear distances from the net number of bonding electrons.

57. Find a mathematical relation among D_e, ω_e, and $x_e\omega_e$ if dissociation of a diatomic molecule occurs when vibrational energies differ only infinitesimally in adjacent levels. Test it with data from Table 8.5, and explain differences in predicted and observed dissociation energies.

Answer: $D_e = \dfrac{\omega_e^2}{4x_e\omega_e}.$

58. Describe the bonding in tetrahedral VCl_4 and octahedral $Mo(CO)_6$.

59. If the heats of formation of $H_{(g)}$, $C_{(g)}$, $CH_{3(g)}$, $CH_{4(g)}$, and $C_2H_{6(g)}$ are 52.1, 171.7, 32.0, -17.9, and -20.2 kcal mole^{-1}, calculate:
(a) The strength of $C-H$ and $C-C$ bonds.
(b) The heat of formation of $C_5H_{12(g)}$.
[Data from F. D. Rossini, *et al.*, *Circular of the National Bureau of Standards 500* (1952).]
Answer: 99.5 kcal for CH.

60. Discuss the structure of $CF_3-C\equiv C-H$ if [J. N. Shoolery, R. G. Shulman, W. F. Sheehan, Jr., V. Schomaker, and D. M. Yost, *Journal of Chemical Physics*, 19, 1364 (1951)]:
(a) $C-H = 1.056$ A.
(b) $C\equiv C = 1.201$ A.
(c) $C-C = 1.464$ A.
(d) $C-F = 1.335$ A.
(e) $\measuredangle$ FCF $= 107.5°$.

61. Explain the electrical conductivities of diamond, ZnS, NaCl, Fe, and CdS containing traces of $CuCl_x$ in place of Cd.

62. Compare the valence-bond and band theories' explanations of electrical conductivity in graphite.

63. Calculate the Bohr radius of an electron in its most stable state near a positively charged $(Z = 1)$ impurity center in n-type semiconducting silicon. How many Si atoms are within a sphere with twice this distance as radius?
Answer: 550 atoms.

64. Indicate by a schematic diagram the contact layer and its distorted bands when:
(a) Two different metals touch.
(b) An insulator contacts a metal.
(c) An n-type semiconductor contacts a metal.

65. Calculate the energy states of a hole-electron combination in a homogeneous dielectric with $\kappa = 2.5$.

FOOTNOTES

1. The ideas of this section are drawn from these sources: Landé, A., *Foundations of Quantum Theory, a Study in Continuity and Symmetry.* New Haven, Conn.: Yale University Press, 1955. Landé, A., *American Scientist*, 41, 439 (1953); Landé, A., *American Journal of Physics*, 20, 353 (1952); Landé, A., *The Physical Review*, 87, 267 (1951).

2. Much of this section is drawn from the sources of Section 8.4.

3. Feynman, R. P., *Reviews of Modern Physics*, 20, 367 (1948).

4. A clear and detailed treatment is given by: Pauling, L. and E. B. Wilson, Jr., *Introduction to Quantum Mechanics.* New York: McGraw-Hill Book Company, Inc., 1935, Chapter III.

5. A clear and detailed treatment is given by: Pauling, L. and E. B. Wilson, Jr., *Introduction to Quantum Mechanics.* New York: McGraw-Hill Book Company, Inc. 1935, Chapter V.

6. Eckart, C., *The Physical Review*, **36**, 878 (1930); Pauling, L. and E. B. Wilson, Jr., *Introduction to Quantum Mechanics*. New York: McGraw-Hill Book Company, Inc., 1935, pp. 180-82.

7. Pauling, L. and E. B. Wilson, Jr., *Introduction to Quantum Mechanics*. New York: McGraw-Hill Book Company, Inc., 1935, pp. 221-24.

8. Pauling, L. and E. B. Wilson, Jr., *Introduction to Quantum Mechanics*. New York: McGraw-Hill Book Company, Inc., 1935, pp. 210, 214-15.

9. Weinbaum, S., *Journal of Chemical Physics*, **1**, 593 (1933).

10. Coulson, C. A., *Transactions of the Faraday Society*, **33**, 1479 (1937).

11. For a comparison of the molecular-orbital and valence-bond methods, see: Coulson, C. A., *Valence*. New York: Oxford University Press, 1952, Chapter VI.

12. Varshni, Y. P., *Reviews of Modern Physics*, **29**, 664 (1957).

13. Pauling, L., *Nature of the Chemical Bond*. Ithaca, N. Y.: Cornell University Press, 1960, pp. 153 et seq.

14. See, for example: Pearson, R. G., *Chemical and Engineering News*, June 29, 1959, p. 72.

15. Schomaker, V., and D. P. Stevenson, *Journal of the American Chemical Society*, **63**, 37 (1941).

16. Pauling, L., *Journal of the American Chemical Society*, **69**, 542 (1947).

17. See, for example: Pauling, L., *Journal of the American Chemical Society*, **69**, 542 (1947); and *Proceedings of the Royal Society (London)*, Series *A*, **196**, 343 (1949).

18. Hedberg, K., *Journal of the American Chemical Society*, **74**, 3486 (1952).

19. Sherman, J., *Chemical Reviews*, **11**, 93 (1932).

20. See, for example: Lefever, R. A., *Journal of Chemical Education*, **30**, 486 (1953).

21. Honig, J. M., *Journal of Chemical Education*, **34**, 343 (1957).

9 / STATISTICAL

MECHANICS

A. THEORY

9.1 Entropy Postulate

It is now time to attempt the ultimate goal of the theoretical chemist: to relate chemical behavior on the macroscopic or molar level to mechanical behavior on the microscopic or single-event level. Much modern research is devoted to this attempt for time-dependent processes. For equilibrium states and reversible processes, however, the broad outlines are well established and previous matter of this book provides several interesting examples that can be discussed properly here.

From the very beginning of this text observed facts have been related at least qualitatively to the structure of matter. The kinetic theory yielded a mechanical explanation of pressure and explained heat as disorganized mechanical motion. Faced with a detailed calculation of the trajectories and collisions of 10^{24} particles, one was forced to admit that the details were of secondary importance. Observables had to be averages and a full and complete knowledge was not only impossible but unnecessary. Still, averages must be used with caution for they involve uncertainties. Moreover, the uncertainties of quantum and wave mechanics are such that a cautious student might rightly question whether a wave-particle view of matter could give anything familiar, especially on the macroscopic level of observation.

Statistical mechanics bridges the gap between single event and thermo-dynamics. It provides a method of calculating the few thermodynamic quan-tities of a macroscopic system from the immense number of individual events that together constitute the state of a system. Many similar but different microscopic states exhibit essentially the same macroscopic variables, so almost any reasonable set of microscopic events will yield thermodynamic sense. Almost any method of averaging also yields essentially the same result; the most probable state has macroscopic properties that differ only negligibly from any kind of average. As a result, the average behavior of an ensemble of similar microscopic systems in a suitable range of states is said to be the aver-age behavior of a particular mechanical system actually studied. While its exact microscopic state may be incompletely specified, its thermodynamic state is indeed well specified.

The first part of this chapter explains in general terms how the stationary energies of quantum mechanics can be averaged to yield the few macroscopic quantities that thermodynamics calls its own. Maxwell-Boltzmann statistics are found to be a limiting case of two new kinds of statistics. In the second part of this chapter, methods of calculation are developed for several simple situations: the perfect gas; crystals at low temperature; electrons in metals; photons. The result for photons is, in fact, the historical starting-point of quantum mechanics.

Boltzmann made a remarkable and most fundamental discovery when he found that the function

$$\iint f(p, q) \ln f(p, q) \, dp \, dq$$

provides a macroscopically suitable measure of the deviation from equilibrium or degree of removal from equilibrium of a system with probability distribu-tion $f(p, q)$. The symbols p and q stand for all the momenta and positions of the particles of the system. This function tends to decrease to a minimum as time passes and as equilibrium is approached. Entropy, on the contrary, tends spontaneously to increase as equilibrium is approached from some arbi-trary initial state described by $f(p, q)$. Gibbs and many others after him thus postulate that

$$S = -k \iiint f \ln f \, dp \, dq . \tag{6.57}$$

The change of sign means that S increases spontaneously on approach to equilibrium and the constant k fixes the dimensions of S, the entropy. Equa-tion (6.57) is classical in that conjugate momenta p and positions q are assumed to have exactly specifiable values.

517

Stationary states, which as time-independent are expected to be the basis of equilibrium predictions, are characterized by their accurately specified energies E_n in quantum mechanics. Time and energy are conjugate variables. The classical formulation of the entropy postulate is thus modified to read

$$S = -k \sum_n P_n \ln P_n \,. \tag{9.1}$$

In (9.1), P_n is the probability of a stationary state with energy E_n. The summation proceeds over all allowed states just as the integrations in the classical expression (6.57) proceeded over all allowed values of p and q. As defined, S is identified with the macroscopically observable entropy of thermodynamics and the thermodynamic energy E is identified with the mean energy as in (9.2).

$$E = \sum_n P_n E_n \,. \tag{9.2}$$

The probabilities P_n of the energies E_n can be calculated by the methods of quantum mechanics by taking appropriate averages of $|\psi|^2$. They are normalized so that

$$1 = \sum_n P_n \,. \tag{9.3}$$

At equilibrium, E is a minimum subject to the constraints of constant S and (9.3). Or again, at equilibrium, S is a maximum subject to the constraints of constant E and (9.3). By the method of undetermined multipliers A and $(\beta k)^{-1}$, either condition for an extremum (or stationary value) requires that

$$\delta E - A - \left(\frac{1}{\beta k}\right) \delta S = 0 \,. \tag{9.4}$$

Since the several energies E_n are specified,

$$\delta E = \sum_n E_n \, \delta P_n = 0 \,. \tag{9.5}$$

From (9.3), a change in probabilities accompanying a virtual change in the system yields

$$\delta(1) = \sum_n \delta P_n = 0 \,. \tag{9.6}$$

Similarly, from (9.1),

$$\delta S = -k \sum_n \left[\delta P_n \ln P_n + P_n \left(\frac{\delta P_n}{P_n}\right) \right] = 0 \,.$$

But because of (9.6), this is equivalent to

$$\delta S = -k \sum_n \delta P_n \ln P_n = 0 \,. \tag{9.7}$$

Substitution of (9.5), (9.6), and (9.7) into (9.4) then yields

$$\sum_n \left[E_n - A + \left(\frac{1}{\beta}\right) \ln P_n \right] \delta P_n = 0 . \qquad (9.8)$$

For arbitrary δP_n, it is necessary that

$$\ln P_n = \beta(A - E_n) \qquad (9.9)$$

$$P_n = e^{\beta(A - E_n)}. \qquad (9.10)$$

The probability distribution of (9.9) and (9.10) is the most likely one and P_n, the probability that the system it represents is in state n with energy E_n, is a maximum. The ensemble from which the mechanical system was chosen is called *canonical*. It represents a thermodynamic system at equilibrium with a constant temperature heat reservoir. The undetermined multipliers A and β have thermodynamic meaning and can be evaluated by (9.2) and (9.3).

9.2 Identification of Thermodynamic Functions

Because ordinary macroscopic systems contain very great numbers of individuals, the probability distribution is quite sharply peaked at its single maximum. As a result, the most probable value of a quantity and its mean value cannot be distinguished experimentally. Such a distinction might be noticed, however, for small systems such as a colloidal particle undergoing Brownian motion. However, for systems of ordinary or molar size, the average, most probable, and observed values are alike. Equation (9.2) states this for energy, and in general for some property G_n, the macroscopic value G is postulated to be

$$G = \sum_n G_n P_n . \qquad (9.11)$$

In particular, with $\ln P_n$ given by (9.9), (9.1) reads

$$S = -k \sum_n P_n [\beta(A - E_n)] = -k\beta[A \sum_n P_n - \sum_n P_n E_n] .$$

By virtue of (9.2) and (9.3), this becomes

$$S = -k\beta(A - E) . \qquad (9.12)$$

The various energies E_n will in general depend upon external parameters that can be specified at will by the experimenter. Such parameters might be electric, magnetic, or gravitational fields or the position of barriers such as vessel walls. If X stands for these external parameters and in particular for the volume, then the statisticomechanical equivalent of (4.88) is (9.13).

$$T = \left(\frac{\partial E}{\partial S}\right)_X . \qquad (9.13)$$

519

Equation (9.13) is the most sophisticated and final definition of absolute temperature T. In particular, with values of δE and δS as given in (9.5) and (9.7),

$$T = \frac{\sum\limits_{n} (\delta P_n) E_n}{-k \sum\limits_{n} (\delta P_n) \ln P_n} = \frac{\sum\limits_{n} (\delta P_n) E_n}{-k\beta \sum\limits_{n} \delta P_n (A - E_n)}.$$

Since $\sum\limits_{n} \delta P_n A = A \sum\limits_{n} \delta P_n = 0$ because of (9.6), it follows at once that β fixes a reciprocal temperature scale, for

$$\beta = \frac{1}{kT}. \tag{9.14}$$

Equation (9.12) then reads

$$S = \frac{E - A}{T}$$

$$A = E - TS. \tag{4.79}$$

The undetermined multiplier A is thus the Helmholtz free energy.

9.3 Partition Function

Actual calculation of values of E, S, A, and other thermodynamic variables generally involves the partition function Q, sometimes called the *sum-of-states.* By definition, the canonical partition function Q is

$$Q = \sum_{n} e^{-(E_n/kT)}. \tag{9.15}$$

Because of (9.3) and (9.10),

$$1 = \sum_{n} P_n = \sum_{n} e^{\beta(A - E_n)}.$$

But $\beta = 1/kT$ and A is independent of n so that

$$1 = e^{A/kT} \sum_{n} e^{-(E_n/kT)}$$

$$e^{-(A/kT)} = Q$$

$$A = -kT \ln Q. \tag{9.16}$$

It happens that the logarithm of Q is more convenient in calculations than is Q itself, as the following calculations show. For statistical mechanics, pressure P is defined by (4.95).

$$-P = \left(\frac{\partial A}{\partial V}\right)_T. \tag{4.95}$$

The partition function Q depends upon external parameters like V because the energies E_n calculated by the wave equation depend upon boundary conditions like positions of vessel walls. By virtue of (9.16),

$$P = kT \left(\frac{\partial \ln Q}{\partial V} \right)_T. \tag{9.17}$$

The logarithm of Q is involved also in E and C_V, for by (9.2) and (9.10),

$$E = \sum_n E_n e^{\beta A - \beta E_n} = e^{\beta A} \sum_n E_n e^{-\beta E_n}.$$

Because of (9.15) and (9.16),

$$E = \frac{1}{Q} \left(- \frac{\partial Q}{\partial \beta} \right)_X$$

$$= - \left(\frac{\partial \ln Q}{\partial \beta} \right)_X \tag{9.18}$$

In terms of T, (9.18) reads

$$E = - \left(\frac{\partial \ln Q}{\partial T} \right)_X \left(\frac{\partial T}{\partial \beta} \right)_X$$

$$= kT^2 \left(\frac{\partial \ln Q}{\partial T} \right)_X. \tag{9.19}$$

Similarly, from the definition of C_V,

$$C_V = \left(\frac{\partial E}{\partial T} \right)_X = k \frac{\partial}{\partial T} \left[T^2 \left(\frac{\partial \ln Q}{\partial T} \right) \right]. \tag{9.20}$$

With values of V specified by the experimenter in advance; with values of E and S as postulated; and with values of T, P, and C_V as calculated from $\ln Q$, all thermodynamic functions can be calculated by the usual methods of thermodynamics.

Example 9.1. Express the Gibbs free energy G in terms of $\ln Q$ and its derivatives. By definition, $G = E + PV - TS = A + PV$; hence, by (9.16) and (9.17),

$$G = kT \left[V \left(\frac{\partial \ln Q}{\partial V} \right)_T - \ln Q \right].$$

9.4 Kinds of Statistics

The straightforward but usually tedious way to evaluate the partition function Q is to sum (9.15) directly over all possible states with known energies E at some temperature T of interest. States with E_n large compared to kT contribute little or almost nothing to Q so that states with energies in excess of a certain value can be neglected in calculating Q within a specified accuracy.

Most, and frequently all, energies of molecules can be found experimentally with great precision by spectroscopic methods since $\Delta E = h\nu$.

Whether observed or calculated energies are used to evaluate the partition function, it is necessary to take account of the fact that identical particles or molecules cannot be distinguished from each other. Classically each individual of a system could in principle be numbered and followed along its observed or predicted trajectory in phase space forever. However, in order to assure that the entropy of a homogeneous system is an extensive property, Gibbs was forced to conclude that only the numbers and not the individual identities of like particles in the several states were of importance. Quantum mechanics by its nature insists on the same idea; identical particles are in principle indistinguishable. Thus, the $N!$ permutations of N identical particles comprising a system cannot even in classical statistical mechanics be considered to lead to new situations. Accordingly, permutations and interchanges of identical units do not generate really different circumstances and the partition function must be divided by $N!$ to take account of this indistinguishability of identical units.

Although in the last analysis any interaction whatsoever removes degeneracies and affects energies, it is often convenient and quite accurate to neglect interactions among almost independent units such as molecules of a perfect gas. Each molecule if isolated would have the same spectrum of energies E_k. By analogy with (9.15) there is for each molecule a partition function

$$Q_1 = \sum_k e^{-\beta E_k} . \qquad (9.21)$$

The system energies E_n become merely a summation of N terms each of which is one of the molecular energies E_k. There is a system energy E_n for each way of distributing the various molecular energies E_k among the N molecules considered as distinguishable. The number of times a particular value of $E_n = E_m$ occurs in Q is the number of ways of distributing the same set of molecular energies among the N distinguishable molecules, namely the coefficients C_m in

$$\left(\sum_k e^{-\beta E_k} \right)^N = \sum_m C_m e^{-\beta E_m} .$$

Here each value of E_m differs from every other. With $(N!)^{-1}$ to correct for indistinguishability,

$$Q = \frac{1}{N!} \sum_n e^{-\beta E_n} = \frac{1}{N!} \sum_m C_m e^{-\beta E_m} = \frac{1}{N!} \left(\sum_k e^{-\beta E_k} \right)^N .$$

Substitution of Q_1 into the expression for Q yields

$$Q = \frac{1}{N!} Q_1^N . \qquad (9.22)$$

In deriving (9.22) no limitation was placed upon the number of identical molecules with like spectra of energies E_k. If the number of energy states available to the molecules greatly exceeds their actual number, (9.22) is adequate because it is unlikely that more than one molecule should achieve the same state as another molecule. Quantum mechanics, however, places limitations upon the number of molecules that can exist in exactly like states.

If each of the N molecules contains an odd number of elementary particles with half-integral spin, the wave function of the system must be antisymmetric with respect to interchange of any two molecules. Since interchange of an even number of elementary particles of half-integral spin does not change the sign of the wave function, the wave function of the system must be antisymmetric only if each molecule contains an odd number of such elementary particles. If their number is even in each molecule and if elementary particles with integral spin (light quanta, π-mesons, and the like) are present, the wave function of the system must be symmetric with respect to interchanges of molecules. Wave functions that are only partly symmetric or antisymmetric are not allowed.

Systems with symmetric wave functions may have any number of molecules in each quantum state, but systems with antisymmetric wave functions may have only one or none per state. Systems that can have only one or none per state are subject to the Pauli exclusion principle and are regulated by Fermi-Dirac statistics. Systems that can have more than one unit in the same state follow Bose-Einstein statistics. In the limit of high temperature or low density of units per available state both these kinds of statistics reduce to Boltzmann statistics for which (9.22) is true.

B. APPLICATIONS

9.5 Perfect Monatomic Gas

With the methods of calculation now developed it is possible to calculate Q explicitly for several situations. One of the simplest of these is the ideal monatomic gas consisting of N identical point masses free in a volume V. The energies E_k are given by (8.38), where k stands for the integer triple (n_x, n_y, n_z).

$$E_k = \frac{\pi^2 \hbar^2}{2m} \left(\frac{n_x^2}{a^2} + \frac{n_y^2}{b^2} + \frac{n_z^2}{c^2} \right). \tag{8.38}$$

If the box with sides a, b, and c is very large, the energies E_k are closely spaced and, if the gas is dilute, (9.22) holds. It is necessary merely to calculate Q_1.

$$Q_1 = \sum_k e^{-\beta E_k} \tag{9.21}$$

$$= \sum_{n_x=1}^{\infty} \sum_{n_y=1}^{\infty} \sum_{n_z=1}^{\infty} \exp \left[-\frac{\beta \pi^2 \hbar^2}{2m} \left(\frac{n_x^2}{a^2} + \frac{n_y^2}{b^2} + \frac{n_z^2}{c^2} \right) \right].$$

In the approximation suitable for a rarified gas in a big box,

$$\sum_{n=1}^{\infty} \exp\left[-\frac{\beta\pi^2\hbar^2}{2m}\left(\frac{n^2}{a^2}\right)\right] = \int_0^{\infty} \exp\left[-\frac{\beta\pi^2\hbar^2 n^2}{2ma^2}\right] dn .$$

By the usual methods of transformation, this becomes

$$\frac{1}{2}\left(\frac{2ma^2}{\beta\pi^2\hbar^2}\right)^{1/2} \int_0^{\infty} x^{-1/2}e^{-x}\,dx = \left(\frac{ma^2}{2\beta\pi^2\hbar^2}\right)^{1/2} \Gamma(\tfrac{1}{2})$$

$$= \left(\frac{ma^2}{2\beta\pi\hbar^2}\right)^{1/2} .$$

If $V = abc$, it therefore follows from (9.21) and (9.22) that

$$Q_1 = \left(\frac{2\pi mkT}{h^2}\right)^{3/2} V \tag{9.23}$$

and

$$Q = \left(\frac{2\pi mkT}{h^2}\right)^{3N/2} \frac{V^N}{N!}. \tag{9.24}$$

In order to obtain a simple expression for $\ln Q$, use is made of the Stirling approximation for factorials of large numbers:

$$\ln N! \approx N \ln N - N + \tfrac{1}{2}\ln 2\pi N . \tag{9.25}$$

Since N is at least of the order of 10^{18}, the last term of (9.25) is negligible. With (9.25), (9.24) yields

$$\ln Q = N \ln \left(\frac{2\pi mkT}{h^2}\right)^{3/2} + N \ln V - \ln N!$$

$$= N \ln \left[\left(\frac{2\pi mkT}{h^2}\right)^{3/2} \frac{Ve}{N}\right]. \tag{9.26}$$

The calculation of the thermodynamic functions given $\ln Q$ is straightforward. By (9.17), with $R = Nk$,

$$P = kT \left(\frac{\partial \ln Q}{\partial V}\right)_T = \frac{RT}{V}.$$

Similarly, by (9.19),

$$E = RT^2 \frac{d \ln T^{3/2}}{dT} = \tfrac{3}{2}RT .$$

Although these expressions are familiar, the absolute value of the entropy S is not.

$$S = \frac{E - A}{T} = \tfrac{3}{2}R + k \ln Q .$$

With $PV = RT$ and $M = Nm$,

$$S = -R \ln P + \tfrac{5}{2} R \ln T + R \ln \left[\left(\frac{2\pi M}{Nh^2} \right)^{3/2} (ke)^{5/2} \right]. \qquad (9.27)$$

If P is expressed in atmospheres and S in calories per mole per degree,

$$S = -R \ln P + \tfrac{5}{2} R \ln T + \tfrac{3}{2} R \ln M - 2.3151. \qquad (9.28)$$

These equations are suitable only for dilute gases in which almost all molecules are in the same single state at the temperature T.

Example 9.2. What is the absolute entropy of He at 298.16°K? The accepted value is 30.126 cal mole^{-1} deg^{-1} [F. D. Rossini, *et al.*, Circular of the National Bureau of Standards 500 (1952)].

Since $M = 4.003$ and $P = 1.000$ atm, (9.28) yields

$$S° = \tfrac{5}{2} R \ln 298.16 + \tfrac{3}{2} R \ln 4.003 - 2.3151 = 28.306 + 4.135 - 2.315$$

$$= 30.126 \text{ cal mole}^{-1} \text{ deg}^{-1}.$$

9.6 Perfect Diatomic Gas

When a molecule consists of mechanical parts or has accessible to it at the temperature of interest more than one intramolecular energy state, the partition function Q_1 depends upon more than just the translational energies of the preceding section. This discussion of intramolecular energies considers four kinds: electronic, vibrational, rotational, and nuclear spin energies. Since these energies merely add to the translational energy of the molecule,

$$Q_1 = \left(\frac{2\pi mkT}{h^2} \right)^{3/2} V Q_i. \qquad (9.29)$$

Here Q_i is an internal partition function, namely,

$$Q_i = \sum_i e^{-(E_i/kT)} \qquad (9.30)$$

where E_i represents the several intramolecular energies.

The energy differences among various nuclear spin states are very small and are comparable to kT at less than 0.01°K even in strong magnetic fields. Accordingly, the several states that arise because of the several possible values of the components of an isotope's spin along the direction of a magnetic field are of almost equal energy. If the spin of the isotope is i, then the number of states of almost equal energy is $2i + 1$. Since each of these states has one term in Q_i, it follows that

$$Q_i = (2i + 1)Q_{im} \qquad (9.31)$$

where Q_{im} is the internal partition function of the monatomic molecule without nuclear spin.

In a diatomic molecule in which both atoms have nonzero nuclear spin, each contributes almost independently to Q_i. If the nucleuses differ,

$$Q_i = (2i_A + 1)(2i_B + 1)Q_{id} \qquad (9.32)$$

where i_A and i_B are the spins on nucleuses A and B and where Q_{id} is the internal partition function of the heteronuclear diatomic molecule without nuclear spin. If the nucleuses are alike, the requirement for a symmetric or antisymmetric molecular wave function requires (9.32) to be modified. The modified form, generally required only for molecules such as H_2 and D_2 at temperatures less than room temperature, is

$$Q_i = i(i + 1)Q_{id}^{(p)} + (i + 1)(2i + 1)Q_{id}^{(o)} . \qquad (9.33)$$

The superscripts refer to para and ortho modifications. For most molecules containing identical nucleuses, several rotational energy levels are well populated at room temperature. If so, (9.33) reduces to $\frac{1}{2}Q_i$ of (9.32) because only half of the rotational states are accessible to each modification.

The net effect of nuclear spin states is thus to add $\ln (2i + 1)$, $\ln (2i_A + 1)(2i_B + 1)$, or approximately $2 \ln (2i + 1) - \ln 2$ to $\ln Q_1$. These terms affect only the entropy. Since only a nuclear reaction can change nuclear spin, this entropy term (except $-\ln 2$) is suppressed or ignored by convention.

Another contribution to entropy that is generally suppressed is the entropy of mixing of isotopes. As long as the change of interest produces no separation of isotopes, the whole system can be classified as one giant molecule that suffers no change in its entropy due to isotope redistribution. Most changes do change electronic, vibrational, and rotational states so that their influence on the several thermodynamic functions must be calculated.

As is generally the case, direct summation over all molecular states except nuclear spin states will yield Q_i. Because electronic energies are commonly great relative to kT and also few in number, Q_i for electronic states of any molecule — monatomic, diatomic, or polyatomic — is best evaluated by direct summation. In addition to its characteristic vibrational and rotational energy, each state of a certain electronic state has a common electronic energy E_e. Each term of Q_i for each electronic state thus has a common factor $e^{-(E_e/kT)}$ so that

$$Q_i = \sum_e Q_e Q_{rv}^{(e)} . \qquad (9.34)$$

Equation (9.34) really says that electronic energy and rotational-vibrational energy are additive. The summation upon e in (9.34) is over electronic states with

$$Q_e = g_e e^{-(E_e - E_o)/kT} \qquad (9.35)$$

where $E_e - E_o$ is the energy difference of the lowest vibrational-rotational state of state e and that of the ground state with energy E_o. Ordinarily E_o

is the origin of energy so that $E_o = 0$. The factor g_e is the degeneracy of state e, that is, the number of electronic states of almost equal energy for every vibrational-rotational state. For most stable chemicals, g_e is unity in the ground state. Oxygen and NO are notable exceptions for which g_e is not unity.

It happens that rotational and vibrational energies are at least approximately additive so that

$$Q_{rv}^{(e)} = Q_r^{(e)} Q_v^{(e)} . \tag{9.36}$$

Except for H_2, HD, CH_4, and other molecules with small moments of inertia, above room temperature Q_r can be evaluated by integration. Moreover, the summation over vibrational states represented by Q_v can be evaluated in closed form if the vibration is harmonic. Thus, Q_{rv} can be expressed explicitly in terms of molecular parameters.

From the development above it is clear that

$$Q_v = \sum_v e^{-[E(v)/kT]} \tag{9.37}$$

where, as in (8.72),

$$E(v) = (v + \tfrac{1}{2})2\pi\hbar\nu_o . \tag{9.38}$$

Substitution and factoring yields

$$Q_v = e^{-(\pi\hbar\nu_0/kT)} \sum_{v=0}^{\infty} e^{-(2\pi\hbar\nu_0 v/kT)} . \tag{9.39}$$

The summation is the sum of a geometric progression; hence,

$$Q_v = e^{-(\pi\hbar\nu_0/kT)} [1 - e^{-(2\pi\hbar\nu_0/kT)}]^{-1} . \tag{9.40}$$

Values of ν_o for several molecules can be calculated from values of ω_e in the ground state in Table 8.5 by the relation $\nu_o = c\omega_e$.

The evaluation of Q_r by integration is justified when $B_e hc \ll kT$. Since there are $(2J + 1)$ states of energy

$$E(J) = hcB_e[J(J + 1)] \tag{9.41}$$

it follows that

$$Q_r = \sum_{J=0}^{\infty} (2J + 1) e^{-\{hcB_e[J(J+1)]/kT\}} . \tag{9.42}$$

If $hcB_e = wkT$ and if $w \ll 1$,

$$Q_r = \int_0^{\infty} (2J + 1)e^{-w(J^2+J)} \, dJ$$

$$= \frac{1}{w} \int_0^{\infty} e^{-x} \, dx = \frac{1}{w} \Gamma(1) = \frac{1}{w}.$$

By (8.121),

$$Q_r = \frac{4\pi c I_e k T}{h \hbar c} = \frac{2 I_e k T}{\hbar^2} \cdot \tag{9.43}$$

Combination of all these results yields for the internal partition function Q_i of a heteronuclear diatomic molecule in its nondegenerate ground electronic state, subject of course to the various restrictions noted above,

$$Q_i = (2i_A + 1)(2i_B + 1)\left(\frac{2I_e k T}{\hbar^2}\right)\left[\frac{e^{-(\pi \hbar \nu_o/kT)}}{1 - e^{-(2\pi \hbar \nu_o/kT)}}\right]. \tag{9.44}$$

If $A = B$, certain rotational levels are unpopulated and Q_i contains an extra factor of $\tfrac{1}{2}$. For a system of N identical diatomic gas molecules, then,

$$\ln Q = N \ln \left[\left(\frac{2\pi m k T}{h^2}\right)^{3/2} \frac{Ve}{N} Q_i\right]. \tag{9.45}$$

Example 9.3. Calculate the heat content function of N_2 at 2000°K and compare with the value of Table 6.3.

Since $H = E + PV$, it seems necessary to calculate PV as well as E by statistical mechanics. But Q_i is independent of V so that $PV = RT$ for N_2 as well as a monatomic perfect gas. Hence, at 0°K, PV vanishes and E is zero by convention. The heat function is thus

$$\frac{H_T^o - H_o^o}{T} = \frac{[E(T) + RT] - [E(0) + 0]}{T} = \frac{E(T)}{T} + R \cdot$$

Only E needs calculation at 2000°K. By (9.19), (9.44), and (9.45), with the effects of nuclear spin in this homonuclear molecule accounted for by an extra factor of $\tfrac{1}{2}$,

$$\frac{E(T)}{T} = kT\left(\frac{\partial \ln Q}{\partial T}\right)_V$$

$$= RT \frac{\partial}{\partial T} \ln\left[\left(\frac{2\pi m k T}{h^2}\right)^{3/2}\left(\frac{Ve}{N}\right)\frac{1}{2}\left(\frac{2I_e k T}{\hbar^2}\right)\left(\frac{e^{-(\pi \hbar \nu_o/kT)}}{1 - e^{-(2\pi \hbar \nu_o/kT)}}\right)\right]$$

$$= RT \frac{\partial}{\partial T}\left\{\ln T^{5/2} - \frac{\pi \hbar \nu_o}{kT} - \ln\left[1 - e^{-(2\pi \hbar \nu_o/kT)}\right]\right\}$$

$$= RT\left[\frac{\tfrac{5}{2}T^{3/2}}{T^{5/2}} + \frac{\pi \hbar \nu_o}{kT^2} + \frac{e^{-(2\pi \hbar \nu_o/kT)}(2\pi \hbar \nu_o/kT^2)}{1 - e^{-(2\pi \hbar \nu_o/kT)}}\right]$$

$$= \tfrac{5}{2}R + \frac{N h \nu_o}{T}\left[\tfrac{1}{2} + \frac{e^{-(2\pi \hbar \nu_o/kT)}}{1 - e^{-(2\pi \hbar \nu_o/kT)}}\right]$$

$$= \tfrac{5}{2}R + \frac{N h \nu_o}{T}\left[\tfrac{1}{2} + \frac{1}{e^{(2\pi \hbar \nu_o/kT)} - 1}\right].$$

According to Table 8.5, $\omega_e = 2359.61$ cm^{-1}; hence,

$$\frac{h\nu_o}{kT} = \frac{hc\omega_e}{kT}$$

$$= \frac{6.624 \times 10^{-27} \times 2.998 \times 10^{10} \times 2.360 \times 10^{3}}{1.380 \times 10^{-16} \times 2.000 \times 10^{3}} = 1.698$$

and

$$e^{1.698} = 5.464 \ .$$

Since the real state at 0°K is given zero energy, the term $N h\nu_o/2T$ must be suppressed for it is due to zero-point energy $N h\nu_o/2$, which has as its reference the minimum of potential energy rather than the lowest vibrational state. Accordingly, at 2000°K,

$$\frac{H_T^o - H_o^o}{T} = R + \tfrac{5}{2}R + \frac{N h\nu_o}{2000} \times \left(\frac{1}{5.464 - 1} \right)$$

$$= \tfrac{7}{2}R + \frac{6.024 \times 10^{23} \times 6.624 \times 10^{-27} \times 2.360 \times 10^{3} \times 2.998 \times 10^{10}}{2.000 \times 10^{3} \times 4.464 \times 4.184 \times 10^{7}}$$

$$= 6.955 + 0.756 = 7.711 \text{ cal mole}^{-1} \text{ deg}^{-1} \ .$$

The value in Table 6.3 is 7.750 cal mole^{-1} deg^{-1}.

Example 9.4. Find Q_i for NO if nuclear spin is ignored.

From the discussion of NO in Section 8.20 it is necessary to conclude that the ground electronic state involves electronic spin and a nonzero component of electronic angular momentum along the internuclear axis. Because the electronic angular momentum states differ little in energy, these π-states with components $+1$ and -1 cause every energy level to be doubled. The two electronic spin states are separated by an energy comparable to kT at 200°K; it is thus improper to correct by a factor of two or to ignore the more energetic state. Since the vibrational and rotational energies of both electronic spin states are almost alike, (9.34), (9.35), and (9.44) yield

$$Q_i = 2\left[1 + e^{-(E_e/kT)} \right]\left(\frac{2I_e kT}{\hbar^2} \right)\left[\frac{e^{-(\pi\hbar\nu_o/kT)}}{1 - e^{-(2\pi\hbar\nu_o/kT)}} \right].$$

9.7 Perfect Polyatomic Gas

Because polyatomic molecules have many more electronic and vibrational energy states than diatomic molecules, their spectra are quite complex compared to diatomic spectra. As a result, the interpretation of their spectra in terms of simple and uniquely identified energy states is difficult. Although the expressions for the several forms of molecular energy are similar in kind to those for diatomic molecules, they are more lengthy. Each added term in the molecular energy adds a factor to the partition function.

If electronic energies are ignored and if other molecular energies can be separated into additive contributions from nuclear spin, rotation, and vibration. there is in the partition function of a molecule (1) a factor $(2i + 1)$ for each nucleus with nonzero spin; (2) a factor $(2I_e kT/\hbar^2)^{1/2}$ for each nonzero moment of inertia; (3) a factor $\{e^{-(\pi\hbar\nu_0/kT)}/[1 - e^{-(2\pi\hbar\nu_0/kT)}]\}^{g_v}$ for each vibrational frequency, where g_v is the degree of vibrational degeneracy; (4) a correction factor $\sqrt{\pi}/\sigma$, where σ is the finite order of the pure rotational subgroup of the point group of the molecule. Diatomic molecules A_2 have $\sigma = 2$. Because molecular symmetry and internal rotations generally require detailed application often tailored to fit a particular kind of molecule, these remarks on polyatomic molecules and their partition functions must suffice here. Further details are available in some of the references at the end of the chapter.

At modest temperatures the partition function of many molecules depends only mildly upon vibrations. Often it is sufficient to use only approximate frequencies of vibration guessed by analogy with similar molecules or by use of an empirical force-constant formula. With moments of inertia from data on molecular structure it is then possible to calculate free energies and equilibrium constants for gaseous reactions.

9.8 Crystals and the Third Law

In a crystal containing N atoms, the energy due to harmonic vibration with $3N$ degrees of freedom is

$$E = \sum_{i=1}^{3N} (n_i + \tfrac{1}{2})h\nu_{oi} . \tag{9.46}$$

Rotational energy is assumed absent because the crystal itself is fixed and because each atom has no moment of inertia. Real crystals of course may contain at lattice sites molecules that may rotate in part or as units either freely or with some hindrance. Electronic energy is also zero, for the crystal is assumed to be in its ground electronic state, the electronic state at absolute zero. This ground state may, however, be degenerate in any of several ways. A simple kind of degeneracy is due to nuclear spin, but even this is presumed to be lost at absolute zero because only one spin state is supposedly most stable.

With g_o as the degeneracy of the ground state of the crystal, the partition function of the whole crystal is

$$
\begin{aligned}
Q &= g_o \sum_{n_i=0}^{\infty} \exp\left[-\frac{1}{kT} \sum_{i=1}^{3N} (n_i + \tfrac{1}{2})h\nu_{oi} \right] \\
&= g_o \prod_{i=1}^{3N} \sum_{n_i=0}^{\infty} e^{-[(n_i+\frac{1}{2})h\nu_{oi}/kT]} \\
&= g_o \prod_{i=1}^{3N} \left[\frac{e^{-(\pi\hbar\nu_{oi}/kT)}}{1 - e^{-(2\pi\hbar\nu_{oi}/kT)}} \right].
\end{aligned}
\tag{9.47}
$$

That is, there is a factor of the form

$$\frac{e^{-(\pi\hbar\nu_{oi}/kT)}}{1 - e^{-(2\pi\hbar\nu_{oi}/kT)}}$$

for each of the $3N$ frequencies or degrees of translational freedom and a factor g_o for the g_o levels of almost equal energy at each vibrational state. Finally, from (9.47),

$$\ln Q = \ln g_o - \sum_{i=1}^{3N} \frac{\pi\hbar\nu_{oi}}{kT} - \sum_{i=1}^{3N} \ln\left[1 - e^{-(2\pi\hbar\nu_{oi}/kT)}\right]. \qquad (9.48)$$

The first term on the right contributes only to the entropy since it is independent of T and external parameters. If $g_o = 1$, the entropy is zero at absolute zero. If there is nuclear spin i at each of N lattice sites,

$$g_o = (2i + 1)^N$$

and the entropy S_o^o at absolute zero due to nuclear spin degeneracy is

$$S_o^o = Nk \ln (2i + 1). \qquad (9.49)$$

This term is usually suppressed. Terms for isotope mixing are also usually suppressed.

Residual entropy is conventionally acknowledged to exist at absolute zero if g_o varies as some quantity to a power of the order of N. For solid CO with complete randomness quenched in, $g_o = 2^N$ for N molecules and

$$S_o^o = Nk \ln 2. \qquad (9.50)$$

For ice with randomly located protons, two to an oxygen, $g_o = (\tfrac{3}{2})^N$ for NH_2O and[1]

$$S_o^o = Nk \ln \tfrac{3}{2}. \qquad (9.51)$$

But if $g_o = C^M$ where M is small compared to N, then

$$S_o^o = \left(\frac{M}{N}\right) Nk \ln C \approx 0. \qquad (9.52)$$

That is, residual entropy will be absent at absolute zero in terms of the third law of thermodynamics if the number M of random-sites per gram-mole is very small compared to Avogadro's number.

The second term of (9.48) yields the zero-point energy of the crystal. Since the conventional zero of energy is at this level of energy, the second term of (9.48) is to be omitted. The last term of (9.48) yields the characteristic T^4-dependence of energy and the T^3-dependence of C_V.

9.9 Degenerate Electron Gas[2]

One of the common circumstances in which Boltzmann statistics utterly fail is for electrons in a metal. The reason is that even at temperatures near the melting points of metals the number of electrons is comparable to the number of states with energy kT. Fermi-Dirac statistics must be used.

Let s be the number of states of about the same energy available to n electrons. Since each state may be either unoccupied or occupied by only one electron because of the exclusion principle, the number of ways of assigning the n electrons to the s states is $s(s - 1)(s - 2) \cdots (s - n + 1)$, for the first electron has s possible states available, the second has $(s - 1)$, the third has $(s - 2)$, and so on until there remain $(s - n)$ vacant states. But

$$s(s - 1)(s - 2) \cdots (s - n + 1) = \frac{s!}{(s - n)!}.$$

Moreover, the n electrons are indistinguishable so that their $n!$ possible orders of being chosen reduces the number of distinguishable arrangements to $s!/n!(s - n)!$. If several groups of states of different ranges of energy exist, the total number of distinguishable eigenstates is the product for all groups of states, namely,

$$P = \prod_i \frac{s_i!}{n_i!(s_i - n_i)!}. \tag{9.53}$$

This product is proportional to the probability that the particular arrangement is achieved from all possible arrangements. By maximizing this probability for a constant total number N of electrons and for a constant energy E, the most likely distribution or arrangement is found. And because of the great numbers of electrons and states, the distribution is sharply peaked so that mean and most probable values do not differ significantly. Thus, P of (9.53) is to be maximized provided

$$E = \sum_i n_i E_i \tag{9.54}$$

and

$$N = \sum_i n_i \tag{9.55}$$

are constant.

According to Stirling's approximation (9.25),

$$
\begin{aligned}
\ln P &= \sum_i \ln (s_i!) - \sum_i \ln (n_i!) - \sum_i \ln (s_i - n_i)! \\
&= \sum_i [s_i \ln s_i. - s_i - n_i \ln n_i + n_i \\
&\qquad\qquad - (s_i - n_i) \ln (s_i - n_i) + (s_i - n_i)] \\
&= \sum_i [s_i \ln s_i - n_i \ln n_i - (s_i - n_i) \ln (s_i - n_i)].
\end{aligned}
$$

Since P is a maximum when $\ln P$ is a maximum, by the method of undetermined multipliers β and F

$$\delta(\ln P) - \beta \, \delta E + \beta F \, \delta N = 0 \, .$$

On adjusting the various numbers n_i of electrons in the available states,

$$\sum_i \left(-\ln n_i + \ln (s_i - n_i) - \beta E_i + \beta F \right) \delta n_i = 0 \, .$$

The most probable distribution is, therefore.

$$\ln \left(\frac{s_i - n_i}{n_i} \right) = \beta(E_i - F) \, . \tag{9.56}$$

The conditions (9.54) and (9.55) fix β and F thus. Equation (9.56) yields the Fermi-Dirac distribution

$$n_i = \frac{s_i}{e^{\beta(E_i - F)} + 1} \, . \tag{9.57}$$

When s_i greatly exceeds n_i, as in an ideal gas subject to Boltzmann statistics,

$$n_i \approx s_i e^{-\beta(E_i - F)}$$

because unity is small compared to $e^{\beta(E_i - F)}$. By (9.55),

$$N = \sum_i s_i e^{-\beta(E_i - F)}$$

$$e^{-\beta F} = \frac{1}{N} \sum_i s_i e^{-\beta E_i} \, .$$

Then, by (9.54),

$$E = \sum_i s_i E_i e^{-\beta(E_i - F)} = \frac{N \sum_i s_i E_i e^{-\beta E_i}}{\sum_i s_i e^{-\beta E_i}} = N \bar{E}_i \, .$$

As expected, this is like (1.116), the Boltzmann distribution, if $\beta = 1/kT$ and if s_i is the number of states of energy E_i.

At absolute zero β is infinite. In order that n_i be greater than zero it is necessary that F exceed E_i. States with energy E_i less than F have $n_i = s_i$ at absolute zero; that is, the electron gas is completely degenerate with all possible states occupied. States with E_i greater than F have $n_i = 0$ at absolute zero. The Fermi energy F thus represents the maximum energy of electrons at absolute zero. As indicated in Sections 8.28 and 8.30, the number of electrons with energy F may be quite great.

Above absolute zero F depends upon T. When kT is small compared to $E_i - F$, it follows from (9.57) that

$$\frac{n_i}{s_i} \approx e^{-[(E_i - F)/kT]} \, .$$

That is, the probability n_i/s_i that a state with energy well removed from the Fermi level is occupied follows Boltzmann statistics with the zero of energy referred to the Fermi level. At any temperature, states with energy equal to F are half-occupied, for by (9.57) with $E_i = F$,

$$n_i = \frac{s_i}{1 + e^0} = \frac{s_i}{2}.$$

9.10 Radiation[3]

The wave function of a system of photons is symmetric for interchanges of identical photons. The statistics are Bose-Einstein and the number of photons possible in any state is unlimited.

The total number of distinguishable eigenstates is best calculated by considering the n photons and the s states available to them in any small range of energies as a line of n photons and $(s - 1)$ markers that divide the n photons into s states of similar energy. These $(n + s - 1)$ objects can be arranged without restriction in $(n + s - 1)!$ ways. But since the $n!$ permutations of the photons and the $(s - 1)!$ permutations of the markers do not lead to distinguishable arrangements, the number of distinguishable arrangements is

$$\frac{(n + s - 1)!}{n!(s - 1)!}.$$

If several groups of states of different ranges of energy exist, the total number of distinguishable eigenstates is

$$P = \prod_i \frac{(n_i + s_i - 1)!}{n_i!(s_i - 1)!}. \tag{9.58}$$

On maximizing $\ln P$ at constant N and E as in the preceding section, there results as the most probable distribution

$$\ln \left(\frac{s_i + n_i - 1}{n_i} \right) = \beta(E_i - F). \tag{9.59}$$

Since n_i and s_i are assumed to be large numbers, unity can be neglected in the term $s_i + n_i - 1$ and

$$n_i = \frac{s_i}{e^{E_i - F/kT} - 1} \tag{9.60}$$

where $1/kT$ replaces β. This is the Bose-Einstein distribution law.

For photons, $F = 0$ and $E_i = h\nu_i$. The total average energy of a system of n_i oscillators with frequency ν_i is

$$E = \sum_i n_i E_i$$

$$= \sum_i \frac{s_i h \nu_i}{e^{h\nu_i/kT} - 1}. \tag{9.61}$$

The number of distinguishable photon states in a volume V with frequencies from ν_i to $\nu_i + d\nu_i$ is

$$\frac{8\pi V \nu_i^2 \, d\nu_i}{c^3}. \tag{9.62}$$

The famous Planck radiation formula for the energy density $E(\nu)$ is, then,

$$E(\nu) = \frac{8\pi V h \nu^3}{c^3 (e^{h\nu/kT} - 1)}. \tag{9.63}$$

It is here that quantum mechanics began in 1900.

Example 9.5. Show that the energy of radiation is proportional to T^4 (Stefan-Boltzmann law).

As implied by (9.63), the total energy is

$$E = \int_0^\infty E(\nu) \, d\nu = \frac{8\pi V h}{c^3} \int_0^\infty \frac{\nu^3 \, d\nu}{e^{h\nu/kT} - 1}.$$

If $x = h\nu/kT$, then $dx = (h/kT) \, d\nu$ and

$$E = \frac{8\pi V k^4 T^4}{c^3 h^3} \int_0^\infty \frac{x^3 \, dx}{e^x - 1}.$$

Since the integral is a function only of its limits, it follows that E varies as T^4.

REFERENCES

Guggenheim, E. A., *Thermodynamics, An Advanced Treatment for Chemists and Physicists*. Amsterdam: North-Holland Publishing Co., 1957.

Herzberg, G., *Molecular Spectra and Molecular Structure*. Princeton, N. J.: D. Van Nostrand Company, Inc. *Vol. I, Spectra of Diatomic Molecules* (1950); *Vol. II, Infrared and Raman Spectra of Polyatomic Molecules* (1945).

Mayer, J. E., and M. G. Mayer, *Statistical Mechanics*. New York: John Wiley & Sons, Inc., 1940.

Tolman, R. C., *The Principles of Statistical Mechanics*. New York: Oxford University Press, 1938.

PROBLEMS

Because of the advanced nature of the matter of this chapter and the limited number of readily tractable problems, only one set of problems is given.

1. Show by classical methods that the probability density of an ensemble of systems of specified constant energy is Ω^{-1}, where Ω is the allowed volume in phase space. Then show that the entropy is $k \ln \Omega$, with Ω proportional to the number of states with the specified constant energy.

2. Find enthalpy as a function of $\ln Q$.

3. Show that for any state of aggregation

$$C_P = C_V + T \left(\frac{\partial P}{\partial T}\right)_V \left(\frac{\partial V}{\partial T}\right)_P .$$

Then find C_P as a function of $\ln Q$.

4. If $E = \frac{3}{2} NkT$ and if $P = -(\partial E/\partial V)$, show that $PV = NkT$. *Hint:* use (8.38).

5. Test the Stirling approximation (9.25) for 5!, 10!, and 100! (N.B.: $\log_{10} 100! = 157.97$.)

6. If the potential energy inside the container of a classical ideal gas is zero and is infinite outside, calculate Q for a classical ideal monatomic gas of N molecules from the Gibbs phase integral

$$Q = \frac{1}{N! h^{3N}} \iint e^{-\beta \mathcal{K}(p,q)} \, dp \, dq.$$

Answer: $Q = \left[\dfrac{2\pi mkT}{h^2}\right]^{3N/2} \dfrac{V^N}{N!} .$

7. Show that $C_V = -T(\partial^2 A/\partial T^2)_X$ and with this expression find C_V of a perfect monatomic gas.
Answer: $C_V = 3Nk/2$.

8. Discuss the analogy between mixing isotopes and allowing one of several nuclear spin states to achieve equilibrium in $(2i + 1)$ states.

9. For the purposes of considering symmetry and antisymmetry, molecular wave functions of homonuclear diatomic molecules can be factored into five parts: center-of-mass (symmetric with respect to interchange of nucleuses); vibrational (symmetric); electronic; rotational (symmetric for even J, antisymmetric for odd); and nuclear spin (symmetric for ortho, antisymmetric for para). Prepare a table listing symmetry of electronic state, ortho- or para-type, and even or odd rotational levels actually populated in H_2 and D_2. The spin of D is unity.

10. Find $\ln Q$, E, and S^o per mole $F_{(g)}$ at 298.16°K from these data [C. E. Moore, *Atomic Energy Levels, Vol. I*, Circular of the National Bureau of Standards 467, Washington, D. C. (1949)]:

STATE OF F	ENERGY (cm^{-1})	DEGENERACY
$^2P_{3/2}$	0.0	4
$^2P_{1/2}$	404.0	2
other	$> 10^5$	—

Answer: $\ln Q = 1.0512 \times 10^{25}$; $E = 965$ cal mole^{-1}; $S^o = 37.918$ cal deg^{-1} mole^{-1}.

11. From data of the preceding problem, calculate the free energy functions of F at 298.16°K, 1000°K, 2000°K, and 4000°K.

12. Show that Q_v of a diatomic molecule at very high temperatures is $kT/h\nu_o$.

13. Derive a formula analogous to (9.28) for the entropy of a perfect diatomic gas.

14. Calculate the free energy function of N_2 at 2000°K.

15. Calculate the absolute entropy of $Br_{2(g)}$ at 298.16°K.

16. Compare $B_e hc$ and kT for Br_2, Cl_2, CO, HCl, and H_2. For which of these molecules is (9.43) adequate at 300°K? At 1000°K?

17. Show that the equilibrium constant K_p takes the form $K_p = \prod_j \left(\dfrac{Q}{N}\right)_j e^{-(\Delta E_o^o/RT)}$

where the product is over all gaseous molecules with products in numerator and reactants in denominator each to a power indicated by the number of moles in the balanced equation, and where ΔE_o^o is the increase in zero-point energy for the reaction.

18. Show that K_p of a gas reaction is greater the larger are the:
(a) Moments of inertia of products.
(b) Vibrational frequencies of reactants.
(c) Number of low-lying molecular energy states of products.

19. Find $\ln Q$ for N molecules of gaseous O_2 in its ground state at temperatures where ortho-para corrections are negligible.

20. Show that in a heteronuclear polyatomic molecule, nuclear spin states contribute $\sum \ln (2i + 1)$ to the entropy.

21. Evaluate the constant C in the formula

$$-\frac{G_T - E_o}{RT} = -\ln P + C \ln T + \cdots$$

for:
(a) Linear molecules.
(b) Nonlinear molecules.
Both translation and rotation contribute to C.

22. Consider a nonlinear molecule of n atoms within which there occurs one free rotation described by one angle relative to axes fixed to part of the molecule.
(a) How many degrees of angular freedom exist?
(b) How many coordinates are needed in the internal potential energy?
(c) Estimate C_V for $CH_3 - C \equiv C - CH_3$ at 300°K if all vibrational frequencies contribute $\frac{1}{2}R$.
Answer: (a) $3 + 1$; (b) $3n - 7$; (c) $C_V = 9R$.

23. Evaluate the partition function of a crystal of N atoms if it displays only one $3N$-fold-degenerate fundamental vibrational frequency ν. Then calculate C_V and plot C_V as a function of T for $h\nu = 300k$ from 0°K to 500°K.

24. Explain why electrons in a crystalline conductor contribute very little to C_V at room temperature. What is expected of N free electrons classically?
Answer: $\frac{3}{2}R$.

25. If the Fermi level of a metal has an energy of 100 kcal mole^{-1}, plot n_i/s_i as a function of E_i at 0°K, 100°K, 300°K, and 500°K.

26. Discuss possible interpretations of the phrase "temperature of radiation."

FOOTNOTES

1. Pauling, L., *Nature of the Chemical Bond.* Ithaca, N. Y.: Cornell University Press, 1960, p. 467.

2. The Fermi-Dirac and Bose-Einstein distributions are derived as in: Tolman, R. C., *The Principles of Statistical Mechanics.* New York: Oxford University Press, 1938, pp. 369-74.

3. See footnote to Section 9.9.

10 / CHEMICAL

KINETICS

A. ZERO- AND FIRST-ORDER REACTIONS

10.1 Measurement of Extent of Reaction

Very few people need be concerned with equilibrium thermodynamics, but everyone is vitally interested in chemical kinetics, the study of the time-rates of chemical change. As viewed by the physical sciences, life itself is a complex set of coordinated and interdependent chemical reactions that sustain for a time a highly improbable system quite out of equilibrium with its surroundings. If all reactions proceeded swiftly or even at the same rate toward equilibrium, our universe would be much less varied than it is. Stability and reasonable permanence often require much effort in slowing spontaneous processes. The engineer must control corrosion, wear, and stability and strength of materials. On the other hand, a manufacturer of chemicals with thousands of dollars invested in expensive equipment depends not only upon a favorable change of free energy. He must produce his product swiftly and efficiently to minimize his investment in equipment and labor. The many scientific publications of difficult and careful observations and controversial interpretations of these data are perhaps the surest criterion of the theoretical chemist's present interest in kinetics.

To measure time quite accurately is easy but it is not always easy to decide when a chemical change began or to measure the degree to which the reaction progresses as time passes. The ideal analytical method is much swifter than the reaction of interest, yields an accurate analysis, and does not disturb the reaction. Measurement of the index of refraction, absorption spectrum, volume, or pressure of a system often fixes the progress of a reaction. In 1850, Wilhelmy followed the rate of inversion of sucrose at constant temperature with a polarimeter. This was the first exact study of the kinetics of a chemical change. Sometimes the rate of growth of crystals of a product or the loss in mass of reactants can also be followed continuously and used as a measure of the extent of a reaction. The most obvious way to analyze is, however, to withdraw typical aliquots from time to time. The withdrawal may be directly into a mass spectrometer or gas chromatograph. Chemical analysis of an aliquot ordinarily requires halting the reaction by quenching or by withdrawing a catalyst in order to allow time for the more leisurely chemical analysis.

Some of the more common methods of continuous analysis of streams of reacting chemicals are: electrical conductivity; electrode potentials; infrared, visible, and ultraviolet absorption spectroscopy; X-ray emission or fluorescence spectroscopy; density; viscosity; dielectric constant; nuclear magnetic resonance; and mass spectroscopy. Instruments that continuously record process data in most of these ways are available commercially. Automation is achieved by feeding such recorded data to a computer that controls the process variables in accord with scientific and economic goals.

Frequently the measurement that is made does not of itself yield an analysis. If X_0 is the value of some physicochemical property at time $t = 0$, if X_t is its value at an intermediate time t, and if X_∞ is its final value at infinite time, then the fraction unreacted and remaining unchanged at time t is

$$\frac{X_\infty - X_t}{X_\infty - X_0}$$

while the fraction reacted or the fractional progress of the reaction is

$$\frac{X_t - X_0}{X_\infty - X_0}.$$

The property X is assumed to be a linear function of the extent of the reaction. This is true of the pressure of an isothermal constant-volume reaction for which $\Delta n_{(g)}$ is not zero. It may be true also of optical activity, dielectric constant, electrical conductivity, and so on. The sum of these two expressions is, of course, unity. In the limit at $t = 0$, the first is unity and the second is zero, while at $t = \infty$, the first is zero and the second is unity.

10.2 Zero-Order Reactions

The rate of a chemical reaction can be stated in terms of the rate of disappearance of reactants or of appearance of products. Sometimes these two rates differ, but here they are supposed equal. Let the sole reaction of interest be

$$\text{A} \quad + \quad 2\,\text{B} \quad \rightarrow \quad \text{D} + 3\,\text{E}\,. \tag{10.1}$$

$$\begin{array}{ccccc}
C_A^o & & C_B^o & t=0 & 0 \quad 0 \\
C_A^o - x & & C_B^o - 2x & t & x \quad 3x
\end{array}$$

As the symbols below the species indicate, species A begins with a concentration C_A^o and species B begins at C_B^o, while none of the products is present at the start. The balanced chemical equation says that 1 mole of D is generated when 1 mole of A reacts. If the change occurs at constant volume, the production of x moles of D per unit volume is accompanied by the loss of x moles of A per unit volume. This loss is indicated by a minus sign. The equation also states that 2 B react with each A; hence, the production of x moles of D per unit volume requires the loss of $2x$ moles B per unit volume so that at some time after the start the concentration of B is $C_B^o - 2x$. Similarly, the equation says that 3 E are produced for every D so that the concentration of E is three times that of D at any instant.

The rate at which D is generated is dx/dt. In general, this derivative and others like it are taken at constant volume. The balanced chemical equation says that this is also the rate at which A is destroyed. If C_A is the instantaneous concentration of A at some time t, then

$$C_A = C_A^o - x\,. \tag{10.2}$$

Since C_A^o is independent of time,

$$\frac{dC_A}{dt} = -\frac{dx}{dt}\,. \tag{10.3}$$

Since x increases with time, dC_A/dt is less than zero. That is, C_A decreases as t increases. Moreover,

$$\frac{dx}{dt} = -\frac{dC_A}{dt} \tag{10.3}$$

that is, the rate at which D is generated equals the rate at which A reacts, $-dC_A/dt$. Similarly,

$$\frac{dC_B}{dt} = \frac{d}{dt}\,(C_B^o - 2x) = -2\,\frac{dx}{dt}$$

$$\frac{dx}{dt} = \frac{1}{2}\left(-\frac{dC_B}{dt}\right)\,. \tag{10.4}$$

541

That is, the rate at which D is generated is one-half the rate at which B disappears. Again, the rate at which E is generated is three times the rate at which D is generated, for

$$\frac{dC_E}{dt} = \frac{d(3x)}{dt} = 3\left(\frac{dx}{dt}\right). \tag{10.5}$$

As stated in terms of the rate of disappearance of a reactant A and the concentrations of all reactants, the rate of (10.1) is, in general,

$$-\frac{dC_A}{dt} = kC_A^a C_B^b. \tag{10.6}$$

The over-all order of the reaction described by this empirically observed rate law is $a + b$. The reaction is of a order with respect to A and of b order with respect to B. The proportionality constant k is a positive number independent of concentration but dependent upon temperature and perhaps other variables.

Equations like (10.6) are generally applicable only to fluids. Mobilities in solid solutions are low and the rates of solid-state transformations, even simple decompositions, depend in general upon formation of favorable crystal nucleuses and upon surface reactions. Even the seemingly simple process of sublimation of a molecular crystal in a vacuum involves several steps: formation of an energetically favorable arrangement, decomposition to yield molecules adsorbed on the decomposing surface, slow desorption of these physically adsorbed molecules, and diffusion of the molecules away from the surface.

Frequently the products of solid state reactions catalyze the reaction. For example, the rate of decomposition of Ag_2O after an induction period is proportional to the amount of silver produced and to the amount of oxide.[1] Once a solid-state decomposition is well under way and no new reaction sites are generated, the reaction rate is frequently proportional to the amount of decomposing substance. Although solid-state reactions are important in geology, propellants, crystallization, and semiconducting materials, their discussion is best left to advanced textbooks.

If the rate of a reaction is independent of the concentrations of reactants, a and b are zero in (10.6) and the reaction is of zero order. This situation results when some factor besides concentration limits the rate or when the concentrations of reactants are artificially maintained constant. A solution may be kept saturated or the presence of a condensed volatile phase may fix the concentration of a gaseous reactant. The intensity of light may limit the rate of a photochemical reaction. Unless such restraints are removed, the true order of the reaction cannot be observed.

When a substance is strongly adsorbed on a catalytic surface, its rate of isomerization or decomposition is independent of time and concentration and the reaction is of zero order. As the adsorption weakens, the order rises until the rate of reaction is first order when a single reactant is weakly adsorbed on a catalytic surface. For the zero-order reaction with strong adsorption,

$$-\frac{dC}{dt} = k_0 \,. \tag{10.7}$$

If C^o is the initial concentration at $t = 0$, then when the concentration is C at some later time,

$$-\int_{C^o}^{C} dC' = k_0 \int_0^t dt'$$

$$C^o - C = k_0 t \,. \tag{10.8}$$

The time $t_{1/2}$ for half of the reactant to disappear depends upon C^o, for if $C = C^o/2$, it follows from (10.8) that

$$t_{1/2} = \frac{1}{k_0}\left(C^o - \frac{C^o}{2}\right) = \frac{C^o}{2k_0} \,. \tag{10.9}$$

Example 10.1. It is possible to follow the rate of decomposition of ammonia on tungsten by noting the increase in pressure of gases at constant volume and temperature. The reaction is

$$2\,NH_{3(g)} \rightarrow N_{2(g)} + 3\,H_{2(g)} \,.$$

At 1100°C, these half-times $t_{1/2}$ and initial pressures P_o were observed [C. H. Kunsman, *Journal of the American Chemical Society*, **50**, 2100 (1928)]:

P_o (mm Hg)	265	130	58
$t_{1/2}$ (min)	7.6	3.7	1.7

Show that the reaction is zero order, calculate k_0 at 1100°C, and predict the total pressure 3.00 min after NH_3 at 200 mm Hg is admitted to a rigid vessel containing tungsten at 1100°C.

Since concentration is proportional to pressure at constant temperature, (10.9) requires that $t_{1/2}$ be proportional to P_o. The constancy of k_0 as given by

$$k_0 = \frac{P_o}{2t_{1/2}}$$

shows that the reaction is zero order. Indeed, $k_0 = 17.4, 17.6, 17.0$ mm Hg min^{-1} from these data, with a mean of 17.3 mm Hg min^{-1}.

As in (10.8), after 3.00 min,

$$P_{NH_3} = P_o - k_0 t = 200 - 17.3 \times 3.00$$

$$= 200 - 52 = 148 \text{ mm Hg} \,.$$

Since 2 moles NH_3 yield four of products, the pressure of products is 104 mm Hg. The total pressure will therefore be $148 + 104 = 252$ mm Hg.

10.3 First-Order Reactions

The first-order differential equation is (10.10).

$$-\frac{dC}{dt} = k_1 C \ . \tag{10.10}$$

Since k_1 is independent of C and t, with C^o as initial concentration, integration yields

$$-\int_{C^o}^{C} \frac{dC'}{C'} = k_1 \int_0^t dt'$$

$$\ln\left(\frac{C^o}{C}\right) = k_1 t \ . \tag{10.11}$$

The ratio C/C^o is the fraction of decaying species that is unreacted at time t. Between any two times t_1 and t_2 with concentrations C_1 and C_2, (10.10) yields similarly

$$-\int_{C_1}^{C_2} \frac{dC}{C} = k_1 \int_{t_1}^{t_2} dt$$

$$\ln\left(\frac{C_1}{C_2}\right) = k_1(t_2 - t_1) \ . \tag{10.12}$$

In terms of the rate of formation of B according to the reaction

$$\begin{array}{cccc}
\text{A} & \rightarrow & \text{B} + n\,\text{D} \\
C^o & t = 0 & 0 & 0 \\
C^o - x & t & x & nx
\end{array}$$

the first-order rate law reads

$$-\frac{dC}{dt} = -\frac{d(C^o - x)}{dt} = \frac{dx}{dt} = k_1(C^o - x) \ .$$

That is,

$$\int_0^x \frac{dx'}{C^o - x'} = -\int_{C^o}^{(C^o - x)} \frac{d(C^o - x')}{(C^o - x')} = k_1 \int_0^t dt'$$

$$\ln\left(\frac{C^o}{C^o - x}\right) = k_1 t \ . \tag{10.13}$$

With $C = C^o - x$, (10.13) is (10.11).

The half-life of a reaction is the time $t_{1/2}$ required for half a reactant to disappear. It is independent of initial concentrations for a first-order reaction and thus is a valuable index of the rate of such a reaction. If $C = \frac{1}{2}C^o$ in (10.11) or if $x = \frac{1}{2}C^o$ in (10.13),

$$\ln 2 = k_1 t_{1/2} = 0.69315 . \tag{10.14}$$

Because k_1 in (10.10) has dimensions of reciprocal time, the units of concentration exactly canceling, $t_{1/2}$ is a time.

The best way to determine whether experimental data fit the first-order rate law (10.10) is to calculate values of the rate graphically or analytically and plot the logarithm of these rates as a function of the logarithm of concentration. If $-\Delta C = -(C_2 - C_1) = C_1 - C_2$ and if $\Delta t = t_2 - t_1$, then an analytic expression for the rate of decay is

$$-\frac{dC}{dt} \approx -\frac{\Delta C}{\Delta t} = \frac{C_1 - C_2}{t_2 - t_1}. \tag{10.15}$$

If the time interval Δt is short compared to the total time of the reaction, (10.15) is a good approximation to the rate and $\frac{1}{2}(C_1 + C_2)$ is a good approximation to the corresponding concentration. The rate may also be found graphically as the slope of $C = C(t)$. The reaction is first order if the slope of the log-log plot is unity, for by (10.10)

$$\ln\left(-\frac{dC}{dt}\right) = \ln C + \ln k_1 .$$

A somewhat less reliable but frequently used method of establishing that a reaction is first order is to calculate k_1 from the integrated equations (10.11), (10.12), or (10.13) for each timed observation of concentration. If the k_1's are constant, the reaction is said to be first order *with respect to time*. It is also sometimes convenient to show experimentally that $t_{1/2}$ is independent of initial concentration.

Some compounds that decompose by a first-order reaction are: N_2O_5, Cl_2O, $NaOCl$, acetone, diethyl ether, and ethylene oxide.

Example 10.2. At 20.0°C, benzene diazonium chloride dissolved in isoamyl alcohol decomposes to yield 1 mole $N_{2(g)}$ for each mole of chloride decomposed. Some of the measurements of volume of N_2 (S.T.P.) generated at various times are [C. E. Waring and J. R. Abrams, *Journal of the American Chemical Society*, 63, 2757 (1941)]:

t (min)	0	40	50	90	100	140	160	200	220	300	320	∞
V (ml)	0.00	6.59	8.21	14.43	15.76	21.08	23.57	28.17	30.32	37.76	39.41	69.84

Show that this reaction is first order and calculate its half-life.

The 69.84 ml N_2 at $t = \infty$ is a linear measure of the initial amount of diazonium salt. In the first 40 min the amount of salt that decomposed was proportional to 6.59 and at $t = 40$ min the amount of salt remaining was proportional to 69.84 −

$6.59 = 63.25$. The amount of salt at 50 min was proportional to $69.84 - 8.21 = 61.63$ so that in the period from 40 to 50 min the average amount of salt $\bar{C}$ was proportional to $\frac{1}{2}(63.25 + 61.63) = 62.44$ and the amount that decomposed was proportional to $8.21 - 6.59 = 63.25 - 61.63 = 1.62$. In the same way the following values of rate and mean concentration are calculated.

Δt	50–40	100–90	160–140	220–200	320–300
$-\Delta C$	1.62	1.43	2.49	2.15	1.65
$\left(-\dfrac{\Delta C}{\Delta t}\right)$	0.162	0.143	0.1245	0.1075	0.0825
$\bar{C}$	62.44	54.74	47.51	40.60	31.26

The logarithms of the rates and mean concentrations $\bar{C}$ are plotted in Figure 10.1. The slope of the line is 0.968; hence, the order is 0.968 or approximately unity.

The rate constants are readily found thus:

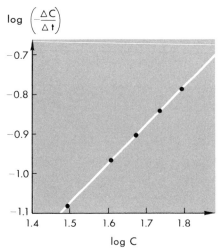

Fig. 10.1. *Decomposition of Benzene-diazonium Chloride.*

$$k_1 = \frac{1}{\bar{C}}\left(-\frac{\Delta C}{\Delta t}\right).$$

The several values of $k_1 \times 10^3$ are: 2.60, 2.61, 2.62, 2.66, and 2.64. Since the mean value is 2.63×10^{-3} min^{-1}, it follows from (10.14) that

$$t_{1/2} = \frac{0.693}{2.63 \times 10^{-3}} = 264 \text{ min}.$$

Example 10.3. At 298.4°C, azomethane decomposes mainly according to the reaction

$$CH_3NNCH_{3(g)} \rightarrow C_2H_{6(g)} + N_{2(g)}.$$

If this is the only reaction and if the first-order rate constant k_1 is 2.50×10^{-4} sec^{-1} [H. C. Ramsperger, *Journal of the American Chemical Society*, **49**, 912 (1927)], what will be the partial pressures of reactant and products when azomethane initially at 200 mm Hg decomposes for 30.0 min?

With pressures replacing concentrations in (10.11), and with $P^o = 200$,

$$2.303 \log\left(\frac{200}{P}\right) = 2.50 \times 10^{-4} \times 30.0 \times 60$$

$$\log\left(\frac{200}{P}\right) = 0.195 = \log 1.566$$

$$P = \frac{200}{1.566} = 128 \text{ mm Hg}.$$

The partial pressure of azomethane is 128 mm Hg after 30.0 min. Since each mole of azomethane decomposed yields one each of ethane and nitrogen, each of the latter has a partial pressure of $200 - 128 = 72$ mm Hg.

10.4 Radioactive Decay

The rate of decay of a radioactive atomic nucleus is proportional to the number of nucleuses that can decay. That is, if N is the number of radioactive nucleuses at time t, as in (10.10),

$$-\frac{dN}{dt} = k_1 N .$$ (10.16)

Definite integration yields

$$-\int_{N_o}^{N} \frac{dN'}{N'} = k_1 \int_0^t dt'$$

$$\ln\left(\frac{N_o}{N}\right) = k_1 t .$$ (10.17)

Since it is customary to list half-lives rather than values of k_1, use of (10.14) yields

$$\ln\left(\frac{N_o}{N}\right) = \frac{t \ln 2}{t_{1/2}}.$$ (10.18)

The most massive stable nucleus is $_{83}\text{Bi}^{209}$. A few lighter nucleuses are naturally radioactive, and many artificially radioactive nucleuses lighter than $_{83}\text{Bi}^{209}$ have been produced by bombardment or in nuclear fusion or fission reactions. The K mesons are said to bind protons and neutrons together by quantum mechanical exchange forces just as two boys playing catch are in a way united by the ball they throw back and forth. Whether or not the decay particles emitted by radioactive species exist as identifiable individuals in nucleuses is uncertain. One successful theory of alpha decay pictures alpha particles as escaping from an unstable nucleus by a quantum mechanical "tunneling" through a barrier that classically would be impenetrable. A main function of high-energy accelerators is to find the distribution and potential energies of fundamental particles in nucleuses.

Hydrogen is the only common nucleus with fewer neutrons than protons. Generally neutrons outnumber protons, and the excess of neutrons increases with atomic number. Seven-eighths of the nucleuses in the crust of the earth have even mass numbers. Elements with even numbers of neutrons or protons are more stable and abundant than those with odd numbers. Only five stable nucleuses have odd numbers of neutrons and odd numbers of protons. Nucleuses with 2, 8, 20, 28, 50, 82, and 126 neutrons or protons are unusually stable, indicating the existence of nuclear energy states analogous to the states of atomic electrons.

There are four disintegration series of heavy radioactive elements. One series decays to $_{83}\text{Bi}^{209}$ and has as its longest-lived radioactive member $_{93}\text{Np}^{237}$, with a half-life of 2 million years. This series was not observed to occur naturally because this half-life does not match the age of the earth, a few billion years. Three of these series are found naturally and terminate in stable isotopes of Pb. They have parents with half-lives of the order of a billion years. These long-lived parents not only preserve the series but each may produce a steady state of decay in its series of radioactive elements, just as a large mountain lake may feed a descending chain of lower lakes which retain their water for rather short times.

In such a state of radioactive equilibrium, the rates of decay of all isotopes in the series are equal. Hence,

$$-\frac{dN_1}{dt} = -\frac{dN_2}{dt} = -\frac{dN_3}{dt} = \cdots .$$

Because of (10.16),

$$k_1N_1 = k_2N_2 = k_3N_3 = \cdots .$$

In terms of half-lives, this becomes

$$\frac{N_1}{(t_{1/2})_1} = \frac{N_2}{(t_{1/2})_2} = \frac{N_3}{(t_{1/2})_3} = \cdots . \tag{10.19}$$

If one half-life is known, others in such a series can be found by a chemical analysis that fixes N_1, N_2, N_3, ... This was once the only way to determine extremely large half-lives. The probable error in determining a decay rate is approximately equal to the square root of the number of decay events measured. For a slowly decaying species this error is relatively large, while the error in chemical analysis is small.

Example 10.4. If the half-life of C^{14} is 5600 years, how many atoms of C^{14} are required to produce an average of five beta emissions per minute?

Since $t_{1/2} = 5600 \times 365 \times 24 \times 60$ min, it follows from (10.14) that

$$k_1 = \frac{0.693}{2.95 \times 10^9 \text{ min}} = 2.35 \times 10^{-10} \text{ min}^{-1} .$$

If $-\Delta N/\Delta t =$ five per minute, by (10.16)

$$N = \frac{-(\Delta N/\Delta t)}{k_1} = \frac{5.00}{2.35 \times 10^{-10}} = 2.13 \times 10^{10} \text{ atoms} .$$

Example 10.5. A piece of wood buried by a glacier had 25.6% as much C^{14} as a recently grown piece of wood. If the amount of C^{14} in the atmosphere was the same when the old wood died as it is now, when did the glacier overrun the forest?

By (10 18) with $N = 0.256N_o$,

$$t = \frac{t_{1/2}}{\ln 2} \ln \left(\frac{N_o}{N}\right) = \left(\frac{5600}{0.693}\right) 2.303 \log \left(\frac{1}{0.256}\right) = 11,000 \text{ years ago} .$$

10.5 Tracers

The use of radioactive tracers in medicine is well known because it is daily news. Artificially produced radioactive phosphorous is useful in locating brain tumors; radioactive iodine traces the path of iodine through the body and can be used to irradiate tissue where it tends to collect, as in cancers of the thyroid.

Radioactive tracers are useful in following the path of mn ute amounts of matter. Use of C^{14} has elucidated the path of carbon in and the processes of photosynthesis. Very low vapor pressures become measurable, it is possible to evaluate the completeness of precipitations and other analytical separations, slight adsorption on surfaces can be detected, and the quality of lubricants and extent of wear can be evaluated by noting the accumulation of radioactive metal in oil used to lubricate radioactive pistons and bearings. The mechanisms of chemical reactions can be determined and the rate of exchange of atoms between different species can be measured. For example, radioactive halogens rapidly react with solutions of like halide ions, for after a short time the halide ions become radioactive.

In order to follow the extent or mechanism of a reaction, unusual concentrations of stable isotopes are often of value. Analysis, however, must be by mass spectroscopy. A famous and early use of water labeled with extraordinary amounts of stable O^{18} established that many esters are hydrolyzed without breaking the alkyl-oxygen bond. That is,

$$R - \overset{\overset{\displaystyle O}{\|}}{C} - O - R' + H_2O^{18} \rightarrow R - \overset{\overset{\displaystyle O}{\|}}{C} - O^{18} - H + H - O - R'.$$

If the $R' - O$ bond had undergone fission, the resulting alcohol would have contained O^{18}.

Example 10.6. In the presence of perchloric acid at $27°C$, the following exchange reaction occurs in H_2O containing the usual normal amount of O^{18}:

$$Co(NH_3)_5H_2O^{18\,+++} + H_2O \rightleftharpoons Co(NH_3)_5H_2O^{+++} + H_2O^{18}.$$

At the beginning of an experiment the mole fraction of O^{18} in the complex ion was 0.006649, after 25.1 hr it was 0.004366, and at equilibrium it was 0.002192 [A. C. Rutenberg and H. Taube, *Journal of Chemical Physics*, **20**, 825 (1952)]. Calculate the first-order rate constant of this exchange reaction and the half-life of the complex ion in aqueous solution.

The amount of complex ion that can be observed to react is proportional to $0.006649 - 0.002192 = 0.004457$. The fraction of this that remains after 25.1 hr is

$$\frac{C}{C^o} = \frac{0.004366 - 0.002192}{0.006649 - 0.002192} = \frac{0.002174}{0.004457}.$$

By (10.11),

$$k_1 = \frac{2.303}{25.1} \log\left(\frac{4.457}{2.174}\right) = 2.86 \times 10^{-2} \text{ hr}^{-1}.$$

549

Then, by (10.14),

$$t_{1/2} = \frac{0.693}{k_1} = \frac{0.693}{2.86 \times 10^{-2}} = 24.2 \text{ hr}.$$

This calculation assumes that the reverse reaction is unimportant and that the concentration of H_2O^{18} in the solvent is constant during the reaction.

10.6 Unimolecular Decomposition

First-order reactions are generally of first order only in certain circumstances. Although Wilhelmy in 1850 found that the rate of hydrolysis of sugar is proportional to the concentration of unhydrolyzed sugar, the first-order rate constant really depends upon the acidity of the aqueous solution and upon the concentration of water. In dilute aqueous solutions, the concentration of water is so great that it is essentially undisturbed by the hydrolytic reaction. Even the homogeneous decomposition of a pure gaseous substance like azomethane may have a first-order rate constant that is a function of concentration or pressure of reactant. Such a functional dependence means, of course, that the process of decomposition is not as simple as radioactive decay.

Chemical reactions proceed at a finite rate because not all molecules of reactants are ready to react. Some of the factors that have long been recognized as important in controlling the rate of a reaction are the number of favorable collisions, the proper orientation of colliding molecules, and a suitable excitation or activation process to overcome chemical stability and inertia. In 1922, Lindemann explained how collisions might supply the extraordinary energy required to effect reaction. One of the latest modifications of the Lindemann mechanism is due to R. A. Marcus.[2] It proceeds thus:

$$\left.\begin{array}{l} A + M \underset{k_{2'}}{\overset{k_2}{\rightleftharpoons}} A^* + M \\[2ex] A^* \quad \overset{k_1{}^*}{\rightarrow} A^{\ddagger} \\[2ex] A^{\ddagger} \quad \overset{k_1}{\rightarrow} \text{products}. \end{array}\right\} \qquad (10.20)$$

Species A^* is an active, energized molecule of reactant A after it has collided with M, which may be A or another species. Active species A^* then becomes an activated complex $A^{\ddagger}$, that crucial state of A which leads to decomposition into products. Only when the energy of activation becomes available at the reactive site in A does A^* become $A^{\ddagger}$. In simple molecules A^* becomes $A^{\ddagger}$ rapidly, but in molecules of many atoms and many degrees of vibrational and rotational freedom, this transformation with rate constant k_1^* may proceed only slowly.

In order to express the mathematical rate law of this mechanism, it is necessary to distinguish the order of a reaction from its molecularity. The *order* of a reaction is the sum of the exponents on concentrations in the rate law like (10.6). The order of a reaction need not be integral. The *molecularity* of a reaction is, however, an integer and is equal to the number of reactant molecules that comprise the activated complex. The mechanism in (10.20) is unimolecular because $A^\ddagger$ consists of only one molecule of A.

The net forward rate of the first reaction of (10.20) is the rate of disappearance of A, namely,

$$-\frac{dC_A}{dt} = k_2 C_A C_M - k_2' C_{A*} C_M . \tag{10.21}$$

The forward rate is proportional to the concentrations of A and M as the mechanism requires, and the reverse rate $k_2' C_{A*} C_M$ is likewise proportional to the number of deactivating collisions of A* and M. When the decomposition proceeds at a steady rate, generally near its initial stages, the rate of change in the concentration of the intermediate A* will be zero. According to the mechanism (10.20), in the steady state

$$0 = \frac{dC_{A*}}{dt} = k_2 C_A C_M - k_2' C_{A*} C_M - k_1^* C_{A*} . \tag{10.22}$$

Solution of (10.22) for the concentration of A* yields

$$C_{A*} = \frac{k_2 C_A C_M}{k_1^* + k_2' C_M} . \tag{10.23}$$

With the aid of (10.22) and (10.23), (10.21) reads

$$-\frac{dC_A}{dt} = k_1^* C_{A*} = \left[\frac{k_1^* k_2 C_M}{k_1^* + k_2' C_M} \right] C_A$$

$$= k_1(C) C_A \tag{10.24}$$

where the unimolecular rate constant $k_1(C)$ is a function of C_M according to (10.25).

$$\frac{1}{k_1(C)} = \left(\frac{k_2'}{k_1^* k_2} \right) \left(1 + \frac{k_1^*}{k_2' C_M} \right) . \tag{10.25}$$

If $k_1^* \ll k_2' C_M$, $k_1(C)$ is independent of C_M, the decomposition is first order, and

$$k_1 = \frac{k_1^* k_2}{k_2'} . \tag{10.26}$$

This holds when deactivation by collision predominates over activation and decomposition. High pressures and many degrees of freedom in the reactant

A favor first-order decay, as in azomethane, acetone, ether, and N_2O_5 at atmospheric pressure. On the other hand, low pressures and few degrees of freedom in A favor $k_1^* \gg k_2' C_M$ so that (10.24) and (10.25) yield

$$-\frac{dC_A}{dt} = k_2 C_A C_M .$$
(10.27)

If M is A, the reaction is second order in A. The simple molecules HI, N_2O, NO, NOCl, NO_2, and CH_3CHO decompose by second-order reactions at atmospheric pressure. Great decreases in pressure frequently change the order of a decomposition reaction continuously from first to second. This happens for the dissociation of Br_2, decomposition of azomethane, isomerization of cyclopropane and cyclobutane, and many other reactions.

Example 10.7. If cyclopropane and propylene are equally effective as M in (10.20), find the limiting values at infinite and low pressure of the first- and second-order decay rate constants at 469.6°C for the isomerization of cyclopropane to propylene. The total pressures P and apparent first-order rate constants $k_1(P)$ are [T. S. Chambers and G. B. Kistiakowsky, *Journal of the American Chemical Society*, 56, 399 (1934)]:

P (mm Hg)	762.7	757.0	388.1	389.1	207.6	213.7	110.2	109.0
$k_1(P) \times 10^4$ (sec^{-1})	1.13	1.09	1.07	1.10	1.05	1.04	0.955	0.961

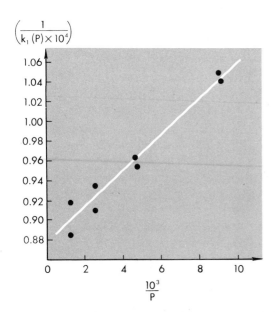

$\left(\dfrac{1}{k_1(P) \times 10^4}\right)$

Fig. 10.2. *Rate Constants for Isomerization of Cyclopropane.*

As (10.25) suggests, $[10^{-4}/k_1(P)]$ is plotted in Figure 10.2 as a linear function of $(10^3/P)$. The best straight line yields the intercept $k_1^{-1} = 0.88 \times 10^4$ at $P = \infty$; whence, $k_1(P = \infty) = 1.14 \times 10^{-4}$ sec^{-1}. The slope of the line in Figure 10.2 is 18.6×10^4 mm Hg sec. According to (10.25), the slope is k_2^{-1} so that

$$k_2 = \frac{10^{-4}}{18.6} = 5.38 \times 10^{-6} \text{ (mm Hg)}^{-1} \text{ sec}^{-1} .$$

Example 10.8. At what pressure is the isomerization of cyclopropane essentially a second-order reaction?

The reaction is second order if $k_1^* \gg k_2' p_M$. According to (10.26) and Example 10.7,

$$\frac{k_1^*}{k_2'} = \frac{k_1(P = \infty)}{k_2} = \frac{1.14 \times 10^{-4}}{5.38 \times 10^{-6}} = 21.2 \text{ mm Hg} .$$

Within 1%, $100 k_2' p_M = k_1^*$ and $p_M = k_1^*/100 k_2' = 0.212$ mm Hg. At pressures less than 0.212 mm Hg, the isomerization of cyclopropane would be essentially second order.

B. SECOND- AND THIRD-ORDER REACTIONS

10.7 Second-Order Reactions

Simple molecules like HI and CH_3CHO tend to decompose at low pressure in the absence of other substances by a second-order reaction. If C is the concentration of the species at time t and C^o is its initial concentration, and if the reaction is irreversible, the second-order rate law is

$$-\frac{dC}{dt} = k_2 C^2 \qquad (10.28)$$

$$-\int_{C^o}^{C} \frac{dC'}{C'^2} = k_2 \int_0^t dt'$$

$$\frac{1}{C} - \frac{1}{C^o} = k_2 t$$

$$\frac{C^o - C}{CC^o} = k_2 t \;. \qquad (10.29)$$

In terms of the formation of x moles l^{-1} of product from an initial concentration C^o by the reaction

$$\begin{array}{ccc} 2\,\text{A} & \longrightarrow & \text{D} + \cdots \\ C^o & t = 0 & 0 \\ C^o - 2x & t & x \end{array} \qquad (10.30)$$

it follows that if (10.30) states the mechanism,

$$\frac{dx}{dt} = k_2 (C^o - 2x)^2 \qquad (10.31)$$

$$\frac{1}{2} \int_0^x \frac{2\,dx'}{(C^o - 2x')^2} = k_2 \int_0^t dt'$$

$$\frac{1}{2}\left[\frac{1}{C^o - 2x} - \frac{1}{C^o} \right] = k_2 t$$

$$\frac{x}{C^o(C^o - 2x)} = k_2 t \qquad (10.32)$$

Since $C = C^o - 2x$, $x = (C^o - C)/2$ and (10.32) is

$$\frac{C^o - C}{2C^o C} = k_2 t \;. \qquad (10.33)$$

The value of k_2 in (10.33) is half as great as k_2 in (10.29) because D forms in (10.30) at half the rate at which A disappears. Equations like (10.29) and

(10.33) describe also the second-order reaction of different species if their initial concentrations are equal.

If $C_A^o \neq C_B^o$ in the second-order reaction

$$A + B \rightarrow D + \cdots \tag{10.34}$$

then

$$-\frac{dC_A}{dt} = -\frac{dC_B}{dt} = k_2 C_A C_B . \tag{10.35}$$

At any time, $dC_A = dC_B$ so that

$$\int_{C_A^o}^{C_A} dC_A' = \int_{C_B^o}^{C_B} dC_B'$$

$$C_A^o - C_A = C_B^o - C_B .$$

Since $C_A^o \neq C_B^o$, it follows that $C_A \neq C_B$ and

$$-\frac{dC_A}{dt} = k_2 C_A [C_A + (C_B^o - C_A^o)]$$

$$\int_{C_A^o}^{C_A} \frac{dC_A'}{C_A'[C_A' + (C_B^o - C_A^o)]} = -k_2 \int_0^t dt'$$

$$\left[\frac{1}{C_B^o - C_A^o}\right] \ln \left[\left(\frac{C_A}{C_A + (C_B^o - C_A^o)}\right)\left(\frac{C_B^o}{C_A^o}\right)\right] = -k_2 t$$

$$k_2 t = \left(\frac{1}{C_B^o - C_A^o}\right) \ln \left(\frac{C_B C_A^o}{C_A C_B^o}\right) . \tag{10.36}$$

The half-life $t_{1/2}$ of a second-order reaction is found from (10.29) if $C = C^o/2$ thus:

$$t_{1/2} = \frac{C^o - (C^o/2)}{k_2 C^o (C^o/2)} = \frac{1}{k_2 C^o} . \tag{10.37}$$

If the half-life of a reaction is inversely proportional to the initial concentration of a reactant, the reaction is second-order in time with respect to that species, all other concentrations being constant in k_2. If observed values of t, C, and C^o yield a constant value of k_2 in (10.29) or (10.36), or if graphing a suitable function of concentrations against time produces a straight line with slope k_2, the reaction is termed second-order in time. The best way, however, to show that a reaction is second-order with respect to a certain species is to show that (10.28) holds for small finite increments in C and t. That is,

$$\left(-\frac{\Delta C}{\Delta t}\right) = k_2 C^2$$

$$\log\left(-\frac{\Delta C}{\Delta t}\right) = \log k_2 + 2 \log C .$$

If the slope of the graph of $\log\left(-\dfrac{\Delta C}{\Delta t}\right)$ vs. $\log C$ is two, the reaction is second order. The value of the ordinate $\log\left(-\dfrac{\Delta C}{\Delta t}\right)$ at $C = 1$ is $\log k_2$.

Some second-order reactions of the type (10.30) are these:

$$2\,NO_2 \rightarrow 2\,NO + O_2$$
$$2\,NOCl \rightarrow 2\,NO + Cl_2$$
$$2\,HI \rightarrow H_2 + I_2 \,.$$

Some second-order reactions of the type (10.34) in which the rate is first-order in each reactant are these:

$$N_2 + O_2 \rightarrow 2\,NO$$
$$H_2 + I_2 \rightarrow 2\,HI$$

and the acid or basic saponification of many esters.

Example 10.9. If $k_2 = 4.00 \times 10^{-6}$ l mole^{-1} sec^{-1} at $600°K$ for the decomposition of HI according to the equation

$$-\frac{dC_{HI}}{dt} = k_2 C_{HI}^2$$

how many molecules of HI decompose per second at $600°K$ at atmospheric pressure if the reverse reaction that forms HI is negligible?

At 1 atm at $600°K$,

$$C_{HI} = \frac{n}{V} = \frac{P}{RT} = \frac{1.00}{0.082 \times 600} = 2.03 \times 10^{-2} \text{ mole l}^{-1}\,.$$

According to (10.28),

$$-\frac{dC}{dt} = 4.00 \times 10^{-6}\,(2.03 \times 10^{-2})^2$$

$$= 16.5 \times 10^{-10} \text{ mole l}^{-1} \text{ sec}^{-1}\,.$$

Hence,

$$-\frac{dN}{dt} = 16.5 \times 10^{-10} \times 0.602 \times 10^{24}$$

$$= 9.9 \times 10^{14} \text{ molecules l}^{-1} \text{ sec}^{-1}\,.$$

Example 10.10. At $600°K$, $k_2 = 6.3 \times 10^2$ ml mole^{-1} sec^{-1} for the reaction

$$2\,NO_2 \rightarrow 2\,NO + O_2\,.$$

At $600°K$, how long will it take for one-tenth of a sample of NO_2 at 400 mm Hg to decompose by this reaction?

If $C = 0.900C^{\circ}$, then by (10.29),

$$t = \frac{C^{\circ} - C}{k_2 C^{\circ} C} = \frac{0.100 C^{\circ}}{k_2 C^{\circ}(0.900 C^{\circ})} = \frac{1}{9k_2 C^{\circ}}\,.$$

But

$$C^o = \frac{P}{RT} = \frac{(400/760)}{82.06 \times 600} = 1.07 \times 10^{-5} \text{ mole ml}^{-1}$$

hence,

$$t = \frac{1}{9 \times 6.3 \times 10^2 \times 1.07 \times 10^{-5}} = 16.5 \text{ sec}.$$

Example 10.11. The reaction

$$2 \text{ NO}_2 + \text{F}_2 \rightarrow 2 \text{ NO}_2\text{F}$$

is first-order with respect to F_2 and NO_2. When

$$-\frac{dC_{\text{F}_2}}{dt} = k_2 C_{\text{F}_2} C_{\text{NO}_2}$$

$k_2 = 3.40 \times 10^4$ cc mole^{-1} sec^{-1} at 25°C [Calculated from R. L. Perrine and H. S. Johnston, *Journal of Chemical Physics*, 21, 2202 (1953)]. If F_2 initially at 2.00 mm Hg reacts with NO_2 initially at 5.00 mm Hg in a rigid vessel at 25°C, what will be their pressures and the pressure of NO_2F after 30.0 sec?

At $T = 298.2$, the initial concentrations are

$$C_{\text{F}_2}^o = \frac{p_{\text{F}_2}^o}{RT} = \frac{(2.00/760)}{82.06 \times 298.2} = 1.075 \times 10^{-7} \text{ mole cc}^{-1}$$

$$C_{\text{NO}_2}^o = \frac{p_{\text{NO}_2}^o}{RT} = \frac{5.00/760}{82.06 \times 298.2} = 2.69 \times 10^{-7} \text{ mole cc}^{-1}.$$

With $t = 30.0$ and $C_{\text{NO}_2}^o - C_{\text{F}_2}^o = 1.62 \times 10^{-7}$ mole cc^{-1} in (10.36),

$$3.40 \times 10^4 \times 30.0 = \frac{2.303}{1.62 \times 10^{-7}} \log \left[\frac{C_{\text{NO}_2} \times 1.075 \times 10^{-7}}{C_{\text{F}_2} \times 2.69 \times 10^{-7}} \right]$$

$$\log \left(\frac{C_{\text{NO}_2}}{C_{\text{F}_2}} \right) = 7.18 \times 10^{-2} + \log \left(\frac{2.69}{1.075} \right) = 0.471$$

hence,

$$C_{\text{NO}_2} = 2.96 \, C_{\text{F}_2}.$$

According to the reaction, at time t

$$2\text{NO}_2 \quad + \quad \text{F}_2 \quad \rightarrow \quad 2 \text{ NO}_2\text{F}.$$
$$C_{\text{NO}_2}^o - 2x \qquad C_{\text{F}_2}^o - x \qquad 2x$$
$$p_{\text{NO}_2}^o - 2y \qquad p_{\text{F}_2}^o - y \qquad 2y$$

Since $p_{\text{NO}_2} = 2.96 \, p_{\text{F}_2}$ after 30.0 sec in the rigid vessel,

$$p_{\text{NO}_2}^o - 2y = 2.96(p_{\text{F}_2}^o - y)$$
$$5.00 - 2y = 2.96(2.00 - y)$$
$$y = 0.96.$$

Whence

$$p_{\text{F}_2} = p_{\text{F}_2}^o - y = 2.00 - 0.96 = 1.04 \text{ mm Hg}$$
$$p_{\text{NO}_2} = p_{\text{NO}_2}^o - 2y = 5.00 - 1.92 = 3.08 \text{ mm Hg}$$
$$p_{\text{NO}_2\text{F}} = 2y = 2 \times 0.96 = 1.92 \text{ mm Hg}.$$

10.8 Third-Order Reactions

A third-order trimolecular gaseous reaction appears to require a triple collision. Since triple collisions are very rare, such reactions are observed only when all possible uni- and bimolecular reactions are very slow. Most known third-order gaseous reactions are of the type

$$2\,A \quad + \quad B \quad \rightarrow \quad D + \cdots . \qquad (10.38)$$

$$\begin{array}{cccc} C_A^o & C_B^o & t = 0 & 0 \\ C_A^o - 2x & C_B^o - x & t & x \end{array}$$

The differential equation for this reaction,

$$\frac{dx}{dt} = \frac{1}{2}\left(-\frac{dC_A}{dt}\right) = -\frac{dC_B}{dt} = k_3(C_A^o - 2x)^2(C_B^o - x) \qquad (10.39)$$

can be integrated whether or not $C_A^o = C_B^o$.

Reactions of NO with O_2, H_2, Cl_2, and Br_2 are perhaps third order according to the mechanism

$$2\,NO + X_2 \rightarrow 2\,NOX . \qquad (10.40)$$

Recombination of species X is a common kind of third-order gaseous reaction.

$$2\,X + M \rightarrow X_2 + M^* . \qquad (10.41)$$

If the third body M is not present, the hypothetical complex X_2^* of fleeting existence tends to dissociate within one vibration of the newly formed bond. For if the species X is an atom, there is no way for the species X_2^* to dissipate its vibrational energy. On the other hand, if the fragments X are large with many degrees of freedom, the vibrational energy of X_2^* can wander about the molecule in these other degrees of freedom until a collision withdraws enough energy to stabilize the newly formed molecule.

The proposed mechanism is

$$\left. \begin{array}{c} X + X \underset{k_1^*}{\overset{k_2}{\rightleftharpoons}} X_2^* \\[2mm] X_2^* + M \xrightarrow{k_2^*} X_2 + M^* . \end{array} \right\} \qquad (10.42)$$

This mechanism may yield either second- or third-order kinetics. The rate of decay of X is

$$-\frac{dC_X}{dt} = k_2 C_X^2 - k_1^* C^* \qquad (10.43)$$

and the rate of formation of X_2^* is zero in the steady state so that

$$0 = \frac{dC^*}{dt} = k_2 C_X^2 - k_1^* C^* - k_2^* C^* C_M . \qquad (10.44)$$

557

Solution of (10.44) for C^* and substitution in (10.43) yields

$$-\frac{dC_X}{dt} = k_2 C_X^2 - k_1^* \left[\frac{k_2 C_X^2}{k_1^* + k_2^* C_M}\right]$$

$$= k_2 C_X^2 \left[1 - \frac{k_1^*}{k_1^* + k_2^* C_M}\right]$$

$$= \frac{k_2 k_2^* C_X^2 C_M}{k_1^* + k_2^* C_M}. \tag{10.45}$$

If $k_1^* \gg k_2^* C_M$, X_2^* is more likely to dissociate than to suffer a stabilizing collision with M. According to (10.14), its half-life $t_{1/2}^*$ would be

$$t_{1/2}^* = \frac{\ln 2}{k_1^*}$$

a time that decreases as k_1^* increases. Equation (10.45) then yields the third-order law

$$-\frac{dC_X}{dt} = \left(\frac{k_2 k_2^*}{k_1^*}\right) C_X^2 C_M . \tag{10.46}$$

The formation of a coordinate covalent bond between BF_3 and alkyl amines of low molecular weight has a mechanism like (10.42).[3] If A represents the amine, the mechanism is

$$\left.\begin{array}{c} A + BF_3 \underset{k_1\bullet}{\overset{k_2}{\rightleftharpoons}} A.BF_3^* \\[2mm] A.BF_3^* + M \overset{k_2\bullet}{\rightarrow} A.BF_3 + M^* \end{array}\right\} \tag{10.47}$$

where M is a diluent gas that carries away energy from the excited adduct $A.BF_3^*$. The life-time of this hot adduct is proportional to the number of its vibrational degrees of freedom. Since $A.BF_3^*$ is longer-lived than X_2^*, k_1^* no longer dominates $k_2^* C_M$, especially when much M is present. The analogue of (10.45) reads

$$-\frac{dC_A}{dt} = \frac{k_2 k_2^* C_A C_{BF_3} C_M}{k_1^* + k_2^* C_M} = k C_A C_{BF_3} \tag{10.48}$$

where

$$\frac{1}{k} = \frac{1}{k_2} + \frac{k_1^*}{k_2 k_2^* C_M}. \tag{10.49}$$

The pseudoconstant k depends upon C_M and causes the over-all order to vary from second to third. When k_1^* is small or C_M is large, k approaches k_2 and the mechanism becomes second order.

10.9 Determination of Order

The order of a reaction can be established in several ways:

1. If the half-life of a reactant, the time for half of it to disappear, is independent of the initial concentration, the reaction is first order in time. If the half-life is proportional to initial concentration, it is zero order; if inversely proportional to initial concentration, second; and so on.

2. If experimental values for time and concentration yield constant rate constants k in an assumed integrated rate law like (10.8), (10.11), (10.29), or (10.36), and if it can be established that this does not prejudice the interpretation, then the order of the reaction with respect to time is established.

3. If the logarithm of rate is plotted against the logarithm of concentration, the slope is the order of reaction with respect to concentration. This method is particularly fruitful with a great excess of all but one reactant. For example, in the third-order reaction

$$\begin{array}{cccc} 2\,A & + & B & \to & D + \cdots \quad (10.38) \\ C_A^o & & C_B^o & t = 0 & 0 \\ C_A^o - 2x & C_B^o - x & t & x \end{array}$$

if $C_A^o \gg 2x$, the differential equation becomes

$$\frac{dx}{dt} = k_3(C_A^o - 2x)^2(C_B^o - x) \quad (10.39)$$

$$\approx k_1(C_B^o - x)$$

where the first-order rate constant is $k_1 = k_3(C_A^o - 2x)^2 \approx k_3(C_A^o)^2$, almost a constant. Adding an excess of a reagent thus reduces the number of variables in the rate law. If a great excess cannot be added, the same sort of reduction in variables can be effected in the first stages of a reaction by holding the concentrations of all but one reactant constant during several different experiments.

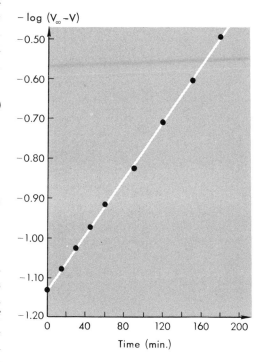

Fig. 10.3. *Hydrolysis of Methyl Acetate.*

Example 10.12. Although the rate of hydrolysis of methyl acetate depends upon the concentrations of acid and water, by effecting hydrolysis in strongly acidic aqueous medium, these concentrations can be assumed constant. From the data below, show that the reaction is first order in time with respect to methyl acetate concentration. The extent of reaction was followed by titrating the total amount of acid in equal aliquots. Here V is the volume of base used per aliquot.

t (min)	0	15	30	45	60	90	120	150	180	∞
V (ml)	24.58	26.12	27.47	28.68	29.87	31.40	32.94	34.03	34.93	38.06

If the reaction

$$H_2O + CH_3 - \overset{\overset{\text{O}}{\|}}{C} - O - CH_3 \rightarrow CH_3 - \overset{\overset{\text{O}}{\|}}{C} - O - H + H - O - CH_3$$

is essentially complete at $t = \infty$, then $V_\infty - V$ is proportional to the concentration of ester at time t. By (10.10),

$$-\int \frac{dC}{C} = k_1 \int dt$$

$$-\ln C = k_1 t + \text{const.}$$

$$-\log (V_\infty - V) = \frac{k_1 t}{2.303} + \text{const.}$$

The logarithms of $V_\infty - V$ are plotted as a function of time in Figure 10.3. Since the slope is constant, the reaction is first order in ester.

C. COMPLEX REACTIONS

10.10 Reversible Reactions

In the early stages of reaction, the opposing reverse reaction is frequently negligible. It often happens also that ΔG^o is less than zero for the forward reaction so that the equilibrium constant is great enough to assure essentially complete reaction. Account has already been taken of reverse reactions in the mechanisms of unimolecular reactions (10.20) and recombination reactions (10.42).

The stoichiometric equation for the net reaction may not indicate the molecularity or order of a reaction. The decomposition of acetaldehyde may be either first or second order:

$$CH_3CHO \rightarrow CH_4 + CO .$$

The reaction

$$2 NO_2 + F_2 \rightarrow 2 NO_2F$$

is second order. But if the balanced net stoichiometric reaction does indicate the mechanism, as it does for

$$H_2 + I_2 \underset{k_2'}{\overset{k_2}{\rightleftharpoons}} 2 HI \qquad (10.50)$$

then it is easy to formulate the rate equation for any extent of reaction.

For (10.50),

$$-\frac{dC_{H_2}}{dt} = -\frac{dC_{I_2}}{dt} = \frac{1}{2}\frac{dC_{HI}}{dt} = k_2 C_{H_2} C_{I_2} - k_2' C_{HI}^2 \,.$$

At equilibrium, when the rate is zero,

$$0 = k_2 C_{H_2} C_{I_2} - k_2' C_{HI}^2$$

$$K_c = \frac{C_{HI}^2}{C_{H_2} C_{I_2}} = \frac{k_2}{k_2'} \,. \tag{10.51}$$

Indeed, for any reaction whose equation describes its mechanism, the equilibrium constant is the ratio of forward rate constant to reverse rate constant.

Example 10.13. If $2k_2' = 4.00 \times 10^{-6}$ l mole^{-1} sec^{-1} at 600°K for the decomposition of HI in the equation

$$-\frac{dC_{HI}}{dt} = 2k_2' C_{HI}^2$$

what is the rate constant k_2 for the formation of HI? At 600°K, $K_c = 73.0$ for (10.50). By (10.51),

$$k_2 = k_2' K_c = 2.00 \times 10^{-6} \times 73.0 = 1.46 \times 10^{-4} \text{ l mole}^{-1} \text{ sec}^{-1} \,.$$

10.11 Consecutive and Competing Reactions

The rate of formation of a final product sometimes differs from the rate of disappearance of a reactant. Two common reasons are competing reactions that lead to more than one product or a series of consecutive reactions that generate intermediate species whose concentrations rise during the early stages of reaction and finally fall to zero. A particularly simple example of consecutive reactions is the transformation of A into C via two first-order reactions, with B as intermediate.

$$A \xrightarrow{k_{1(1)}} B \xrightarrow{k_{1(2)}} C \,. \tag{10.52}$$

$$C_A^o - x \qquad x - y \qquad y$$

The first-order rates are

$$\frac{dx}{dt} = k_{1(1)}(C_A^o - x) \tag{10.53}$$

$$\frac{dy}{dt} = k_{1(2)}(x - y) \,. \tag{10.54}$$

These simultaneous differential equations can be solved for x and y as follows. As in (10.13),

$$\int_0^x \frac{dx'}{(C_A^o - x')} = k_{1(1)} \int_0^t dt'$$

$$\ln\left(\frac{C_A^o}{C_A^o - x}\right) = k_{1(1)}t$$

$$\frac{x}{C_A^o} = (1 - e^{-k_{1(1)}t}) . \tag{10.55}$$

Elimination of x from (10.54) with (10.55) yields

$$\frac{dy}{dt} = k_{1(2)}\{C_A^o[1 - e^{-k_{1(1)}t}] - y\}$$

$$\frac{dy}{dt} + k_{1(2)}y = C_A^o k_{1(2)}[1 - e^{-k_{1(1)}t}] . \tag{10.56}$$

Multiplication by $e^{k_{1(2)}t}$, an integrating factor, transforms the left-hand member of (10.56) into an exact derivative, namely,

$$\frac{d}{dt}[ye^{k_{1(2)}t}] .$$

Upon integration with respect to t with $y = 0$ at $t = 0$, (10.56) becomes

$$\left(\frac{y}{C_A^o}\right)e^{k_{1(2)}t} = \int_{t'=0}^{t'=t} [1 - e^{-k_{1(1)}t'}] \, d[e^{k_{1(2)}t'}]$$

$$= [e^{k_{1(2)}t} - 1] - \left[\frac{k_{1(2)}}{k_{1(2)} - k_{1(1)}}\right] \int_{t'=0}^{t'=t} d\{e^{[k_{1(2)} - k_{1(1)}]t'}\}$$

$$= [e^{k_{1(2)}t} - 1] - \left[\frac{k_{1(2)}}{k_{1(2)} - k_{1(1)}}\right]\{e^{[k_{1(2)} - k_{1(1)}]t} - 1\} .$$

Whence,

$$\frac{y}{C_A^o} = [1 - e^{-k_{1(2)}t}] + \left(\frac{k_{1(2)}}{k_{1(2)} - k_{1(1)}}\right)[e^{-k_{1(2)}t} - e^{-k_{1(1)}t}]$$

$$= \frac{k_{1(2)}[1 - e^{-k_{1(1)}t}] - k_{1(1)}[1 - e^{-k_{1(2)}t}]}{[k_{1(2)} - k_{1(1)}]} . \tag{10.57}$$

Figure 10.4 shows how the concentrations of A, B, and C vary with time if $k_{1(2)} = 2k_{1(1)}$. Although A decays according to simple first-order kinetics, the formation of B delays the formation of C. The steady-state approximation corresponds to the maximum concentration of B. If this maximum is broad and flat, as it often is in more complex reactions, the steady state is a good approximation. It is, however, preceded by an induction period similar to the one that in Figure 10.4 precedes the maximum in B.

Competing reactions are common in organic syntheses where isomeric products abound. Let the competing reactions be similar second-order reactions such as

$$
\left.\begin{array}{c}
\mathrm{A} + \mathrm{B} \xrightarrow{k_{2(1)}} \mathrm{D} + \cdots \\
\mathrm{A} + \mathrm{B} \xrightarrow{k_{2(2)}} \mathrm{E} + \cdots .
\end{array}\right\} \qquad (10.58)
$$

If x moles of D and y moles of E have formed by time t from reactants originally at concentrations C_A^o and C_B^o, then

$$
\frac{dx}{dt} = k_{2(1)}[C_A^o - (x + y)][C_B^o - (x + y)]
$$

$$
\frac{dy}{dt} = k_{2(2)}[C_A^o - (x + y)][C_B^o - (x + y)].
$$

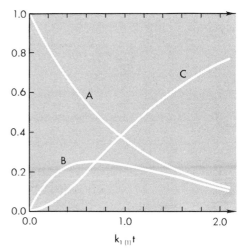

Concentration

Fig. 10.4. *Consecutive First-Order Reactions.*

If these are the only reactions to use A and B, the rate of disappearance of A or B is the sum of these rates. The ratio of D to E is

$$
\frac{dx}{dy} = \frac{k_{2(1)}}{k_{2(2)}}. \qquad (10.59)
$$

A successful synthesis often involves adjusting experimental conditions to obtain as favorable a set of rates as possible.

10.12 Reaction Mechanisms

The order of a reaction is best thought of as an empirically observed exponent. The molecularity is more remote from experiment inasmuch as it involves an interpretation of observed data in terms of a mechanism or series of reactions that seem plausible. The importance of a suitable mechanism is paramount, however, in really understanding reaction rates. On the other hand, mechanisms are so varied and sometimes appear even to be so much a matter of personal taste that any attempt at generality is gross simplification. Rather than attempt a survey here, only one mechanism is discussed in the hope that it presents typical problems and that "a picture is worth a thousand words." The particular example chosen is

$$2 \, NO_2 + F_2 \rightarrow 2 \, NO_2F \, . \tag{10.60}$$

It has been explained in detail in the literature.[4]

At low pressures, the reaction is first order in both F_2 and NO_2. The mechanism (10.47) does not apply because at low pressures it requires third-order kinetics. The most reasonable initial reaction is then a slow, rate-limiting, bimolecular one,

$$NO_2 + F_2 \xrightarrow{k_2} NO_2F + F \, . \tag{10.61}$$

The fluorine atoms thus generated can be removed in several ways, namely,

$$F + NO_2 + M \xrightarrow{k_3} NO_2F + M^* \tag{10.62}$$

$$F + F + M \xrightarrow{k_3'} F_2 + M^* \tag{10.63}$$

$$F + NO_2F \xrightarrow{k_2'} NO_2 + F_2 \tag{10.64}$$

or by side reactions. Species M is any third body of the reaction. The purpose of this discussion is to show that one or two of these reactions are of minor importance.

Reaction (10.64) is merely the reverse of the initial reaction (10.61), but (10.62) and (10.63) may be either second or third order; for each of the latter is a bimolecular recombination in the presence of a third body M that removes energy. At the low pressures used to establish the second-order rate law for the over-all reaction (10.60), only third-order kinetics are suitable for (10.62) or (10.63). If (10.63) is excluded, the steady-state condition for F yields

$$\frac{dC_F}{dt} = 0 = k_2 C_{NO_2} C_{F_2} - k_2' C_F C_{NO_2F} - k_3 C_F C_{NO_2} C_M \, .$$

Solution for C_F and substitution in the equation

$$\frac{dC_{NO_2F}}{dt} = k_2 C_{NO_2} C_{F_2} - k_2' C_F C_{NO_2F} + k_3 C_F C_{NO_2} C_M$$

yields for the rate

$$\frac{1}{2} \left(\frac{dC_{NO_2F}}{dt} \right) = k_3 C_{NO_2} C_M \left[\frac{k_2 C_{NO_2} C_{F_2}}{k_2' C_{NO_2F} + k_3 C_{NO_2} C_M} \right] .$$

If $k_3 C_{NO_2} C_M \gg k_2' C_{NO_2F}$, the rate is $\frac{1}{2}(dC_{NO_2F}/dt) = k_2 C_{NO_2} C_{F_2}$, as observed. The reaction is not slowed by large values of C_{NO_2F} so that this condition means that k_2' is very small and (10.64) is negligible. That is, (10.61) and (10.62) alone are sufficient to explain the observed order of the over-all reaction. If (10.63) competes with (10.62) and (10.64), there results a complex rate expression that does not fit observations.

If (10.63) is the only means of destroying F atoms,

$$\frac{dC_F}{dt} = k_2 C_{NO_2} C_{F_2} - k_3' C_F^2 C_M$$

and

$$\frac{1}{2}\left(\frac{dC_{NO_2F}}{dt}\right) = \tfrac{1}{2} k_2 C_{NO_2} C_{F_2} .$$

Although this last expression satisfies the rate law, the concentration of F is not observed to increase with time so that $k_3' C_F^2 C_M$ must equal $k_2 C_{NO_2} C_{F_2}$. Instead of showing that the third-order recombination is much slower than the rate of the over-all reaction so that $k_3' C_F^2 C_M \neq k_2 C_{NO_2} C_{F_2}$, it is more convenient to show that (10.62) is faster than (10.63). The ratio of their rates is

$$\frac{k_3 C_F C_{NO_2} C_M}{k_3' C_F^2 C_M} \approx \frac{C_{NO_2}}{C_F}$$

for M is probably equally effective as third body in both reactions and k_3 is at least as great as k_3'. Indeed, k_3 should be greater than k_3' because NO$_2$F* has more degrees of vibrational freedom than F_2^* and should therefore be longer-lived. That is, (10.62) should become second order at lower pressures than (10.63). Since NO$_2$ is present in concentrations typical of a reactant, while F is a minor species generated by the reaction, this ratio greatly exceeds unity and (10.63) is of minor importance. The most reasonable mechanism is, therefore, simply

$$NO_2 + F_2 \xrightarrow{slow} NO_2F + F$$
$$F + NO_2 + M \xrightarrow{fast} NO_2F + M^* .$$

D. EFFECTS OF TEMPERATURE, SOLVENTS, AND RADIATION

10.13 Rate as a Function of Temperature

Although van't Hoff had proposed that the logarithm of a rate constant k_n should depend upon absolute temperature in the way that an equilibrium constant does, it was Arrhenius in 1889 who showed with the data available to him that

$$k_n = se^{-(\Delta H_a/RT)} . \qquad (10.65)$$

He found s and ΔH_a to be independent of temperature, and over modest

565

ranges of temperature they are indeed practically constant. Accordingly, if independent of T,

$$\ln k_n = \ln s - \frac{\Delta H_a}{RT} \tag{10.66}$$

$$\frac{d \ln k_n}{dT} = \frac{\Delta H_a}{RT^2}. \tag{10.67}$$

Everyone knows that reactions generally increase in rate as T increases, and therefore ΔH_a is greater than zero. Having the dimensions of energy, ΔH_a is called the *activation energy*, the energy that must be acquired by reactants in order to overcome their chemical inertia and achieve that critical intermediate state which leads to products.

Definite integration of (10.67) between temperature T_1 at which the rate constant is $k_{n(1)}$ and temperature T_2 at which the rate constant is $k_{n(2)}$ yields (10.68) if ΔH_a is independent of T.

$$\int_{k_{n(1)}}^{k_{n(2)}} d(\ln k_n) = \frac{\Delta H_a}{R} \int_{T_1}^{T_2} \frac{dT}{T^2}$$

$$\ln \left(\frac{k_{n(2)}}{k_{n(1)}} \right) = \frac{\Delta H_a(T_2 - T_1)}{RT_1T_2}. \tag{10.68}$$

Because the precision of observed rate constants is generally less than that of vapor pressures or equilibrium constants, (10.66) and (10.68) are quite suitable, especially over small ranges of temperature. There is no reason to expect, however, that ΔH_a be really independent of temperature. Like any increase in enthalpy, it varies with T in accord with Kirkhoff's law.

If the activation energy is ascribed to a violent bimolecular collision, the exponential factor in (10.65) represents the fraction of collisions with energy in excess of ΔH_a and s is the total number of double collisions. If so, s should vary as $\sqrt{T}$, and it often does for bimolecular reactions. Simple collision theory does not provide a suitable method of predicting rate constants from microscopic data such as molecular structure; for it cannot predict with suitable precision the efficiency of collisions, the probability that a favorable orientation is achieved at impact, or the effective collision diameter of a molecule.

A semithermodynamic approach is more fruitful. If H_1 is the absolute enthalpy of reactants and if H_a is the absolute enthalpy of the intermediate state of extraordinary energy that lies between reactants and products, then

$$\Delta H_a = H_a - H_1. \tag{10.69}$$

When the increase in enthalpy for the over-all reaction is

$$\Delta H = H_2 - H_1 \tag{10.70}$$

where H_2 is the absolute enthalpy of products, then

$$\Delta H = H_2 - H_a + H_a - H_1$$
$$= -\Delta H_a' + \Delta H_a . \tag{10.71}$$

In (10.71),

$$\Delta H_a' = H_a - H_2 \tag{10.72}$$

and is the increase in enthalpy on going from products to intermediate state. It therefore is the heat of activation of the reverse reaction.

This semithermodynamic approach is in accord with the results of equilibrium thermodynamics. In general, the forward and reverse rate constants k_n and k_n' are related to the equilibrium constant K by (10.73).

$$K = \frac{k_n}{k_n'} . \tag{10.73}$$

This, together with (10.67) and (10.71), yields the familiar thermodynamic result

$$\frac{d \ln K}{dT} = \frac{d \ln k_n}{dT} - \frac{d \ln k_n'}{dT} = \frac{\Delta H_a}{RT^2} - \frac{\Delta H_a'}{RT^2} = \frac{\Delta H}{RT^2} .$$

Similarly, if G_1^o, G_a^o, and G_2^o represent the absolute standard free energies of initial, intermediate, and final states,

$$\Delta G^o = G_2^o - G_1^o = G_a^o - G_1^o + G_2^o - G_a^o$$
$$= \Delta G_a^o - \Delta G_a^{o'} . \tag{10.74}$$

In view of (10.73) and the well-known relation

$$K = e^{-(\Delta G^o/RT)}$$

it follows that

$$\frac{k_n}{k_n'} = \frac{e^{-(\Delta G_a^o RT)}}{e^{-(\Delta G_a^{o'}/RT)}} . \tag{10.75}$$

With a factor A to adjust dimensions of concentration and time, this yields

$$k_n = s e^{-(\Delta H_a^o/RT)} = A e^{-(\Delta G_a^o/RT)}$$
$$= A e^{\Delta S_a^o/R} e^{-(\Delta H_a^o/RT)} \tag{10.76}$$

and

$$s = A e^{\Delta S_a^o/R} . \tag{10.77}$$

The familiar ideas concerning entropy and disorder can often be applied in a qualitative way in interpreting trends in s for related reactions or in explaining values of s that differ greatly from the expected collision rate for simple spheres. Perhaps the intermediate state is a tightly knit complex resulting from a collision or perhaps its formation is sterically hindered, the direction and relative orientations of reactants being of critical importance. Such an intermediate state is rather organized and rather unlikely relative to reactants so that ΔS_a^o would be expected to be less than zero. The effective frequency s of fruitful collisions would then be less than A, the total frequency. On the other hand, if the intermediate state greatly resembles in order and organization its reactant precursor, ΔS_a^o should be near zero and $s = A$. Or, finally, if the intermediate state is loosely bound or tending toward dissociation, ΔS_a^o should reflect this increase in disorder in being greater than zero. If so, s exceeds the usual collision frequency A. Such qualitative ideas are often of mnemonic but seldom of quantitative value.

Example 10.14. Calculate the activation energy ΔH_a for the decomposition of HI if k_2 is 3.95×10^{-6} l mole^{-1} sec^{-1} at 321.4°C and is 1.07×10^{-6} l mole^{-1} sec^{-1} at 300.0°C, where

$$- \frac{dC_{HI}}{dt} = k_2 C_{HI}^2 .$$

[Data from G. B. Kistiakowsky, *Journal of the American Chemical Society,* **50**, 2315 (1928).]

Since $T_2 - T_1 = 594.6 - 573.2 = 21.4$°C, (10.68) yields

$$\Delta H_a = \frac{RT_1 T_2}{T_2 - T_1} \ln \left(\frac{k_{2(2)}}{k_{2(1)}} \right)$$

$$= \frac{1.987 \times 573.2 \times 594.6 \times 2.303}{21.4} \log \left(\frac{3.95}{1.07} \right)$$

$$= 41,300 \text{ cal mole}^{-1} .$$

Example 10.15. If the only reaction is decomposition of HI, how long will it take for 1% pure HI to decompose at 1 atm at 400°C? Use data from Example 10.14.

By (10.68), the rate constant k_2 at 400°C is found thus:

$$\ln \left(\frac{k_2}{3.95 \times 10^{-6}} \right) = \frac{41,300 \, (673 - 595)}{1.987 \times 673 \times 595} = 4.05$$

$$k_2 = 57.2 \times 3.95 \times 10^{-6} = 2.26 \times 10^{-4} .$$

After 1% decomposition, $C = 0.99 C^o$ and, by (10.29),

$$\frac{C^o - 0.99 C^o}{C^o (0.99 C^o)} = 2.26 \times 10^{-4} t$$

$$t = \frac{44.8}{C^o} .$$

Since

$$C^o = \frac{P}{RT} = \frac{1.00}{0.08205 \times 673}$$

$$t = 44.8 \times 0.08205 \times 673 = 2470 \text{ sec} .$$

A simpler method of solution begins with (10.28) and $-\Delta C = C^o \times 10^{-2}$ for 1% decomposition.

$$t = -\frac{\Delta C}{k_2 C^2} = \frac{C^o \times 10^{-2}}{2.26 \times 10^{-4} \times (C^o)^2} = \frac{0.08205 \times 673 \times 10^{-2}}{2.26 \times 10^{-4}} = 2440 \text{ sec} .$$

Example 10.16. With data from Example 10.14, calculate the characteristic collision diameter of HI in its decomposition at 321.4°C.

If C_{HI} is the number of moles of HI per milliliter, the number of molecules of HI that decompose per liter per second is $Nk_2(C_{HI} \times 10^3)^2$. The number that decompose per milliliter per second is therefore $Nk_2 C_{HI}^2 \times 10^3$. Since two molecules of HI decompose together in one collision according to the reaction $2\ HI \rightarrow H_2 + I_2$, it follows that

$$Nk_2 C_{HI}^2 \times 10^3 = 2Z_2 e^{-(\Delta H_a / RT)}$$

where Z_2 is the total number of bimolecular collisions of HI per milliliter per second. By (1.91),

$$Z_2 = 2\sigma^2 (NC_{HI})^2 \left(\frac{\pi RT}{M}\right)^{1/2} .$$

Whence, with cgs units everywhere except in the exponential and k_2,

$$\sigma^2 = \frac{k_2 \times 10^3}{4N} \left(\frac{M}{\pi RT}\right)^{1/2} e^{\Delta H_a / RT}$$

$$= \frac{3.95 \times 10^{-6} \times 10^3}{4 \times 6.02 \times 10^{23}} \left(\frac{128}{\pi \times 8.314 \times 10^7 \times 595}\right)^{1/2} e^{41,300/(1.987 \times 595)}$$

$$= 16.4 \times 10^{-28} \times (8.24 \times 10^{-10})^{1/2} \times 1.45 \times 10^{15}$$

$$= 68.3 \times 10^{-18} \text{ cm}^2$$

$$\sigma = 0.827 \times 10^{-8} \text{ cm} .$$

This cross section is considerably smaller than the value of about 3×10^{-8} cm derived from viscosities. Besides, the interatomic distance in HI is 1.60 A, also in excess of 0.83 A.

10.14 The Activated Complex

The theory of absolute reaction rates, developed by Eyring and others,[5] provides a method of calculating the rates of chemical reactions. The intermediate state of extraordinary energy that leads from reactants to products is called the *activated complex*. In unimolecular reactions it consists of one reactant molecule with the energy of activation so localized that nothing more is needed for dissociation to products except time and proper movements of the parts that are to become products. In a bimolecular reaction the activated complex is the double-molecule produced by the union of the two reactants. The activated complex of a trimolecular reaction is the triple-molecule formed, from three reactant molecules.

The activated complex stands atop the energy-pass of lowest height between the energy-valleys of reactants and products. With respect to all but one of its internal coordinates, it is stable; with respect to the coordinate that describes the extent of reaction, usually a bond-stretching or vibrational coordinate, it is unstable. That is, the activated complex lies at a saddle-point from which all but one coordinate lead to higher energies, that one leading to the lower energies of reactants or products.

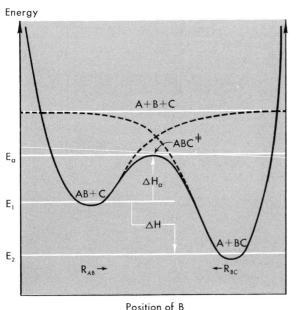

Figure 10.5 describes this one reaction coordinate for an exothermic reaction in which atom C attacks diatomic molecule AB according to the reaction

$$AB + C \rightarrow A + BC .$$

The reaction is pictured as the movement of B away from A to form the linear activated complex $ABC^{\ddagger}$ and subsequent approach of B toward C. The dashed curves indicate the electronic energies of isolated AB and BC as in Figure 8.10 if each dissociated to atoms. The activated complex $ABC^{\ddagger}$ is the molecule that exists atop the energy pass that separates the stable states of AB + C and A + BC. At absolute zero for 1 mole,

Fig. 10.5. *A View of the Reaction Coordinate for the Reaction* $AB + C \rightarrow ABC\ddagger \rightarrow A + BC.$

$$\begin{aligned} \Delta H &= N(E_2 - E_1) \\ \Delta H_a &= N(E_a - E_1) \\ \Delta H_a' &= N(E_a - E_2) . \end{aligned} \quad \left.\begin{aligned}\\\\\\\end{aligned}\right\} \quad (10.78)$$

Just as the energy of a diatomic molecule can be calculated by the methods of quantum mechanics, so also can the energy of $ABC^{\ddagger}$ and the curves of Figure 10.5. Although one coordinate is enough if it is chosen properly, it is often simpler to think in terms of more than one. The reaction of AB with C would have r_{AB} and r_{BC}, these being simplified to one of approximately the correct form in Figure 10.5. In general, then, the energy E_a of the activated complex is the energy of the lowest energy-pass connecting reactants and products in a space wherein energy is a function of one or more space variables.

With the energy and configuration of the activated complex known by such calculation, and with vibrational and rotational frequencies known from the shape of the energy-parameter surface, the theory of absolute reaction rates then uses the methods of statistical mechanics to evaluate the rate constant k_n. It is assumed, with ample justification through agreement of calculated and observed rates, that the activated complex is in equilibrium with reactants. The equilibrium

$$A + B + \cdots \rightleftharpoons AB^{\ddagger} \tag{10.79}$$

between reactants A, B, $\cdots$ and activated complex $AB^{\ddagger}$ has an equilibrium constant

$$K_c^{\ddagger} = \frac{C_{AB\ddagger}}{C_A C_B \cdots} = e^{-(\Delta A^{\ddagger}/kT)} . \tag{10.80}$$

If, as commonly happens, the activated complex always decomposes to products as it is formed, the rate of the reaction is equal to the frequency $\nu^{\ddagger}$ of vibration along the reaction coordinate times the concentration of activated complex. If $N_{\ddagger}$ molecules of $AB^{\ddagger}$ exist in a volume V, the rate (molecules per unit volume per unit time) is

$$-\frac{d}{dt}\left(\frac{N_{\ddagger}}{V}\right) = \nu^{\ddagger}\left(\frac{N_{\ddagger}}{V}\right). \tag{10.81}$$

With one molecule per unit volume as the standard state, (10.80) then yields for the rate:

$$-\frac{d}{dt}\left(\frac{N_A}{V}\right) = -\frac{d}{dt}\left(\frac{N_B}{V}\right) = -\frac{d}{dt}\left(\frac{N_{\ddagger}}{V}\right)$$

$$= \nu^{\ddagger}\left(\frac{N_A}{V}\right)\left(\frac{N_B}{V}\right) \cdots e^{-(\Delta A^{\ddagger}/kT)} . \tag{10.82}$$

By analogy with (10.6), which holds at constant V,

$$-\frac{dC_A}{dt} = kC_A^a C_B^b \tag{10.6}$$

it is clear that the rate constant is

$$k_n = \nu^{\ddagger}e^{-(\Delta A^{\ddagger}/kT)} . \tag{10.83}$$

Chapter 9 discusses the calculation of $\Delta A^{\ddagger}$ and other thermodynamic properties from molecular properties. Here it is convenient to make the calculation for one molecule in unit volume; the translational partition function (9.23) for $V = 1$ is merely

$$Q_{tr} = \left(\frac{2\pi mkT}{h^2}\right)^{3/2} . \tag{10.84}$$

Then, for one molecule per unit volume, as in (9.29) and (9.16),

$$Q_1 = Q_{tr}Q_i \quad \text{and} \quad A = -kT \ln Q_1 . \tag{10.85}$$

Equations (10.84) and (10.85) as applied to (10.79) yield

$$\Delta A^{\ddagger} = A_{\ddagger} - (A_{\mathrm{A}} + A_{\mathrm{B}} + \cdots)$$

$$= -kT \ln \left(\frac{Q_{tr}^{\ddagger} Q_i^{\ddagger}}{Q_{tr}^{(\mathrm{A})} Q_i^{(\mathrm{A})} Q_{tr}^{(\mathrm{B})} Q_i^{(\mathrm{B})} \cdots} \right).$$

Finally, by (10.83)

$$k_n = \nu^{\ddagger} \left(\frac{Q_{tr}^{\ddagger} Q_i^{\ddagger}}{Q_{tr}^{(\mathrm{A})} Q_i^{(\mathrm{A})} Q_{tr}^{(\mathrm{B})} Q_i^{(\mathrm{B})} \cdots} \right). \qquad (10.86)$$

The methods of evaluating Q_i have been discussed in Sections 9.6 and 9.7. Here only two features need to be clarified: how the activation energy originates and how the very low frequency $\nu^{\ddagger}$ of vibration along the reaction coordinate is to be handled.

The activation energy originates from the electronic parts of the Q_i's. Each electronic state of a species has an energy E_e from which vibrational and rotational levels of that electronic state are calculated. As in (9.34) and (9.35),

$$Q_i = \sum_e g_e e^{-(E_e - E_o)/kT} Q_{rv}^{(e)}.$$

The energy of the ground (or most stable) state of most molecules is usually so much less than the energies of all excited states that the sum is dominated by the one term for that one most stable state and

$$Q_i = g_e e^{-(E_e - E_o)/kT} Q_{rv}^{(e)}.$$

With one species it is best to let $E_o = E_e$ and Q_i is simply $g_e Q_{rv}^{(e)}$, where g_e is the electronic degeneracy of the ground state.

As in Figure 10.5, it is common to assume that the transition from reactants to products via activated complex can be effected adiabatically in the quantum mechanical sense (that is, with $g_e^{\ddagger} = g_e^{\mathrm{A}} g_e^{\mathrm{B}} \cdots$). In the end, therefore, the g_e's cancel in (10.86) and there remains only the factor

$$\exp - \frac{1}{kT} \left\{ (E_{\ddagger} - E_o) - [(E_{\mathrm{A}} - E_o) + (E_{\mathrm{B}} - E_o) + \cdots] \right\}.$$

These energies are the lowest vibrational-rotational energies of the most stable electronic states of the several species and E_o is the one arbitrary reference energy common to all. It is customary to choose the lowest vibrational state of each electronic state as the zero of energy in computing $Q_{rv}^{(e)}$ for each species. The activation energy per molecule at absolute zero is

$$\Delta E^{\ddagger} = (E_{\ddagger} - E_o) - [(E_{\mathrm{A}} - E_o) + (E_{\mathrm{B}} - E_o) + \cdots].$$

In Figure 10.5, E_o would be chosen as E_1 and $E_{\ddagger}$ as E_a. The zero-point energy of $\mathrm{ABC}^{\ddagger}$ is not shown in the figure because it involves bendings and stretching along coordinates not depicted there.

The second feature of (10.86) concerns the decomposition vibration $\nu^{\ddagger}$ of the activated complex. If the reference of energy in calculating Q_v of a molecule such as the activated complex is its lowest energy level, its vibrational partition function, as in (9.47), is

$$Q_v = \prod_i [1 - e^{-(2\pi\hbar\nu_i/kT)}]^{-1} .$$

For most frequencies, $2\pi\hbar\nu_i \gg kT$ so that Q_v is close to unity. The one low frequency $\nu^{\ddagger}$ of the activated complex corresponding to vibration along the reaction coordinate contributes thus:

$$\lim_{\nu^{\ddagger}\to 0} \left(1 - e^{-(2\pi\hbar\nu^{\ddagger}/kT)}\right)^{-1} = \lim_{\nu^{\ddagger}\to 0} \left[1 - \left(1 - \frac{2\pi\hbar\nu^{\ddagger}}{kT} + \cdots\right)\right]^{-1}$$

$$= \frac{kT}{2\pi\hbar\nu^{\ddagger}}. \tag{10.87}$$

A nonlinear activated complex of N atoms is treated, therefore, like an ordinary molecule with $3N - 7$ internal degrees of freedom. Six of the total of $3N$ degrees of freedom are rotation and translation and the seventh, not included among the $3N - 7$, is the weak vibration with frequency $\nu^{\ddagger}$.

The internal partition function $Q_i^{\ddagger}$ of the activated complex is the product of (10.87) and an internal partition function $Q_i^{(\ddagger)}$ of the complex devoid of the vibration $\nu^{\ddagger}$. That is, $Q_i^{\ddagger} = (kT/h\nu^{\ddagger})Q_i^{(\ddagger)}$. It follows, therefore, from (10.86) and subsequent equations that

$$k_n = \left(\frac{kT}{h}\right)\left(\frac{Q_{tr}^{(\ddagger)}Q_i^{(\ddagger)}}{\prod_{j=1}^{n} Q_{tr}^{(j)}Q_i^{(j)}}\right) e^{-(\Delta E^{\ddagger}/kT)} . \tag{10.88}$$

The $(n + 1)Q_{tr}$'s are given by (10.84) and the Q_i's are calculated for the most stable electronic state whose lowest vibrational-rotational state is the reference of energy for each. The universal frequency factor (kT/h) is 6.21×10^{12} sec^{-1} at $25°C$.

The observed activation energy ΔH_a of (10.67) differs slightly from $N \Delta E^{\ddagger}$ of (10.88) for several reasons. While $N \Delta E^{\ddagger}$ applies at $T = 0$, ΔH_a may obtain at any T. In general for ideal gases in (10.79), $\Delta H = \Delta E + (1 - n)RT$ and the choice of standard state is immaterial to ΔE or ΔH. It happens, however, that observed values of ΔH_a and ΔE_a in equations like (10.67) exceed calculated values $N \Delta H^{\ddagger}$ or $N \Delta E^{\ddagger}$ by RT because of the factor kT/h in (10.88). That is, $\Delta H_a = N \Delta H^{\ddagger} + RT = N \Delta E^{\ddagger} + (1 - n)RT + RT = N \Delta E^{\ddagger} + (2 - n)RT$. With this result and $R = Nk$, (10.88) finally yields

$$k_n = e^{2-n} \left(\frac{kT}{h}\right)\left(\frac{Q_{tr}^{(\ddagger)}Q_i^{(\ddagger)}}{\prod_{j=1}^{n} Q_{tr}^{(j)}Q_i^{(j)}}\right) e^{-(\Delta H_a/RT)} . \tag{10.89}$$

Example 10.17. If all molecules are rigid, if all rotational partition functions $(2I_e kT/\hbar^2)^{1/2}$ are $10^{1.5}$, and if all Q_{tr} are 10^{26}, show that bimolecular reactions between nonlinear reactants are much slower than between atoms even when the activation energies of both reactions are equal.

For bimolecular reactions $n = 2$. If all vibrations are suppressed, the molecules being rigid, all Q_v are unity. For the diatomic activated complex, there are two nonzero moments of inertia and $Q_i = Q_r = (10^{1.5})^2 = 10^3$. For a rigid nonlinear molecule or activated complex, there are three nonzero moments of inertia and $Q_i = (10^{1.5})^3$. The bimolecular reaction between atoms has a rate constant k_{2a} as given by (10.89) of

$$k_{2a} = \left(\frac{kT}{h}\right)\left(\frac{10^{26} \cdot 10^3}{10^{26} \cdot 10^{26}}\right) e^{-(\Delta Ha/RT)}.$$

Similarly, for the reaction between nonlinear molecules,

$$k_{2m} = \left(\frac{kT}{h}\right)\left(\frac{10^{26} \cdot 10^{4.5}}{10^{26} \cdot 10^{4.5} \cdot 10^{26} \cdot 10^{4.5}}\right) e^{-(\Delta Ha/RT)}.$$

It follows at once that $k_{2a} = k_{2m} \times 10^{7.5}$. The rate between atoms exceeds that between nonlinear molecules by 3×10^7. What must be explained by steric factors and collision efficiencies in the collision theory is here explained simply in terms of rotational degrees of freedom.

10.15 Reaction Rates in Solution

Some reactions such as the decomposition of N_2O_5 or Cl_2O proceed in some solvents at about the same rate as in the gaseous state. The reason is that the mechanism and activated complex are the same in both phases. The theory of absolute reaction rates is readily extended from gases to include reactions in solution merely by formulating the theory in terms of activities instead of concentrations. Just as in equilibrium thermodynamics, an activity coefficient of unity means ideal behavior. And so if a reaction rate is unchanged upon going from gas to solution, the solvent is essentially an inert diluent which does not modify mechanism or states of reactants and activated complex.

An inert solvent is expected to modify a rate in at least two ways: by limiting diffusion and by increasing the collision rate. Although a solvent may prevent free mixing of reactants, it also slows their motion away from each other once they have come together. The increase in the frequency of collisions is an increase in the number of both activating and deactivating collisions. Thus it happens that by its presence the inert solvent tends to speed and slow the rate to about the same extent.

If the reactants or activated complex interact with the solvent, the rate may vary through changes in mechanism or through changes in s and ΔH_a. Essentially the same mechanism might occur because the interaction with solvent is weak, as in solvation. Solvation of activated complex without appreciable solvation of reactants leads to a somewhat more stable intermediate and thus to smaller ΔH_a. The result is a greater rate for a mechanism essentially the same as in an inert solvent or none at all.

Many reactions occur in solution but not in the gaseous phase because reactants are not volatile. Ionic reactions are generally of this kind. Increasing the ionic strength of a solution generally speeds reactions involving ions but does not affect the rate of reactions involving nonionic reactants. Increasing the dielectric constant κ of a solvent may increase or decrease the rate of a reaction. If the reactants are oppositely charged ions, increasing κ usually decreases the rate by reducing the interionic attraction of reactants.

When the solvent actually is a reactant, it is present in excess. A huge excess of a reactant of course speeds the reaction and masks its true order. In 1850, Wilhelmy found that sugar was hydrolyzed by a first-order reaction only because the concentrations of water, a reactant, and H^+, a catalyst, were almost constant during his observations. The rate of this hydrolysis is really proportional to the concentrations of sugar, water, and hydronium ion.

10.16 Laws of Photochemistry

The two laws of photochemistry are simple. Only absorbed radiation can act, and one photon activates one molecule in the primary step. What happens after the initial primary step can be and usually is rather complicated.

The laws of Beer and Lambert relate the intensity of radiation transmitted through a substance to the length of the optical path and the concentration of absorber. The combined law of Beer and Lambert says that the rate of decrease in transmitted intensity I with respect to optical path length x is proportional to the intensity and to the concentration C of the absorber. Mathematically,

$$-\frac{dI}{dx} = \epsilon I C . \tag{10.90}$$

If I_o is the initial intensity when the thickness of absorber x is zero, then integration of (10.90) yields

$$-\int_{I_o}^{I} \frac{dI'}{I'} = \epsilon C \int_0^l dx$$

$$\ln\left(\frac{I_o}{I}\right) = \epsilon C l . \tag{10.91}$$

The proportionality constant ϵ depends upon the wavelength of radiation as well as upon the nature of the absorber and the units of C and x. Since absorption spectroscopists prefer decadic logarithms for calculations, (10.91) is usually written

$$A = \log\left(\frac{I_o}{I}\right) = aCl \tag{10.92}$$

where $2.303a = \epsilon$. Here A is called the absorbancy or optical density and a is the molar absorbancy if C is given in moles per unit volume.

If one absorbtion cell of length l contains several species i (such as solvent and solutes), at wavelength λ_1, (10.92) reads

$$A^{(1)} = l \sum_i a_i^{(1)} C_i . \tag{10.93}$$

That is, each of the i species that absorb are assumed to act independently upon the intensity transmitted by the others. Because the various molar absorbancies depend upon wavelength in a way that varies according to the nature of the absorber and its various excited energy states, at λ_j for the same mixture in the same cell

$$A^{(j)} = l \sum_i a_i^{(j)} C_i . \tag{10.94}$$

If the matrix of molar absorbancies $a_i^{(j)}$ is known at the several wavelengths λ_j for the several species i, (10.94) represents simultaneous linear equations that can be solved for the several C_i. The number of equations must exceed or equal the number of concentrations to be found.

If the values of I_o and I are measured absolutely in terms of ergs per square centimeter per second, then $I_o - I$ is the energy absorbed per square centimeter per second. If the radiation is monochromatic with frequency ν, the energy per photon is $E = h\nu$. The total number of photons absorbed per second per square centimeter is therefore $(I_o - I)/h\nu$. Even when the intensity is not uniform over an irradiated area $\mathcal{C}$, the second law requires that $[(I_o - I)/h\nu]\,\mathcal{C}$ be the number of molecules that absorb per second. The number of moles of absorber that disappear in a volume $V = \mathcal{C}l$ per second is therefore

$$-\frac{dC}{dt} = \left(\frac{I_o - I}{N h\nu}\right)\frac{1}{l}$$

$$= \frac{I_o(1 - e^{-\epsilon Cl})}{N h\nu l}. \tag{10.95}$$

When λ, ϵ, and l are fixed and absorption is modest so that $\epsilon Cl \ll 1$, (10.95) becomes

$$-\frac{dC}{dt} = \frac{I_o \epsilon C}{N h\nu}. \tag{10.96}$$

That is, for the reaction

$$A + h\nu \rightarrow A^*$$

the rate of disappearance of A and the rate of formation of A^* are proportional to I_o, C_A and ϵ if absorption is weak. Equation (10.96) is ordinarily suitable even for a small range of frequencies if the absorption coefficient does not vary greatly with ν.

Example 10.18. The concentrations of two solutes were estimated in the same solution by absorption spectroscopy at 2 wavelengths. At λ_1, the molar absorbancies were 300 and 30 l mole^{-1} cm^{-1}; at λ_2, 10 and 200 l mole^{-1} cm^{-1}. When measured in a cell 2.00 cm in length, the percentage transmitted (after correction for solvent and cell-window absorption) was 1.77% at λ_1 and 20.3% at λ_2. What were the concentrations of the two solutes?

At λ_1, by (10.92) and (10.93),

$$\log \left(\frac{100}{1.77} \right) = 2.00(300C_A + 30C_B) .$$

At λ_2, similarly,

$$\log \left(\frac{100}{20.3} \right) = 2.00(10C_A + 200C_B) .$$

Simultaneous solution of these equations yields

$$C_A = 2.76 \times 10^{-3} \text{ mole } l^{-1}$$
$$C_B = 1.59 \times 10^{-3} \text{ mole } l^{-1} .$$

10.17 Chain Reactions

A chain reaction is a reaction that proceeds by the repetition of a certain sequence of reactions. One or more of the reactants in the repeated series of reactions is itself a product of those reactions. This product, which is also a reactant, is generally a radical or excited atom, ion, or molecule. When it is destroyed the chain of reactions is broken and the reaction ceases until another reactive species is generated. This highly reactive intermediate may be generated thermally, by absorption of radiation, or in other ways. Often it is generated in an induction period during which no obvious reaction occurs.

Chain reactions differ from ordinary reactions in exhibiting a rate that is constant or even explosively accelerated. Ordinary reactions decrease in rate as reactants are consumed. Because an induction period is often required to generate the reactive intermediate that propagates the chain, a typical chain reaction is slow at first, swift or even explosive later, and finally slow as reactants are exhausted. Their complicated mechanisms often make their rates complicated functions of concentrations and even of impurities. Finally, their rate constants are unusually great because of apparently large frequency factors.

The classic examples of chain reactions are the reactions of hydrogen with bromine or chlorine. Reaction begins with the production of halogen atoms. In the thermal reaction, there exists the equilibrium $X_2 \rightleftharpoons 2\,X$. In the photochemical mechanism, halogen atoms X are generated by photolysis of X_2 and are eventually destroyed by a three-body collision.

$$X_2 + h\nu \xrightarrow{k_I} X + X \tag{10.97}$$

$$X + X + M \xrightarrow{k_3} X_2 + M^* . \tag{10.98}$$

The chain reaction involves just two steps, namely,

$$\left. \begin{array}{l} X + H_2 \xrightarrow{k_X} HX + H \\[2mm] H + X_2 \xrightarrow{k_H} HX + X . \end{array} \right\} \tag{10.99}$$

These two steps can occur repeatedly until reactants disappear or until the atomic chain carriers are destroyed by (10.98) or (10.100).

$$H + H + M \rightarrow H_2 + M^* . \tag{10.100}$$

The production of HX is slowed by the addition or formation of HX because (10.99) is reversed.

$$X + HX \rightarrow X_2 + H \tag{10.101}$$

$$H + HX \xrightarrow{k_2} H_2 + X . \tag{10.102}$$

These reverse reactions do not, however, decrease the number of chain-propagating atoms. Reaction (10.100) is relatively unimportant because the concentration of H is small. The photolysis of X_2 yields enough X, however, to make (10.98) of some importance. Reaction (10.101) is highly endothermic and thus is slow because of a great ΔH_a.

The mathematical formulation in a steady state proceeds in the usual way. Without (10.100) and (10.101),

$$\frac{dC_{HX}}{dt} = k_X C_{H_2} C_X + k_H C_{X_2} C_H - k_2 C_{HX} C_X \tag{10.103}$$

$$0 = \frac{dC_H}{dt} = k_X C_{H_2} C_X - k_H C_{X_2} C_H - k_2 C_{HX} C_H \tag{10.104}$$

$$0 = \frac{dC_X}{dt} = -k_X C_{H_2} C_X + k_H C_{X_2} C_H + k_2 C_{HX} C_H$$

$$-k_3 C_M C_X^2 + \tfrac{1}{2} k_I I C_{X_2} . \tag{10.105}$$

The last term in (10.105) follows from (10.96). In view of (10.104), (10.105) becomes simply

$$C_X = \left(\frac{k_I I C_{X_2}}{2 k_3 C_M} \right)^{1/2} \tag{10.106}$$

and (10.103) reduces to

$$\frac{dC_{HX}}{dt} = 2k_H C_{X_2} C_H .$$ (10.107)

Solution of (10.104) for C_H and use of (10.106) to eliminate C_X yields finally

$$\frac{dC_{HX}}{dt} = 2k_H C_{X_2} \left(\frac{k_X C_{H_2}}{k_H C_{X_2} + k_2 C_{HX}}\right)\left(\frac{k_I I C_{X_2}}{2k_3 C_M}\right)^{1/2} .$$ (10.108)

In the reaction of Cl_2 with H_2, the chain (10.99) may occur up to one million times before it is broken by recombination of atoms at the wall or in a three-body collision. Both chain reactions are swift because they have small activation energies. With Br_2, however, the reaction

$$Br + H_2 \rightarrow HBr + H$$

is endothermic. Since ΔH_a is at least as great as ΔH, the rate of this reaction is slow and recombination can compete, thus limiting the chain length.

The quantum yield of a photochemical reaction is a measure of the efficiency with which radiation is used in a reaction. It is the ratio of the number of molecules of product produced to the number of quanta absorbed. For the production of HCl it may be as high as 10^6; in photosynthesis it is 0.25; in cis-trans isomerizations, it may be as low as 0.05.

E. CATALYSIS

10.18 Industrial Catalysis

A catalyst is a substance that changes the rate of a chemical reaction without itself undergoing a net change in the over-all reaction. It partakes in the reaction as an intermediate or by modifying the activity of reactant or activated complex. Solvation may stabilize the activated complex more than it does the reactants; if so, ΔH_a is lowered and the rate of the reaction is increased. Many organic decompositions are accelerated by I_2 because I_2 can remove a hydrogen atom as HI, combine with and stabilize molecular fragments, and later by a bimolecular reaction be regenerated as I_2, leaving the original molecule in fragments. The I_2 thus offers a reaction route of lower energy and greater speed and ease. The main action of a catalyst is its effect on ΔH_a.

The economic importance of catalysts is great. Exothermic reactions are reversed by a temperature rise. A suitable catalyst not only decreases capital outlay in equipment by speeding a reaction, but it may also increase yields in exothermic reactions by allowing profitable operation at reduced temperatures. Examples are the production of SO_3 and NH_3 from the elements.

Industrial catalysts are usually solids of high surface area. The active species may be supported on silica or alumina with surface areas of the order of 10^2 m^2 g^{-1}. Heterogeneous catalysis, usually gaseous reactants on solid catalyst, involves several steps: transport of reactants to surface, adsorption, activation, reaction, desorption, and transport away from the surface. The surface of catalyst contains inert regions, regions of high activity, strains and defects, pores and holes, and various other features to attract and activate reactants. The action may often be specific enough to favor a reaction whose competitor would in the absence of catalyst quite dominate the mode of reaction.

A true catalyst is unchanged after the reaction has been completed. Hydrogenation catalysts of Ni and Pt may approach this ideal by acting as matrices in which atomic hydrogen can dissolve preparatory to reaction. Many industrial catalysts must be regenerated from time to time because side reactions gradually deposit products that obstruct the surface. Still other reasons for loss in activity of a catalyst are gradual loss of active regions through sintering or through accumulation of trace impurities that deactivate centers of activity. Sulfur and arsenic deactivate platinum by forming such things as PtS$_2$ and PtAs$_2$.

A common regeneration problem concerns removal of carbon and "coke" from silica-alumina cracking catalysts. These catalysts may contain from 5-30% alumina supported on silica. The particles of catalyst are so small that they can be circulated with hot petroleum vapors in a so-called fluidized state. As cracking occurs, deposits of graphitic carbon build up. These particles of coke are removed in a regenerator by controlled burning with air. Such rough treatment inevitably causes sintering and a loss in activity. Hence, old catalyst with surface areas of about 150 m^2 g^{-1} is withdrawn from time to time and gradually replaced by new catalyst with an area of about 500 m^2 g^{-1}. Although silica-alumina is not a catalyst in the strict sense because it is changed during reaction, it does speed a desired change, the production of gasoline from petroleum by decreasing the molecular weight of the hydrocarbons.

Reactions that proceed by chain reaction can be very effectively stopped by what are sometimes called *negative catalysts*. These are substances that react with and remove chain-carrying species such as free radicals. Hydrogen peroxide is commonly stabilized in this way.

10.19 Biological Catalysis

Although inorganic and organic decompositions, polymerizations, and syntheses often proceed well only with the aid of highly specific catalysts, biological catalysts are undoubtedly the most specialized. A biological catalyst, called an *enzyme*, may do nothing but attack a certain type of hydrogen atom.

But in proper order with respect to its fellow enzymes it supports and even is life.

One common mechanism by which enzymes work is the famous Michaelis-Menten mechanism.[6]

$$
\left.
\begin{aligned}
\text{A} + \text{X} &\underset{k_2'}{\overset{k_2}{\rightleftharpoons}} \text{AX} \\
\text{AX} &\overset{k_1}{\rightarrow} \text{D} + \text{X}
\end{aligned}
\right\}
\tag{10.109}
$$

where X is the enzyme that transforms the substrate A into the products D. As the mechanism requires,

$$
\frac{dC_{\text{AX}}}{dt} = k_2 C_{\text{A}} C_{\text{X}} - k_2' C_{\text{AX}} - k_1 C_{\text{AX}}
\tag{10.110}
$$

and

$$
\frac{dC_{\text{D}}}{dt} = k_1 C_{\text{AX}} .
\tag{10.111}
$$

Since the total or initial concentration C_{X}^o of enzyme is $C_{\text{X}} + C_{\text{AX}}$, in the steady state when the concentration of AX is constant, (10.110) yields

$$
0 = k_2 C_{\text{A}} (C_{\text{X}}^o - C_{\text{AX}}) - (k_2' + k_1) C_{\text{AX}} .
$$

Whence

$$
C_{\text{AX}} = \frac{k_2 C_{\text{A}} C_{\text{X}}^o}{k_2 C_{\text{A}} + (k_2' + k_1)} .
\tag{10.112}
$$

The rate of formation of product is then

$$
\frac{dC_{\text{D}}}{dt} = \frac{k_1 k_2 C_{\text{A}} C_{\text{X}}^o}{k_2 C_{\text{A}} + (k_2' + k_1)} .
\tag{10.113}
$$

When a great excess of substrate A is present, $k_2 C_{\text{A}} \gg k_2' + k_1$ and

$$
\frac{dC_{\text{D}}}{dt} \approx k_1 C_{\text{X}}^o
\tag{10.114}
$$

first order in enzyme concentration but zero order in substrate concentration. However, when substrate is almost lacking, the rate is first order in both, for $k_2 C_{\text{A}} \ll k_2' + k_1$ and

$$
\frac{dC_{\text{D}}}{dt} \approx \left(\frac{k_1 k_2}{k_2' + k_1} \right) C_{\text{A}} C_{\text{X}}^o .
\tag{10.115}
$$

REFERENCES

Dainton, F. S., *Chain Reactions, An Introduction.* London: Methuen & Co., Ltd., 1956.

Garner, W. E., ed., *Chemistry of the Solid State.* London: Butterworth's Scientific Publications, 1955.

Glasstone, S., K. J. Laidler, and H. Eyring, *The Theory of Rate Processes, The Kinetics of Chemical Reactions, Viscosity, Diffusion and Electrochemical Phenomena.* New York: McGraw-Hill Book Company, Inc., 1941.

Hinshelwood, C. N., *The Kinetics of Chemical Change.* New York: Oxford University Press, 1940.

Laidler, K. J., *Chemical Kinetics.* New York: McGraw-Hill Book Company, Inc., 1950.

Morrison, R. T., and R. N. Boyd, *Organic Chemistry.* Boston: Allyn and Bacon, Inc., 1959.

Rollefson, G. K., and M. Burton, *Photochemistry and the Mechanism of Chemical Reactions.* Englewood Cliffs, N. J.: Prentice-Hall, Inc., 1939.

PROBLEMS

1. Explain how the extent of a reaction might be followed by absorption spectroscopy.

2. Formulate mathematically the rate of a zero-order reaction in terms of the rate of appearance of products and integrate the differential equation.

3. At 900°C in a rigid vessel in the presence of W, pure NH_3 at 200 mm Hg initial pressure decomposes by a zero-order reaction until after 160 min the total pressure of all gases is 300 mm Hg. If in a similar experiment the initial pressure of NH_3 is to be 150 mm Hg, predict the pressure of NH_3 after 1.00 hr. [Data from C. H. Kunsman, *Journal of the American Chemical Society*, **50**, 2100 (1928).]

4. Calculate the average life of a substance that decomposes by a first-order reaction. *Answer:* $1/k$.

5. Near atmospheric pressure at 427°C, the apparent first-order rate constant for the irreversible decomposition of cyclobutane according to the reaction $C_4H_8 \rightarrow 2\ C_2H_4$ is $k_1 = 1.23 \times 10^{-4}$ sec^{-1} [C. T. Genaux, F. Kern, and W. D. Walters, *Journal of the American Chemical Society*, **75**, 6196 (1953)]. If 0.0300 mole C_4H_8 is placed in a 1-l vessel at 427°C, calculate the total pressure expected in the vessel after 2.00 hr. *Answer:* 2.73 atm.

6. One curie of radiation is 3.7×10^{10} disintegrations sec^{-1}. If the half-life of Co^{60} is 5.3 yr, what mass of pure Co^{60} will provide the activity of 1.00 millicurie? *Answer:* 0.890 microgram.

7. At 499.5°C and various total pressures P, a few of the apparent first-order rate constants for the isomerization of cyclopropane are: $k_1 = 5.94 \times 10^{-4}$ sec^{-1} at 710.4 mm Hg; 5.12×10^{-4} sec^{-1} at 99.4 mm Hg; 4.11×10^{-4} sec^{-1} at 24.4 mm Hg [T. S. Chambers and G. B. Kistiakowsky, *Journal of the American Chemical Society*, **56**, 399 (1934)]. Find the limiting value of the first-order rate constant at infinite pressure and the second-order rate constant at low pressure.

8. Describe mathematically this second-order reaction $3\ A + B \xrightarrow{k_2} D + \ldots$ in terms of the rate of formation of D if the rate is first order in A and first order in B.

9. Show that the half-life of a reaction of order n in one species is inversely proportional to the $(n-1)$th power of the initial concentration of that species.

10. The fraction of methyl acetate that remains at various times during saponification at 25°C when ester and base begin at the same concentration are [J. Walker, *Proceedings of the Royal Society (London)*, *A*78, 157 (1906)]: 0.740 after 3 min; 0.683 after 4; 0.634 after 5; 0.589 after 6; 0.550 after 7; 0.519 after 8; 0.464 after 10; 0.416 after 12; 0.363 after 15; 0.319 after 18; 0.288 after 21; 0.254 after 25. Determine the order of the reaction in two ways.
Answer: Second.

11. State and explain the probable effect of increasing complexity of M on the mechanism (10.42).

12. Determine the rate constant for the hydrolysis of methyl acetate in aqueous 1 NHCl from Figure 10.3.

13. Criticize the validity of deriving the thermodynamic equilibrium constant by equating forward and reverse reaction rates.

14. Find the time at which B in (10.52) reaches its maximum concentration.

15. In isoamyl alcohol, benzene diazonium chloride decomposes to nitrogen and other products by a first-order reaction with these rate constants:

T (°C)	20.0	30.0	40.0	50.0
$10^3 \times k_1$ (min^{-1})	2.61	11.6	47.5	192.

[C. E. Waring and J. R. Abrams, *Journal of the American Chemical Society*, **63**, 2757 (1941).] What is the activation energy of this reaction and what is the half-life of the salt in this solution at 0°C?
Answer: $\Delta H_a = 27,000$ cal; 8100 min.

16. From data in Example 10.1 and Problem 3, find the activation energy for the decomposition of NH_3 on W at 1000°C.

17. What is the activation energy of a reaction the rate of which at 100°C is doubled by a rise in temperature of 10°C?
Answer: $\Delta H_a = 19,200$ cal.

18. Show that the mechanism of formation of the activated complex is of no concern in calculating the rate of a reaction in which the complex always yields products.

19. The rate constants of some reactions change with pressure even though there is no hint of a change in molecularity or mechanism. What can be said of the volume of the activated complex?

20. A 1-molar solution 0.200 mm thick transmits 10% of a beam of light. With neglect of absorption by solvent and cell windows, what percentage of the initial intensity will be transmitted by a 2-molar solution in a cell 0.150 mm thick?

21. Explain how some of the rate constants in (10.108) might be measured using thermal and photochemical information.

22. The quantum yield of HI from H_2 and I_2 is two. Explain this upper limit of two.

23. A cracking catalyst used in a petroleum refinery has a surface area of 300 m² g⁻¹. If the catalyst consists of tiny independent identical spheres with a density of 2.00 g cc⁻¹, what is the radius of one of these tiny spheres?
Answer: 50 A.

24. Near 225°C at about 120 mm Hg, diethyl peroxide decomposes by a first-order rate law in which $k_1 = 2 \times 10^{13} \exp [- (31.7 \times 10^3)/RT]$ sec^{-1}, where R is 1.987 cal mole^{-1} deg^{-1} [R. E. Rebbert and K. J. Laidler, *Journal of Chemical Physics*, **20**, 574 (1952)]. At 225°C, how long will it take for 30.0% of a sample of pure diethyl peroxide to decompose?
Answer: 1.4 sec.

25. If $t_{1/2}$ of Sr^{90} is 28 yr, how long will it take for 95% of a sample of Sr^{90} to decay?

26. If the half-lives of U^{238} and Th^{234} are 4.5×10^9 yr and 24 days, calculate the mass ratio of Th^{234} to U^{238} in a mineral at radioactive equilibrium.

27. Show that (10.25) results from (10.20) only if the rate of transformation of A‡ to A* is negligible compared to the rate with which A‡ becomes products.

28. At 290°C, azomethane (CH$_3$NNCH$_3$) decomposes to ethane and nitrogen by a unimolecular process. The apparent first-order rate constants ($k_1 \times 10^5$ sec^{-1}) at various initial pressures (P mm Hg) are [H. C. Ramsperger, *Journal of the American Chemical Society*, **49**, 1495 (1927)]: 13.5 at 707.9; 13.7 at 375.0; 13.7 at 320.0; 13.2 at 191.0; 11.8 at 44.07; 9.7 at 23.51; 9.0 at 12.03; 6.9 at 5.818; 5.8 at 2.587; 5.3 at 1.989; 4.5 at 0.879; and 3.2 at 0.309 mm Hg. From these data find the apparent first-order rate constants at 100 mm Hg and at 2000 mm Hg. How long would it take for 75% of a sample of azomethane to decompose at 290°C at these two initial pressures?

29. From 540°K to 727°K, the bimolecular second-order reaction CO + NO$_2$ $\xrightarrow{k_2}$ CO$_2$ + NO has $k_2 = 1.2 \times 10^{13} \exp (-31,600/RT)$ where $R = 1.987$ cal mole^{-1} deg^{-1} and the units of k_2 are cc mole^{-1} sec^{-1} [H. S. Johnston, W. A. Bonner, and D. J. Wilson, *Journal of Chemical Physics*, **26**, 1002 (1957)]. If CO at an initial pressure of 5.00 mm Hg is mixed with NO$_2$ at an initial pressure of 7.00 mm Hg at 600°K, what will be the partial pressure of NO after 10.0 hr?

30. Integrate (10.39) and evaluate the integration constant.

31. Hypophosphites decompose thus:

$$H_2PO_2^- + OH^- \rightarrow HPO_3^{--} + H_2 .$$

In a certain experiment, 19.5 cc H$_2$ (S.T.P.) were generated in 20 min when the concentration of H$_2$PO$_2^-$ was 0.50 and that of OH$^-$ was 1.28. A second experiment yielded 25.0 cc H$_2$ (S.T.P.) in 50 min when the concentrations of H$_2$PO$_2^-$ and OH$^-$ were 0.25 and 1.28. A third experiment yielded 135.0 cc H$_2$ (S.T.P.) in 30 min when the concentrations of H$_2$PO$_2^-$ and OH$^-$ were 0.25 and 3.94. What is the order of the reaction with respect to H$_2$PO$_2^-$ and OH$^-$?
Answer: First in H$_2$PO$_2^-$; second in OH$^-$.

32. Prepare a graph like Figure 10.4 for $k_{1(1)} = 2k_{1(2)}$ and discuss the differences between it and Figure 10.4.

33. The rate constants k_2 for the reaction of Section 10.12 are 4.8×10^4 cc mole^{-1} sec^{-1} at 27.7°C, 1.35×10^5 at 50.4°C, and 3.4×10^5 at 70.2°C. Calculate s and ΔH_a. To which part of the mechanism does ΔH_a apply?

34. Show that the values of ΔH_a associated with similar reactions are proportional to the various temperatures at which the reactions achieve the same rate.

35. Show that the collision theory and the absolute reaction rate theory predict the same rate constant for bimolecular reactions of atoms.

36. In 0.8 NH$_2$SO$_4$ irradiated by Co^{60}, H$_2$O$_2$ is generated in proportion to the time of irradiation [T. J. Sworski, *Journal of Chemical Physics*, **21**, 375 (1953)]. If 285 micromoles H$_2$O$_2$ are generated per hour, how many micromoles of H$_2$O$_2$ are generated in 25 min of irradiation?

37.   If the half-life of M* is 1.0×10^{-8} sec, what ϵ is required at 1 atm at 27°C to maintain a pressure of M* of 1.0×10^{-7} mm Hg with $I_o = 5.00$ ergs mm^{-2} sec^{-1}? Express ϵ as a function of ν.

Answer: $\epsilon/\nu = 7.3 \times 10^{-8}$ cm^2 sec mole^{-1}.

38.   At high pressures of Cl_2, the chain-terminating step in the production of HCl may be

$$Cl_3 + Cl_3 \xrightarrow{k_3} 3\,Cl_2$$

where Cl_3 is generated from and is in near-equilibrium with Cl_2 and Cl.

$$Cl + Cl_2 \underset{k''}{\overset{k'}{\rightleftharpoons}} Cl_3$$

If this is so, derive the rate law that describes the photoproduction of HCl from H_2 and Cl_2 at high Cl_2 pressures.

Answer: $\dfrac{dC_{HCl}}{dt} = \dfrac{2k_H k_X C_{H_2}}{k'(k_H C_{Cl_2} + k_2 C_{HCl})} \left[\left(\dfrac{k''2 k_I I C_{Cl_2}}{2k_3} \right)^{1/2} + \dfrac{k_I I C_{Cl_2}}{2} \right].$

---

39.   At 45°C, phenylmalonic acid (H_2A) and its singly charged anion (HA^-) undergo decarboxylation, but the doubly charged anion (A^{--}) is stable. Per 1 l of solution, the number of moles of CO_2 generated per hour is equal to $11.2 \times 10^{-3}\,C_{H_2A} + 35 \times 10^{-3}\,C_{HA^-}$ [E. Gelles, *Journal of the American Chemical Society*, 75, 6199 (1953)]. The first ionization constant of H_2A is 2.7×10^{-3}; the second is 9.4×10^{-6}. If 20.0 millimoles H_2A were dissolved in a l of buffer, how many moles of CO_2 would be evolved after 20.0 hr at 45°C if the buffer had a *p*H of:
(a)   0.00?
(b)   3.00?
(c)   5.00?

40.   Equation (10.17) relates the number of radioactive nucleuses to time, but it is common practice to use the time rate of decay in place of N_o and N when using this equation. Justify this use and indicate circumstances in which such practice is in error.

41.   Formulate the mathematics of the unimolecular mechanism of decomposition of A when collisions of A with A differ in efficiency of energy transfer from collisions of A with M.

42.   The oxidation of C_2H_2 by O_3 is first order in each reactant with $k_2 = 0.0025$ mm^{-1} sec^{-1} at 30°C [R. D. Cadle and C. Schadt, *Journal of Chemical Physics*, 21, 163 (1953)]. How long will it take for 1% of an equimolar mixture of C_2H_2 and O_3 to react if the initial total pressure is 4.00 mm Hg? How long will it take for 1% of the C_2H_2 in a mixture containing it at 3.00 mm Hg and O_3 at 1.00 mm Hg to react? *Answer:* 2.00 sec; 4.00 sec.

43.   In the recombination mechanism (10.42) for $X = CH_3$, $k_2 = 3.7 \times 10^{13}$ cc mole^{-1} sec^{-1} at 165°C. [G. B. Kistiakowsky and E. K. Roberts, *Journal of Chemical Physics*, 21, 1637 (1953)]. The ratio of k_1^* to k_2^* is 68×10^{16} molecules cc^{-1} for $M = He$ and 4.0×10^{16} molecules cc^{-1} for $M = CH_3COCH_3$ [K. U. Ingold, I. H. S. Henderson, and F. P. Lossing, *Journal of Chemical Physics*, 21, 2239 (1953)]. What is the half-life of CH_3 initially at a pressure of 5×10^{-7} mm Hg:
(a)   In the absence of a third body?
(b)   In the presence of He at a pressure of 10 mm Hg?
(c)   In the presence of CH_3COCH_3 at a pressure of 1.0 mm Hg?

44. The law of microscopic reversibility requires that, at equilibrium, the rate of the forward reaction equal the rate of the reverse reaction for each path of the mechanism. [Thermodynamics requires merely that the over-all forward rate equal the over-all reverse rate.] If the decomposition of NO is bimolecular, show that $N_2 + O_2 \rightarrow 2$ NO is also bimolecular.

45. Prepare a graph of the concentrations of A, B, and C for the mechanism of first-order reactions

$$A \xrightarrow{k_1} B \underset{k_1'}{\overset{k_1}{\rightleftharpoons}} C$$

when $k_1 > k_1'$.

46. From data in Problem 7 and Example 10.7 calculate the activation energies associated with the mechanism (10.20) for the isomerization of cyclopropane if $\Delta H^\circ = -5$ kcal mole^{-1} for the over-all isomerization.

47. In view of Problem 46, will the isomerization of cyclopropane tend to remain first order to lower pressures as the temperature is increased or decreased from 500°C?

48. By the theory of absolute reaction rates and the kinetic theory, estimate the order of magnitude of the apparent efficiency of collisions in a gas reaction at 300°K between an atom and a rigid diatomic molecule when the activated complex, rigid except for $\nu^\ddagger$, is:
(a) Linear.
(b) Nonlinear.

49. At 40°C with radiation of wavelength 4358 A, the photochemical reaction

$$Cl_{2(g)} + C_2Cl_{4(g)} \rightarrow C_2Cl_{6(s)}$$

proceeds at a rate that depends upon the intensity of light and the concentration of Cl_2. When p_{Cl_2} was 46.7 mm Hg and $p_{C_2Cl_4}$ was 5.8 mm Hg, the total pressure decreased by 3.40×10^{-3} mm Hg sec^{-1} in a rigid glass vessel of volume 1110 cc when 5.66×10^{-10} einsteins sec^{-1} were absorbed. The energy of 1 einstein is $Nh\nu$. Later, when p_{Cl_2} was 43.2 mm Hg and $p_{C_2Cl_4}$ was 2.3 mm Hg, the total pressure decreased by 1.48×10^{-3} mm Hg sec^{-1} when 1.47×10^{-10} einsteins sec^{-1} were absorbed. If the rate law is

$$-\frac{dC_{Cl_2}}{dt} = kI_a^n C_{Cl_2}$$

where I_a is the intensity of *absorbed* radiation, find k and n. Determine also the quantum yield for each set of conditions if only half of the Cl_2 that disappears absorbs radiation in the primary event. [Data from R. G. Dickinson and J. L. Carrico, *Journal of the American Chemical Society,* 56, 1473 (1934).]

50. If the primary event in the photochlorination of C_2Cl_4 is $Cl_2 + h\nu \rightarrow 2$ Cl, invent a mechanism that leads to the rate law stated in Problem 49. N. B.: $I_a = I_0 \epsilon C / Nh\nu$.

51. At constant light intensity from 82°C to 132°C, the rate of disappearance of Br_2 in the photo-bromination of toluene (T) to yield benzyl bromide and HBr is

$$-\frac{dC_{Br_2}}{dt} = \frac{kC_{Br_2}^{1/2}C_T^{1/2}}{1 + n\left(\dfrac{C_{HBr}}{C_{Br_2}}\right)}$$

where k and n depend upon temperature thus:

$$\log k = 1.497 - \frac{1742}{T}$$

$$\log n = 3.007 - \frac{1176}{T}$$

[H. E. Anderson, Jr., H. A. Scheraga, and E. R. Van Artsdalen, *Journal of Chemical Physics*, **21**, 1258 (1953)]. Propose a mechanism for this gaseous chain reaction that does not involve hydrogen atoms, and by comparison with the observed rate law discuss the relative efficiencies of Br_2 and toluene as third bodies in recombination of Br atoms.

52. By making suitable assumptions about activation energies of reactions in the chain mechanism for bromination of toluene in the previous problem, find the heat of formation of benzyl radical. For gaseous toluene, $\Delta H_f^o = 12$ kcal mole^{-1}. *Answer:* 50 kcal mole^{-1}.

53. Justify this statement: The partition function of a strongly adsorbed (i.e., chemisorbed) reactant on a solid catalyst is unity.

54. Show how the Michaelis-Menten constant $(k_2' + k_1)/k_2$ is related to the rate of formation of product when substrate is present in excess.

FOOTNOTES

1. Lewis, *Zeitschrift für physikalische Chemie*, **52**, 310 (1905).

2. Lindemann, F. A., *Transactions of the Faraday Society*, **17**, 598 (1922); Marcus, R. A., *Journal of Chemical Physics*, **20**, 359 (1952).

3. Garvin, D., and G. B. Kistiakowsky, *Journal of Chemical Physics*, **20**, 105 (1952); Kistiakowsky, G. B. and R. Williams, *Journal of Chemical Physics*, **23**, 334 (1955).

4. Perrine, R. L., and H. S. Johnston, *Journal of Chemical Physics*, **21**, 2202 (1953).

5. Glasstone, S., K. J. Laidler, and H. Eyring, *The Theory of Rate Processes.* New York: McGraw-Hill Book Company, Inc., 1941.

6. Michaelis, L., and M. L. Menten, *Biochemische Zeitschrift*, **49**, 333 (1913).

APPENDIXES

A. LINE INTEGRATION; EXACT AND INEXACT DIFFERENTIALS*

A definite integral is a function of its limits when it is of the form

$$\int_a^b \frac{df(x)}{dx} \, dx = f(b) - f(a).$$ (1)

It is possible, however, for a definite integral of the form

$$\int_a^b \phi(x, y) \, dx$$ (2)

to depend not only on the limits a and b but also on the many possible values of y in the interval $a \leqslant x \leqslant b$. If the values of y are given as a function of x by the relation $y = F(x)$, then substitution of $F(x)$ for y in (2) gives an integral like (1) in one variable x. This is readily evaluated by (1) if the integration can be done. When the variable of integration is y, the expression analogous to (2) is

$$\int_{a'}^{b'} \chi(x, y) \, dy \, .$$ (3)

---

* The matter of this appendix is highly abbreviated. For ample development, the student is referred to the latest editions of the two sources of this appendix, which were: Granville, W. A., P. F. Smith, and W. R. Longley, *Elements of the Differential and Integral Calculus*. Boston: Ginn & Company, 1941; Woods, F. S., *Advanced Calculus*. Boston: Ginn & Company, 1934. The latest edition of the former is 1957; of the latter, 1954.

In general, (2) and (3) seldom occur alone. Integrals of this type are commonly of the form

$$\int_{(a,a')}^{(b,b')} [\phi(x, y)\, dx + \chi(x, y)\, dy] .\tag{4}$$

When the function $y = F(x)$ is specified, the integral (4) can be calculated. Because the curve $y = F(x)$ specifies that the integration be performed along a certain curve or *path*, the integral (4) is called a *line integral*.

The value of (4) generally depends upon the curve or path of integration. For example, let the integral be

$$I = \int_{(0,0)}^{(2,1)} [(y + 1)\, dx + (x^2)\, dy] .$$

When $y = x/2$, substitution for y yields

$$I = \int_0^2 \left[\left(\frac{x}{2} + 1 \right) dx + (x^2)\, \frac{dx}{2} \right] = \frac{13}{3} .$$

However, if the path be along $y = 0$ for $0 \leqslant x \leqslant 2$ and then along $x = 2$ for $0 \leqslant y \leqslant 1$, the integral along $y = 0$ becomes $\int_0^2 dx = 2$ while along $x = 2$ it becomes $\int_0^1 4\, dy = 4$. The second path along $y = 0$ and $x = 2$ thus yields $I = 6$, a value which differs from $13/3$.

If the function $\phi(x, y)$ in (2) were merely y, then

$$\int_a^b \phi(x, y)\, dx = \int_a^b y\, dx$$

would be the area bounded by $y = \phi(x)$, $y = 0$, $x = a$ and $x = b$. Since curves like C_1 and C_2 of Figure A1 can be followed in two directions, it is necessary to define one direction as positive and the other as negative. When the curve bounds a certain region A, the positive direction along the curve C is that direction which keeps the region A on the left of a person traversing the curve. Integration along C_1, namely,

$$A_1 = \int_a^b y_1\, dx\tag{5}$$

would give the area A_1 bounded by C_1, $y = 0$, $x = a$ and $x = b$. Similarly, integration along C_2 with the region A on the left would give the area bounded by C_2, $y = 0$, $x = b$ and $x = a$. The expression for this area A_2 would be negative because dx is everywhere negative; hence,

$$-A_2 = \int_b^a y_2\, dx .\tag{6}$$

Since the infinitesimal element of area dA is $(y_2 - y_1)\,dx$ for the enclosed region A, this enclosed region has the area

$$A = \int_a^b (y_2 - y_1)\,dx = A_2 - A_1 .\tag{7}$$

As C_1 and C_2 are traversed in the positive sense with the enclosed region on the left,

$$\oint y\,dx = \int_a^b y_1\,dx + \int_b^a y_2\,dx = A_1 - A_2 \tag{8}$$

where the symbol $\oint$ indicates integration in the positive sense along C along a closed path which begins and ends at (a, a'). By (5), (6), and (7), it follows that

$$\oint y\,dx = -A .\tag{9}$$

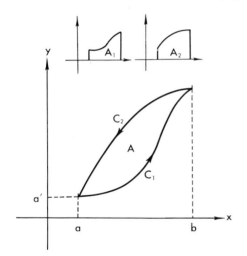

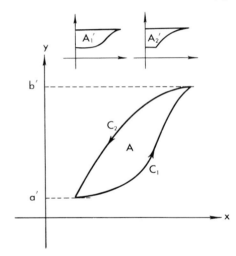

Fig. A1. *Line Integral and Area.*   **Fig. A2.** *Line Integral and Area Again.*

Similarly, it can be shown that

$$\oint x\,dy = +A .\tag{10}$$

For if A_1' is the area bounded by C_1, $x = 0$, $y = a'$, and $y = b'$, then as in Figure A2,

$$A_1' = \int_{a'}^{b'} x_1\,dy .$$

And for A_2' bounded by C_2, $x = 0$, $y = a'$ and $y = b'$,

$$-A_2' = \int_{b'}^{a'} x_2\,dy .$$

Since $A = A_1' - A_2'$,

$$A = \int_{a'}^{b'} x_1 \, dy + \int_{b'}^{a'} x_2 \, dy = \oint x \, dy$$

for the region A is always on the left as the curve is followed from (a, a') along C_1 to (b, b'), thence along C_2 to (a, a').

From (9) and (10),

$$2A = \oint (x \, dy - y \, dx) . \qquad (11)$$

This formulation and (9) and (10) assume that there are only two points on the curve C for each value of x or y in the interval and that there is only one point on C at the ends of the interval. Equation (11) is, however, quite general, for any region can be divided into areas that satisfy these requirements. Moreover, the path of integration may consist of portions of two different curves.

The area bounded by the parabola $y = 2x^2$ and the line $y = 2x$ can be calculated by (11). As shown in Figure A3, these curves intersect at $x = y = 0$ and at $x = 1$, $y = 2$. Along the parabola where $y = 2x^2$ and $dy = 4x \, dx$,

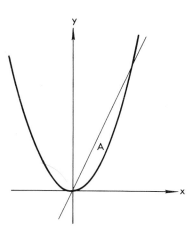

Fig. A3. *An Area Calculated.*

$$\int_{(0,0)}^{(1,2)} (x \, dy - y \, dx) = \int_0^1 [x(4x \, dx) - (2x^2) \, dx] = \int_0^1 2x^2 \, dx = \tfrac{2}{3} .$$

Along the line where $y = 2x$ and $dy = 2 \, dx$,

$$\int_{(1,2)}^{(0,0)} (x \, dy - y \, dx) = \int [x(2 \, dx) - (2x) \, dx] = 0 .$$

By (11),

$$A = \tfrac{1}{2} \oint (x \, dy - y \, dx) = \tfrac{1}{2}(\tfrac{2}{3} + 0) = \tfrac{1}{3} .$$

Let $\phi(x, y)$ and $(\partial\phi)/\partial y)_x$ be functions that are continuous in a region A and along a curve C as in Figure A1 or A2. If there are only two points on C for each value of x between the end points of the interval from a to b and if there is but one point on C at the end points a and b, then by (1),

$$\iint \left(\frac{\partial\phi}{\partial y}\right)_x dx \, dy = \int_a^b dx \int_{y_1}^{y_2} \left(\frac{\partial\phi}{\partial y}\right)_x dy$$

$$= \int_a^b [\phi(x, y_2) - \phi(x, y_1)] \, dx$$

$$= -\int_a^b \phi(x, y_1) \, dx - \int_b^a \phi(x, y_2) \, dx .$$

591

Since $\phi(x, y_1)$ is C_1 while $\phi(x, y_2)$ is C_2, and since the limits establish the direction so as to keep the region A on the left, this is the line integral of $\phi(x, y)$ along C with reversed sign. That is,

$$\iint \left(\frac{\partial \phi}{\partial y}\right)_x dx\, dy = -\oint \phi(x, y)\, dx . \tag{12}$$

Similarly, if $\chi(x, y)$ and $(\partial \chi/\partial x)_y$ behave like $\phi(x, y)$ and $(\partial \phi/\partial y)_x$ in the region A and along the curve C,

$$\iint \left(\frac{\partial \chi}{\partial x}\right)_y dx\, dy = +\oint \chi(x, y)\, dy . \tag{13}$$

The signs of (12) and (13) resemble those of (9) and (10). From (12) and (13), the general form of the line integral can be expressed in terms of a surface integral over the region A as

$$-\oint [\chi(x, y)\, dy + \phi(x, y)\, dx] = \iint \left[\left(\frac{\partial \phi}{\partial y}\right)_x - \left(\frac{\partial \chi}{\partial x}\right)_y\right] dx\, dy . \tag{14}$$

Equation (14) is a form of Green's theorem in the plane.

If everywhere in the region A

$$\left(\frac{\partial \phi}{\partial y}\right)_x = \left(\frac{\partial \chi}{\partial x}\right)_y \tag{15}$$

then the line integral of (14) around A, which can be any region suitably divided, is zero.

$$\oint [\chi(x, y)\, dy + \phi(x, y)\, dx] = 0 . \tag{16}$$

On the other hand, if (16) is true, then (15) is also true. If (15) were not true, then it would be possible to choose the region A so that $(\partial \phi/\partial y)_x - (\partial \chi/\partial x)_y$ would be positive, with the result that the line integral would not be zero as supposed. Equation (15) is therefore the necessary and sufficient condition that the line integral around A be zero.

If (16) is true, the integral along C_1 between any two points is equal in magnitude but opposite in sign to the integral along C_2 for the return trip; for the sum of these two integrals is the round trip and must be zero. If the return trip along C_2 be performed in reverse, it becomes an alternate route from the initial state (a, a') to the final state (b, b'). Since these states and the alternate routes are quite arbitrary and are subject only to the conditions set forth in deriving (14), (15), and (16), the necessary and sufficient condition that a line integral (14) depend only on the initial and final states is that (15) or (16) be true.

The statements (15) and (16) can be formulated in another way in terms of an *exact differential*. The expression $\phi \, dy + \chi \, dx$ shall have the same meaning as above. If $\phi \, dy + \chi \, dx$ is an exact differential, then there exists some function $z = z(x, y)$ such that

$$dz = \phi \, dx + \chi \, dy \, . \tag{17}$$

Then,

$$\left(\frac{\partial z}{\partial x}\right)_y = \phi \quad \text{and} \quad \left(\frac{\partial z}{\partial y}\right)_x = \chi \, . \tag{18}$$

If the second mixed partial derivatives of z are found and if they are equal, as is generally true in physical applications, then

$$\frac{\partial}{\partial x}\left(\frac{\partial z}{\partial y}\right) = \frac{\partial^2 z}{\partial x \, \partial y} = \frac{\partial^2 z}{\partial y \, \partial x} = \frac{\partial}{\partial y}\left(\frac{\partial z}{\partial x}\right).$$

Or, by (18), $\partial \chi / \partial x = \partial \phi / \partial y$, which is the same as (15). On the other hand, let (15) be true. Then since $\phi = \phi(x, y)$,

$$\int \phi \, dx = f(x, y) + C(y) \, . \tag{19}$$

The constant of integration $C(y)$ is a function of y because the integration was performed only upon x and $\int \phi \, dx$ depends on y. Let

$$z(x, y) = f(x, y) + C(y) \, . \tag{20}$$

Then,

$$\frac{\partial z}{\partial y} = \frac{\partial f}{\partial y} + \frac{dC}{dy} \, . \tag{21}$$

If z exists, (18) is true and all that remains is to determine C, which can be done by (21):

$$\frac{dC}{dy} = \chi - \frac{\partial f}{\partial y} \, . \tag{21}$$

But dC/dy is not a function of x, so that differentiation of (21) gives

$$0 = \frac{\partial \chi}{\partial x} - \frac{\partial^2 f}{\partial x \, \partial y} \, . \tag{22}$$

That is, by (19) and (22),

$$\frac{\partial \chi}{\partial x} = \frac{\partial^2 f}{\partial x \, \partial y} = \frac{\partial}{\partial y}\left\{\frac{\partial}{\partial x}\left[\int \phi \, dx - C(y)\right]\right\}$$

$$\frac{\partial \chi}{\partial x} = \frac{\partial \phi}{\partial y} \tag{15}$$

which is again (15). Since z is given by (20) and C is given by (21), the condition (15) is sufficient.

Since the integral of an expression that satisfies (15) is the integral of an exact differential dz, the function $z = z(x, y)$ exists and can be evaluated at the initial and final states. The value is thus independent of everything except the initial and final states.

If (15) or (16) is not satisfied, as sometimes happens in physical situations, then the expression $\phi\, dx + \chi\, dy$ is called an *inexact differential*. The value of an integral of an inexact differential depends not only on the initial and final states but also upon the path. Heat and work are examples of inexact differentials, and suitable examples and exercises illustrating the dependence upon the process as well as upon the initial and final states are given in the text.

Although heat and work depend upon the intermediate states of a changing system as it proceeds from a certain initial state to a certain final state, there are several thermodynamic functions that do depend only upon the initial and final states of a system. Accordingly, the increment in such a function, such as the energy, is independent of the process by which the change is effected. Any path that is mathematically convenient or conceptually simple provides a suitable path of integration and the unique increment in the value of the function between the two end states. Illustration of the behavior of exact differentials is, as for inexact ones, reserved to the main text.

Although heat is an inexact differential, it has been found that dividing the infinitesimal amount of heat absorbed reversibly by a system by the absolute temperature gives an exact differential. The reciprocal of the absolute temperature is called an *integrating factor*, for its use allows integration independent of the path. This fundamental mathematical nature of the laws of thermodynamics was discovered by Caratheodory. Without the aid of fictitious engines, he was able to develop the laws of thermodynamics from a study of a certain differential equation.

B. NOTATION AND SYMBOLS

Symbols	Meanings in Numbered Equations
$'$	Value for reverse process; used also to distinguish variables.
$-$	Mean value of; with subscript, partial molar quantity.
(Subscripts)	Used to designate species, state, order of reaction, etc.
(Superscripts)	Used to designate phase or system.
$+,-$	As subscripts, value for cation, anion.
$*$	As superscript, refers to complex conjugate, excited, or energy.
$\ddagger$	As superscript, activated or involving activated complex.

$\displaystyle\int_{(1)}^{(2)} \ldots dx$	Definite integration from state (1) with value x_1 to state (2) with value x_2.
$\displaystyle\oint \ldots dx$	Integration on a closed path.
A	Helmholtz free energy; a constant; Madelung constant; optical density or absorbancy.
A	A reactant.
A_o	Beatty-Bridgeman constant.
$\mathcal{Q}$	Area.
a	Attractive constant in equation of state of fluid; lattice or other parameter; an integer; Debye length; molar absorbancy; as subscript, activation.
a_+, a_-	Activity of cation, anion.
$a_\pm$	Mean molal activity.
a_i	Activity of species i; molar absorbancy of species i.
a_i'	Arbitrary activity of species i, especially a nonequilibrium value.
a_n	Constant.
aq	As subscript, aqueous.
A_aB_b	Typical compound of elements A and B.
B	Second virial coefficient; a constant; as subscript, Boyle.
B	A reactant.
B_e	Spectroscopic rotational constant.
B_o	Beatty-Bridgeman constant.
b	Effective volume in equation of state of fluid; lattice or other parameter; an integer; force constant; as subscript, boiling.
C	Molar heat capacity; proportionality, integration, or other constant; centered on C face; Beatty-Bridgeman constant; third virial coefficient; as subscript, Charles.
C	Number of components.
C_i	Molarity of species i; moles of gas i per liter.
C_P	Molar heat capacity at constant pressure.
C_V	Molar heat capacity at constant volume.
c	Velocity of light in vacuo; lattice parameter; as subscript, critical.
D	A product.
D	Dissociation energy.
D	Electric displacement.
d	Differential operator; Bragg spacing; an integer; a distance; as subscript, diatomic.
d_{hkl}	Bragg spacing for planes indexed (hkl).
dq	Inexact differential of heat absorbed by system.
dw	Inexact differential of work done on system.
E	A product.

595

E	Energy; as subscript, electric.
$\mathbf{E}$	Electric field intensity (volts cm^{-1}).
$\mathscr{E}$	Potential difference.
E_e	Electron affinity.
$\mathscr{E}_j$	Junction potential.
$\mathscr{E}_t$	Potential difference of cell with transference.
e, exp	Base of natural logarithms.
e	Electronic charge; an integer; as subscript, engine, electrode, equilibrium, or electronic.
F	Force; structure factor; face-centered; Fermi energy.
$\mathbf{F}$	Degrees of freedom.
$\mathscr{F}$	Faraday.
F_i	Formality (number of gram formula weights of i per liter).
f	Function; as subscript, formation, fusion, or cryoscopic.
f_i	Fugacity of species i; atomic scattering factor.
f_i'	Arbitrary fugacity of species i, especially a nonequilibrium value.
f	Function, especially a distribution function.
$\mathscr{f}_i$	Activity coefficient (pressures).
G	Gibbs free energy, with or without subscript; number of distributions.
g	Mass; acceleration of gravity; osmotic coefficient.
g	As subscript, gaseous.
g_e	Electronic multiplicity.
H	Enthalpy, with or without subscript; Hermite function $H_n(\xi)$.
$\mathbf{H}$	Hamiltonian operator.
$\mathscr{H}$	Classical Hamiltonian; Magnetic field strength.
h	Planck's constant; Miller index.
$\hbar$	$h/2\pi$.
I	Ionic strength; intensity of radiation; moment of inertia; body-centered.
I_o	Ionization energy.
$\mathscr{g}$	Electric current.
$\mathscr{g}_+,\ \mathscr{g}_-,\ \mathscr{g}_\pm$	Current carried by ion.
i	van't Hoff i; $\sqrt{-1}$; with subscript, nuclear spin; as subscript, summation index, inversion, or internal.
J	Rotational quantum number.
j	As subscript, summation index or junction.
K	Kelvin.
K	Equilibrium constant; proportionality or other constant.
K_A	Acidic ionization constant.
K_B	Basic ionization constant.
K_W	Ion product of water.

K_a	Equilibrium constant (activities).
K_b	Ebullioscopic constant.
K_c	Equilibrium constant (molarities).
$K_c^{\ddagger}$	Equilibrium constant (molarities) involving activated complex.
K_e	Equilibrium constant (fugacities).
K_f	Cryoscopic constant.
K_p	Equilibrium constant (pressures).
k	Boltzmann constant; rate constant of nonintegral order; proportionality constant; Miller index.
k_n	Rate constant for forward reaction of order n.
k_n'	Rate constant for reverse reaction of order n.
L	Electric conductance or conductivity; Langevin function.
l	Mean free path; a distance; azimuthal quantum number; Miller index.
l	As subscript, liquid.
$l_+, l_-, l_\pm$	Equivalent ionic conductance.
log	Decadic logarithm.
ln	Natural logarithm.
M	Molecular or formula weight; collision species; as subscript, molar.
M_i	Molecular or formula weight of species i.
m	Mass of molecule, atom, or electron; magnetic quantum number; as subscript, migration, mean, or mass.
$m_\pm$	Mean ionic molality.
m_i	Molality of species i.
N	Avogadro's number (or any number converting microscopic to macroscopic); number of molecules.
N	Number distribution.
$N_{\pm i}$	Normality of ionic species i (with or without i).
N_i	Mole fraction of species i.
n	Number of moles (often with subscript to identify species); order of reflection or reaction; an integer; number of protons or electrons lost or gained; principal quantum number; bond number.
n_L	Index of refraction.
n_x, n_y, n_z	Integer.
o	As subscript or superscript, standard, initial, pure, ideal value or value at absolute zero or infinite dilution; ortho.
0	As subscript, initial.
P	Total uniform normal pressure; probability; as subscript, isobaric.
P	Number of phases; polarization per unit volume.
$\mathscr{P}_M$	Molar polarization.

597

P_n	Probability distribution
p	Momentum or momentum coordinate; pressure, especially of a condensed phase; para; multiplicity of reflection.
$p\mathrm{H}$	Potential of hydrogen.
p_i	Partial pressure of species i.
Q	Electric charge; partition function, with or without subscripts; with subscript, a function of activities and fugacities like K.
$Q_+,\ Q_-$	Charge carried by ion.
q	Heat absorbed by system from surroundings; a space coordinate; probability, with subscripts.
R	Gas constant; radius; internuclear distance; radial part of wave function.
R_N	Reynolds number.
$\mathcal{R}$	Electric resistance.
R_{ij}	Radial distance between i and j.
R_M	Molar refraction.
r	Radial distance; as subscript, reduced, reservoir, or rotational.
r_{ij}	Radial distance between i and j.
rev	As subscript, reversible.
S	Entropy; overlap integral.
$\bar{S}_i$	Partial molar entropy.
s	Frequency or collision factor; scattering variable $[(4\pi \sin\theta)/\lambda]$; as subscript, surroundings or sublimation.
s	As subscript, solid.
sp	As subscript, specific.
T	Absolute temperature.
t	Time; as subscript, transference.
$t_{1/2}$	Half-life.
$t_+,\ t_-,\ t_\pm$	Transference number of ion.
tr	As subscript, transition or translational.
U_o	Lattice energy.
u	Root mean square velocity; mobility; an integer; time-independent wave function.
V	Total volume; potential energy; as subscript, at constant volume.
$\mathbf{V}$	Electrode potential.
$\bar{V}_i$	Partial molar quantity, especially partial molar volume.
v	Velocity; an integer; volume, as of unit cell or condensed phase; variation function; vibrational quantum number; as subscript, vaporization or vibrational.
v_i	Partial volume of species i.
$v_+,\ v_-,\ v_\pm$	Velocity of ion.
W_i	Mass or weight of species i.

w	Work done on system by surroundings; an integer.
w'	Work done by system on surroundings.
X	Fraction liquefied; wave function; parameters of external force.
x	Cartesian coordinate; a variable; a fraction; concentration of product.
x_i	Fractional displacement along a axis; parameter of external force; electronegativity of species i.
y	Cartesian coordinate; a variable; a parameter.
y_i	Fractional displacement along b axis.
Z	Collision frequency (with subscript); number of lattice sites per unit cell.
$\mathbf{Z}$	Number of charges per particle.
z	Cartesian coordinate; height; fractional ionic character; compressibility factor.
z_+	Charge on cation in units of fundamental charge.
z_-	Charge on anion (a negative integer) in units of fundamental charge.
z_i	Fractional displacement along C axis.
α	Coefficient of expansion at constant pressure; Lagrangian multiplier; polarizability; crystalline phase; degree of dissociation; Debye-Huckel coefficient; spin function; degree of ionization.
α_R	Angle of rotation.
β	Angle; Lagrangian multiplier; statistical temperature variable; crystalline phase; spin function; compressibility coefficient.
Γ	Gamma function.
γ	Ratio of heat capacities (C_P/C_V); surface tension or energy; a constant.
$\gamma_\pm$	Mean ionic activity coefficient (molality).
γ_i	Activity coefficient (molality).
Δ	Increment in (final less initial).
δ	Virtual variation; root mean square displacement.
$\dfrac{\partial}{\partial x}$	Partial derivative operator.
ϵ	Energy per molecule; efficiency; molar absorption coefficient; a variable less than unity.
ζ	Electrokinetic potential.
η	Coefficient of viscosity; number of equivalents.
Θ	Angular part of wave function.
θ	Angle, especially in spherical polar coordinates; Bragg angle; Debye characteristic temperature.

599

κ	Dielectric constant.	
Λ	Equivalent electric conductance.	
λ	Wavelength; parameter.	
μ	Dipole moment; magnetic permeability; Joule-Thomson coefficient; reduced mass.	
μ_o	Permanent dipole moment.	
μ_i	Chemical potential of species i (partial molar Gibbs free energy $\overline{G}_i$); induced dipole moment.	
$\boldsymbol{\mu}_i$	True chemical potential in electric field.	
ν	Frequency; total number of fragments per mole.	
$\bar{\nu}$	Wave number.	
ξ	Progress variable; Hermite variable.	
Π	Osmotic pressure; product operator.	
ρ	Density.	
Σ	Summation operator.	
σ	Effective collision diameter; electric charge per unit area.	
τ	Celsius temperature; $d\tau$ = element of volume.	
Φ	Absolute electric potential; angular part of wave function.	
ϕ	Function; probability amplitude; probability distribution function; angle, as of incidence, of reflection, or in spherical polar coordinates; work function.	
ψ	Wave function with time.	
ω	Spin variable; angular velocity.	
ω_e	Spectroscopic vibrational constant.	

C. PHYSICAL CONSTANTS*

Values of the Basic Constants

c	velocity of light	$2.997902 \pm 0.000013 \times 10^{10}$	cm/sec
$\mathscr{F}$	Faraday constant	$96,493.1 \pm 1.0$	coulombs/equiv.
h	Planck constant	$6.62377 \pm 0.00027 \times 10^{-27}$	erg-sec/molecule
N	Avogadro constant	$6.02380 \pm 0.00016 \times 10^{23}$	molecules/mole
$\lim\limits_{P \to 0} (PV)_o$	(PV) product	2271.16 ± 0.04	joules/mole
T_o	absolute temp of 0°C	273.160 ± 0.010	degrees K

* F. D. Rossini, F. T. Gucker, Jr., H. L. Johnston, L. Pauling, and G. W. Vinal, *Journal of the American Chemical Society*, 74, 2699 (1952).

Values of the Derived Constants

c^2	Einstein constant	$8.987416 \pm 0.000081 \times 10^{13}$	joules/gram
e	electronic charge $(\mathcal{F}/N)$	$1.601864 \pm 0.000036 \times 10^{-19}$	coulomb
hc/k	second radiation const.	1.438676 ± 0.000091	cm-degree
k	Boltzmann constant (R/N)	$1.380257 \pm 0.000067 \times 10^{-16}$	erg/degree-mole
Nhc	wave number-energy const.	11.96171 ± 0.00026	joule-cm/mole
R	gas constant $[(PV)_o/T_o]$	8.31439 ± 0.00034 .082054	joules/degree-mole liter atm/mole deg

Values of the Defined Constants

g	standard gravity	980.665	cm/sec-sec
P	standard atmosphere	1,013,250	dynes/cm-cm
P	standard mm Hg	1/760	atmosphere
—	thermochemical calorie	4.1840	joules

Values of Certain Auxiliary Relations*

1 mean solar second $= 1.00273791$ sidereal second
1 joule $\quad = 0.999835 \pm 0.000052$ international joule (NBS)
1 ohm $\quad = 0.999505 \pm 0.000015$ international ohm (NBS)
1 ampere $\quad = 1.000165 \pm 0.000025$ international ampere (NBS)
1 volt $\quad = 0.999670 \pm 0.000029$ international volt (NBS)
1 coulomb $\quad = 1.000165 \pm 0.000025$ international coulomb (NBS)
1 watt $\quad = 0.999835 \pm 0.000052$ international watt (NBS)
1 liter $\quad = 1000.028 \pm 0.004$ cubic centimeters

Values of the Various Constants Expressed in Different Units*

	2271.16	joules/mole
$(PV)_o$	22,414.6	cm³-atm/mole
	22.4140	liter-atm/mole
$\mathcal{F}$	96,493.1	coulombs/equiv.
	23,062.4	cal/volt equiv.

* All electrical units are absolute unless otherwise indicated.

	1.601864×10^{-19}	coulomb
e	1.601864×10^{-20}	e.m.u.
	4.80223×10^{-10}	e.s.u.
	8.31439	joules/degree-mole
R	1.98719	cal/degree-mole
	82.0567	cm^3-atm/degree-mole
	0.0820544	liter-atm/degree-mole
Nhc	11.96171	joule-cm/mole
	2.858917	cal-cm/mole
c^2	8.987416×10^{13}	joules/gram
	2.148044×10^{13}	cal/gram
1 cal	4.184000	joules
	4.18331	international joules
	41.2929	cm^3-atm
	0.0412917	liter-atm

INDEX *

A

Absolute entropy, 206–209, 371
  calculation by statistical mechanics, 385, 524–525, 531
  isotopes, 282
Absolute reaction rate theory, 570ff
Absolute temperature, 5
Absolute zero, 203, 459–460
  unattainability, 203–205
Absorbancy, 576
Absorption of light:
  Beer-Lambert law, 575–576
  solids, 508–509
Acetone-water system, 290–295
Acid, 414–421
  concentration, 421
  definitions, 415
  dibasic, 416–417
  ionization, 416–417
  Lewis, 415, 558
  nonideality, 288
  transference in, 392
Activated complex, 550–551, 569–574
  solvation, 574–575
Activation, 550
  photo-, 576–577
  thermodynamic approach, 566–568
Activation energy, 566ff, 572–573
  observed value, 573
  size, 579
Activity, 264 (*See* Activity coefficient)
  cell potentials, 429
  osmotic coefficient, 336–337
Activity coefficient, 335–338
  calculation, 338
  cell potentials, 441–443
  ionic, 336–338, 416
  use, 416, 439
  value of concept, 336
Actual process, 184
Additivity of atomic radiuses, 499
Adiabatic chemical reaction, 171–177
Adiabatic demagnetization, 203–205, 255
Adiabatic expansion, 146–150
Adiabatic process, 119, 127, 141ff, 186–188, 191, 193

impossible, 187–188
  real gas, 146–150
  spontaneous, 224–227
Adiabatic work, 127, 143–144, 199
Adsorption, 98, 402, 580
Air, 277, 279
  solubility in water, 289–290
Allowed reflections, 71–74
Alloys:
  absolute zero, 203
  order in, 87, 91, 203
Alpha decay, 475, 547
Amagat's law, 278–279
American sign convention, 436
Amino-acids, 400
Ammonia:
  electrode potentials in, 435
  equilibrium constants, 384
  ionization, 414–415
  rate of decomposition, 543
  solvent, 411
Ampere, definitions, 387
Analysis:
  chemical, 282, 392
  continuous, 540
  extent of reaction, 392, 539–540
  radioactive, 548, 549
  spectroscopic, 576, 577
  X-ray, 69, 71
Angular momentum, 462, 487ff
Aniline point, 303
Anode, 388
Antibonding orbitals, 489–492
Antiparticles, 482
Antisymmetry, 480ff, 484, 487ff, 523, 536
  molecular, 487ff
  orbital, 495
  wave function, 523, 536
Area, calculation, 588ff
Arrhenius, 415, 565
Asymmetric carbon, 106
Atmosphere, standard, 22, 601
Automation, 540
Average value, 28, 376–377, 517
Avogadro's law, 7–8
Avogadro's number, 8, 203
  determination, 53, 75, 391

---

* Symbols for physical quantities are listed alphabetically in Appendix B, pp. 594–600.